INSTRUCTOR MANUAL FOR TEXT AND LABORATORY MANUAL
for
Conceptual Integrated Science

Paul G. Hewitt

Suzanne Lyons

John Suchocki

Jennifer Yeh

PEARSON

Addison
Wesley

San Francisco   Boston   New York
Capetown   Hong Kong   London   Madrid   Mexico City
Montreal   Munich   Paris   Singapore   Sydney   Tokyo   Toronto

Editor-in-Chief: Adam R.S. Black, Ph.D.
Senior Acquisitions Editor: Lothlo'rien Homet
Editorial Assistant: Ashley Taylor Anderson
Managing Editor: Corinne Benson
Production Supervisor: Lori Newman
Manufacturing Buyer: Pam Augspurger
Cover Designer: Richard Whitaker, Seventeenth Street Studios
Project Management: Progressive Publishing Alternatives
Composition: Progressive Information Technologies
Illustrations: Progressive Publishing Alternatives
Cover and Text Printer: Offset Paperback Manufacturers

ISBN: 0-8053-9043-X

PEARSON

Addison
Wesley

6 7 8 9 10 –OPM– 10
www.aw-bc.com

Table of Contents

Introduction

This guide describes a way to teach integrated science conceptually. People with a conceptual and integrated understanding of science are more alive to the world. A botanist taking a stroll through a wooded park is more alert than others to the trees, plants, mosses, and the life that teems in them. An astronomer gazing at the stars appreciates more than just the visual beauty of their twinkling light; he or she can marvel at their tempestuous life cycles and feel the awe that comes from knowing we are all literally made of stardust. The geologist doesn't view rocks as dull, inert, and boring. Rather, to him or her, rocks are the stuff of which Earth is made; they flow slowly over time, stretch, bend, shatter, shift, and metamorphose. To the geologist's educated eye, rocks hold fascinating secrets about Earth's past. We authors believe that the integrated scientist is the most fortunate of all scientists, for he or she can partake in all these delights. The integrated scientist is enriched by knowledge of the full gamut of natural sciences.

The integrated science instructor plays a unique role—he or she gets to point out the connections in the natural world. Such a teacher is in a good position to add meaning to students' lives. Your influence goes beyond the students you face in class, for it is passed on to others through them. Perhaps, many of your students will become teachers themselves. If they are elementary school teachers, yours may be the only science course they take in preparation for their teaching. They should feel good about science so as to pass on a sense of excitement about it to their students. In our profession, we can never tell where our influence stops. It will touch young adults, as they exercise their sharp and analytical minds. And it may extend to children who wonder about stars, clouds, wind, rocks, mechanical and electronic gadgets, plants animals, and food.

Science courses are too often the "killer courses" in schools. Do not let integrated science be one of them! The rigor in tilling a field has more to do with the depth of the plow setting than the field itself. Conceptual Integrated Science, with the plow not too deep and not too shallow, can be a favorite course for both you and your students.

On Class Lectures

Students are known to grumble when a lecture seems detached from the chapter being studied or when the lecture is a verbatim presentation of it. A successful lecturer avoids both of these extremes. A lecture can provide additional examples and explanations to chapter material (which is provided in this manual). Educational research shows that students learn by attaching new ideas to what they already know. This is the essence of constructivism. Knowledge is acquired one layer at a time, each layer depending on the layer beneath—hence the emphasis on *analogies* in the text. In your teaching too, the authors encourage you to use analogies whenever possible. You may find that your students are an excellent source of new analogies and examples to supplement those in the text. To stimulate this, you can make the following assignment:

> Choose one (or more) of the concepts presented in the reading assignment, and cite any illustrative analogies or examples that *you* can think of.

To paraphrase William James, who stated that "wisdom is knowing what to overlook," we agree that good teaching is knowing what to omit. It is important to distinguish between what to skim over and what to dig into. Too often an instructor will spend precious class time digging into noncentral and nonessential material. How nice for the student when class time is stimulating and the material covered is central and relevant.

This text begins with physics, with its supply of equations. These are important in a conceptual course—not as a recipe for plugging in numerical values but as a guide to thinking. The equation tells the student what variables to consider in treating an idea. In physics, for example, how much an object accelerates depends not only on the net force but on mass as well. The formula $a = F/m$ reminds one to consider both quantities. Does gravitation depend on an object's speed? Consideration of $F \sim mM/d^2$ shows that it doesn't, and so forth. The problem sets at the ends of many chapters involve computations that help to illustrate concepts rather than challenge your student's mathematical abilities. They are fewer in number than exercises to avoid course emphasis on number crunching.

A note of caution: Please don't overwhelm your students with excessive written homework! (Remember those courses you took as a student where you were so busy with the chapter-end material that you didn't get into the chapter material itself?) The exercises are numerous only to provide you with a wide selection to consider. Depending on your style of teaching, you may find that posing and answering exercises in class makes a successful lecture.

Answers and solutions to odd-numbered exercises and problems appear for students in the *Practice Book*. Answers to all exercises and problems are in the back of this manual. These are suitable for copying and posting or distributing, or whatever. It's your course.

In lecture, we think that before moving on to new material it is important to provide the student with a self-check after important ideas and concepts are presented. We do this by posing the following, after presenting an idea and supporting it with example: "If you understand this—if you really do—then you can answer the following question." Then we pose the question slowly and clearly, usually in multiple-choice form or such that a short answer is called for, and ask the class to make a response—usually written. We can't overestimate the importance of the "check-your-neighbor" practice, which is catching on in education. One excellent way to facilitate this is with the use of whiteboards (pieces of white Masonite) that students can write responses on with markers. Faster and better are the clicker questions provided on the Conceptual Integrated Science Media Manager. With the immediate feedback to clicker questions, you can tailor your lecture to your students, as well as check their attendance.

On No Class Lectures

Most students expect classes to consist of lectures plus demonstrations. A great class is one where the lectures are engaging and the demonstrations are many. A boring class is one where the instructor makes little attempt to be animated and the demonstrations are nonexistent. Either way, students remain seated, equipped with pen and paper to record the events as accurately as possible so that they can study them later in greater detail on their own.

This traditional class format can be effective at helping students learn. Educational research suggests, however, that better results are obtained when the instructor is able to engage students as active participants. The aforementioned "check-your-neighbor" type questions are a good starting point. In taking this interactive approach a step further, students can collaborate in teams to work on projects, worksheets, or hands-on activities—all the better if the curriculum is designed to assist students in articulating what they have learned. Students themselves can be given access to the science demonstrations and be asked to explain the underlying concepts. Any lecture presentation they receive is short and sweet, and provided "on the fly" in response to their specific needs. In such a scenario, students find themselves in the spotlight. They find that class is akin to a grand study session where the instructor is their tutor, migrating from student to student and providing expert assistance on demand. These are the hallmarks of what we call a "student-centered" class. Lectures are minimized for the sake of increased class participation.

Students Must Come Prepared

The prerequisite to an effective student-centered class is that the student comes to class prepared. Assignments need to have been read *beforehand* and exercises attempted *beforehand* such that a hazy understanding has already begun to take form. But as any instructor knows, student resistance to coming to class prepared can be intense. How then can we motivate students to come to class prepared? There are numerous tools. First of all, it is vital that the textbook be as user-friendly as possible—students should enjoy reading it! In developing *Conceptual Integrated Science,* we took it to heart that the student should be able to learn about concepts on their own with minimal assistance from the instructor. This, in turn, supports the instructor who wishes to conduct a student-centered class.

Another important tool for encouraging students to study is a short quiz given at the beginning of class, or even *before* class with the quiz posted on the course website. Quizzes should assess students for their familiarity with—not their expertise of—the material about to be covered. Following the quiz and a brief introduction, students work on various activities within teams. If a student comes ill-prepared, he or she then faces perhaps one of the greatest motivators: peer pressure. Of course, not everyone can always come prepared, but students quickly come to realize that it is difficult to hide when the spotlight is on them, even in large lecture halls.

If you want to make your classes more student-centered, you should let your students know right away how this approach will help their learning, provide for an enjoyable experience, and, ultimately, improve their test scores. (The interpersonal skills gained through collaborative learning is an added plus.) Also, students are much more willing to participate if the in-class activities are unequivocally related to the quizzes and exams they take.

Lastly, a student-centered approach, though it provides a greater opportunity to facilitate student learning, consumes a large portion of class and thus gives you less time to deliver content. In order to keep pace with a traditional syllabus, the instructor will need to decide whether there will be material on exams which is not covered directly in class. If so, the instructor should be mindful to reserve class time for the more challenging concepts.

Students Are the Players and You Are Their Coach

There is great potential to transform a class from one geared towards passive learning to one geared towards active learning. All you need is a willingness to get creative and push the responsibilities of learning more squarely on your students. You can do this not necessarily by providing good *answers,* but by providing good *questions.* We can think of students as team players out on the field doing all the hard work; your job is to act as coach, directing their learning efforts. Sometimes the best way to do this is by knowing when to cheer and when to remain silent.

Getting Started

So, is it better to retool one's teaching methods in a single semester or to explore new activities one at a time over many years? Revolution or evolution? If you're like us, the thought of revamping everything within a single semester is most undesirable. Indeed, implementing any student-centered activity requires a fair amount of trial and error. Imagine introducing several new activities all within a few weeks, only to have them fail miserably! This would be a disservice to your students, to yourself, and to the student-centered learning approach. The best approach is to introduce only the activities you think will work best for your students in a time frame that allows for successful development. Too much too soon can be self-defeating.

The techniques presented here are a select few that we know work well from experience. Some work for large classes while others are better suited for smaller classes. Chances are that you have already implemented techniques of your own or that new ideas will soon be coming to you as you forge ahead. Also, you need look no further than journals such as those of the National Science Teachers Association, or go to the web to, find a constant flow of student-centered learning innovations. Some good references are included at the end of this essay. The point is that student-centered learning is fertile ground, even for those of us who have already nailed down our lecture presentations and are wondering what to do next.

Student-Centered Assessment Techniques

(What students can do to articulate what they've learned)

The Concepts Inventory

The Concepts Inventory is short test taken anonymously by students at the beginning and end of the semester to measure increased understanding of basic concepts. Inventory questions should reflect concepts that the instructor hopes the ideal student will learn by taking the course. A good inventory will also include questions that address common misconceptions. At the end of the semester, the same Concept Inventory is given or the same questions can be snuck into the final exam. Typically, student scores on an inventory don't improve by very much. This can be explained, in part, by the idea that it is most difficult to lead students away from their well-entrenched misconceptions.

The Minute Quiz

It is valuable to give students a single-question quiz at the beginning of class to assess whether or not they have come prepared. Such a quiz might be designed to test for a *familiarity* of the material about to be covered rather than an *understanding* of this material. Note that these quizzes needn't take much time. In our classes they are known as "minute quizzes" because the students have only one minute to answer it. They can put their quiz, which is printed on a narrow strip of paper, into a blue box that gets passed around the class. A right answer is worth 25 points while a wrong answer is worth 10 points. If a student opts not to put their quiz into the blue box, they may hold onto their quiz until the word is given that they are allowed to open their notes, their textbooks, and talk with their neighbors about the possible answer. After another one minute period they place the quiz into a red box which means they get 20 points for a right answer and 15 points for a wrong answer. Students soon catch onto their best strategy. With this system the prepared students are preferentially rewarded. By the end of the semester all of the quiz scores add up to a significant portion of the course grade, which is added incentive for students to come to class prepared.

Collaborative Exams

For a real learning experience, an exam may be offered in three phases: individual, team, and class. In the first phase each student takes the exam individually while also filling out a duplicate exam that contains their answers but not their name. Assessment for this individual effort should be weighted the greatest. For example, each question may be worth 5 points, while for the second phase each question is worth 3 points, and for the third phase just 1 point.

A ten minute warning is given to assure that all students finish with the first phase at about the same time. Exams are turned in while the duplicate exams are spread out onto a broad table. Students then congregate into their teams to take the exam again, but this time working together and with resources, such as the textbook. They are also permitted to send a scout to inspect the duplicate exams to see how the rest of the class answered specific questions. Each member of the team should have a copy of the exam, but only one exam is to be turned in for assessment. Meanwhile, the instructor and/or TA is quickly grading the individual exams (use a Scantron if available). Ideally, the individual exams are graded by the time the teams are finished with their team exams and the individual exam average score is posted on the chalkboard.

After teams turn in their exams they are ready for the third phase in which they take the exam yet again together as a class. The instructor records their answers on a single master copy of the exam. Teams vote for an answer by holding up color-coded flash cards. Teams are allowed to argue their answers, but majority wins. If there is a tie among teams, then there is a recount after some healthy debate. After each class answer is recorded, students are then told the correct answer, which is often followed by the cheers or groans.

The length of the exam is determined by the duration of the class. For a 75 minute class, the exam can contain up to 25 questions. For 50 minute class, the exam should be narrowed down to about 15 questions. Timing is an important issue with this sort of collaborative exam. In particular, students should finish the first phase of the exam all at about the same time. Slower students can be encouraged to come to class early for a head start. It is also helpful to have a second room where slower students can go in the event they need another 5 or 10 minutes to finish the first phase. For the second phase, which is the team phase, it helps to include a "toughie" bonus short-essay question at the end of the exam. This is useful for teams who finish early—it keeps them busy while other teams are still working on the regular questions. There is not always sufficient time to have the third phase, which is when the class takes the exam together as a whole. To expedite the third phase, the instructor lays out the team answers so he or she can see all the team answers at a glance. Instant credit is given to questions that are unanimously correct. This allows the instructor to move on to some of the more difficult questions, which tend to have different answers from different teams.

By the time the class period is over, students have taken the exam three times and know their final score. Individual effort is preferentially rewarded, yet students still get the valuable experience of working together as a team. Furthermore, with such a format, the instructor is able to fill the exam with juicy, but tough questions. The individual phase of the exam, for example, may average 65%. This is balanced, however, by the team and class phases, which may run 80% and 95%, respectively, so that the overall average is within the mid-70's. One serious drawback to this format is that it consumes a lot of paper. If each student has access to a computer, however, the paper can be replaced by online delivery, which would also assist with the intensive instant grading.

Appeals

With end-of-semester course evaluations, a number one concern shown by most students is whether or not the course was fair. Towards satisfying this need, students may be permitted to appeal any question for which they believe they deserve credit. The instructor, of course, sets up the conditions of the appeal. For example, the students' explanation for why they think they deserve credit must be hand-written and submitted within a certain time frame. Also, only those who were actively involved in the appeal, as indicated by their signature, have the possibility of gaining points. Appeals are reviewed by the instructor in the safety of his or her home or office where he or she may assign full, partial, or no credit. Aside from providing students a sense of fairness on your part, the appeals provide the feedback you need to modify questions that might not be worded so optimally.

Student-Centered Learning Activities

(What students can do in-class when the instructor is not lecturing)

Team Formations

Collaborative learning tends to work best when students are grouped together in teams consisting of either 3 or 4 students. For a team of 5 students, invariably, the fifth student takes a back seat and is less involved. For a team of 2 students, there is not a sufficient diversity of ideas. Who goes on what team is the difficult responsibility of the instructor who knows that each team needs to be well-balanced in terms of academic abilities and gender. At the start of the semester, you can eye-ball who should go where. Putting friends together initially is a good thing. Alternatively, you can await the results of a non-anonymous Concept Inventory and use student scores as the basis for team formations.

You should consider new team formations after each mid-term. Students thus work together in the same team up through the mid-term, which is collaborative as described above. Mid-term exam scores are then used as the basis for new team formations.

Active Explorations

At the end of each chapter in *Conceptual Integrated Science* is a select list of hands-on science activities we call Active Explorations. These do-at-home activities, including many others found within the *CIS Laboratory Manual*, are a good centerpiece for team learning. As you can imagine, students appreciate the exploratory nature of these activities—they really help to liven up a class.

Practice Pages

An important supplement to *Conceptual Integrated Science* is the *Practice Book*, which is a comprehensive set of concept review worksheets we prefer to call practice pages. These practice pages are designed as a study guide that students can work on outside of class. They are far more effective, however, when students work on them together as a team under the expert supervision of the course instructor, who can help each team of students as necessary. It's common that the practice page will prompt a question from a student that, in turn, prompts the instructor to give a short lecture presentation to the team. In such instances, neighboring teams can be encouraged to eavesdrop. We call this "targeted teaching" and it arises not just from the practice pages, but also from whenever the instructor is roaming about checking on team progress. Occasionally, it prompts the instructor to switch gears and give his or her mini-presentation to the whole class.

Think-Pair-Share

Present a multiple choice question to the class. Students contemplate the question on their own and then commit to an answer preferably in writing or via flash cards so that the instructor can quickly gauge student performance. Students then discuss their reasoning with an adjacent student. After student-student discussions, a second survey of answers is taken. To accommodate this technique you will find on the *Conceptual Integrated Science Media Manager CD-ROM* an extensive set of multiple choice clicker questions in PowerPoint® format.

Class Presentations with Activity Intervals

Assign select exercises from the textbook to teams of students who then have a short period of time (10 minutes) to prepare and practice articulating an answer. Students as individuals or as a team then get up in front of the class and present a cogent answer to the exercise taking no more than 2 minutes per exercise. They then ask if there are any questions. The instructor, meanwhile, has planted some well thought-out questions among the audience who then ask these questions, probing deeper into the concepts. The presenting student or students can either respond or choose to serve as moderators of a class discussion. Beyond this, certain exercises lend themselves to short but effective activities. After a student presentation of surface tension, for example, the class can be challenged to float a paperclip on water. Or after an exercise on condensation, the instructor can invert a steam filled soda can in water. Students are then prompted to explain why the can imploded. Of course, if they can't figure it out, it is the responsibility of the instructor to remain silent.

Focused Listing

On a blank sheet of paper, students write down a list of 4 or 5 terms or phrases that help to portray the content of a particular section of the textbook or of some reading assignment. This activity quickly assesses what key concepts have been picked up and whether or not the student has studied the reading assignment. A related activity is called "The Muddiest Point" whereby students write down what concepts from a chapter were most unclear. The instructor then uses this information to launch a class presentation (mini-lecture or demonstration) or a class discussion *à la* the Socratic method whereby everything the instructor says is phrased as a question.

Talk to the Wall

Students hate this activity. But that's okay because you're their coach, not their friend. Short, easy to read "Explain This" questions are posted around the classroom. There are as many posted questions as there are students, which means this works only for relatively small classes. Beneath each question is a grid that allows the student to rate on a scale of 1 to 5. To begin, each student is placed in front of a question. At the sound of a bell, all students vocalize their explanation or answer. They tend to speak softly at first, but the instructor keeps insisting that they speak louder. Ideally the classroom becomes quite noisy. Students must continue to articulate, no pauses allowed, until the bell rings once again. At that point they rate on the grid how well they think they did. The whole class then rotates in the same direction so that everyone is before a new question. This continues for as long as the instructor thinks is appropriate. When finished, the instructor runs around the room grabbing all the questions. Ones in which students gave themselves low marks are the ones that become the focus of subsequent class discussions.

The main point to emphasize to students through this activity is that there is a vast difference between thinking you know something and articulating that which you think you know. A true test for understanding is whether or not the student is able to explain that understanding verbally. So when one student explains a concept to another, who benefits the most? The sender or the receiver? Likewise, who is getting the best learning experience: the new professor refining his or her lecture presentation, or the students listening to this lecture presentation? We can't emphasize enough that if a student really wants to learn something, a good way to start is by moving the mouth, whether to a friend or a brick wall—it doesn't matter. It is not comfortable. But that's okay. Learning isn't meant to be comfortable. The best ice skaters are the ones who have fallen down the most.

Reward Race

A set of not-so-easy multiple choice questions are posted around the room. Students work in teams to answer these questions. The first team to get all answers correct wins the prize, preferably something made of chocolate. Strategies are important. Some teams will decide to split up. Others will stay huddled as they migrate from one question to the next. Also, if a team submits answers but gets at least one wrong, they are not allowed to submit answers again until either all the other teams have had a chance or after a specified amount of time. Furthermore, the instructor doesn't tell teams which questions they got wrong, only the number of them they got wrong. This is certainly one of the more fun activities.

Office Visits

While class is occupied with some learning activity (pensive activities, such as the Practice Pages are best), the instructor pulls individual students away for a brief office visit. The instructor inquires about how things are going and whether the student has any general or specific questions or concerns. This is also a good time to show the student his or her present course grade and provide advice on how to do well in the course. Furthermore, this activity serves as an important ice-breaker that makes students more inclined to take advantage of your regular office hours.

Field Trip

Class-size permitting, take students on a tour of the department's teaching and research laboratories. Ask your colleagues if they would be willing to talk to your students about the appeal of science and why they chose it as a profession.

Salon de Science (pronounced "see-aunce")

Bring in a stack of recent science journals, both popular and technical, and set the classroom up as though it were a coffee house—background music, tea, donuts, etc. Students merely spend the class time reading through these journals and discussing science-related topics with their peers as well as the instructor. Strange but true, many if not most of your students have never read through a science journal or magazine. Perhaps down the road this activity will help them to think twice about throwing away one of those pervasive science magazine subscription offers.

Readiness Assurance Test (RAT)

Hands down, this is the students' favorite activity—not for the joy of it but because it is most related to helping them perform well on their exams. The RAT is simply a trial exam given the class before the actual exam. It helps students assess how ready they may or may not be for the exam. Everything about the RAT should be identical to the exam except that the points don't count and the questions are different. So should the RAT questions be easier or harder? We recommend you make them harder. A good RAT is one whereby the students mope out of class with their heads hanging low. They feel it in their hearts that they really need to buckle down if they want to do well on the upcoming real exam. Depending on what psychology you want to use, you may or may not tell them that the questions on the RAT were relatively tough. Either way, their subsequent improved performance on the real exam can be a great confidence builder, which is especially important for these students—many of whom are science phobic.

If you are implementing collaborative exams (described above) or any other new and unusual exam format, a RAT also affords you the opportunity to learn how the exam format is best implemented.

Instructor-Centered Learning Activities

(What the instructor can do outside of class)

Class Journal

Student-centered learning is such fertile ground for educational innovation. As soon after class as possible, we encourage you to open up your Class Journal and start recording what went well and what went wrong. We can almost guarantee that through this process, ideas for improvements and new ideas altogether will arise. You should document the details of each class session even if you don't think anything unusual occurred. Unbeknownst to you, many ideas are likely brewing within your sub-conscious. The process of writing in your journal, especially soon after class, is a great way to allow these ideas to bubble up to the surface where you can consider them in fuller detail.

Think-Pair-Share

Think about your curriculum using your Class Journal. Discuss your experiences and ideas with your colleagues. Then share your ideas with others through departmental seminars or regional or national meetings. The key word here is synergy. We instructors don't work in a vacuum. In working together we can fast-forward to better ways of reaching our non-science oriented students. Today, we find a growing gap between those who embrace science and those who shun science. Our efforts to bridge this gap and to bring everyone to understand science as a beautiful and effective way of viewing the universe is of ultimate importance.

Explore References

Here are a few references to that you might find helpful as a starting point for learning more about student-centered learning techniques.

Thomas A. Angelo, K. Patricia Cross, *Classroom Assessment Techniques, A Handbook for College Teachers, 2nd ed.*, Jossey-Bass, 1993.

Eric Mazur, *Peer Instruction: A User's Manual*, Prentice-Hall, 1997.

Jeffrey P. Adams, Timothy F. Slater, *Strategies for Astro 101*, Prentice-Hall, 2003.

Chemical Concepts Inventory
http://jchemed.chem.wisc.edu/JCEDLib/QBank/collection/CQandChP/CQs/ConceptsInventory/CCIIntro.html

Or just type "Chemical Concepts Inventory" into google

Collaborative learning activities
www.wcer.wisc.edu/nise/cl1/cl/

Field-Tested Assessment Guide (CATs)
www.flaguide.org

Just in Time Teaching
www.JiTT.org

Teaching Tips

- Your attitude toward students and attitude about science in general is of utmost importance: Consider yourself not the master in your classroom, but the main resource person, the pace setter, and the guide. Consider yourself a bridge between your students' ignorance and some of the information you've acquired in your study. Guide their study—steer them away from the dead ends you encountered, and keep them on essentials and away from time-draining peripherals. You are there to help them. If they see you so, they'll appreciate your efforts. This is a matter of self-interest. An appreciated instructor has an altogether richer teaching experience than an underappreciated instructor.

- Don't be a "know-it-all." When you don't know the answer to a question, don't pretend you do. You'll lose more respect faking knowledge than not having it. If you're new to teaching, students will understand you're still pulling it together and will respect you nonetheless. But if you fake it, and some of your students *can* tell, any respect you've earned plummets.

- Be firm, and expect good work of your students. But be fair and get papers graded and returned quickly. Be sure the bell curve of grades reflects a reasonable average. If you have excellent students, some should score 100% or near 100% on exams. The least respected teacher in this author's memory was one who made exams so difficult that the class average was near the noise level, where the highest marks were some 50%. That practice was devastating.

- Be sure that the knowledge you want your students to acquire is reflected by your test items. The student question, "Will that be on the test?" is a *good* question. What is important—by definition—is what's on the test. If you consider a topic important, include it so you allow your students credit for their feedback on it.

- Consider having students repeat work that you judge to be poor—before it gets a final grade. A note on a paper saying you'd rather not grade it until they've given it another try is the mark of a concerned and caring teacher.

- Do less professing and more questioning. Information that is of value ought to be the answer to a question. "Check your neighbor" should be an important feature of your class. Beware of the pitfall of too quickly answering your own questions.

- Show your students respect. Although all your students are more ignorant of science than you are, some are more intelligent than you are. Underestimating their intelligence is likely overestimating your own. Respect is a two-way street.

Ancillaries

Conceptual Integrated Science PRACTICE BOOK (0-8053-9039-1): This, the most important of the ancillaries, is a book of 150 practice sheets that helps students develop concepts quite differently than with traditional workbooks that are seen as drudgery by students (sample on page xv). These are insightful and interesting activities that prompt your students to engage their minds and DO integrated science. Used in class, they are ideal for cooperative learning. Out of class they play the role of a tutor. The book is low priced so it can be offered as a suggested supplement to the text in your student bookstore. If you're planning on light coverage, consider photocopying selected pages for student handouts. Reduced practice pages with answers are at the back of the book, along with answers to the odd-numbered exercises and problems from the textbook.

TEST BANK (0-8053-9072-3): A book with about 2000 multiple-choice questions, with a much fewer number of short-answer exercises. They are rated by three levels of difficulty as well as by emphasis on mathematical or conceptual understanding.

COMPUTERIZED TEST BANK (0-8053-9044-8): Contains the same questions that are in the printed Test Bank, on a cross-platform CD-ROM. The software provides options to scramble questions, print different versions of a test, edit questions and answers, or add to and modify existing question files. Documentation for the test-generating software and a description of how it works is contained in an accompanying booklet. Windows or Macintosh.

LABORATORY MANUAL (0-8053-9073-1): The laboratory manual is rich with simple activities to precede to coverage of course material, as well as experiments that apply course material. The instructions and answers to most of the lab questions are included at the end of this manual.

TRANSPARENCY ACETATES (0-8053-9071-5): Features more than 100 important figures from the text, which are available to qualified adopters from your Addison Wesley Longman rep.

THE CONCEPTUAL SCIENCE PLACE: (www.ConceptualSciencePlace.com) In addition to the wealth of resource available for students, The Conceptual Science Place offers an easy-to-use Gradebook which allows you to assign activities such as interactive tutorials and quizzes each week that are automatically tracked and graded. The Class Manager feature also allows you to post your syllabus, create a class roster, track grades, and more.

CONCEPTUAL INTEGRATED SCIENCE MEDIA MANAGER CD-ROM (0-8053-9068-5): The Media Manager multi-CD-ROM package provides the largest library available of purpose-built in-class presentation materials, including Interactive Figures™, Hewitt's renowned demonstration videos, high-resolution figures and photos from the book, and chapter-by-chapter PowerPoint® slides and clicker questions. The Media Manager also offers Hewitt's acclaimed Next-Time Questions, along with the Instructor Manual and Test Bank in Word format.

You'll better serve your students by employing the ancillaries. On the next page is a sample **Next-Time Question**, with answer page. They can be displayed in a glass case, or if you're an overhead-projector person, consider showing one or two at the end of a class—with the answer shown "next time." Or use them in PowerPoint® presentations. These are intended for students after they've studied related material. It's important that there be a sufficient delay between seeing the questions and seeing the answers. A week is fine. Answering questions too quickly sabotages the learning process. Alternatively, they can be used as an interest builder to introduce material. Then answers can be shown after you've treated the related concept. (When students come to you for an early answer, suggest they consult their friends. And if they say their friends don't have a clue, suggest they make new friends!)

What would happen to the weight
when the iron rusts? Assume that
not fall off the bar.

a) The weight of the bar would inc
it is gaining oxygen.

b) The weight would be the same b
is neither created nor destroye
reaction.

c) The weight would decrease bec
less dense than iron.

What would happen to the weight of an iron bar
when the iron rusts? Assume that the rust does
not fall off the bar.

a) The weight of the bar would increase because
it is gaining oxygen.

b) The weight would be the same because
matter is neither created nor destroyed in a
chemical reaction.

c) The weight would decrease because rust is
less dense than iron.

Answer: a

As the iron rusts, it reacts with the oxygen in the air to form
the compound iron oxide, Fe_2O_3. So, the added oxygen atoms
add to the weight of the bar.

**A rusty piece of iron is slightly
heavier than it was before rusting
occurred. How about that!**

Shown below is a sample page from the *Practice Book*, which the authors consider the most important ancillary to the text. Reduced pages with answers are at the back of the *Practice Book*, along with the solutions to odd-numbered exercises and problems from the textbook.

The concept of systems is nicely shown in this Practice Sheet.

Chapter 4: Momentum and Energy

Systems

Momentum conservation (and Newton's Third Law) apply to *systems* of bodies. Here we identify some systems.

1. When the compressed spring is released, Blocks A and B will slide apart. There are three systems to consider here, indicated by the closed dashed lines below—System A, System B, and System A+B. Ignore the vertical forces of gravity and the support force of the table.

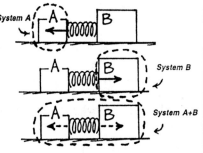

   a. Does an external force act on System A?   (yes)   (no)

      Will the momentum of System A change?   (yes)   (no)

   b. Does an external force act on System B?   (yes)   (no)

      Will the momentum of System B change?   (yes)   (no)

   c. Does an external force act on System A+B?   (yes)   (no)

      Will the momentum of System A+B change?   (yes)   (no)

2. Billiard ball A collides with billiard ball B at rest. Isolate each system with a closed dashed line. Draw only the external force vectors that act on each system.

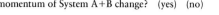

   System A   System B   System A+B

   a. Upon collision, the momentum of System A   (increases) (decreases) (remains unchanged).
   b. Upon collision, the momentum of System B   (increases) (decreases) (remains unchanged).
   c. Upon collision, the momentum of System A+B (increases) (decreases) (remains unchanged).

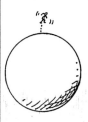

3. A girl jumps upward from Earth's surface. In the sketch to the left, draw a closed dashed line to indicate the system of the girl.

   a. Is there an external force acting on her?   (yes)   (no)

      Does her momentum change?   (yes)   (no)

      Is the girl's momentum conserved?   (yes)   (no)

   b. In the sketch to the right, draw a closed dashed line to indicate the system [girl + Earth]. Is there an external force due to the interaction between the girl and Earth that acts on the system?   (yes)   (no)

      Is the momentum of the system conserved?   (yes)   (no)

4. A block strikes a blob of jelly. Isolate three systems with a closed dashed line and show the external force on each. In which system is momentum conserved?

5. A truck crashes into a wall. Isolate three systems with a closed dashed line and show the external force on each. In which system is momentum conserved?

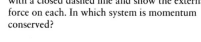

Classroom Drawing Techniques

From Paul Hewitt

I vividly remember as a student how annoyed I was with a professor who couldn't draw a simple cube in his lectures. He'd make an attempt, step back and look at it, wipe part of it from the board, and patch it here and there with little improvement. He always ended up with a "cube" with nonparallel sides. I thought, "He's forever overloading us with homework assignments that take up entire weekends and he won't take a few minutes of his own time to learn how to draw a simple cube." Instructors have a responsibility to improve their art skills if that art is part of their presentation. Only a small amount of practice is needed.

A step-by-step method for drawing a cube is shown at the right. The important key is keeping the vertical lines vertical, and the other two sets of lines parallel to one another. Simply draw a "square" tilted for perspective, draw its twin slightly displaced, and then connect the two with parallel lines. For a finishing touch, wipe away part of the lines to indicate which lines are behind.

Copy your favorite comic strip characters a few times, and you'll have developed enough skill to show improved drawing with your classes. The added respect you'll get from your students is well worth the effort.

Stick figures are easiest to draw. If you learn to draw a few of these, you can go a step further and use double lines for a full figure, as shown. Either way has merit.

The number of individual drawings you'll do in class is likely small in number—perhaps a dozen or so. Variations on a few basic drawings result in many drawings. For example, a person running along the street can be easily changed to a person pitching a ball. This and others are shown on the following three pages, step by step. I suggest you try your hand at these on your chalkboard or overhead transparencies. Take your time doing these, and after the motor skill is programmed in you, work on speed. You're highly successful when you can casually draw an illustration at about the pace you write a formula on the board. So give these a try, then try copying your favorite comic strip characters. Good Energy!

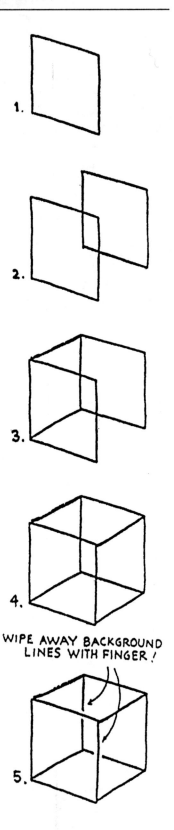

WIPE AWAY BACKGROUND LINES WITH FINGER!

Draw Me . . . *Step by Step!*

Draw Me . . . Step by Step!

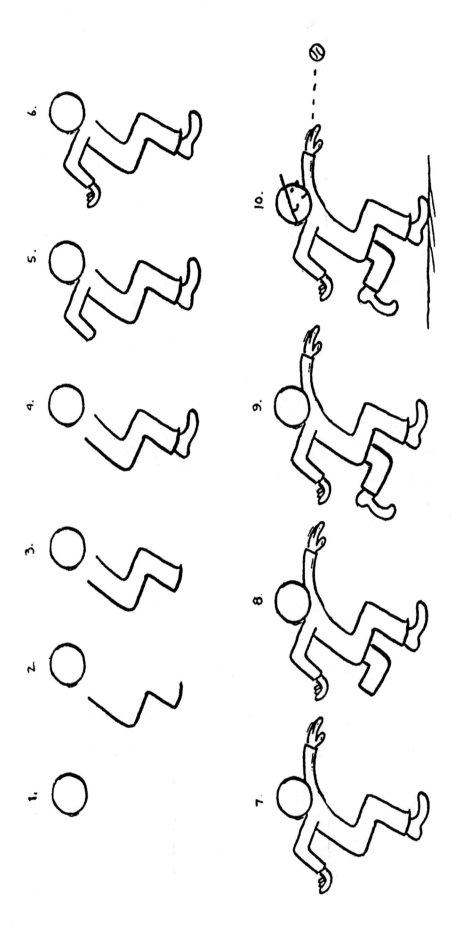

Draw Me . . . *Step by Step!*

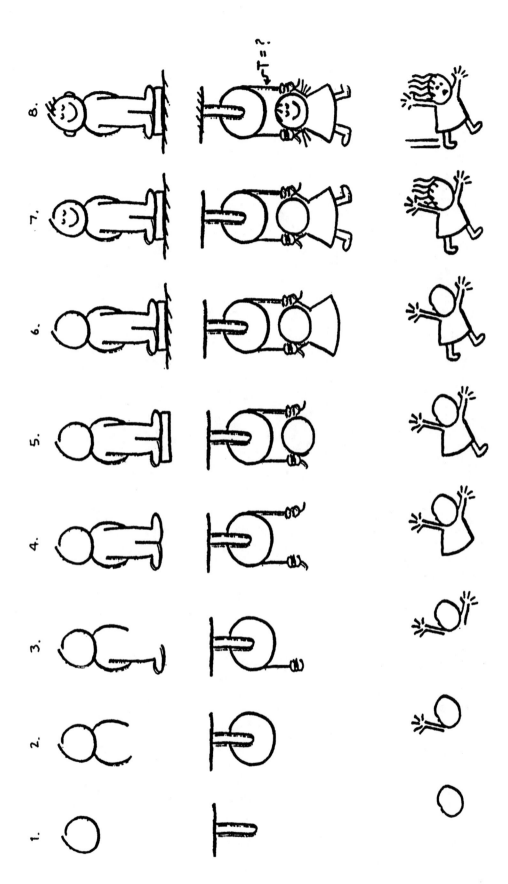

1   About Science

A common practice is spending the first week of a science class on the tools of science—unit conversions, significant figures, making measurements, and using scientific notation. This is anything but exciting to most students. The authors of this book believe that this is pedagogical folly. How much better it is if the first week acts as a hook to promote class interest, with tools introduced if and when they are needed later in the course. So, this book begins by introducing the nature of science, the value of integrated science, the scientific method, the role of science in society, and other topical issues such as pseuodoscience, the relationship between science and religion, and the similarities and differences among science and art.

In *Next-Time Questions*:
• Hypotheses

In the *Lab Manual*:
• Tuning the Senses (enhancing perception)
• Making Cents (introduces the mass balance and the making of a simple graph)

Transparencies:
Math Connection Direct proportion, *Math Connection* Inverse proportion

Suggested Presentation

A Brief History of Advances in Science
Science is organized knowledge. Its roots are found in every culture. The Chinese discovered printing, the compass, and rockets; Islamic cultures developed algebra and lenses; mathematicians in India developed the concept of zero and infinity. This text, nevertheless, emphasizes Western science. Science did advance faster in Western than in Eastern cultures, largely because of the different social and political climates.

While early Greeks, in an era of experimental democracy and free thinking, were questioning their speculations about the world, their counterparts in the more authoritarian eastern parts of the world were largely occupied in absorbing the knowledge of their forebears. In regions like China, absorbing this knowledge was the key to personal success. So scientific progress in Eastern cultures was without the early period of questioning that accelerated the scientific advances of Europe and Eurasia. In any event, it is important to emphasize throughout your course that all *science is a human endeavor*. In addition to being a legacy of what humans have learned about nature, it's also a human activity that answers questions of human interest. It is done by and for humans.

You may consider elaborating the idea that the test of correctness in science is experiment. As Einstein once said, "many experiments may show that I'm right, but it takes only one experiment (that can be repeated) to show that I'm wrong." Ideas must be verifiable by other scientists. In this way science tends to be self-correcting.

Mathematics and Conceptual Integrated Science
The mathematical structure of science is evident in this book by the many equations. These are shorthand notations of the connections and relationships of nature. They are seen primarily as guides to thinking, and only secondarily as recipes for solving problems. Many instructors bemoan students who reach for a formula

when asked a scientific question. We authors take a more positive view of this, for formulas are shorthand statements about the connections of concepts. For example, if asked if speed affects the force of gravity on earth satellites, a look at the equation for gravitation tells us no—only mass and distance affect force. Now if speed changes the distance, then in that case, yes. When equations are seen as guides to thinking, then conceptual thinking is present. Hooray!

You can provide a specific example of "equations as guides to thinking" by going over the Math Connection box. This feature is meant to clarify the role of math in *Conceptual Integrated Science* rather than to challenge students. The notions of direct and inverse proportions are intuitively easy to grasp—showing that science often has a mathematical structure, but this structure need not be difficult to grasp.

The Scientific Method—A Classic Tool

The scientific method is given in a six-step form. We say that science is structured common sense. The scientific method is an example. The scientific method is to be seen as a sensible way to go about investigating nature. Although the six steps are useful, they don't merit your students memorizing them. And most often, they are not the specific steps used in scientific discoveries. The *scientific attitude*, more than a particular method, underlies scientific discovery.

A Scientific Attitude Underlies Good Science Expand on the idea that honesty in science is not only a matter of public interest but is also a matter of self-interest. Any scientist who misrepresents or fudges data, or is caught lying about scientific information, is ostracized by the scientific community. There are no second chances. The high standards for acceptable performance in science, unfortunately, do not extend to other fields that are as important to the human condition. For example, consider the standards of performance required of politicians.

Scientific Hypotheses

Distinguish between *hypothesis*, *theory*, *fact*, and *concept*. Point out that theory and hypothesis are not the same. A *theory* applies to a synthesis of a large body of information. The criterion of a theory is not whether it is true or untrue, but rather whether it is useful or not. It is useful even though the ultimate causes of the phenomena it encompasses are unknown. For example, we accept the theory of gravitation as a useful synthesis of available knowledge that relates to the mutual attraction of bodies. The theory can be refined, or with new information, it can take on a new direction. It is important to acknowledge the common misunderstanding of what a scientific theory is, as revealed by those who say, "But it is not a fact; it is *only* a theory." Many people have the mistaken notion that a theory is tentative or speculative, while a fact is absolute.

Impress upon your class that a *fact* is not immutable and absolute, but it is generally a close agreement by competent observers of a series of observations of the same phenomena. The observations must be verifiable. Because the activity of science is the determination of the most probable, there are no absolutes. Facts that were held to be absolute in the past are seen altogether differently in the light of present-day knowledge and observational equipment.

By *concept*, we mean an intellectual framework that is part of a theory. We speak of the concept of time, the concept of energy, or the concept of a force field. Time is related to motion in space and is the substance of the Theory of Special Relativity. We find that energy exists in tiny grains, or quanta, which is a central concept in the Quantum Theory. An important concept in Newton's Theory of Universal Gravitation is the idea of a force field that surrounds a material body. A concept is an idea with various applications. Thus, when we think "conceptually," we use a generalized way of looking at things.

Prediction in science is different from prediction in other areas. In the everyday sense, one speaks of predicting what has not yet occurred, like whether or not it will rain next weekend. In science, however, prediction is not so much about what *will* happen, but about what *is* happening and is not yet noticed, like what the properties of a hypothetical particle are or are not. A scientist predicts what can and cannot happen, rather than what will or will not happen.

Science Has Limitations

Just as a great strength of a democracy is its openness to criticism, likewise with science. This is in sharp contrast to dogma, which is seen as absolute. The limitations of science, like those of democracy, are open for improvement. The world has suffered enormously from those who have felt their views were beyond question. Author K. C. Cole says it well when she asserts that belief in only one truth and being the possessor of it is the deepest root of all the evil that is in the world.

Pseudoscience

The material on pseudoscience should be excellent for student discussions. A stimulating exercise is to ask students to formulate a series of questions that help determine whether a given claim is a case of pseudoscience. Such a list might include the following questions, and more:

- Does the claim use technical-sounding jargon that is not precisely defined?
- Does the claim use scientific words imprecisely and in a nonscientific context (e.g., "energy," "frequency," "vibration")?
- Do proponents complain of being overly criticized?
- Is one reason given for the supposed validity of the claim that it has been around a long time (so it must be true)?
- Do proponents of the claim use the logical fallacy of the ad hominum to respond to critics? (An ad hominem argument is a challenge directed at he who expresses an idea rather than at the idea itself.)

Pseudoscience is very big business, and examples of it abound. Help students understand the difference between nonscience, science, pseudoscience, and *protoscience* (a new science trying to establish legitimacy).

The Search for Order—Science, Art, and Religion

Einstein said, "Science without religion is deaf; religion without science is blind." The topic of religion in a science text is rare. We treat it briefly only to address what is foremost on many students' minds. Do religion and science contradict each other? Must one choose between them? We hope our very brief treatment presents a satisfactory answer to these questions. Our take is that religion and science are compatible when they address different realms.

Technology—Practical Use of the Findings of Science

In discussions of science and technology and their side effects, a useful statement is: *You can never do just one thing.* Doing *this* affects *that*. Or, You can never *change* only one thing. Every time you show an equation, it's evident that changing a variable on one side of the equation changes one or more on the other side. This idea is nicely extended with "there is never just one force" in discussions of Newton's third law.

The Natural Sciences: Physics, Chemistry, Biology, Earth Science, and Astronomy

With regard to science courses and liberal arts courses, there is a central factor that makes it difficult for liberal arts students to delve into science courses the way that science students can delve into liberal arts courses—and that's the *vertical nature of science courses*. They build upon each other, as noted by their prerequisites. A science student can take an intermediate course in literature, poetry, or history at any time. But in no way can a humanities student take an intermediate physics or chemistry course without first having a foundation in elementary physics and mathematics. Hence the importance of this conceptual course.

Integrated Science

Coming into this course, students may be hazy about what integrated science is. Yet, once you explain it to them, they will readily grasp the value of it. When asked "Why study integrated science?" one student simply stated "Because life is integrated." We fully agree. Point out to students that they will see over and over in this text—and in their everyday lives—that the branches of science are interconnected. How can one understand the host of interesting and important scientific phenomena—from global warming to the origin of the solar system to forensic medicine—without integrating concepts from different branches of science?

An Investigation of Sea Butterflies This case study examines the scientific method as actually applied as well as provides a specific example of integrated science. Another important point discussed is the idea of a scientific *control*—a basic feature of a valid scientific experiment. This idea can be rather subtle, so you may want to emphasize it in your lecture. Consider using the concept check questions for this feature as check-your-neighbor questions—they get at the main ideas of this section.

IN YOUR TEACHING, BETTER TO BE A GUIDE ON THE SIDE THAN A SAGE ON THE STAGE!

2 **Describing Motion**

Demonstration Equipment

Coat hanger and clay blobs

Wooden block stapled to a piece of cloth (to simulate tablecloth pull)

Tablecloth (without a hem) and a few dishes (for the tablecloth pull)

Piece of rope for a classroom tug-of-war

Wooden cube that will fit on a pan balance (another material such as cardboard will do)

Pan balance

This chapter introduces students to kinematics and dynamics. Kinematics is the study of motion without regard to the forces that produce it. When forces are considered, the study is then of dynamics. The authors believe that one of the great follies of physics instruction is overtime on kinematics. Whereas many physics books begin with a chapter on kinematics, this is downplayed in this book. Only the amount of kinematics that is needed is blended into this and the following chapter. As such, please do not focus undue attention on the kinematics concepts of speed, velocity, and acceleration. And please spare your students graphical analysis of these topics, which is better left to a math class or a follow-up physics course. Mastering motion graphs is more of an uphill task than getting a grip on the concepts themselves (but try telling that to a teacher who has a passion for graphical analysis!) Too-early emphasis on kinematics can bog a course down at the outset. So, lightly treat the sections on speed, velocity, and acceleration. Take greater care in developing the concept of force then move as smoothly as you can to where the meat is—the next chapter on Newton's laws of motion.

Of particular interest to me (Hewitt) is the Personal Essay in the chapter, which relates to events that inspired me to pursue a life in physics—my meeting with Burl Grey on the sign-painting stages of Miami, Florida. Relative tensions in supporting cables is what first caught my interest in physics, and I hope to instill the same interest in your students with this chapter.

So force, rather than kinematics, is the emphasis of this chapter. And force vectors, only parallel ones at this point, are the easiest to understand. They underlie the equilibrium rule: $\sum F = 0$ for systems in equilibrium. These are further developed in the *Practice Book*. (Not using the *Practice Book* is like teaching swimming away from water. This is an important book—the authors' most imaginative and pedagogically useful tool for student learning!)

Note that in introducing force, we first use pounds—most familiar to your students. A quick transition, without fanfare, introduces the newton. We don't make units a big deal and don't get into the laborious task of unit conversions, which is more appropriate for physics majors.

A brief treatment of units and systems of measurement is provided in Appendix A.

If you get deeply into motion, you can consider the *Sonic Ranger* lab, which uses a sonar ranging device to plot in real time the motion of students, rolling balls, or whatever. This lab can be intriguing, so be careful that it doesn't swallow too much time. Again, overtime on kinematics is the black hole of physics teaching!

In the *Practice Book*:
• Vectors and Equilibrium
• Free Fall Speed
• Acceleration of Free Fall

In *Next-Time Questions*:
• The Scaffold in Equilibrium
• The Bee and the Bicycle

In the *Lab Manual*:
• Go Go Go! (experiment on graphing motion)
• Sonic Ranger (activity on graphing motion)
• Walking the Plank (activity)

Transparencies:
Figures 2.4, 2.9, 2.13, 2.15, 2.19, 2.22, 2.24

Suggested Presentation

Begin by holding up the textbook and remarking on its vast amount of information. A look at the table of contents shows there is much to cover. Whereas some material will be covered in depth, some will not. State that they will come to feel quite comfortable with an understanding of much of the content, but not all. There isn't time for a thorough treatment of all material. So rather than bogging down at the beginning of your course and ending up racing over material at the term's end, you're going to do it the other way around, and race through this beginning chapter. Rather than tilling this soil with a deep plow setting, you're going to skim it and dig in later. (This will help you avoid overtime on kinematics!)

Your first question: What means of motion has done more to change the way cities are built than any other? [Answer: The elevator!]

Explain the importance of simplifying. Explain that motion, for example, is best understood by first neglecting the effects of air resistance, buoyancy, spin, and the shape of the moving object. Beneath these factors are simple relationships that may otherwise be masked. So you'll concentrate on simple cases and avoid complexities. State that you're not trying to challenge them, but to teach them some of the physical science that you yourself have learned. Better they understand a simple case than be miffed by a complicated one that less clearly focuses on the main concept being treated.

Aristotle's Classification of Motion

Briefly discuss Aristotle's views on motion. His views were a good beginning for his time. They were flawed from the point of view of what we know today, but his efforts to classify all things, motion being one of them, was a boost in human thinking. Perhaps we remember him too much for his errors, when in total, he did much to shape good thinking in his time.

Galileo's Concept of Inertia

Acknowledge the chief difference between Aristotle's approach and that of Galileo. The big difference between these two giant intellects was *the role of experiment*—emphasized by Galileo. The legendary experiment at the Leaning Tower of Pisa is a good example. Interestingly, legend has it that many people who saw the falling objects fall together continued to teach otherwise. Seeing is not always believing. Ideas that are firmly established in one's thinking are difficult to change. People in science must be prepared to have their thinking challenged often.

Point to an object in the room and state that if it started moving, one would reasonably look for a cause for its motion. We would say that a force of some kind was responsible, and that would seem reasonable. By force, you mean quite simply, a push or a pull. Tie this idea to the notion of force maintaining motion as Aristotle saw it. State that a cannonball remains at rest in the cannon until a force is applied, and that the force of expanding gases drives the ball out of the barrel when it is fired. But what keeps the cannonball moving when the gases no longer act on it? Galileo wondered about the same question when a ball gained speed in rolling down an incline but moved at constant speed on a level surface. This leads you into a discussion of inertia. In the everyday sense, inertia refers to a habit or a rut. In physics, it's another word for laziness, or the resistance to change as far as the state of motion of an object is concerned. Inertia was first introduced not by Newton, but by Galileo as a result of his inclined-plane experiments. You'll return to this concept when Newton's first law is treated in the following chapter.

How much inertia an object has is related to the amount of mass the object has. Mass is a measure of the amount of material in an object. Weight is the gravitational attraction of the earth for this amount of material. Whereas mass is basic, weight depends on location. You'd weigh a lot more on Jupiter than on Earth, and a lot less on the surface of the moon. Mass and weight are proportional; hence, they are often confused.

Mass is sometimes confused with volume. Comparing an overstuffed fluffy pillow to a small automobile battery should convince anyone that mass and volume are different. The unit of mass is the kilogram, and the unit of volume is cubic meters or liters.

Density is a concept of fundamental importance and is often confused with both mass and volume. Try the following demo to make the concept of density clear. Measure the dimensions of a large wooden cube in centimeters, and find its mass with a pan balance. Define density = mass/volume. (Use the same cube when you discuss flotation later.) Some of your students will unfortunately conceptualize density as massiveness or bulkiness rather than massiveness per bulkiness, even when they give a verbal definition properly. This can be helped with the following:

> CHECK YOUR NEIGHBOR: Which has the greater density, a cupful of water or a lake-full of water? A kilogram of lead or a kilogram of feathers? A single uranium atom or the world?

I jokingly relate breaking a candy bar in two and giving the smaller piece to my friend who looks disturbed. "I gave you the same density of candy bar as I have."

Contrast the density of matter and the density of atomic nuclei that comprise so tiny a fraction of space within matter. From about 2 g/cm^3 to 2×10^{14} g/cm^3. And in a further crushed state, the interior of neutron stars, about 10^{16} gm/cm^3.

Mass Versus Weight

To distinguish between mass and weight, compare the efforts of pushing horizontally on a block of slippery ice on a frozen pond versus lifting it. Or consider the weightlessness of a massive anvil in outer space and how it would be difficult to shake. And if it were moving toward you, it would be harmful to be in its way because of its great tendency to remain in motion. The following demo (often used to illustrate impulse and momentum) makes the distinction nicely:

> DEMONSTRATION: Hang a massive ball by a string and show that the top string breaks when the bottom is pulled with gradually more force, but the bottom string breaks when the string is jerked. Ask which of these cases illustrates weight. (Interestingly enough, it's the weight of the ball that makes for the greater tension in the top string.) Then ask which of these cases illustrates inertia. (When jerked, the tendency of the ball to resist the sudden downward acceleration, its inertia, is responsible for the lower string breaking.) This is the best demo we know of for showing the different effects of weight and mass.

One Kilogram Weighs 9.8 Newtons

Suspend a 1-kg mass from a spring scale and show that it weighs 9.8 N. We can round this off to 10 N, for precision is not needed.

Units of Force—Newtons

I suggest not making a big deal about the unfamiliar unit of force—the newton. I simply state that it is the unit of force used by physicists, and if students find themselves uncomfortable with it, simply think of "pounds" in its place. Relative magnitudes, rather than actual magnitudes, are the emphasis of conceptual integrated science anyway. Do as my mentor Burl Grey does in Figure 2.10 and suspend a familiar mass from a spring scale. If the mass is a kilogram and the scale is calibrated in newtons, it will read 9.8 N. If the scale is calibrated in pounds, it will read 2.2 pounds. State that you're not going to waste valued time in unit conversions. (Students can do enough of that in one of those dull physics courses they've heard about.)

> CHECK YOUR NEIGHBOR: Which has more mass, a 1-kg stone or a 1-lb stone? [A 1-kg stone has more mass, for it weighs 2.2 lb. But we're not going to make a fuss about such conversions. If the unit newton bugs you, think of it as a unit of force or weight in a foreign language for now!]

Net Force

Discuss the idea of more than one force acting on something, and the resulting net force. Figure 2.9 captures the essence. Here's where you can introduce vectors. Note that the forces in the figure are represented by arrows. Drawn to scale, these are vectors. Briefly distinguish between vector quantities (like force, velocity, and, as we shall see, acceleration) and scalar quantities (time, mass, volume).

Equilibrium for Objects at Rest

Cite other *static* examples, where the net force is zero as evidenced by no changes in motion. Hold the 1-kg mass at rest in your hand and ask how much net force acts on it. Be sure they distinguish between the 9.8 N gravitational force on the object and the zero net force on it—as evidenced by its state of rest. (The concept of acceleration is introduced shortly.) When suspended by the spring scale, point out that the scale is pulling up on the object, with just as much force as the earth pulls down on it. Pretend to step on a bathroom scale. Ask how much gravity is pulling on you. This is evident by the scale reading. Then ask what the net force is that acts on you. This is evident by your absence of any motion change. Consider two scales, one foot on each, and ask how each scale would read. Then ask how the scales would read if you shifted your weight more on one scale than the other. Ask if there is a rule to guide the answers to these questions. There is: $\Sigma F = 0$. For any object in equilibrium, the net force on it must be zero. Before answering, consider the skit outlined below.

Sign Painter Skit   Draw on the board the sketch below, which shows two painters on a painting rig suspended by two ropes.

Step 1: If both painters have the same weight and each stands next to a rope, the supporting force in the ropes will be equal. If spring scales were used, one on each rope, the forces in the ropes would be evident. Ask what the scale readings in each rope would be in this case. [The answer is that each rope will support the weight of one man + half the weight of the rig—both scales will show equal readings.]

Step 2: Suppose one painter walks toward the other as shown in the sketch, which you draw on the chalkboard (or show via overhead projector). Will the reading in the left rope increase? Will the reading in the right rope decrease? Grand question: Will the reading in the left rope increase exactly as much as the decrease in tension in the right rope? And if so, how does either rope "know" about the change in the other rope? After neighbor discussion, be sure to emphasize that the answers to these questions lie in the framework of the Equilibrium Rule: $\Sigma F = 0$. Because there is no change in motion, the net force must be zero, which means the upward support forces supplied by the ropes must add up to the downward force of gravity on the two men and the rig. So a decrease in one rope must necessarily be met with a corresponding increase in the other. (This example is dear to my heart. Both Burl and I didn't know the answer way back then—because neither he nor I had a model for analyzing the problem. We didn't know about Newton's first law and the Equilibrium Rule. How different one's thinking is depends on whether there is a model or guidance. If Burl and I had been mystical in our thinking, we might have been more concerned with how each rope "knows" about the condition of the other. This is the approach that intrigues many people with a nonscientific view of the world.)

The Support Force (Normal Force)

Ask what forces act on a book at rest on your lecture table. Then discuss Figure 2.12, explaining that the atoms in the table behave like tiny springs. This upward support force is equal and opposite to the weight of the book, as evidenced by the book's state of rest. The support force is a very real force. Because it is always perpendicular to the surface, it is called a *normal force*. Without it, the book would be in a state of free fall.

Friction—A Force That Affects Motion

Drag a block at constant velocity across your lecture table. Acknowledge the force of friction, and how it must exactly counter your pulling force. Show the pulling force with a spring balance. Now, because the block moves without accelerating, ask for the magnitude of the friction force. It must be equal and opposite to your scale reading. Then the net force is zero. While sliding, the block is in dynamic equilibrium. That is, $\Sigma F = 0$.

Equilibrium of Moving Things

If you're in the car of a smoothly moving train and you balance a deck of cards on a table, they are in equilibrium whether the train is in motion or not. If there is no change in motion (acceleration), the cards don't "know the difference."

Speed and Velocity

Define speed, writing its equation in longhand form on the board while giving examples (automobile speedometers, etc.). Similarly define velocity, citing how a race car driver is interested in his *speed,* whereas an airplane pilot is interested in her *velocity* (speed and direction).

Motion Is Relative

Acknowledge that motion is relative to a frame of reference. When walking down the aisle of a train at 1 m/s, your speed relative to the floor of the train is different than your speed relative to the ground. If the train is moving at 50 m/s, then your speed relative to the ground is 51 m/s if you're walking forward, or 49 m/s if you're walking toward the rear of the train. Tell your class that you're not going to make a big deal about distinguishing between speed and velocity, but you are going to make a big deal of distinguishing between speed or velocity and another concept—*acceleration.*

Galileo and Acceleration

Define acceleration, identifying it as a vector quantity, and cite the importance of *change.* That's change in speed, or change in direction. Hence, both are acknowledged by defining acceleration as a rate of change in velocity rather than speed. Ask your students to identify the three controls in an automobile that enable the auto to *change* its state of motion—that produce *acceleration* (accelerator, brakes, and steering wheel). State how one lurches in a vehicle that is undergoing acceleration, especially for circular motion, and state why the definition of velocity includes direction to make the definition of acceleration all-encompassing. Talk of how without lurching one cannot sense motion, giving examples of coin flipping in a high-speed aircraft versus doing the same when the same aircraft is at rest on the runway.

Units for Acceleration

Give numerical examples of acceleration in units of kilometers/hour per second to establish the idea of acceleration. Be sure that your students are working on the examples with you. For example, ask them to find the acceleration of a car that goes from rest to 100 km/h in 10 seconds. It is important that you not use examples involving seconds twice until they taste success with the easier kilometers/hour per second examples. Have them check their work with their neighbors as you go along. Only after they get the hang of it, introduce meters/second/second in your examples to develop a sense for the units m/s^2.

Falling Objects

Round off $9.8 \ m/s^2$ to $10 \ m/s^2$ in your discussions, and you'll more easily establish the relationships between velocity and distance. Later you can move to the more precise $9.8 \ m/s^2$, when more precision is wanted.

> CHECK YOUR NEIGHBOR: If an object is dropped from an initial position of rest from the top of a cliff, how *fast* will it be traveling at the end of 1 second? (You might add, "Write the answer on your notepaper." And then, "Look at your neighbor's paper—if your neighbor doesn't have the right answer, reach over and help him or her—talk about it.")

After explaining the answer when class discussion dies down, repeat the process, asking for the speed at the end of 2 seconds, and then for 10 seconds. This leads you into stating the relationship $v = gt$, which by now you can express in shorthand notation. After any questions, discussion, and examples, state that you are going to pose a different question—not asking for how *fast,* but for how *far.* Ask how far the object falls in 1 second.

Ask for a written response and then ask if the students could explain to their neighbors *why* the distance is only 5 m rather than 10 m. After they've discussed this for almost a minute or so, ask, "If you maintain a speed of 60 km/h for 1 hour, how far do you go?"—then, "If you maintain a speed of 10 m/s for 1 second, how far do you go?" *Important point:* You'll appreciably improve your instruction if you allow some thinking time after you ask a question. Not doing so is the folly of too many teachers. Then continue, "Then why is the answer to the first question not 10 meters?" After a suitable time, stress the idea of *average* velocity and the relation $d = vt$.

For accelerating objects that start from a rest position, the average velocity is half the final velocity (average velocity = [initial velocity + final velocity]/2).

> CHECK YOUR NEIGHBOR: How far will a freely falling object that is released from rest fall in 2 seconds? In 10 seconds? (When your class is comfortable with this, then ask how far in 1/2 second.)

Investigate Figure 2.23 and have students complete the speed readings. Ask what odometer readings (that measure distance) would be for the speeds shown. To avoid information overload, we restrict all numerical examples of free fall to cases that begin at rest. Why? Because it's simpler that way. (We prefer our students understand simple physics rather than be confused about not-so-simple physics!) We do go this far with them:

Two-Track Demo
Look ahead at the two tracks shown in Exercise 25. With your hand, hold both balls at the top end of the tracks and ask which will get to the end first. Or you can quip, which will win the race, the slow one or the fast one? Or, the one with the greatest average speed or the one with the smaller average speed? Asked these latter ways, the question guides the answer. But be ready to find that most students will intuitively know the balls will reach the end with the same speed. (This is more obvious from a conservation of momentum point of view.) But the question is not of speed, but of *time*—which gets there first. And that's a challenge to realize that! The speed gained by the ball on the lower part of the dipped track is lost coming up the other side, so, yes, they reach the end with the same speed. But the gained speed at the bottom of the dip means more average speed overall. You'll get a lot of discussion on this one. You can make your own tracks quite simply. I got this idea from my friend and colleague, Chelcie Liu, who simply bought a pair of equal length bookcase supports and bent them by hand. They are more easily bent with the aid of a vice.

Integrated Science—Biology, Astronomy, Chemistry, and Earth Science: Friction Is Universal
To make the point that friction is indeed universal, break students into small groups and ask them to list examples of friction that relate to each of the major science subject areas—physics, chemistry, biology, earth science, and astronomy. Have students state their examples so all can appreciate the diversity of friction applications. Also, you might have a brick available to students interested in verifying the concept discussed in the Concept Check question for themselves.

Integrated Science—Biology: Hang Time
This fascinating idea completes the chapter. Most students (and other instructors) are amazed that the best athletes cannot remain airborne for a second in a standing jump. This prompts great class discussion. You can challenge your students by saying you'll award an *A* to any student who can do a 1-second standing jump! You'll have takers; but you'll award no *A*'s for this feat.

3   Newton's Laws of Motion

Demonstration Equipment

Spring balance and wood block (that you'll pull across the table at constant speed)

Iron ball, about 1 kilogram, with hooks for attached strings (mass vs. weight demo)

Hammer and heavy weight (or sledgehammer and blacksmith anvil) for inertia demo

This is a central chapter—the backbone of classical mechanics. The concept of inertia has already been introduced, so you begin here with more illustrations of the same concept under the banner of Newton's first law. The second and third follow, and the chapter culminates with a treatment of vectors. This is a heavy chapter that needs time and care.

In the *Practice Book*:
* Newton's First Law and Friction
* Nonaccelerated and Accelerated Motion
* A Day at the Races with Newton's Second Law: $a = \dfrac{F}{m}$
* Dropping Masses and Accelerating Cart
* Mass and Weight
* Converting Mass to Weight
* Bronco and the Newton's Second Law
* Newton's Third Law
* Nellie and Newton's Third Law
* Vectors and the Parallelogram Rule
* Vectors
* Force Vectors and the Parallelogram Rule
* Force-Vector Diagrams

In the *Lab Manual*:
* Putting the Force Before the Cart (activity)

In *Next-Time Questions*:
* Pellet in the Spiral
* Ball Swing
* Falling Elephant and Feather
* Falling Balls
* Dart Guns
* Skydiver
* Truck and Car Collision
* Acceleration at the Top
* Net Force Halfway Up
* Acceleration on the Way Up
* Scale Reading
* Tug of War
* Tug of War 2
* Leaning Tower of Pisa Drop
* Nellie Suspended by Ropes

Transparencies:
Figures 3.4, 3.5, 3.8, 3.13, 3.14, 3.15, 3.17, 3.24, 3.25, 3.31, *Math Connection* Vector calculations, *Math Connection* Horizontal and vertical vector components

Suggested Presentation

Newton's First Law of Motion—The Law of Inertia

Begin with a demonstration, such as the tablecloth pull.

> DEMONSTRATION: Show that inertia refers also to objects at rest with the classic *tablecloth-and-dishes demonstration*. [Be sure to pull the tablecloth slightly downward so there is no upward component of force on the dishes!] I precede this demo with a simpler version, a simple block of wood on a piece of cloth—but with a twist. I ask what the block will do when I suddenly whip the cloth toward me. After a neighbor check, I surprise the class when they see that the block has been stapled to the cloth! This illustrates Newton's zeroth law—be skeptical. Then I follow up with the classic tablecloth demo. Don't think the classic demo is too corny, for your students will really love it.

Of course when we show a demonstration to illustrate a particular concept, there is almost always more than one concept involved. The tablecloth demo is no exception, which also illustrates impulse and momentum (Chapter 4 material). The plates experience two impulses: friction between the cloth and the dishes, and friction between the sliding dishes and the table. The first impulse moves the dishes slightly toward you. It is brief, and very little momentum builds up. Once the dishes are no longer on the cloth, the second impulse acts in a direction away from you and prevents continued sliding toward you, bringing the dishes to rest. Done quickly, the brief displacement of the dishes is hardly noticed. Is inertia really at work here? Yes, for if there were no friction in the demo, the dishes would remain at rest.

> DEMONSTRATION: Continuing with inertia, do as Jim Szeszol does and fashion a wire coat hanger into an *m* shape as shown. Two globs of clay are stuck to each end. Balance it on your head, with one glob in front of your face. State you wish to view the other blob and ask how you can do so without touching the apparatus. Then simply turn around and look at it. It's like rotating the bowl of soup only to find the soup remains put. Inertia in action! (Of course, like the tablecloth demo, there is more physics here than inertia; this demo can also be used to illustrate rotational inertia and the conservation of angular momentum.)

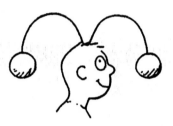

A useful way to impart the idea of mass and inertia is to place two objects, say a pencil and a piece of chalk, in the hands of a student and ask for a judgment of which is heavier. The student will likely respond by shaking them, one in each hand. Point out that in so doing, the student is really comparing their inertias and is making use of the intuitive knowledge that weight and inertia are directly proportional to each other. In the next chapter, you'll focus more on the distinctions between mass and weight and between mass and volume.

> CHECK YOUR NEIGHBOR: How does the law of inertia account for removing dirt from your shoes by stamping on the porch before entering a house? Removing snow from your shoes by doing the same? Removing dust from a coat by shaking it?

> DEMONSTRATION: Do as Marshall Ellenstein does and place a metal hoop atop a narrow jar. On top of the hoop balance a piece of chalk. Then whisk the hoop away, and the chalk falls neatly into the narrow opening. The key here is to grab the hoop on the inside, on the side farthest from your sweep. This elongates the hoop horizontally and the part that supports the chalk drops from beneath the chalk. (If you grab the hoop on the nearer side, the elongation will be vertical and pop the chalk up into the air!)

> DEMONSTRATION: Lie on your back and have an assistant place a blacksmith's anvil on your stomach. Have the assistant strike the anvil rather hard with a sledgehammer. The principles here are the same as the ball and string demo. Both the inertia of the ball and the inertia of the anvil resist the changes in motion they would otherwise undergo. So, the string doesn't break, and your body is not squashed. (Be sure that your assistant is skillful with the hammer. When I began teaching I used to trust students to the task. In my fourth year, the student who volunteered was extra nervous in front of the class and missed the anvil entirely—but not me. The hammer smashed into my hand, breaking two fingers. I was lucky I was not seriously injured.)

Relate the idea of tightening a hammerhead by slamming the opposite end of the handle on a firm surface to the bones of the human spine after jogging or even walking around. Interestingly, we are similarly a bit shorter at night. Ask your students to find a place in their homes that they can't quite reach before going to bed—a place that is 1 or 2 centimeters higher than their reach. Then tell them to try again when they awake the next morning. Unforgettable, for you are likely instructing them to discover something about themselves they were not aware of!

The Moving Earth
Stand facing a wall and jump up. Then ask why the wall does not smash into you as the earth rotates under you while you're airborne. Relate this to the idea of a helicopter ascending over San Francisco, waiting motionless for 3 hours and waiting until Washington, DC, appears below, then descending. Hooray, this would be a neat way to fly across the country! Except, of course, for the fact that the "stationary" helicopter remains in motion with the ground below. "Stationary" relative to the stars means it would have to fly as fast as the earth turns (what jets attempt to do!).

Acceleration Relates to Force
Acceleration was introduced in the previous chapter and polished a bit with the falling speedometers, á la the *Practice Book*. Now we move on to the cause of acceleration—force. State that acceleration is produced by an imposed force. Write this as $a \sim F$, and give examples of doubling the force and the resulting doubling of the acceleration, and so forth. Introduce the idea of net force, with appropriate examples—like applying twice the force to a stalled car gives it twice as much acceleration—three times the force, three times the acceleration.

Newton's Second Law Links Force, Acceleration, and Mass
Point out that although Galileo introduced the idea of inertia, discussed the role of forces, and defined acceleration, he never made the connections to these ideas as Newton did with his second law. Although Galileo is credited as the first to demonstrate that in the absence of air resistance, falling objects fall with equal accelerations, he was unable to say why this is so. The answer is given by Newton's second law.

SKIT: Hold a heavy object like a kilogram weight and a piece of chalk with outstretched hands, ready to drop them. Ask your class which will strike the ground first if you drop them simultaneously. They know. Ask them to imagine that you ask the same of a bright child, who responds by asking to handle the two objects before giving an answer. Pretend you are the child judging the lifting of the two objects. "The metal object is heavier than the chalk, which means there is more gravity force acting on it, which means it will accelerate to the ground before the chalk does." Write the child's argument in symbol notation on the board, $a \sim F$. Then go through the motions of asking the same of another child, who responds with a good argument that takes inertia rather than weight into account. This child says, after shaking the metal and chalk back and forth in his or her hands, "The piece of metal is more massive than the chalk, which means it has more inertia than the chalk, which means it will be harder to get moving than the chalk. So the chalk will race to the ground first, while the inertia of the metal causes it to lag behind." Write this kid's argument with $a \sim \dfrac{1}{m}$. State that the beauty of science is that such speculations can be ascertained by experiment. Drop the weight and the chalk to show that however sound each child's argument seemed to be, the results do not support either. Then bring both arguments together with $a \sim \dfrac{F}{m}$, Newton's second law.

CHECK YOUR NEIGHBOR (similar to one in the text): Suppose in a high-flying airplane the captain announces over the cabin public address system that the plane is flying at a constant 900 km/h, and the thrust of the engines is a constant 80,000 newtons. What is the acceleration of the airplane? [*Answer*: Zero, because velocity is constant.] What is the combined force of air resistance that acts all over the plane's outside surface? [*Answer*: 80,000 N. If it were less, the plane would speed up; if it were more, the plane would slow down.]

Objects in Free Fall Have Equal Acceleration
The falling speedometers of Figure 2.23 of the previous chapter show that acceleration of free fall is constant. Speed picks up, and distance of fall increases, but acceleration remains a constant 10 m/s^2. Newton's second law provides the explanation. This is importantly illustrated in the falling bricks and feathers of Figure 3.9. Emphasize it!

Acceleration of Fall is Less When Air Resistance Acts

DEMONSTRATION: After you have made clear the cases with no friction, then make a transition to practical examples that involve friction—leading off with the dropping of sheets of paper, one crumpled and one flat. Point out that the masses and weights are the same, and the only variable is air resistance. Bring in the idea of net force again, asking what the net force is when the paper falls at constant speed.

CHECK YOUR NEIGHBOR: What is the acceleration of a feather that "floats" slowly to the ground? The net force acting on the feather? If the feather weighs 0.01 N, how much air resistance acts upward against it?

These questions lead into a discussion of the parachutists in Figure 3.10. They also lead the way to exercises in the *Practice Book*.

For your information, the terminal velocity of a falling baseball is about 150 km/h (95 mi/h), and for a falling Ping-Pong ball about 32 km/h (20 mi/h).

So far we have regarded a force as a push or a pull. We will now consider a broader definition of force.

A Force Is Part of an Interaction
Hold a piece of tissue paper at arm's length, and ask if the heavyweight champion of the world could hit the paper with 50 pounds of force. Ask your class to check their answers with their neighbors. Then don't give your answer. Instead, continue with your lecture.

Reach out to your class and state, "I can't touch you, without you touching me in return—I can't nudge this chair without the chair in turn nudging me—I can't exert a force on a body without that body in turn exerting a force on me. In all these cases of contact, there is a *single* interaction between *two* things—contact requires a *pair* of forces, whether they be slight nudges or great impacts, between *two* things. This is Newton's third law of motion. Call attention to the examples of Figure 3.17.

Newton's Third Law—Action and Reaction
Extend your arm horizontally, and show the class that you can bend your fingers upward only very little. Show that if you push with your other hand, and thereby apply a force to them, or have a student do the same, they will bend appreciably more. Then walk over to the wall and show that the inanimate wall does the same (as you push against the wall). State that everybody will acknowledge that you are pushing on the wall, but only a few realize the fundamental fact that the wall is simultaneously pushing on you also—as evidenced by your bent fingers!

CHECK YOUR NEIGHBOR: Identify the action and reaction forces for the case of a bat striking the ball. [Ball strikes bat.]

Simple Rule Distinguishes Action and Reaction
When body A acts on body B, body B reacts on body A. It makes no difference which is called action and which is called reaction. Figure 3.17 captures the essence.

Discuss walking on the floor in terms of the single interaction between you and the floor, and the pair of action and reaction forces that comprise this interaction. Contrast this to walking on frictionless ice, where no interaction occurs. Ask how one could leave a pond of frictionless ice. Make the answer easy by saying one has a massive brick in hand. By throwing the brick there is an interaction between the thrower and the brick. The reaction to the force on the brick, the recoiling force, sends one to shore. Or without such a convenient brick, one has clothing. Or if no clothing, one has air in the lungs. One could blow air in jet fashion. Exhale with the mouth facing away from shore, but be sure to inhale with the mouth facing toward shore.

CHECK YOUR NEIGHBOR: Identify the force that pushes a car along the road. [Interestingly enough, the force that pushes cars is provided by the road. Why? The tires push on the road (action), and the road pushes on the tires (reaction). So roads push cars along. A somewhat different viewpoint!]

Action and Reaction on Objects of Different Masses
Most people say that the Moon is attracted to Earth by gravity. Ask most people if Earth is also attracted to the Moon, and if so, which pulls harder, Earth or the Moon? You'll get mixed answers. Physicists think differently than most people on this topic: Rather than saying the Moon is attracted to Earth by gravity, a physicist would say there is an attractive force between Earth and the Moon. There is an important difference here.

Asking if the Moon pulls as hard on the Earth as the Earth pulls on the Moon is similar to asking if the distance between New York and Los Angeles is the same as the distance between Los Angeles and New York. Rather than thinking in terms of two distances, we think of a single distance *between* New York and Los Angeles. Likewise, there is a single gravitational interaction between Earth and the Moon.

Action and Reaction Forces Act on Different Objects

Show your outstretched hand where you have a stretched rubber band between your thumb and forefinger. Ask which is pulling with greater force, the thumb or the finger. Or, as you increase the stretch, which is being pulled with more force toward the other—the thumb toward the finger or the finger toward the thumb? After discussion with a neighbor, stress the single interaction between things that pull on each other. Earth and the Moon are each pulling on each other. Their pulls on each other comprise a single interaction. This point of view makes a moot point of deciding which exerts the greater force, the Moon on Earth or Earth on the Moon, or the ball on the bat or the bat on the ball, and so forth. Pass a box of rubber bands to your class and have them do it.

> DEMONSTRATION: Tug-of-war in class. Have a female team engage in a tug-of-war with a male team of men. If you do this on a smooth floor, with the guys wearing socks and gals wearing rubber-soled shoes, the gals will win. The team who wins in this game is the team who pushes harder on the floor.

Discuss the firing of a cannonball from a cannon, as treated in the chapter. Illustrate Newton's third law with a skit about a man who is given one last wish before being shot, who states that his crime demands more punishment than being struck by a tiny bullet, who wishes instead that the mass of the bullet match the magnitude of his crime (being rational in a rigid totalitarian society), that the mass of the bullet be much, much more massive than the gun from which it is fired—and that his antagonist pull the trigger!

Return to your question about whether a heavyweight boxer could hit a piece of tissue paper with a force of 50 pounds or so. Now your class understands (hopefully) that the fist can't produce any more force on the paper than the paper exerts on the fist. The paper doesn't have enough mass to do this, so the answer is no. The fighter can't hit the paper any harder than the paper can hit in return. Consider solving Problem 9 from the end-of-chapter questions here.

Importance of Identifying Systems

Much of the confusion of Newton's third law has to do with failure to define a system. This is covered at length in Figures 3.22–3.25 in the text (the apple and the orange). In the system of only the cart, there is a net force—the one provided by the pull of the apple minus the small friction of the wheels on the ground. In the system of only the apple, the net force is the ground pushing on it minus the reaction pull by the cart. In the system of the orange–apple, the net force is that of the ground pushing on the apple. This point is worth developing.

Consider the following three systems: pool ball A, pool ball B, and balls A + B. Only in the two-ball system, A + B, is the net force zero.

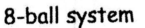

8-ball system　　**cue-ball system**　　**cue-ball + 8 ball system**

Vectors

Exercises in the *Practice Book* nicely get your students into vectors. Use care with vectors, for this is a topic that can be overdone in a course. Although introduced in this chapter, a real need for discussion will occur when projectiles are studied in Chapter 5. However, an easier beginning is with forces.

Forces at an Angle

Again, the *Practice Book* nicely develops force vectors. As a demonstration, support a heavy weight with a pair of scales, as shown. Show that as the angles between supporting strings are wider, the tensions increase. This explains why one can safely hang from a couple of strands of vertical clothesline, but can't when the clothesline is horizontally strung. Interesting stuff.

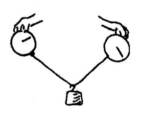

Tell your students that humankind struggled for nearly 2000 years in developing the ideas of this chapter. With this in mind, remind them that they should be patient with themselves if it takes a few days or weeks to achieve as much.

Integrated Science—Biology: Gliding

This feature extends the ideas presented in the section *When Acceleration Is Less than g—Non-Free Fall*, relating surface area to air resistance and reaching terminal speed. Besides mentioning the intriguing adaptations of Draco lizards and flying frogs (whetting students' appetites for biology), this feature explains that one of the evolutionary advantages of gliding is its energy efficiency. Gliding animals can move fast and far with a minimum of energy expenditure. You might give your students a heads-up that energy efficiency is a topic that is important across the sciences—indeed, it is formally explained in Chapter 4 as it relates to machines and energy conservation.

Integrated Science—Biology: Animal Locomotion

Animals consistently make use of Newton's third law for locomotion. Brainstorm examples with students. Or, for a hands-on (actually feet-on) activity, ask students to get up, take off their shoes if they want, and take a few steps. Challenge them to feel the forces of the floor on their feet. Can they verify Figure 3.27 for themselves—that is, can they feel that in walking, a person pushes off the back foot while the forward foot is involved in a controlled fall? The back foot is ever pushing the walker forward due to the third-law force of the floor on it.

We teachers learned our physics when we started teaching it — when we *talked* about it. Your students can learn this way also, right in your class. Become proficient at the Check-Your-Neighbor way of teaching. Learn to ask good questions that promote peer discussions. More questioning, more student interaction, and less professing!

4   Momentum and Energy

Demonstration Equipment

Air track and carts of equal and unequal mass (if you're so fortunate!)

A simple pendulum (any ball tied to a length of string)

The swinging balls apparatus (optional)

This chapter begins by continuing where Chapter 3 leaves off. Newton's second and third laws lead directly to momentum and its conservation. We emphasize the impulse–momentum relationship with applications to many examples that have been selected to grab the students' interest. In presenting your own, the exaggerated symbol technique as shown in Figures 4.4–4.6 is suggested. Draw a comparison between momentum conservation and Newton's third law in explaining examples such as rocket propulsion. You might point out that either of these is fundamental—that is, momentum conservation may be regarded as a consequence of Newton's third law, or equally, Newton's third law may be regarded as a consequence of momentum conservation. Momentum continues to energy, the most central concept in physics, which is discussed in various forms throughout the remainder of the text.

A system is not only isolated in space, but also in time. When we say that momentum is conserved when one pool ball strikes the other, we mean that momentum is conserved during the brief duration of interaction when outside forces can be neglected. After the interaction, friction quite soon brings both balls to a halt. So, when we isolate a system for purposes of analysis, we isolate both in space and in time. System identification is developed further in the *Practice Book*.

The concept of reduced force for collisions involving extended times is wonderfully employed by air bags in cars. Some airlines use the same idea with similar air bags inside seatbelts. Softer speedway barriers, which extend times of contact during collisions, are now on some racing tracks, including the Indianapolis Motor Speedway. These barriers consist of vertically stacked rectangular steel tubes and up to 14 inches of polystyrene foam, which together absorb more than a third of the energy of impact. Air-bag vests are now available for motorcycle riders (www.dainese.com).

In the *Practice Book*:
* Momentum
* Systems
* Impulse–Momentum
* Conservation of Momentum
* Work and Energy

- Conservation of Energy
- Energy and Momentum

In *Next-Time Questions*:
- Momentum Conservation of Jocko the Clown
- Fired Gun
- Long Cannon
- Car–Truck Collision
- Ball Toss
- Roller Coaster

In the *Lab Manual*:
- Egg Toss (activity)
- Bouncy Board (activity)
- An Uphill Climb (experiment)
- Rolling Stop (experiment)
- Dropping the Ball (experiment)

Transparencies:
Figures 4.4, 4.5, 4.6, 4.10, 4.11, 4.17, 4.18, 4.19, 4.20, 4.23

Suggested Presentation

Momentum—Inertia in Motion
Begin by stating that there is something different between a massive cement truck and a roller skate—they each have a different inertia. And that there is still something different about a moving cement truck and a moving roller skate—they have different momenta. Define and discuss momentum as inertia in motion.

> CHECK YOUR NEIGHBOR: After stating that a cement truck will always have more inertia than an ordinary roller skate, ask if a cement truck will always have more momentum than a roller skate.

Cite the case of the supertankers that cut off their power when they are 25 or so kilometers from port. Because of their huge momentum (due mostly to their huge mass), about 25 kilometers of water resistance are needed to bring them to a halt.

Impulse Changes Momentum
Derive the impulse–momentum relationship. In Chapter 2, you defined acceleration as $a = \Delta\frac{v}{t}$ (really Δt, but you likely used t as the "time interval"). Then you defined acceleration in terms of the force needed, $a = \frac{F}{m}$. Now simply equate: $a = a$, or $\frac{F}{m} = \Delta\frac{v}{t}$; with simple rearrangement, you have $Ft = \Delta mv$ (as in the footnote in Section 4.3).

Then choose your examples in careful sequence: First, those where the object is to increase momentum—pulling a slingshot or arrow in a bow all the way back, the effect of a long cannon for maximum range, driving a golf ball. Second, those examples where small forces are the object when decreasing momentum—pulling your hand backward when catching a ball, driving into a haystack vs. a concrete wall, falling on a surface with give vs. a rigid surface. Then lastly, those examples where the object is to obtain large forces when decreasing momentum—karate. To follow the sequence in the text, discuss karate in the context of the Integrated Science feature, *The Impulse–Momentum Relationship in Sports*.

Point of confusion: In boxing, one "follows through," whereas in karate (or more properly called "tae kwon do"), one "pulls back." But this is not so—an expert does not pull back upon striking his target. He or she strikes in such a way that the hand is made to bounce back, yielding up to twice the impulse to the target (just as a ball bouncing off a wall delivers nearly twice the impulse to the wall than if it stuck to the wall).

> CHECK YOUR NEIGHBOR: Why is falling on a wooden floor in a roller rink less dangerous than falling on the concrete pavement? [Superficial answer: Because the wooden floor has more "give."] Emphasize that this is the beginning of a complete answer—one that is prompted if the question is reworded as follows: Why is falling on a floor with more give less dangerous than falling on a floor with less give? (Answer: Because the floor with more give allows a greater time for the impulse that reduces the momentum of a fall to zero. A greater time for change in momentum means less force.)

The loose coupling between railroad cars is a fascinating example of impulse–momentum. The loose coupling brings a long train initially at rest up to speed in a longer time. If the cars were tightly fastened, too much of a load would have to be moved in the same time. The looseness breaks the times of momentum change into segments. This is important in braking the train as well. (I compare this to taking school load in proper sequence, rather than all at once, where for sure one's wheels would simply spin.)

Bouncing
Discuss bouncing if you have time for this interesting, but nonessential, topic.

Bouncing does not necessarily increase impact force. That depends on impact time. Point out that bouncing involves some reversing of momentum, which means greater momentum change and, hence, greater impulse. If the greater impulse is over an extended time (bouncing from a circus net), impact force is small. If over a short time (plant pot bouncing from your head), the impact force is large. Damage from an object colliding with a person may depend more on energy transfer than on momentum change, so in some cases, damage can be greater in an inelastic collision without bouncing.

Conservation of Momentum
Distinguish between external and internal forces and lead into the conservation of momentum. Show from the impulse–momentum equation that no change in momentum can occur in the absence of an external net force. This is your introduction to the all-important concept of conservation in physics. Soon you'll treat conservation of energy, then conservation of charge, then conservation of nucleons in nuclear reactions. In Appendix B, you'll treat conservation of angular momentum. The conservation principles of physics are very important.

Defining Your System
Momentum is not conserved in a system that experiences an external net force. Consider the simple case of a pool ball striking one at rest. If the system is the ball at rest, then an external force acts on it, and momentum is increased. Momentum for this ball is not conserved. Or if the system is the moving ball, then a reaction force acts on it when it strikes the ball at rest. This external force stops the ball in its tracks. Momentum for this ball is not conserved. Now consider the system of interest to be both balls. For this system, no external force acts. The action and reaction forces occur within the system. For this system, net momentum doesn't change, and momentum is conserved. (It is merely transferred from one part of the system to the other without net change.) How deeply you want to treat the notion of systems is your call. It can be glossed over for general students, or delved into in depth with students who value further study in physics.

Collisions
The numerical example of the air-track carts in the Math Connections box in Section 4.4 might be discussed. This emphasizes the vector nature of momentum—particularly for the case of the carts approaching each other. The emphasis you give to this coverage will vary from class to class. It will be important if you are fortunate enough to have an air-track apparatus. Relate this to the Problems at the end of the chapter, particularly Problems 2, 3, 4, and 5.

DEMONSTRATION: Show momentum conservation with an air-track performance.

(Note: This is a good breaking place.)

The Concept of Energy
Begin by standing on a chair against a wall with an extended heavy pendulum bob held at the tip of your nose. Say nothing. Release the bob and let it swing out, then back to your nose. Don't flinch. Then comment on your confidence in physical laws and lead into a distinction between potential and kinetic energy. That is, point out that where the bob is moving fastest, it is lowest, and where it is highest, it doesn't move at all. The bob transforms energy of motion to energy of position in cyclic fashion. Allow the pendulum to swing to-and-fro while you're talking. Its motion decays. Why? Then point out the transformation of energy from the moving bob to the molecules of air that are encountered, and to the molecules in the bending string or wire at the pivot point. The energy of the pendulum will end up as heat energy. I quip that on a very hot day, somebody, somewhere, is swinging a giant pendulum to-and-fro.

Work—Force × Distance
Define work, and compare it to impulse. In both cases, the effect of exerting a force on something depends on how long the force acts. In the previous case, how long was meant as time, and we spoke of impulse. Now, however, how long is meant as distance, and we speak of work. Cite the examples of the drawn slingshot and the long-barreled cannon, where the added length produces greater speed. We described this greater speed in terms of greater momentum. Now we describe this greater speed in terms of greater energy—that is, greater kinetic energy (KE).

Work is done on an object only when an applied force moves it. Emphasize work done on an object. If work is done on an object, then its energy state is different than before work was done on it. Confusion about work often involves exactly what the work acts on. This is highlighted by this check question.

CHECK YOUR NEIGHBOR: Is work done when a weight lifter holds a barbell stationary above her head? [Yes and no. With each contraction of the weight lifter's heart, a force is exerted through a distance on her blood and so does work on the blood. But this work is not done on the barbell.]

Power
Power has to do with how quickly work gets done. A watt of power is the work done in vertically lifting a quarter-pound hamburger with cheese (approximately 1 N) 1 meter in 1 second.

Mechanical Energy
Cite the various forms of energy, and state that we'll consider only mechanical energy for now, which takes the forms of potential energy (PE) and kinetic energy.

Potential Energy
Return to your pendulum: With the pendulum at equilibrium, show how the force necessary to pull it sideways (which varies with the angle made by the string) is very small compared to the force necessary to lift it vertically (its weight). Point out that for equal elevations, the arced path is correspondingly longer than the vertical path, with the result that the product of the applied force and distance traveled—the work done—is the same for both cases. (Without overdoing it, this is a good place to let your students know about integral calculus—how calculus is required to add up the work segments that continuously increase in a nonlinear way.) Then discuss the work needed to elevate the ball in Figure 4.17.

CHECK YOUR NEIGHBOR: Does a car hoisted for lubrication in a service station have PE? How much work will raise the car twice as high? Three times as high? How much more PE will it have in these cases?

You can give the example of dropping a bowling ball on your toe—first from a distance of 1 mm above your toe, then to various distances up to 1 m above your toe. Each time, the bowling ball would do more work on your toe, because it would possess more gravitational potential energy when released.

Kinetic Energy
Relate force × distance = ΔKE to examples of pushing a car, and then to braking a car as treated in the text. To a close approximation, skidding force is independent of speed. Hence, a change in KE is approximately equal to change in skidding distance. When the car's brakes are applied, the car's kinetic energy is changed into internal energy in the brake pads, tire, and road as they become warmer.

You may or may not at this point preview future material by relating the idea of the KE of molecules and the idea of temperature. State that molecules in a substance having the same temperature have the same average KE. If the masses of the molecules are the same, then it follows that the speeds of the molecules are the same. But what if the masses are different, for example, in a sample of gas made up of light and heavy molecules at the same temperature? Which molecules would move faster? (If you shook a container of billiard balls mixed with Ping-Pong balls so that both kinds of balls had the same kinetic energy, which would move faster in the container?) (If an elephant and a mouse run with the same kinetic energy, which is to say both will do the same amount of work if they bump into the door of a barn, can you say which of the two is running faster?) You might consider the demonstration of inhaling helium and talking at this point—particularly if you are not including the chapters on sound in your course design. Relate the higher temperature due to the faster-moving helium molecules to the higher temperature in a bugle when faster-moving air is blown through it.

Work–Energy Theorem
When discussing whether or not work is done, be sure to specify *done on what*. If you push a stationary wall, you may be doing work on your muscles (that involve forces and distances in flexing), but you do no work *on the wall*. *Key point*: If work is done on something, then the energy of that something changes. Distinguish between the energy one expends in doing things, and the work that is actually done *on* something.

CHECK YOUR NEIGHBOR: When a car slows down due to air resistance, does its KE decrease? [Most certainly!]

CHECK YOUR NEIGHBOR: Which is greater, 1 joule or 1 newton? [Whoops! The comparison is silly, for they're units of completely different things—work and force. An idea about the magnitude of 1 joule is that it is the work done in vertically lifting a quarter-pound hamburger with cheese (approximately 1 N) 1 meter.]

Call attention to the pair of photos showing the heat generated by friction on a skidding bicycle tire (Figure 4.22). How interesting it would be to see infrared photos of the heat generated when a couple of carts collide. Recall that half the KE for a collision of identical cars goes into heat. Seeing that via an infrared photo would be interesting.

Conservation of Energy
Discuss Figures 4.17 and 4.18 and then return to your pendulum. Explain how the kinetic energy and, hence, the speed of the bob at the bottom of its swing, is equal to the speed it would have if dropped vertically through the same height. This is shown in Figure 4.20.

CHECK YOUR NEIGHBOR: Consider a block of wood freely sliding down an incline. When released from rest, it will slide to the bottom with a certain speed. Suppose it slid down a steeper incline, but through the same vertical distance. Will the speed at the bottom be different? [It is impressive that the speeds will be the same. The lesser acceleration down the sloped ramp is compensated for by a longer time. But return to the situation and ask how the *times* to reach the bottom compare and be prepared for an incorrect response, "The same!" Quip and ask if the colors and temperatures will also be the same. Straightforward physics can be confusing enough!]

Discuss conservation of energy as applied to cars. When gasoline combines with oxygen in a car's engine, the chemical potential energy stored in the fuel is converted mainly into molecular KE (thermal energy). Some of this energy, in effect, is transferred to the piston, and some of this causes motion of the car.

Conclude by discussing the central role conservation of energy plays in science. Therefore, conservation of energy is a unifying concept of this book. You will find it pops up over and over again in these chapters in a diversity of contexts. To help your students appreciate the importance of this concept, ask students to browse through the unifying concepts list at the back of this book.

Machines
Show how a lever is a simple machine, obeying the "work in = work out" principle. And show that a pulley is an extension of a simple lever.

Efficiency
It should be enough that your students become acquainted with the idea of efficiency, so I don't recommend setting the plow setting too deep for this topic. The key idea to impart is that of useful energy. To say that an incandescent lamp is 10% efficient is to say that only 10% of the energy input is converted to the useful form of light. All the rest turns to heat. But even the light energy converts to heat upon absorption. So all the energy input to an incandescent lamp is converted to heat. This means that it is a 100% efficient *heater* (but not a 100% device for emitting light).

Sources of Energy
It is important that students don't see electricity, steam, and other transporters of energy as energy sources. Sources include solar, geothermal, and nuclear. Electricity, for example, involves some source such as a waterfall (potential energy) or fuel to produce steam. Look ahead to the Integrated Science feature in Chapter 13 on fuel cells. Another contender for electric power is the concept of undersea turbines activated by tidal flows. Test sites are being researched in Norway, the United Kingdom, and the United States. Watch for development in tidal generators of electricity.

It has been correctly said that hydrogen is the ultimate fuel. When burned in vehicles, as is presently being done with commercial vehicles in Iceland, only water vapor is ejected by the exhaust. This makes it seem like a dream fuel. The big problem is that there is no free hydrogen to burn. It must be removed from molecules where it is abundant. And the removal takes energy, which must come from some energy source. If gasoline is the source, then it is argued that it might as well be used in the vehicles to begin with, for even more pollutants would result at the conversion site. Proponents of a hydrogen economy usually sidestep this basic physics. Saying cars should be powered with hydrogen is akin to saying they should be powered with electricity. Both are not sources of energy—but carriers of energy.

Sooner or later, all the sunlight that falls on an ecosystem will be radiated back into space. Energy in an ecosystem is always in transit—you can rent it, but you can't own it.

End this section on an integrated note by saying that when biologists talk of energy in living systems, they're talking about the same energy discussed in this chapter. Our bodies obey the same principles that levers and other machines obey.

Dark Energy

Not discussed in the text is the current serious speculation of dark energy, which is postulated to be speeding up the expanding universe. You may want to discuss this current finding, which may be one of the most important discoveries in science in the past quarter century.

Integrated Science—Biology: The Impulse–Momentum Relationship in Sports

Break students into pairs and ask them to come up with examples of the impulse–momentum relationship in sports. Have them write a few sentences analyzing their example in terms of $Ft = \Delta mv$.

Note the potential point of confusion: In boxing, one "follows through," whereas in karate (or tae kwon do), students may think one "pulls back." But this is not so—an expert does not pull back upon striking his or her target. He or she strikes in such a way that the hand is made to bounce back, yielding up to twice the impulse to the target (just as a ball bouncing off a wall delivers nearly twice the impulse to the wall than if it stuck to the wall).

Integrated Science—Biology and Chemistry: Glucose—Energy for Life

The idea that energy for most life comes from the sun via the process of photosynthesis is introduced in this feature. Students will continue to develop and refine their understanding of this idea throughout the book. Devote a bit of time to it here to lay the foundation. In terms of this chapter, the integrated concept is that energy can be transformed and is conserved and that this happens as solar energy is trapped by plants and then used by nonphotosynthesizing organisms. Figure 4.13 sums up the relationship.

The details of cellular respiration and the chemical reaction for photosynthesis are presented here to give students a taste of things to come. Please don't hold your students responsible for this material yet—it will be developed in much more detail in Parts 2 and 3 of this book. Depending on their previous science courses, students may be very familiar or completely unfamiliar with cellular structure and the chemistry of photosynthesis. That being said, you may want to discuss the nature of chemical energy at this point, explaining that chemical energy is essentially potential energy stored in chemical bonds. Tie this to the discussion of potential energy earlier in this chapter by explaining (without going into too much depth) that chemical bonds are forces of attraction between oppositely charged particles (protons and electrons). The particles are attracted to one another and possess potential energy as a result of their separation.

Sample Advanced Problem and Solution

(Shows how an equation guides thinking! Note how each step dictates the next step.)

Problem: A car traveling along a level road at speed v slams on the brakes and skids to a stop. If the force of friction on the car is half the car's weight, how far does the car slide? (*Hint:* Use the work–energy theorem and solve for d.)

Solution: By the work–energy theorem,

$$W = \Delta KE$$

Work done on the car is Fd, so

$$Fd = \Delta(1/2 \, mv^2)$$

The only force F that does work to reduce the kinetic energy is the force of friction. This force acts through d, the distance of skidding. The mass of the car is m, and its initial speed is v. In this problem, the final speed of the car will be zero, so the change in kinetic energy is simply the initial kinetic energy at speed v. You're looking for distance, so write the equation in a "$d =$" form. It becomes

$$d = \frac{\Delta(1/2 \, mv^2)}{F} = \frac{1/2 \, mv^2}{f} = \frac{1/2 \, mv^2}{mg/2} = \frac{v^2}{g}$$

where F is half the car's weight, $\frac{mg}{2}$.

Note how the terms in the equation dictate subsequent steps and guide your thinking. The final expression tells you the stopping distance is proportional to speed squared, which is consistent with it being proportional to KE. It also tells you that if g were greater, the force of friction would be greater and skidding distance less—which is quite reasonable. Cancellation of mass tells you that the mass of the car doesn't matter. All cars skidding with the same initial speed, with friction equal to half their weights, will skid the same distance. And as for units, note that $\frac{v^2}{g}$ has the unit $(m^2/s^2)(m/s^2) = m$, a distance, as it should be. How nice that much can be learned by a thoughtful examination of a simple equation.

5   Gravity

This chapter offers a good place to reiterate the idea of a scientific theory and comment on the all-too-common and mistaken idea that because something has the status of scientific theory it is somehow short of being valid. This view is evident in those who say, "But it's *only* a theory." The theory of universal gravitation is *only* a theory—a theory that put astronauts on the Moon!

There is a wonderful oldie but goodie film by NASA, "Zero g," showing footage taken aboard Skylab in 1978, narrated by astronaut Owen Garriott. Newton's laws of motion are reviewed with excellent and entertaining examples. You might share this with your students.

You can compare the pull of the Moon that is exerted on you with the pull exerted by more local masses, via the gravitational equation. Consider the ratio of the mass of the Moon to its distance squared:

$$\frac{7.4 \times 10^{22}\,\text{kg}}{(4 \times 10^5\,\text{km})^2} = \frac{5 \times 10^{12}\,\text{kg}}{\text{km}^2}$$

This is a sizable ratio, one that buildings in your vicinity cannot match (city buildings of greatest mass are typically on the order of 10^6 or 10^7 kilograms). However, if you stand 1 kilometer away from the foot of a mountain of mass 5×10^{12} kilograms (about the mass of Mt. Kilimanjaro), then the pull of the mountain and the pull of the Moon are about the same on you. Simply put, with no friction, you would tend to gravitate from your spot toward the mountain—but you experience no tendency at all to gravitate from your spot toward the Moon! That's because the spot you stand on undergoes the same gravitational acceleration toward the Moon as you do. Both you and the entire Earth are accelerating toward the Moon. Whatever the lunar force on you, it has no tendency to pull you off a weighing scale.

Dark matter is not discussed in the text, to prevent information overload. You may be inclined to mention it as a supplementary topic. Dark matter greatly affects the behavior of the universe, which appears to be accelerating outward, rather than slowing down. A different form of energy, referred to as the dark energy, apparently works against the force of gravity to accelerate the expansion of the universe. The concepts of dark matter and dark energy are at the forefront of physics at this point, and are quite mysterious.

This is an intriguing chapter, for the material is interesting in itself, is interesting historically, and is closely related to areas of space science that are currently in the public eye.

In the *Practice Book*:
• The Inverse-Square Law—Weight
• Ocean Tides
• Projectile Motion
• Tossed-Ball Vectors

- Circular and Elliptical Orbits
- Mechanics Overview

In *Next-Time Questions*:
- Block on a Plane
- Ball Toss from Tower
- Monkey and Banana
- Cannonball Orbit
- Satellite in Orbit

In the *Lab Manual*:
- The Weight (experiment)
- Reaction Time (activity)
- The Big BB Race
- Bull's Eye

Transparencies:
Figures 5.6, 5.7, 5.8, 5.22, 5.24, 5.25, 5.26, 5.30, 5.39

Suggested Presentation

Begin by briefly discussing the simple codes and patterns that underlie the complex things around us, whether musical compositions or DNA molecules, and then briefly describe the harmonious motion of the solar system, the Milky Way, and other galaxies in the universe—stating that the shapes of the planets, stars, and galaxies and their motions are all governed by an extremely simple code, or, if you will, a pattern. Then write the gravitational equation on the board. Give examples of bodies pulling on each other to convey a clear idea of what the symbols in the equation mean and how they relate. (Acknowledge that many other texts and references use the symbol r instead of the d used in this text. The r is used to indicate the radial distance from a body's center of gravity, and to emphasize the center-to-center rather than surface-to surface nature for distance. We don't set our plow that deep, however, and use d for distance.)

The Legend of the Falling Apple
The equation for gravitation begins with the legend of the falling apple. Seeing one event was wonderfully linked to another—the orbiting moon. Or put another way, the falling moon. For it's true: The moon is falling. It always has been. Why doesn't it reach ground? Answer this by establishing what tangential velocity is. If this is not clear, then what follows will not be clear either. Stress the direction of tangential velocity (always parallel to the circumference of a circle—or at right angles to a radius).

The Law of Universal Gravitation
This is Newton's grandest discovery. Define and give examples of the terms in the equation for gravity. The equation to the physical science student should be what sheet music is to a musician.

> CHECK YOUR NEIGHBOR: How is the gravitational force between a pair of planets altered when one of the planets is twice as massive? [Twice.] When both are twice as massive? [Four times as much.] When they are twice as far apart? [One-fourth as much.] When three times as far apart? [1/9 as much.] Ten times as far apart? [1/100 as much.]

> CHECK YOUR NEIGHBOR: What do you say to a furniture mover who claims that gravity increases with increased distance from the earth, as evident to him when he's carrying heavy loads up flights of stairs? [Make a distinction between how tired you get with time and the pull of gravity.]

The Inverse-Square Law
Discuss the inverse-square law and go over Figures 5.5 and 5.6. Mention they could as well represent the intensity of radioactivity.

> CHECK YOUR NEIGHBOR: A sheet of photographic film is exposed to a point source of light that is a certain distance away. If the sheet were instead exposed to the same light four times as far away, how would the intensity on the film compare? [1/16 as much.] A radioactive detector registers a certain amount of radioactivity when it is a certain distance away from a small piece of uranium. If the detector is four times as far from the uranium, how will the radioactivity reading compare? [Again, 1/16 as much.]

The Universal Gravitational Constant, *G*

Don't make a big deal out of *G*. It serves to unite the unit of force with the other units of mass and distance. What *is* interesting, however, is that finding *G* enabled science types to calculate the earth's mass. This was a big deal to the general public back then.

Gravitation Is Universal

Few theories have affected science and civilization as much as Newton's theory of gravitation. The successes of Newton's ideas ushered in the so-called Age of Enlightenment, for Newton had demonstrated that by observation and reason and by employing mechanical models and deducing mathematical laws, people could uncover the very workings of the physical universe. How profound that all the moons, planets, stars, and galaxies have such a beautifully simple rule to govern them; namely,

$$F = G\frac{m_1m_2}{d^2}$$

The formulation of this simple rule is one of the major reasons for the success in science that followed, for it provided hope that other phenomena of the world might also be described by equally simple laws.

This hope nurtured the thinking of many scientists, artists, writers, and philosophers of the 1700s. One of these was the English philosopher John Locke, who argued that observation and reason, as demonstrated by Newton, should be our best judge and guide in all things and that all of nature and even society should be searched to discover any "natural laws" that might exist. Using Newtonian physics as a model of reason, Locke and his followers modeled a system of government that found adherents in the thirteen British colonies across the Atlantic. These ideas culminated in the Declaration of Independence and the Constitution of the United States of America.

Projectile Motion

Roll a ball off the edge of your lecture table and call attention to the curve it follows. The ball is a projectile. Discuss the idea of the "downwardness" of gravity, and how there is no "horizontalness" to it and, therefore, no horizontal influence on the projectile.

Pose the situation of the horizontally held gun and the shooter who drops a bullet at the same time he pulls the trigger, and ask which bullet strikes the ground first.

> DEMONSTRATION: Show the independence of horizontal and vertical motion with a spring-gun apparatus that will shoot a ball horizontally while at the same time dropping another that falls vertically. (This is the gist of "The Big BB Race" activity in the *Lab Manual*.) Follow this up with the popular "monkey and hunter" demonstration.

> CHECK YOUR NEIGHBOR: Point to some target at the far side of your classroom, and ask your students to imagine you are going to project a rock to the target via a slingshot. Ask if you should aim at the target, above it, or below it. Easy stuff. Then ask your class to suppose it takes 1 second for the rock to reach the target. If you aim directly at the target, it will fall beneath and miss. How far beneath the target would the rock hit (supposing the floor weren't in the way)? Have your students check with their neighbors on this one. Then ask how far above you should aim to hit the target. Do a neighbor check on this one. (Here we're ignoring the fact that the horizontal component is less when aimed upward. Note the *Next-Time Question* that features this.)

Projectile Altitude and Range

Point out that the relationship of the curved path of Figure 5.24 and the vertical distance of a fall of 5 meters in 1 second. Stress that the projectile is falling beneath the straight line it would otherwise follow. This idea is important for a later understanding of satellite motion.

Discuss the boy's pitching speed from the 5-m-high tower in Figure 5.31. Ask for the pitching speed if the ball traveled 30 m instead of 20 m. (Note the vertical height is 5 m. If you use any height that does not correspond to an integral number of seconds, you're diverting your focus from physics to algebra.) More interesting is considering greater horizontal distances—great enough for the curvature of the Earth to make a difference in arriving at the answer. It's easy to see that the time the projectile is in the air increases when the Earth curves beneath the trajectory.

> DEMONSTRATION: Here's a great one. Tie strings along the length of a meter stick, and suspend small balls from them. At the 25-cm mark, have the string 5 cm long. At the 50-cm mark, the string

should be 20 cm long, and at the 75-cm mark, 45 cm long. At the end of the stick, at the 100-cm mark, the string should be 80 cm long. Aha, the positions of the balls describe an accurate trajectory—even when the stick is tipped from the horizontal. Consider having your students make this for you.

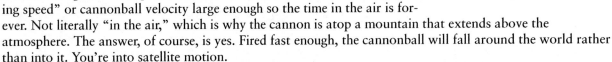

Acknowledge the large effect that air resistance (air drag) has on fast-moving objects such as bullets and cannonballs. A batted baseball, for example, travels only about 60% as far in air as it would in a vacuum. Its curved path is no longer a parabola, as Figure 5.32 indicates.

Fast-Moving Projectiles—Satellites

Sketch "Newton's Mountain," and consider the longer and longer time intervals for greater and greater horizontal speeds. Ask if there is a "pitching speed" or cannonball velocity large enough so the time in the air is forever. Not literally "in the air," which is why the cannon is atop a mountain that extends above the atmosphere. The answer, of course, is yes. Fired fast enough, the cannonball will fall around the world rather than into it. You're into satellite motion.

> CHECK YOUR NEIGHBOR: Why is it confusing to ask why a satellite doesn't fall? [All satellites are continuously falling, in the sense that they fall below the straight line they would travel if they weren't. Why they don't crash to Earth is a different question.]

Earth Satellites

Calculating Satellite Speed   An effective skit that can have your class calculating the speed necessary for close Earth orbit is as follows: call attention to the curvature of the Earth, Figure 5.34. Consider a horizontal laser standing about a meter above the ground with its beam shining over a level desert. The beam is straight, but the desert floor curves 5 m over an 8000-m or 8-km tangent, which you sketch on your chalkboard (or overhead projector). Stress this is not to scale:

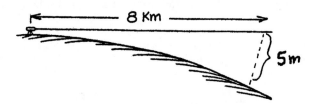

Now erase the laser, and sketch in a supercannon positioned so it points along the laser line. Consider a cannonball fired at, say, 2 km/s, and ask how far downrange it will be at the end of 1 second. A neighbor check should yield an answer of 2 km, which you indicate by drawing a cannonball 2 km from the cannon. But it doesn't really get there, you say, for it falls beneath that point because of gravity. How far? 5 m if the sand weren't in the way.

Ask if 2 km/s is sufficient for orbiting the Earth. Clearly not, for the cannonball strikes the ground. If the cannonball is not to hit the ground, we'd have to dig a trench first, as you show on your sketch, which now looks like this:

Continue by considering a greater muzzle velocity, say 4 km/s, so the cannonball travels 4 km in one second. Ask if this is fast enough to attain an Earth orbit. Student response should indicate that they realize that the cannonball will hit the ground before 1 second is up. Then repeat the previous line of reasoning, again having to dig a trench, and your sketch looks like this:

Continue by considering a greater muzzle velocity—great enough so the cannonball travels 6 km in 1 second. This is 6 km/s. Ask if this is fast enough not to hit the ground (or equivalently, if it is fast enough for Earth orbit). Then repeat the previous line of reasoning, again having to dig a trench. Now your sketch looks like this:

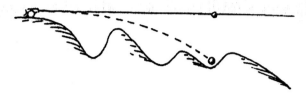

You're almost there: Continue by considering a muzzle velocity great enough so the cannonball travels 8 km in 1 second. (Don't state the velocity is 8 km/s here, as you'll diminish your punch line.) Repeat your previous reasoning, and note that this time you don't have to dig a trench! After a pause, and with a tone of importance, ask the class what speed the cannonball must have to orbit the Earth. Done properly, you have led your class into a "derivation" of orbital speed about the Earth with no equations or algebra.

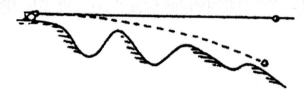

Acknowledge that the gravitational force is less on satellites in higher orbits so they do not need to go so fast. (Actually, not stated in the text, $v = \sqrt{GM/d}$, so a satellite at four times the Earth's radius needs to travel only half as fast, 4 km/s.)

You can wind up your brief treatment of satellite motion and catch its essence via the following skit: Ask your students to pretend they are encountered by a bright youngster, too young to have much knowledge of physics and mathematics, but who, nevertheless, asks why satellites seem to defy gravity and stay in orbit. You ask what answer could correctly satisfy the curiosity of the kid, then pose the following dialogue between the kid and the students in your class (you're effectively suggesting how the student might interact with the bright kid). Ask the kid to observe and then describe what you do, as you hold a rock at arm's length and then simply drop it. The kid replies, "You dropped the rock and it fell to the ground below," to which you respond, "Very good—now what happens this time?" as you move your hand horizontally and again drop the rock. The kid observes and then says, "The rock dropped again, but because your hand was moving, it followed a curved path and fell farther away." You continue, "Very good—now again—" as you throw the rock still farther. The kid replies, "I note that as your hand moves faster, the path follows a wider curve." You're elated at this response, and you ask the kid, "How far away will the rock hit the ground if its curved path matches the curved surface of the Earth?" The kid at first appears very puzzled, but then beams, "Oh—I get it! The stone doesn't hit at all—it's in Earth orbit." Then you interrupt your dialogue and ask the class, "Do YOU get it?" Then back to the kid who asks, "But isn't it really more complicated than that?" to which the answer is no. The essential idea of satellite motion is that simple.

Elliptical Orbits

Refer to Newton's Mountain. Fire the cannonball at 9 km/s. It overshoots a circular path. Your sketch looks like the one here. Ask, at the position shown, is the cannonball moving at 9 km/s, more than 9 km/s, or less than 9 km/s? And why? After a neighbor check, toss a piece of chalk upward and say you toss it upward at 9 m/s. When it's halfway to the top of its path, is it moving 9 m/s, more than 9 m/s, or less than 9 m/s? Equate the two situations. [In both cases, the projectile slows because it is going against gravity.]

Continue your sketch and show a closed path—an ellipse. As you draw the elliptical path, show with a sweeping motion of your arm how the satellite slows in receding from the Earth, moving slowest at its farthermost point, then how it speeds in falling toward the Earth, whipping around the Earth and repeating the cycle over and over again. Move to a fresh part of the chalkboard and redraw with the mountain at the bottom, so your sketch is more like Figure 5.38. (It is more comfortable seeing your chalk moving slowest when farthest coincides with the direction "up" in the classroom. I quip that Australians have no trouble seeing it the first way.)

Sketch in larger ellipses for still greater cannon speeds, with the limit being 11.2 km/s, beyond which the path does not close—escape speed.

Escape Speed
Distinguish between ballistic speed and sustained speed, and that the value 11.2 km/s refers to ballistic speed. (One could go to the moon at 1 km/s, given a means of sustaining that speed and enough time to make the trip!) Compare the escape speeds from different bodies via Table 5.1.

Integrated Science—Biology: Your Biological Gravity Detector
This feature, strictly for enrichment, discusses the *vestibular system,* sometimes called the *balance system.* This material will interest students fascinated by the intricacy of biological adaptations but is not essential reading.

The vestibular system in the inner ear senses the orientation of the body in space as well as movement. Not surprisingly, malfunctions of the vestibular system are frequently accompanied by nausea and dizziness. Astronauts are prone to vestibular problems, and as a result, NASA has studied this system extensively. A tidbit for your students: Interestingly, biologists report that the vestibular sense was one of the first sensory systems to evolve. This makes sense, because the force of gravity is one of the most constant conditions on earth that organisms have had to adapt to.

Integrated Science—Biology: Center of Gravity of People
This feature introduces the concept of center of gravity. This is a useful and easy to grasp idea, so we recommend spending a bit of time on it. Once students understand that pigeons bob their heads back and forth to keep their center of gravity over their base and avoid toppling, they will likely never look at pigeons the same way again. Many animals besides pigeons jerk while they walk to maintain balance in the same way. It's fun to ask students to think of a few examples.

You can do this activity with a group of males and females. Ask your volunteers to stand exactly two foot lengths away from a wall as shown in the figure. They then lift a chair that is placed between them and the wall while their head is still leaning against the wall. With the chair in lifted position, volunteers try to straighten up. They then bend over with a straight back and let their head lean against the wall. Ask students to give two reasons why women can generally do this but males cannot? (Answer: Women have smaller feet and a lower center of gravity.)

Do you want your students to read chapter material *before* coming to class? Then reward them for doing so! Give them a quickie quiz at the outset of each class — or if not every class, then frequently at unannounced times. My students know they'll be quizzed on the chapter-end *Review Questions* of the assigned chapters. They *do* come to class prepared. Common sense — reward the behavior you want!

6   Heat

Demonstration Equipment

Bimetallic strip and a flame

Aluminum soda pop cans, hot plate, pan of water

Ice, test tube, test tube holder, steel wool, flame

Metal bar, sheet of paper, and a flame

Paper cup filled with water and a flame

The concept of heat flow between temperature differences provides some background to the concept of current flow between electric voltage differences later in Chapter 7. Here we introduce the concept of kinetic energy (KE)/molecule, *temperature*, which is analogous to the later concept of potential energy (PE)/charge, *voltage*. Both high temperatures and high voltages are ordinarily harmful only when large energies are transferred in a relatively short time (that is, when large power is transferred). The white-hot sparks of a Fourth-of-July sparkler have very high temperatures, but their energies are very small. So they are quite harmless. Similarly, a balloon rubbed on your hair may have thousands of volts, but the energy stored is very small. Energy per molecule or energy per charge may be high, but if the molecules or charges involved are small in number, the energy content is also small.

In the text, temperature is treated in terms of the kinetic energy per molecule of substances. Although, strictly speaking, temperature is directly proportional to the kinetic energy per molecule only in the case of ideal gases. We take the view that temperature is related to molecular translational kinetic energy in most common substances. Rotational kinetic energy, on the other hand, indirectly relates to temperature, as is illustrated in a microwave oven. There the H_2O molecules are set oscillating with considerable rotational kinetic energy. But this doesn't cook the food. What does is the translational kinetic energy imparted to neighboring molecules that are bounced from the oscillating water molecules. It's the neighboring molecules that are set flying in all directions when they encounter the spinning blades of fans that raises the temperature of the food and cooks it. If neighboring atoms did not interact with the oscillating H_2O molecules, the temperature of the food would be no different before and after the microwave oven was activated. Temperature has to do with the translational kinetic energy of molecules. Degrees of freedom, rotational and vibrational states, and the complications of temperature in liquids and solids are not treated. That's waiting in a dedicated physics course!

Quantity of heat is spoken of in terms of calories and joules. The definition of the calorie in the text implies that the same amount of heat will be required to change the temperature of water 1°C—whatever the temperature of the water. Although this relation holds true to a fair degree, it is not exactly correct: A calorie is precisely defined as the amount of heat required to raise a gram of water from 14° to 15° Celsius.

Be aware of accidents with microwave ovens. Still water may not boil, even when heated to boiling temperature or above. The water is superheated. Suddenly moving it can cause a sudden and violent eruption. This is similar to the spewing of a carbonated beverage when opened after being shaken.

In the *Practice Book*:
• Temperature Mix
• Absolute Zero
• Thermal Expansion
• Transmission of Heat

In *Next-Time Questions*:
• Holiday Sparkler
• Twice as Hot
• Metal Ring
• Metal Gap
• Firewalk
• Space Shuttle Convection
• Coffee Cream Right Away
• Hot Water Radiators

In the *Lab Manual*:
• Dance of the Molecules (activity)
• Temperature Mix (experiment)
• Spiked Water (experiment)
• Specific Heat Capacities (experiment)
• Canned Heat I (experiment)
• Canned Heat II (experiment)
• I'm Melting! I'm Melting! (activity)

Transparencies:
Figures 6.12, 6.18, 6.21, 6.34

Check questions are few in the following suggested presentation. By now it is hoped that this technique is a major part of your teaching. Take pity on students who are bored by a teacher who poses questions that he or she immediately answers without involving the students. This puts the student in the role of a passive observer rather than a participant in the learning process. Pose check questions before you move onto new material. And ideally, have students show their answers on whiteboards—or, if you're so equipped, electronically. We heartily recommend using the clicker questions for this and all chapters!

Suggested Presentation

The Kinetic Theory of Matter
Most of your students will likely be familiar with the basic concepts of the kinetic theory of matter; namely, that matter consists of small, moving particles called atoms and molecules. But you'll want to check to be sure all students are equipped with this picture. Explain that students will learn much more about the kinetic theory of matter in the chemistry portion of the text. For now, it is sufficient just to know that matter is particulate, and that atoms and molecules behave much like billiard balls, or popcorn in a popper.

Temperature
Begin by asking what the difference is between a hot cup of coffee and a cold cup of coffee. Think small for the answer: The molecules in the hot cup of coffee are moving faster—they are more energetic. Heat and temperature have to do with the kinetic energies of the molecules in substances. Heat and temperature are different: To begin with, *heat* is energy that is measured in joules, or calories. *Temperature* is measured in degrees.

Distinguish thermal energy from temperature. A neat example is the Fourth-of-July-type sparkler. The sparks that fly from the firework and strike your face have temperatures in excess of 2000°C, but they don't burn. Why? Because the thermal energy of the sparks is extremely low. It is the amount of energy you receive that burns, not the ratio of energy/molecule. Even with a high ratio (high temperature), if a relatively few molecules are involved, the energy transfer is low. (Again, this is similar to the high voltage of a balloon rubbed against your hair. It may have thousands of volts, which is to say thousands of joules per charge. But if there are a relatively small number of charges, the total energy they possess is small.)

Describe how the increased jostling of molecules in a substance results in expansion, and show how this property underlies the common thermometer. Sketch a noncalibrated thermometer on the board, with its mercury vessel at the bottom, and describe how the energy of jostling molecules is transferred from the outer environment to the mercury within. If placed in boiling water, energy of the jostling water molecules would be transferred to the mercury, which would expand and squeeze up the tube. State that one could make a scratch on the glass at this level and label it 100. And then describe how, if placed in a container of ice water, the molecules of mercury would give energy to the cold water and slow down, contract, and fall to a lower level in the tube. One could again make a scratch and call this point zero. Then, if 100 equally spaced scratches are made between the two reference points, one would have a centigrade thermometer.

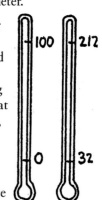

In a vein of humor, draw a second noncalibrated thermometer on the board and repeat your discussion (in abbreviated fashion) of placing it in boiling water. State that the upper level needn't be called 100, that any number would do so long as all thermometers were calibrated the same. Ask the class for any random number. Someone will say 212. Then casually acknowledge the 212 response and write that on your diagram. Repeat the bit about placing the instrument in ice water and state that the position on the scale needn't be called zero, that any number would do. Ask for a random number. You'll have several students volunteer 32, which you graciously accept. The class should be in a good mood at this point, and you briefly discuss the two scales and lead into the idea of absolute zero and the Kelvin scale. (Named after "Lord Scale"?)

Did Fahrenheit have a fever on the day he calibrated his temperature scale? Was a 1.4° above normal responsible for his placement of the 100° mark where he wished to be the standard for 100°? Your class may wish to speculate how he placed his zero.

CHECK YOUR NEIGHBOR: Which has the largest degrees, a Celsius thermometer or a Fahrenheit thermometer? [Celsius.]

CHECK YOUR NEIGHBOR: True or false: Cold is the absence of fast-moving molecules. [False; cold refers to very slow-moving molecules, not their absence. If you have no molecules at all, the concept of temperature is meaningless.]

Absolute Zero

Review the temperature scales and lead into the thermodynamic temperature scale. To lead into an understanding of the absolute temperature scale, begin by considering the ordering of a piece of hot apple pie in a restaurant and then being served cold pie—ice cold pie, at 0°C. Suppose you ask the waiter to heat the pie in the oven. How hot? Say twice as hot. *Question:* What will be the temperature of the pie? Move your class to the "check-your-neighbor" routine. Change your mind about the 0°C initial temperature of the piece of pie, and ask if the problem is easier if you begin with, say, a 10°C piece of pie. Tell your class to beware of neighbors who say the problem is simplified, and the answer is (wrongly) 20°C. This should spark interest. Now you're ready for the "Celsius, the Village Tailor" story.

SKIT: CELCIUS, THE VILLAGE TAILOR: Hold a measuring stick against the wall of the lecture room (so that the bottom of the vertically oriented stick is about 1 meter above the floor) and state that you are Celsius, the village tailor, and that you measure the heights of your customers against the stick, which is firmly fastened to the wall. You state that there is no need for the stick to extend to the floor, nor to the ceiling, for your shortest and tallest customers fall within the extremities of the stick. Mention that all tailors using the same method could communicate meaningfully with each other about the relative heights of their customers, providing the measuring sticks in each shop were fastened the same distance above the "absolute zero" of height. It just so happens that the distance to the floor, the "absolute zero," is 273 notches—the same size notches on the stick itself. Then one day, a very short lady enters your shop and stands against the wall, the top of her head coinciding with the zero mark on the measuring stick. As you take her zero reading, she comments that she has a brother who is twice her height. Ask the class for the height of her brother. Then ask for the temperature of the twice-as-hot apple pie. When this is understood, ask why the pie will not *really* be 273°C. Or that for the initially 10°C pie, the temperature will not really be 293°C. [Considerable heat has gone into changing the state of the water in the pie, which accounts for it being "dried out." If you wish to avoid the change-of-phase factor, begin your discussion with the temperature of something such as a piece of metal that will not change phase for the temperature range in question.]

Heat

Distinguish between *heat* and *temperature*. Heat has to do with energy flow, while temperature is a ratio of energy per molecule. They are very different. A Fourth-of-July-type sparkler emits sparks with temperatures exceeding 2000°C, but the heat one receives when one of these sparks lands on one's face is very small. High temperature means a high ratio of heat per molecule. The *ratio* and the *amount* of heat energy transferred are different things. Relatively few molecules comprise the tiny bit of white-hot matter that makes up the sparks of the sparkler. (Later you'll invoke a similar argument when you discuss the small energy associated with the high voltage of a charged party balloon rubbed on your hair.) Thermal energy is the total molecular energies, kinetic plus potential, internal to a substance. Heat is thermal energy in transit.

> CHECK YOUR NEIGHBOR: How are the sparks from a sparkler that strike your skin akin to tiny droplets of boiling water striking your skin? [Both have high temperatures but safe levels of thermal energy to transfer to your skin.]

Define the calorie, and compare it to the joule. Distinguish the calorie from the Calorie, the concern of people who watch their diet.

The Laws of Thermodynamics

First Law of Thermodynamics   Introduce the first law of thermodynamics by citing the findings of Count Rumford: When cannon barrels were being drilled and became very hot, it was the friction of the drills that produced the heating. Recall the definition of work, *force × distance*, and cite how the metal is heated by the frictional force × distance that the various parts of the drill bit move. Have your students rub their hands together and feel them warming up. Or warm part of the chair they sit on by rubbing.

Follow this up with the account of Joule with his paddle-wheel apparatus and his measuring the mechanical equivalent of heat. Of interest is Joule's attempt to extend this experiment to a larger scale while on his honeymoon in Switzerland. Joule and his bride honeymooned near the Chamonix waterfall. According to Joule's conception of heat, the gravitational potential energy of the water at the top should transfer into increasing the internal energy of the water when at the bottom. Joule made a rough estimate of the increased difference in water temperature at the bottom of the waterfall. His measurements did not substantiate his predictions, however, because considerable cooling occurred due to evaporation as the water fell through the air. Without this added complication, however, his predictions would have been supported. What happens to the temperature of a penny, after all, when you slam it with a hammer? Likewise with water. Emphasize that the first law is simply the law of energy conservation for thermal systems.

Second Law of Thermodynamics   Introduce the second law by considering what occurs when you immerse a hot teacup in a large container of cold water. Thermal energy passes from the hot cup to the cool water. If the flow were in the opposite direction, the cup would become even warmer at the expense of the cold water becoming cooler. Even in this case, the first law would not be violated. You're on your way with the second law.

According to Paul's friend Dave Wall who many years ago worked in the U.S. patent office, the greatest shortcomings of would-be inventors were their lack of understanding the laws of thermodynamics. The patent office has long been besieged with schemes that promise to circumvent these laws. Much effort goes into debunking these schemes, and none has survived scrutiny. The patent office now directs their efforts to matters of more importance.

Specific Heat Capacity

Lead into a distinction between the difference between calories and degrees, and the concept of specific heat capacity, by asking your class to consider the difference in touching an empty iron frying pan that has been placed on a hot stove for 1 minute (ouch!) and doing the same with a frying pan of water. With the water, you could place your hand in it safely even if it were on the stove for several minutes. Ask which has the higher temperature, the empty pan or the one filled with water. Clearly, it is the empty pan. Ask which absorbed the greater amount of energy. The answer is the water-filled pan, if it was on the stove for a longer time. The water absorbed more energy for a smaller rise in temperature! Physics and chemistry types have a name for this idea—*specific heat capacity*, or for short, *specific heat*. Cite the different specific heats of cooked foods, of a hot TV dinner and the aluminum foil that can be removed with bare hands while the food is still too hot to touch. Heat capacity can be viewed as thermal inertia.

Thermal Expansion

State that steel lengths expand about one part in 100,000 for each 1°C increase in temperature. Show a steel rod, and ask if anybody would be afraid to stand with their stomach between the end of the rigidly held steel rod and a wall while the temperature of the rod is increased a few degrees. This is a safe activity, for the slight expansion of the rod would hardly be noticeable. Now ask for volunteers for a steel rod several kilometers in length. This is much different, for although the rate of change in length is the same, the total change in length could well impale you! Then discuss the expansion joints of large structures (Figures 6.16 and 6.17).

DEMONSTRATION: Place the middle of a bimetallic strip in a flame to show the unequal expansions of different metals, and the subsequent bending.

Point out that different substances expand or contract (length, area, and volume) at their own characteristic rates (coefficients of expansion). Cite examples such as the need for the same expansion rate in teeth and teeth fillings; iron reinforcing rods and concrete; and the metal wires that are encased in glass lightbulbs and the glass itself. Provision must be made when materials with different expansion rates interact; like the piston rings when aluminum pistons are enclosed in steel cylinders in a car, and the rockers on bridges (Figure 6.16), and the overflow pipe for gasoline in a steel tank.

CHECK YOUR NEIGHBOR: How would a thermometer differ if glass expanded with increasing temperature more than mercury? [*Answer:* The scale would be upside down, because the reservoir would enlarge (like the hole enlarged in the heated metal ring), and mercury in the column would tend to fill it up with increasing temperature.]

4°C Water
To lead into the idea of water's low density at 4°C, you can ask if anyone in class happens to know what the temperature at the bottom of Lake Michigan was on a particular date, New Year's Eve in 1905, for example. Then for the bottom of Lake Tahoe in California for any other date. And for another, until many are responding "4°C."

CHECK QUESTION: Ask the same for the bottom of a rain puddle outside the building, and be prepared for some to say 4°C.

Then ask why 4°C was the right answer for the deep lakes but the wrong answer for the puddle. Then go into the explanation as given in the book—how the microscopic slush forms as the freezing temperature is approached, yielding a net expansion below 4°C. (We haven't done this, but we have thought of showing a Galileo-type thermometer in class—a small flask with a narrow glass tube filled with colored water, so changes in temperature would be clearly evident by different levels of water in the narrow tube. Then surround the flask with perhaps dry ice to rapidly chill the water. The water level drops as the temperature of the water decreases, but its rate slows as it nears 4°C, and then the direction reverses as cooling continues. This expansion of the water is due to the formation of "microscopic slush.")

Ice Formation on Lakes
Discuss the formation of ice and why it forms at the surface and why it floats. And why deep bodies of water don't freeze over in winter because all the water in the lake has to be cooled to 4°C, before colder water will remain at the surface to be cooled to the freezing temperature, 0°C. State that before one can cool a teaspoonful of water to 3°C, let alone 0°C, all the water beneath must be cooled to 4°C, and that winters are neither cold nor long enough for this to happen in the United States.

Conduction—Heat Transfer via Particle Collision
Begin by asking why pots and pans have wooden or plastic handles, why one can safely touch wood at a high temperature—then discuss conduction from an atomic point of view, citing the role of the electrons in both heat and electrical conductors. You might demonstrate the oldie of melting wax on different metal rods equidistant from a hot flame, and illustrate relative conductivities. Other materials can be compared in their ability to conduct heat, like newspaper when having to sleep outdoors. Discuss the poor conductivity of water, which ties to the previous chapter where you discussed the 4°C temperature of the bottom of deep lakes all year round.

DEMONSTRATION: Wedge some pieces of ice at the bottom of a test tube with some steel wool. Then heat the top part of the tube in a flame. It is impressive to see that the water at the top is brought to a boil by the flame of a burner, while the ice below barely melts!

DEMONSTRATION: Wrap a piece of paper around a thick metal bar and attempt to burn it in the flame. The paper does not reach its ignition temperature, because heat is conducted into the metal.

DEMONSTRATION: Extend the previous demo and place a paper cup filled with water in the flame. Again, the paper will not reach its ignition temperature and burn, because heat from the flame is conducted into the conductor—this time water. Water is not *that* poor a conductor—its high specific heat comes into play here as well.

Discuss the poor conductivity of air, and its role in insulating materials—like snow. Discuss thermal underwear, and how the fish-net open spaces actually trap air between the skin and the undergarment. Discuss double-window thermopane.

Convection—Heat Transfer via Movements of Fluid
Illustrate convection by considering the case of rising warm air.

> CHECK YOUR NEIGHBOR: Why does smoke from a candle rise and then settle off? [It's interesting to note that helium, unlike smoke particles, continues rising even when cool. That's because the small mass of the helium finds it faster than more massive molecules at the same KE. Interestingly, helium is not found in the air but must be mined from beneath the ground like natural gas. (The helium nucleus is the alpha particle that emanates from radioactive ores.) This idea of faster-moving helium underscores the relationship of kinetic energy to temperature.]

> Convection is important in earth science and astronomy. Convection cycles in earth's mantle underlie tectonic plate movement; convection cycles in the atmosphere create wind; and convection cycles in the Sun's convection zone transfer energy from the solar core to its surface. For more ideas on integrating earth science with the physics of convection, check the Integrated Science section below.

Radiation—Heat Transfer via Radiant Energy
Discuss the radiation one feels from red hot coals in a fireplace and how the radiation decreases with distance. Consider the radiation one feels when stepping from the shade to the sunshine. Amazing! The heat is not so much because of the sun's temperature, because like temperatures are to be found in the torches of some welders. One feels hot not because the sun is hot, but because it is *big*. Comfortably big!

Acknowledge that everything emits radiation—everything that has any temperature. But everything does not become progressively cooler, because everything absorbs radiation. We live in a sea of radiation, everything emitting and everything absorbing. When emission rate equals absorption rate, temperature remains constant. Some materials, because of their molecular design, emit better than others. They also absorb better than others. They're easy to spot, because they absorb visible radiation as well and appear black.

> DEMONSTRATION: Pour hot water into a pair of vessels, one black and the other shiny silver. Ask for a neighbor check as to which will cool faster. Have thermometers in each that you ask a student to read aloud at the beginning and a few minutes later. (You can repeat this demo with initially cold water in each vessel.)

Whereas color affects both absorption and reflection in the visible part of the spectrum, for infrared a dominant role is played by the surface texture—polished vs. dull. Hence, a white-painted house will reflect more sunlight but not necessarily more infrared light.

Integrated Science
There are ample opportunities to tie chapter material to earth science. Extend thermal expansion to the earth sciences with this *Next-Time Question*:

> NEXT-TIME QUESTION: Ask your students to place an ice cube in a glass of ice water at home, and compare the water level at the side of the glass before and after the ice melts. Ask them to account for the volume of ice that extends above the water line after it melts. The answer to the original question is, of course, that the level remains unchanged. It so happens that the floating ice cube displaces its own weight of water, which is why it floats. (More on this in Appendix E.) So if the cube weighs a newton, then when placed in the glass, 1 newton of water is displaced, and the water level rises. If it is first melted and then poured in the glass, again the water line would be higher, but by the volume taken by 1 newton, the same amount. More interesting is to account for the volume of all those billions and billions of open spaces in the ice crystals. Their combined volume is essentially that of the part of ice extending above the water line! When the ice melts, the part above the water line fills in the open structures as they collapse. Discuss this idea in terms of icebergs, and whether or not the coastline would change if all the floating icebergs in the world melted. The oceans would rise a bit, but only because icebergs are composed of fresh water. (They form above sea level and break off and then fall into the sea.) The slight rise is more easily understood by exaggerating the circumstance—think of ice cubes floating in mercury. When they melt, the depth of fluid (water on mercury) is higher than before. [Exaggeration of factors is a useful technique in greater-than, equal-to, or less-than-type questions!]

Take note that ocean levels also rise due to thermal expansion. If you had a water-filled test tube that was 2 miles high (the average depth of the ocean), even a slight increase in temperature would raise the level of water appreciably. Similarly, a warmer ocean means a deeper ocean and quite different coastlines in many places! (Too often we attribute rising oceans only to ice-cap melting.)

Another earth-science-related idea you can discuss is the expansion of air as it cools. This idea will be greatly utilized in Chapter 25. First treat the warming of compressed air. The familiar bicycle pump offers a good example. Why does the air become warm when the handle is depressed? It's easy to see that the air molecules speed up when the piston slams against them. A Ping-Pong ball similarly speeds up when a paddle hits it. Now, consider what happens to the speed of a Ping-Pong ball when it encounters a receding paddle! Can your students see that its rebound speed will be less than its incident speed? Now you're ready to discuss the cooling of expanding air and compare it to the case of the slowing Ping-Pong balls with molecules that are, on the average, receding from one another.

Here's a great one: Have everyone in class blow against their hands with open mouths. Their breaths feel warm. Then repeat with very small mouth openings. Their breaths are remarkably cooler. They *experience* firsthand that expanding air *really does* cool!

You can do more integration of earth science and physics here by discussing why the Earth is warmer at the equator than at the poles, and getting into the idea of solar energy per unit area. This is treated in detail in Chapter 25, but you can treat it here as a physics topic, then just review it when you get to earth science. Draw a large circle on the board that represents the Earth (like the one below, only without the sun's rays at this point). Ask for a neighbor check, and speculate why it is warm near the equator and cold at the poles. To dispel the idea that the farther distance to the poles is the reason, do the following:

SKIT: Ask the class to pretend there is a vertical rainfall, into which you reach out your window with two sheets of paper—one held horizontally and the other held at an angle as shown. You bring the papers inside as a friend strolls by and inquires what you're doing. You remark that you have been holding the sheets of paper out in the rain. Your friend sees that the horizontally held paper is much

wetter and asks why. You repeat with both papers held outward as before, and your friend says, "Oh, I see why. You're holding the tilted sheet farther away from the clouds!" Ask your class if you are holding it farther away from the overhead clouds. The answer is yes. Ask if this is the reason the paper is not as wet. The answer is no!

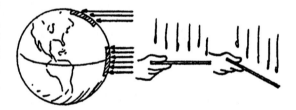

Integrated Science—Chemistry and Biology: Entropy—The Universal Tendency Toward Disorder
The concept of entropy is introduced here but will be explored in more detail in Chapter 13 as it applies to chemical reactions. (Chemical reactions that result in a net entropy increase proceed spontaneously.) If your students have sufficient chemistry background, preview Section 13.10, Entropy and Chemical Reactions, with them now. Brainstorm examples of entropy in other subject disciplines and in everyday life. Interested students could undertake a special multimedia or film project showing events that illustrate entropy. Events could include water spilling, ice melting, a match being lit, air escaping from a tire, a stack of dice or other small object collapsing and dispersing, steam dispersing from the spout of a teakettle, a house of cards collapsing, and so forth. Run the film backwards to show how impossible it is to imagine the Second Law of Thermodynamics being violated.

Integrated Science—The Specific Heat Capacity of Water Affects Global Temperature
Cite examples of water's high specific heat—hot water bottles on cold winter nights, cooling systems in cars, and the climate in places where there is much water. Figure 6.15 shows the sameness of latitudes for England and the Hudson Bay, and the French and Italian Rivieras with Canada. State how the fact that water requires a long time to heat and to cool enables the Gulf Stream to hold thermal energy long enough to reach the North Atlantic. There it cools off. But if the water cools, then according to the conservation of energy, something else has to warm. What is that something? The air. The cooling water warms the air, and the winds at that latitude are westerly. So warmed air moves over the continent of Europe. If this weren't the case, Europe would have the same climate as regions of northern Canada. A similar situation occurs in the United States. The Atlantic Ocean off the coast of the eastern states is considerably warmer than the Pacific Ocean off the coast of Washington, Oregon, and California, yet in winter months, the East coast is considerably colder.

This has to do with the high specific heat of water and the westerly winds. Air that is warmed by cooling water on the West coast moves landward and gives mild winters to Washington, Oregon, and California. But on the East coast, this warmed air moves seaward, leaving the East coast frigid in winter months. In summer months, when the air is warmer than the water, the air cools and the water warms. So, summer months in the West coast states are relatively cool, while the East coast is relatively hot. The high specific heat of water serves to moderate climates. The climates on islands, for example, are fairly free of temperature variations. Even San Francisco, a peninsula that is close to being an island, has the most stable climate of any city in the continental United States.

7   Electricity and Magnetism

Demonstration Equipment

Ballon, fur, silk, rubber rod, glass or plastic rod, suspended pith balls

Wooden 2″ × 4″ board, electrophorus

Wimshurst machine, electrostatic generator

Puffed rice, fluorescent lamp, batteries, bulbs, and connecting wires

A 12-volt automobile battery with metal rods extended from the terminals with alligator clips used to fasten lamps between them

Iron filings, magnet, and transparent plastic

Compass and wire that carries DC current

DC current-carrying wire and a horseshoe magnet

Galvanometer, loop of wire, horseshoe magnet

Demonstration motor-generator device

Hand-cranked generators and lamps to light them with

Here we begin with electrostatics, continue on to electric current, to series and parallel electric circuits, and end our study of electricity with electric power. We then do our survey of magnetism and end with electromagnetic induction, setting the stage for the study of electromagnetic waves in the following chapter. There's easily enough material here for two or three more chapters. This is heavy stuff, so unless you're going to spend more than a week or so on this chapter, you may want to skim over this topic. The material in this chapter should be supported with lecture demonstrations.

For electrostatics, you'll want charging apparatus such as rubber and glass rods, silk and cat's fur or the equivalent, the electrophorus (a metal plate charged by induction that rests on a sheet of Plexiglas which has been charged with cat's fur, or equivalently, a pizza pan that rests on a charged phonograph record), and the Wimshurst machine (electrostatic generator). If you're equipment lucky, toss in demonstrations with a Van de Graaff generator.

For electric currents, you must use an automobile storage battery with extended terminals as shown here. The extended terminals are simply a pair of rigid rods, welding rods, or pieces of thick wire. They are easily inserted and removed if female connectors are permanently fastened into the battery terminals. Also, fasten alligator clips to the ends of three short lengths of wire fastened to lamps of equal resistance. This is a MUST! It puts the *conceptual* in *Conceptual Integrated Science*!

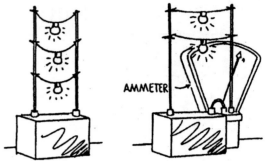

James Redmond tells Paul there are car batteries with side terminal mounts, already threaded to accept a standard bolt, so the rods can simply be threaded in. No fuss, no muss!

If you're into puns in your lectures on rainy days, Marshall Ellenstein has a few pictorial puns on the symbol for resistance that he and coworkers Connie Bownell and Nancy McClure came up with ("Ohmwork" or $\Omega F \times D$, *The Physics Teacher*, September 1991, page 347). A few are as shown:

[Answers in order are Mobile Ohm; Ohm Run; Ohm Stretch; Ohm Sick; Ohmwork; Ohmless; Ohm on the Range; Broken Ohm.]

Tom Senior reports that a good source of free batteries may be your local fire department when they're promoting smoke detectors. Ann Brandon says you may be able to get free 9-volt batteries from your Theatre department, as they are often used for only a single show.

The order of topics in the lecture sequence below departs somewhat from the order of topics in the chapter. The ideas of each demo flow nicely to the next. Have your lecture table set up with rods, pith ball, and charging demos at one end of the table, then an electrophorus, then a Wimshurst or whatever electrostatic machine, and possibly, the Van de Graaff generator. Then your lecture begins at one end of the table and proceeds in order to the opposite end.

Make iron-filing permanent displays by spraying water on iron filings on a paper atop a magnet. The rust stains will leave a permanent impression of the magnetic field. (This idea is from Matt Keller.)

In the *Practice Book*:
- Electric Potential
- Series Circuits
- Parallel Circuits
- Compound Circuits
- Magnetism
- Field Patterns
- Electromagnetism

In *Next-Time Questions*:
- High-Voltage Terminals
- Van de Graaff Generator
- Series Circuit
- Parallel Circuit
- Tack and Magnet
- Trick Magnet

- Wire in Magnetic Field
- Induction

In the *Lab Manual*:
- A Force to Be Reckoned (activity)
- Charging Ahead (activity)
- Ohm, Ohm on the Range (experiment)
- Batteries and Bulbs (activity)
- An Open and Short Case (activity)
- Be the Battery (activity)
- Magnetic Personalities (activity)
- Electric Magnetism (activity)
- Motor Madness (experiment)
- Generator Activator (activity)

Transparencies:
Figures 7.5, 7.6, 7.9, 7.10, 7.12, 7.15, 7.21, 7.22, 7.36, 7.38, 7.45

Suggested Presentation

Begin by comparing the strength of the electric force to gravitational force—billions of billions of times stronger. Acknowledge the fundamental rule of electricity: That *like charges repel and unlike charges attract.* Why? Nobody knows. Hence, we say it is fundamental.

Electric Charge

Electrical effects have to do with electric charges—minus for the electron and plus for the proton. Discuss the near balance that exists in common materials, and the slight imbalance when electrons transfer from one material to another. Different materials have different affinities for electrons, which explains why charge transfers from fur to rubber when rubbed. It also explains why it's painful for people with silver fillings in their teeth to chew aluminum spitballs. Silver has more affinity for acquiring electrons than aluminum. The mildly acidic saliva in your mouth facilitates a flow of electrons, which when transmitted to the nerves of your teeth produce that familiar unpleasant sensation. Discuss *charging*.

> DEMONSTRATION: Bring out the cat's fur, rubber and glass rods, and suspended pith balls (or their alternatives). Explain the transfer of electrons when you rub fur against rubber rod (and silk against glass). Explain what it means to say an object is electrically charged, and discuss the *conservation of charge.*

Coulomb's Law

Call attention to the similarity and difference between Newton's law of gravitation and Coulomb's law.

Charge Polarization

> DEMONSTRATION: Rub a balloon on your hair, and show how it sticks to the wall. Sketch on the board and show in induction how the attracting charges are slightly closer than the repelling charges. Closeness wins, and it sticks! (Induction will be treated in greater detail in Chapter 12.)

> DEMONSTRATION: Show the effects of electrical force and polarization by holding a charged rod near the ends of a more-than-a-meter-long wooden 2 × 4 that balances and easily rotates sideways at its midpoint on a protrusion such as the bottom of a metal spoon. You can easily set the massive piece of wood in motion. This is quite impressive!

> DEMONSTRATION: Charge the electrophorus, place the insulated metal disk on top of it, and show that the disk is not charged when removed and brought near a charged pith ball. Why should it be, for the insulating surface of the electrophorus has more grab on the electrons than the metal plate. But rest the plate on the electrophorus again, and touch the top of the plate. You're grounding it (producing a conducting path to ground for the repelling electrons). Bring the plate near the pith ball, and show that it is charged. Then show this by the flash of light produced when the charged metal plate is touched to the end of a gas discharge tube or a fluorescent lamp. Engage neighbor discussion of the process demonstrated. Only after this is generally understood, proceed to the next demo.

DEMONSTRATION: Move up the lecture table to the Wimshurst machine, explaining its similarity to the electrophorus (actually a rotating electrophorus). Show sparks jumping between the spheres of the machine and so forth, and discuss the sizes (radii of curvature) of the spheres in terms of their capacity for storing charge. [The amount of charge that can be stored before discharge into the air is directly proportional to the radius of the sphere.] Fasten a metal point, which has a tiny radius of curvature and hence a tiny charge storing capacity, to one of the Wimshurst spheres, and demonstrate the leakage of charge.

Under mutual repulsion, charges gather to the region of greatest curvature, the point. Although all parts of the needle are charged to the same electric voltage, the charge density is greatest at the point. The *electric field* intensity about the needle, on the other hand, is greatest about the point, usually great enough to ionize the surrounding air and provide a conducting path from the charge concentration. Hence, charge readily gathers at points and readily leaks from points. Demonstrate this leakage and the reaction force (ion propulsion) with a set of metal points arranged to rotate when charged. This is the "ion propulsion" that science fiction buffs talk about in space travel. Interestingly enough, this leaking of charge from points causes static with radio antennas and, hence, the small metal ball atop automobile antennas.

Discuss *lightning rods* and show how the bottoms of negatively charged clouds and the resulting induced positive charge on the surface of the Earth below are similar to the electrophorus held upside down; where the charged Plexiglas plate is analogous to the clouds, and the metal plate is analogous to the Earth. After sketching the charged clouds and Earth on the chalkboard, be sure to hold the inverted electrophorus pieces against your drawing on the board in their respective places. Discuss the lightning rod as a means to prevent lightning while showing the similar function of the metal point attached to the Wimshurst machine. [Notice that one idea is related to the next in this sequence—very important, as the ideas of electricity are usually difficult to grasp the first time through. So, be sure to take care in moving through this sequence of demonstrations and their explanations.]

Benjamin Franklin's kite, by the way, was not struck by lightning. If it had been, he would likely have not been around to report his experience. Franklin showed that the kite collected charges from the air during a thunderstorm. Hairs on the kite string stood apart, implying that lightning was a huge electric spark.

After establishing the idea that charge capacity depends on the size and curvature of the conductor being charged, advance to what your students have been waiting for: the *Van de Graaff generator* (for humor, invented by Robert Generator).

DEMONSTRATION: When showing the long sparks that jump from the dome of the generator to the smaller grounded sphere, do as Bruce Bernard suggests and hold a lightning rod (any sharp, pointed conductor) in the vicinity of the dome and the sparking will stop. Bring the lightning rod farther away and the frequency of sparking will resume.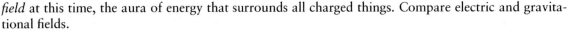

DEMONSTRATION: Set a cup of puffed rice or puffed wheat on top of the Van de Graaff generator. Your students will like the fountain that follows when you charge it. Or do as Marshall Ellenstein does and place a stack of aluminum pie plates on the dome and watch them one by one levitate and fly away. Then snuff out a match by holding it near the charged dome. Introduce (or reintroduce) the idea of the *electric field* at this time, the aura of energy that surrounds all charged things. Compare electric and gravitational fields.

DEMONSTRATION: Hold a fluorescent lamp tube in the field to show that it lights up when one end of the tube is closer to the dome than the other end. Relate this to potential difference, and show that when both ends of the fluorescent tube are equidistant from the charged dome, light emission ceases. (This can be effected when your hand is a bit closer to the dome than the far end of the tube, so current does not flow through the tube when the dome discharges through you to the ground. There is no potential difference across the tube and therefore no illuminating current, which sets the groundwork for your next lecture on electric current.)

The Van de Graaff generator nicely illustrates the difference between *electric potential energy* and *electric voltage*: Although it is normally charged to thousands of volts, the amount of charge is relatively small, so the electric potential energy is relatively small. That's why you're normally not harmed when it discharges through your body. Very little energy flows through you. In contrast, you wouldn't intentionally become the short-circuit for household 110 volts, because although the voltage is much lower, the transfer of energy is appreciable. There is less energy per charge but many, many more charges! [All this is analogous to thermal energy—high temperature may or may not be associated with high or low thermal energy. Recall the white hot sparks of the fireworks sparkler—similarly, high energy per molecule, but not many molecules. Both the high-temperature sparkler and the high-voltage generator are relatively harmless.]

Your electrostatics lecture should end with the Van de Graaff demo and discussion of electric fields, potential energy, and potential. The following question is a bridge to your next lecture on electric currents.

NEXT-TIME QUESTION: Why does current flow when one end of the fluorescent tube is held closer to the charged Van de Graaff generator, but not when both ends are equidistant? [The simplified answer you're looking for at this point is that the close end is in a stronger part of the field than the far end. More energy per charge means more voltage at the near end. With a voltage difference across the tube, you get a current. When both ends are equidistant, there is no voltage difference across the tube, and no current. This leads into electric current. Strictly speaking, the current path is more than simply between the ends of the tube; it goes through you also and to ground where it returns to the generator.]

Electric Current

Define electric current and relate it to the lighting of the lamp via the Van de Graaff generator from your previous lecture. Explain this in terms of current being directly proportional to a difference in voltage. That is, one end of the lamp was in a stronger part of the energy field than the other—more energy per charge on one end than the other—more voltage at one end than the other. Write on the board *Current ~ voltage difference*. (You're on your way to Ohm's law.)

Electric Current and Voltage

Relate voltage to the idea of electrical pressure. Emphasize that a *difference* in electric voltage must exist. Cite how a battery provides this difference in a sustained way compared to suddenly discharging a Van de Graaff generator. Generators at power plants also provide a voltage difference across wires that carry this difference to consumers. Cite examples of voltage differences in cases of birds sitting on bare high-voltage wires, walking unharmed on the third rail of electric-powered train tracks, and the inadvisability of using electric appliances in the bathtub. Electric current is measured in amperes, named after Andre Ampere (who was forced to witness the guillotine death of his father during the French Revolution).

Electrical Resistance

Introduce the idea of electrical resistance, and complete Ohm's law. Compare the resistances of various materials, and the resistances of various thicknesses of wires of the same metal. Call attention to the glass supports on the wires that make up high-voltage power lines and the rubber insulation that separates the pair of wires in a common lamp cord.

Ohm's Law

Complete your chalkboard equation by introducing resistance, and you have Ohm's law.

DEMONSTRATION: Connect two or three lamps to a battery and relate the current, as viewed by the emitted light, to the voltage of the battery and the resistance of the lamps. (Be sure the lamps are not bright enough to make viewing uncomfortable.) Interchange lamps of low and high resistance, relating this to the brightness of the lamps.

Direct Current and Alternating Current

Discuss the differences between DC and AC. Compare the DC current that flows in a circuit powered with a battery to the AC current that flows in a household circuit (powered by a generator). A hydrodynamic analogy for AC is useful: Imagine powering a washing-machine agitator with water power. Verbally describe with gestures a pair of clear plastic pipes connected to a paddle wheel at the bottom of the agitator, fashioned so water that sloshes to-and-fro in the pipes causes the agitator to rotate to-and-fro. Suppose the free ends of the plastic pipe are connected to a special socket in the wall. The socket is powered by the power utility. It supplies no water but consists of a couple of pistons that exert a pumping action, one out and the other in, then vice versa, in rapid alternation. When the ends of the pipe containing water are connected to the pistons, the water in the pipes is made to slosh back and forth: Power is delivered to the washing machine. There is an important point to note here: The *source* of flowing substance, water or electrons, is supplied by you. The power company supplies no water, just as the power utilities supply no electrons! The greater the load on the agitator, the more energy the power company must deliver to the action of the alternating pistons, affording a visual model for household current—especially with the transparent plastic pipes where your students can "see" the sloshing water!

Speed of Electrons in a Circuit

To impart the idea of how DC current travels in a circuit, use the following analogy. Ask the class to suppose that there is a long column of marchers at the front of the room, all standing at rest close together. Walk to the end of this imaginary column and give a shove to the "last person." Ask the class to imagine the resulting impulse traveling along the line until the first marcher is jostled against the wall. (Or use the analogy of loosely coupled railroad cars.) Then ask if this is a good analogy for how electricity travels in a wire. The answer is no. This is a good analogy for how sound travels, but not electricity. Cite how slowly the disturbance traveled and how slowly sound travels compared to light or electricity. Again call attention to the column of marchers and walk to the far end and call out, "Forward march!" As soon as the command reaches each individual, each steps forward. The marcher at the beginning of the column, except for the slight time required for the sound to reach her, steps immediately. State that this is an analogy for electricity. Except for the brief time it takes for the electric *field* setup at the power source to travel through the wire, nearly the speed of light, electrons at the far end of the circuit respond immediately. State that the speed at which the command "forward march" traveled is altogether different from how fast each marcher moved upon receiving that command—and that the velocity of the electric signal (nearly the speed of light) is quite a bit different than the drift velocity of electrons [typically 0.01 cm/s] in a circuit.

> CHECK YOUR NEIGHBOR: When turning the key to start a car, electrons migrate from the negative battery terminal through the electric network to the starter motor and back to the positive battery terminal. What's a ballpark time for electrons to leave the negative terminal, go through the circuit, and return to the battery? Less than a millisecond? Less than a second? About a second or two? Or about a day? [Amazingly, the latter answer!]

Ask for an estimate of the number of electrons pumped by the local power plant into the homes and industries locally in the past year. [Zero.] Stress the idea that power plants sell not electrons, but energy. Discuss the origin of electrons in electric circuits.

Electric Power—The Rate of Doing Work

Distinguish between energy and power. Electric power is usually expressed in kilowatts and electric energy in kilowatt-hours. It is effective if you use an actual electric bill to make your point. Note that a kilowatt-hour is 1000 joules per second times 3600 seconds, or 3600 kJ.

Electric Circuits—Series and Parallel

We recommend introducing series and parallel circuits using only equal resistances. Use small lamps of equal resistance connected to short wires with alligator clips at their ends for easy connection to the extended terminals of the auto battery described earlier. Three lamps are sufficient. Sketches are repeated for emphasis.

> DEMONSTRATION: Connect the ends of one of the lamps directly to the battery terminals. It glows, evidence of current flow. Then insert the rods and repeat. It glows as before. Slide the lamp farther up the rods, and the glow is unchanged. It is easily accepted that the 12-volt potential difference between the terminals is also established along and across the full length of the rods. State how the rods could extend across campus to similarly light a lamp. State how the resistance of the rods is very small compared to the resistance of the lamp filament. Compare the rods to a long lamp cord and then to power lines from power plants to consumers. Take your time with these ideas, for they are central!

Series Circuits

> DEMONSTRATION CONTINUED: Attach two lamps in series via alligator clips. Before connecting the double lamp circuit to the rods, ask for a neighbor check about the relative brightness of light. [Because the resistance is doubled, the current is halved and the brightness diminished—brightness is "less than half," because most of the energy is going to heat and not light. The effects of heat can be discerned for low currents when no light is seen.] Point out that the voltage across each lamp is 6 volts when connected in series. Repeat the process for three lamps in series, where three lamps share the 12 volts, and describe the reduced current in terms of Ohm's law. A bonus is connecting a lecture-size ammeter to your circuit.

Parallel Circuits

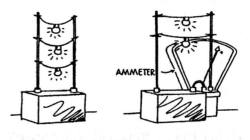

DEMONSTRATION CONTINUED: Now connect a pair of lamps in parallel. Before making the second connection, ask for a neighbor check about the relative brightnesses. It's easy to see that the voltage across each lamp is not reduced as with the series connection, but each is impressed with a full 12 volts. [Nearly a full 12 volts; line voltage diminishes with increased current through the battery—perhaps information overload at this stage of learning.] Repeat with three lamps after a neighbor check. Ask about the "equivalent resistance" of the circuit as more lamps are attached in parallel (or the equivalent resistance to people flow if more doors are introduced to the classroom). The lesser resistance is consistent with Ohm's law. An ammeter between one of the rods and the terminal shows line current, which is seen to increase as lamps are added. This is the simplest and most visually comprehensible demo of parallel circuits I have discovered. Neat?

CHECK YOUR NEIGHBOR: Consider two resistors to be connected in a circuit. Which will have more resistance, if they are connected in series or in parallel? [A series connection will have more resistance, regardless of the values of resistance; the equivalent resistance of a parallel connection will always be less than that of the smaller resistor.]

Home Circuits and Fuses

Discuss home lighting circuits. Draw a simple parallel circuit of lamps and appliances on the board. Estimate the current flowing through each device, and point out that it makes no difference how many of the other devices are turned on. Show on your diagram the currents in the branches and in the lead wires. Show where the fuse goes and describe its function. Then short your circuit and blow the fuse.

Overloading

Discuss the consequences of too many appliances operating on the same line, and why different sets of lines are directed to various parts of the home. Most home wiring is rated at 30 amperes maximum. A common air conditioner uses about 2400 watts, so if operating on 120 volts the current would be 20 amps. To start, the current is more. (Why the starting current is larger would be premature to explain here—if it comes up you can explain that every motor is also a generator, and the input electricity is met with a generated output that reduces the net current flow.) If other devices are drawing current on the same line, the fuse will blow when the air conditioner is turned on, so a 220-volt line is usually used for such heavy appliances. Point out that most of the world operates normally at 220–240 volts.

Magnetism

Begin by holding a magnet above some nails or paper clips on your lecture table. State that the nails or clips are flat on the table, because every particle of matter in the entire world is gravitationally pulling them against the table. Then show that your magnet out-pulls the whole world and lifts the nails or clips off the table.

Show that iron is not the only ferromagnetic substance. Certain Canadian nickels and quarters (1968 to 1981, which are pure nickel) are easily attracted to a magnet. The U.S. 5-cent piece is no longer pure nickel, but 75% copper, and won't respond to a magnet.

Magnetic Poles—Attraction and Repulsion

Show how a bar magnet affects a large lecture compass and discuss magnetic poles. Similar to the fundamental rule of electricity, *like poles repel and opposite poles attract.*

Magnetic Fields

Show field configurations about bar magnets as per Figures 7.26 and 7.27. For a large class, use an overhead projector and iron filings. Simply lay a magnet on the glass surface of the projector and cover it with a sheet of plastic, and sprinkle iron filings over the plastic.

Magnetic Domains—Clusters of Aligned Atoms

Acknowledge the alignment of magnetic domains in the magnet material. (Figure 7.29 shows an idealized representation.)

Magnetic Induction

Explain magnetic induction, and show how bringing a nonmagnetized nail near a magnet induces it to become a magnet and be attracted. Then contrast this with an aluminum rod—discuss unpaired electron spins and magnetic domains. Stress the similarities of electrically inducing charge polarization and magnetically inducing the alignment of magnetic domains.

Magnetic Fields

Discuss the source of magnetism—the motion of charges. All magnetism begins with a moving electric charge: in the spin of the electron about its own axis (similar to a top), in the revolution about the nuclear axis, and as it drifts as part of an electric current.

> DEMONSTRATION: Place a lecture compass near a wire and show the deflection when current is passed through the wire.

The magnetic field is actually a relativistic "side effect" or "distortion" in the electric field of a moving charge. (Einstein's paper on special relativity, after all, was entitled, *On the Dynamics of Moving Charges*.)

Side point: When the magnetic field about a current-carrying wire is undesirable, double wires are used, with the return wire adjacent to the wire. Then the net current for the double wire is zero, and no magnetic field surrounds it. Wires are often braided to combat slight fields where the cancellation is not perfect.

Electromagnets

Call attention to the circular shape of the magnetic field about a current-carrying wire (Figures 7.31 and 7.32, and the photos of field lines of Figure 7.33). It's easy to see how the magnetic field is bunched up in a loop of current-carrying wire and then in a coil of many loops. Then place a piece of iron in the coil and the added effect of aligned domains in the iron produces an electromagnet.

> DEMONSTRATION: Make a simple electromagnet in front of your class. Simply wind wire around a spike and pick up paper clips when you place a current through the wire. Mimic the operation of a junkyard magnet, where the clips are dropped when the current is turned off.

> DEMONSTRATION: Show your department's electromagnets, and your superconducting electro-magnets!

If you have an electromagnetic levitator, discuss the train application when you are fascinating your students with its demonstration. The idea of a *magnetically levitated train* was described in 1909 by Robert Goddard, an American better known for inventing the liquid-fueled rocket. Although Europe and Japan now have the lead in this field, the first modern design for a maglev train comes from Americans, nuclear engineer James R. Powell and particle-acceleration physicist Gordon T. Danby. They were awarded a patent in 1968 for their design.

Whatever the present variations in design, once the train is levitated, there is no mechanical friction to contend with, so only modest force is needed to accelerate it. Fixed electromagnets along the guideway alternately pull and push by switching polarity whenever one of the train's propulsion magnets passes it. The phased switching is timed by computers under the control of the driver to accelerate or decelerate the train, or simply keep it moving. Various designs have the overall result of propelling the train like a surfboard riding a wave. Speculation by coinventor Danby is that future travel in partially evacuated tubes will permit cross-country passage in about an hour. Maglev trains may play a large role in transportation in this new century.

Magnetic Forces Are Exerted on Moving Charges

> DEMONSTRATION: Show how a magnet distorts the electron beam of an oscilloscope or TV picture. Stress the role of motion.

Discuss the motion of a charged particle injected into a magnetic field perpendicularly, and explain how it will follow a circle. The perpendicular push is a centripetal force that acts along the radius of its path. (This is what underlies cyclotrons and bevatrons with radii ranging from less than a meter to more than a kilometer.)

Magnetic Force on Current-Carrying Wires

Simple logic tells you that if forces act on electrons that move through a magnetic field, then forces act on electrons traveling through a wire in a magnetic field.

> DEMONSTRATION: Show how a wire jumps out of (or into) a magnet when current is passed through the wire (Figure 7.38). Reverse current (or turn wire around) to show both cases.

If you have a large lecture galvanometer, show your class the coil of wire that is suspended in the magnetic field of the permanent magnet (Figure 7.40). The same is found in ammeters and voltmeters. Now you are ready to extend this idea to the electric motor.

> DEMONSTRATION: Show the operation of a DC demonstration motor.

Electromagnetic Induction

Up to this point, you have discussed how one can begin with electricity and produce magnetism. The question was raised in the first half of the 1800s: Can it be the other way around—can one begin with magnetism and produce electricity? Indeed it can, enough to light entire cities with electric lighting! Now you produce your galvanometer, magnet, and wire loop—conspicuously well away from your previous electric power source.

DEMONSTRATION: Plunge a magnet in and out of a single coil, as in Figure 7.44, and show with a galvanometer the current produced. This is nice with a large lecture demonstration galvanometer.

This need not be mysterious, for it follows from the deviations of electrons in a magnetic field. Invoke the argument shown previously in Figure 7.36. [Electrons are moved across the magnetic field lines when you push the wire downward, and they experience a sideways force. This time there *is* a path for them and they move along the wire.] Then repeat with the wire bent into two coils—twice the effect. Many coils (Figure 7.46), many times more current.

DEMONSTRATION: Drop a small bar magnet through a vertically held copper or aluminum pipe. It will take appreciably longer to drop through than an unmagnetized piece of iron (which you show first). The explanation is that the falling magnet constitutes a changing magnetic field in the metal pipe. It induces a voltage and hence a current flow in the conducting pipe. The magnetic field set up by the current loops repels the falling magnet and accounts for its slow fall. Electromagnetic induction! [The magnetic field so induced opposes the change in the original field—Lenz's law. If the induced field enhanced the change in the original field, the falling magnet would be attracted rather than repelled and increase in its acceleration and gain more kinetic energy (KE) than its decrease in potential energy (PE). A conservation of energy no-no!] (This demo is a kit available from Pasco Scientific Company in Roseville, CA.)

Faraday's Law

We have seen that charges moving in a magnetic field experience forces. We have seen that the force deviated the direction of electrons, both in a free beam and traveling along a wire, in which case the wire was deviated. Now we see that if we push electrons that are in a wire into a magnetic field, the deviating force will be along the direction of the wire and current is induced. Another way to look at this is to say that *voltage* is being induced in the wire. The current, then, is an outcome of that voltage. Faraday states that the voltage induced in a closed loop equals the time rate of change of the magnetic field in that loop, which is another way of looking at induction. So rather than saying current is induced, Faraday says voltage is induced, which produces current.

DEMONSTRATION: Show the various demonstrations with the classical Elihu Thompson Electromagnetic Demonstration Apparatus (shown at right). With the power on, levitate an aluminum ring over the extended pole of the Elihu Thompson device.

CHECK YOUR NEIGHBOR: Do you know enough physics to state how much electromagnetic force supports this 1-newton aluminum ring (assuming the ring weighs 1 N)? [*Answer:* 1 N, not particularly from a knowledge of electromagnetic forces, but from a knowledge about forces in general that go back to Newton's laws. Because the ring is at rest and not accelerating, the upward electromagnetic force (in newtons!) must be equal to the downward force of gravity.]

DEMONSTRATION: With the power off, place the ring at the base of the extended pole. When you switch on the power, the current induced in the ring via electromagnetic induction converts the ring into an AC electromagnet. (By Lenz's law, not developed in the text, the polarity of the induced magnet is always such to oppose the magnetic field imposed.)

CHECK YOUR NEIGHBOR: Do you know enough physics to state whether or not the electromagnetic force that popped the ring was more than, equal to, or less than the electromagnetic force that produced levitation earlier? [Answer: More, because it accelerated upward, evidence the upward force was more than the weight. This is also understandable because the ring was lower and intercepting more changing magnetic field lines.]

Emphasize the importance of this discovery by Faraday and Henry, and how its application transformed the world. Isn't it difficult to imagine having no electric lights—to live in a time when illumination after the sun goes down is by candles and whale-oil lamps? This was not so long ago, really. In our older cities, many buildings still have pre-electric light fixtures: gas and oil lamps.

State that underlying all the things discussed and observed is something more basic than voltages and currents—the induction of *fields*, both electric and magnetic. And because this is true, we can send signals without wires—radio and TV. Furthermore, electromagnetic induction underlies the energy we get from the Sun.

Meters, Motors, and Generators
Point out that, strictly speaking, generators do not generate electricity—nor do batteries. What they do is pump a fluid composed of electrons. As stressed in the previous chapter, they don't make the electrons they pump. The electron fluid is in the conducting wires.

> DEMONSTRATION: Return to the motor demo and show that when you reverse the roles of input and output, and apply mechanical energy, it becomes a generator. Light a bulb with the hand-cranked generator, and show how the turning is easier when the bulb is loosened and the load removed. Allow students to try this themselves during or at the end of class.

Compare motors and generators—in principle, the same. When electric energy is put in it converts it to mechanical energy—motor. When mechanical energy is put in it converts it to electrical energy—generator. In fact, a motor acts also as a generator and creates a "back voltage" (back emf) and an opposing current. The net current in a motor is the input current minus the generated back current. The net current in a power saw will not cause its overheating and damage to its motor windings—as long as it is running and generating a back current that keeps the net current low. But if you should jam the saw so that it can't spin, without the back current generated by the spinning armature, the net current is dangerously high and can burn out the motor.

Power Production
Continue with a historical theme: With the advent of the generator, the task was to design methods of moving coils of wire past magnetic fields, or moving magnetic fields past coils of wire. Placing turbines beneath waterfalls, and boiling water to make steam to squirt against turbine blades and keep them turning were concepts that pushed toward the industrial revolution.

The Induction of Fields—Both Electric and Magnetic
Point to the similarity of the field induction laws of Faraday and Maxwell—how a change in either field induces the other. This concept led Einstein to the development of his special theory of relativity. Einstein showed that a magnetic field appears when a purely electric field is seen by a moving observer, and an electric field appears when a purely magnetic field is seen from a moving vantage point.

Because of the electric and magnetic induction of fields in free space, we can "telegraph" signals without wires—hence, radio and TV—and furthermore, we shall see that because of field induction, there is light.

Integrated Science—Biology: Electric Shock
Discuss electric shock and why electricians place one hand behind their back when probing questionable circuits [to prevent a difference in potential across the heart of the body]. Discuss how being electrified produces muscle contractions that account for such instances as "not being able to let go" of hot wires, and "being thrown" by electric shock.

Discuss the function of the *third prong on electric plugs* (that it provides a ground wire between the appliance and the ground). The ground prong is longer than the pair of flat prongs. Why? (It will be first to be connected when plugging it into a socket, establishing a ground connection slightly before the appliance is electrically connected. This path to ground prevents harm to the user if there is a short circuit in the appliance that would otherwise include the user as a path to ground.)

Integrated Science—Biology and Earth Science: Earth's Magnetic Field and the Ability of Organisms to Sense It
Discuss the field configuration about the Earth and how cosmic rays are deflected by the magnetic field lines. You might also discuss pole reversals, adding that the magnetic field of the sun undergoes reversals about every 11 years. If you want to discuss the origin of Earth's magnetic field, have your students flip to Chapter 22. They can read about the moving charges in Earth's core that give rise to the planet's magnetic field. Acquaint yourself with the latest findings regarding magnetic field sensing by living things. Some organisms are listed in the text, but the list grows with new findings. Don't leave your students with the impression that organisms rely exclusively on a magnetic sense for navigation. Recent research shows that some organisms construct "mental maps" that allow them to navigate using their memory.

8   Waves—Sound and Light

Demonstration Equipment

Simple pendulum and meterstick

Slinky or loose coil of wire

Large tuning fork and container of water

Large bare loudspeaker and power source

Pair of matched tuning forks to show resonance

Stereo tape player with mono mode, matching speakers, and switch or jacks to reverse the polarity of one of the speakers

Three lamps, red, green, and blue, that can be clamped to a lecture table (or the equivalent)

Two trays of tuning forks

Transparent container of water and powdered milk, and a source of white light that gives a strong beam

Glass tank of water with dye added, prism, mirror, and light source (laser)

Rainbow sticks

Some instructors begin the study of the physics part of integrated science with waves, vibrations, and sound, and light—topics that have greater appeal to many students than mechanics and thermodynamics. Your course could begin here, and you could pick up mechanics later. A useful feature of this text is that for a large part, chapters can stand alone.

This chapter lends itself to whatever interesting lecture demonstrations you can muster from the list above.

Forced vibrations, resonance, and interference provide a very useful background for the same concepts applied to light in the following two chapters.

In the *Practice Book*:
• Vibrations and Wave Fundamentals
• Color
• Diffraction and Interference

- Reflection
- Refraction
- Wave-Particle Duality

In *Next-Time Questions*:
- Radio Waves
- Concert and the Speed of Sound
- Radiating Lamps
- Red, Green, and Blue Lamps
- Girl with Mirror
- Full-Length Mirror
- Pocket Mirror
- Bridge Reflection
- Coin Refraction
- Underwater Viewing
- Candle projection

In the *Lab Manual*:
- Slow-Motion Wobbler (activity)
- Sound Off (activity)
- Pinhole Image (activity)
- Pinhole Camera (activity)
- Mirror, Mirror, on the Wall . . . (activity)

Transparencies:
Figures 8.1, 8.5, 8.10, 8.11, 8.13, 8.14, 8.22, 8.23, 8.28, 8.29, 8.30, 8.32, 8.33, 8.34, 8.38, 8.39, 8.40

Suggested Presentation

This is a long chapter that discusses many different topics related to waves, so covering the entire chapter would take quite a bit of time. Lots of teaching strategies are given for all of the topics, though you will doubtless pick and choose among them to fit the needs of your course.

Note that the "depth of the plow" in the treatment of light is respectably deep. In treating selective reflection and transmission of light, we introduce a model of the atom in which electrons behave as tiny oscillators that resonate or are forced into vibration by external influences. So even if you have not treated the subject of sound, be sure to demonstrate resonance with a pair of tuning forks before treating selective reflection and transmission of light.

Special Wiggles—Vibrations and Waves
Demonstrate the periods of pendula of different lengths, and compare the strides of short and tall people and animals with short and long legs. Giraffes certainly run at a different stride than dachshunds!

Wave Description
Move a piece of chalk up and down, tracing and retracing a vertical straight line on the board. Call attention to how "frequently" you oscillate the chalk, and tie this to the definition of frequency. Also discuss the idea of amplitude. With appropriate motions, show different frequencies and different amplitudes. Then do the same while walking across the front of the board tracing out a sine wave. Show waves of different wavelengths.

> DEMONSTRATION: Show waves on a Bell Telephone torsion-type wave machine (if you're fortunate enough to have one).

> DEMONSTRATION: In jest, do as Tom Gordon at Bronx High School does and suspend a harmonica from a spring, bob it up and down, and ask, "What do we have here?" Answer: Simple "harmonica" motion!

Swing a pendulum to-and-fro and discuss the reciprocal relationship between frequency and period: $f = 1/T$, and $T = 1/f$. Or $fT = Tf = 1$.

Distinguish between wiggles in time—vibrations, and wiggles in space and time—waves. Stress the sameness of the frequency of a wave and the frequency of its vibrating source.

Wave Motion—Transporting Energy

Explain or derive the *wave speed = frequency × wavelength* formula. Calculate the wavelength of one of your local popular radio stations. If you discuss electromagnetic waves, be sure to contrast them with longitudinal sound waves and distinguish between them. You may refer ahead to the family of electromagnetic waves introduced in the next chapter.

Transverse and Longitudinal Waves

Distinguish between transverse and longitudinal waves. This is best done with a Slinky.

> DEMONSTRATION: You and a student hold the ends of a stretched spring or a Slinky and send transverse pulses along it, stressing the idea that only the disturbance rather than the medium moves along the spring. Shake it and produce a sine wave. Then send a stretch or compression down the spring, showing a longitudinal pulse, and wave. After some discussion, produce standing waves.

Sound—A Longitudinal Wave

Begin by stating that the source of sound, or all wave motion, is a vibrating object. Ask your class to imagine a room filled with Ping-Pong balls and that you hold a giant Ping-Pong paddle. When you shake the paddle to-and-fro, you set up vibrations of the balls. Ask how the frequency of the vibrating balls will compare with the frequency of the vibrating paddle. Sound is understood if we "think small."

> DEMONSTRATION: Tap a large tuning fork and show that it is vibrating by dipping the vibrating prongs in a cup of water. The splashing water is clear evidence that the prongs are moving! (Small forks do not work as well.)

> DEMONSTRATION: Hold an aluminum rod (a meter long or so) horizontally at the midpoint and strike one end with a hammer. You will create vibrations that travel and reflect back and forth along the length of the rod. The sustained sound heard is due to energy "leaking" from the ends, about 1% with each reflection. So at any time the sound inside is about 100 times as intense as that heard at the ends. (This is similar to the behavior of light waves in a laser.) Shake the rod to-and-fro as Paul Doherty does, and illustrate the Doppler effect.

> DEMONSTRATION: Rub some pine pitch or rosin on your fingers and stroke the aluminum rod. If you do it properly, it will "sing" very loudly. Do this while holding the rod at its midpoint and then at different places to demonstrate harmonics. (Of course you practiced this first!)

Media That Transmit Sound

Discuss the speed of sound through different media—four times as fast in water than in air, and about eleven times as fast in steel. The elasticity of these materials rather than their densities accounts for the different speeds. Cite how the American Indians used to place their ears to the ground to hear distant hoofbeats, and how one can put the ear to a track to listen for distant trains.

Speed of Sound

Discuss the speed of sound and how one can estimate the distance from a lightning storm.

Compute or state that a radio signal takes about 1/8 second to go completely around the world, while in the same time, sound travels about 42.5 m. Pose the following: Suppose a person attends a concert that is being broadcast over the radio, and that he sits about 45 m from the stage and listens to the radio broadcast with a transistor radio over one ear and the nonbroadcast sound signal with the other ear. Which signal will reach his ear first? The answer is that the radio signal would reach his ear first, even if the radio signal traveled completely around the world before reaching his radio!

Reflection of Sound

Bats and echoes, charting of the ocean bottom, reverberations in the shower, and acoustics in music halls—go to it.

Refraction of Sound

Explain refraction with a chalkboard drawing similar to Figure 8.36. As an example different than the sound of the bugle waking the dog, consider the temperature inversion over a lake at night, and how one can hear whispers of people on the opposite side of the lake. You may want to follow this up with the similar case of refraction by wind, where wind speed is greater higher up than near the ground.

A useful medical application of sound refraction is ultrasound technology, especially in examining the unborn children in pregnant women. Fortunately, the method appears to be relatively free of dangerous side effects. Detailed sonograms are now common, giving a three-dimensional effect.

The most fascinating example of reflection and refraction of sound is the dolphin. Dolphins have been doing all along what humans have just learned to do. Add to the boxed material about dolphins, that unlike humans, dolphins breathe voluntarily. They cannot be put to sleep for medical operations because they will cease breathing and die. They are subject to drowning, as any mammal is. When in trouble, other dolphins hold the troubled dolphin at the surface so breathing can occur. When sick, they will beach themselves so they won't drown. Many shipwrecked sailors owe their lives to dolphins who have beached them. Fascinating creatures!

Forced Vibrations and Natural Frequency
Tap various objects around you and explain what is happening at the atomic level—that crystalline or molecular structures are made to vibrate, and that due to the elasticity and bonding of the material constituents, natural modes of vibration are produced. Objects have their own characteristic frequencies. The organs of humans have a natural frequency of about 7 hertz.

Resonance
> DEMONSTRATION: Show resonance with a pair of tuning forks, explaining how each set of compressions from the first fork pushes the prongs of the second fork in rhythm with its natural motion. Compare this to pushing somebody on a playground swing. Illuminate the forks with a strobe light for best effect!

When you are adjusting the frequency of one of your tuning fork boxes, by moving the weights up or down the prongs, call attention to the similarity of this with tuning a radio receiver. When one turns the knob to select a different station, one is adjusting the frequency of the radio set to resonate with incoming stations.

Cite other examples of resonance—the chattering vibration of a glass shelf when a radio placed on it plays a certain note, the loose front end of a car that vibrates at only certain speeds, a crystal wine glass shattering by a singer's voice, and troops breaking step in bridge crossing.

Interference—The Addition and Subtraction of Waves
Introduce interference by sketching a sine wave on the board—actually a water wave. Then superpose another identical wave on it and ask what happens. Nothing spectacular, simply a wave of twice the amplitude. Now repeat, and superpose the second wave a half wavelength out of step. State that physicists don't say "out of step," but "out of phase."

> DEMONSTRATION: Play a stereo radio, tape, or CD player on a mono setting and demonstrate the different quality of sound when the speakers, set apart from each other, are out of phase. I have mine connected to a DPDT switch to flip the phase. Face the stereo speakers toward each other, at arm's length apart. Flip one speaker out of phase and gradually bring them closer. The volume of sound fades dramatically as they are brought face to face—interference. This may likely be one of the more memorable of your demos.

The question may arise as what happens to the sound energy when sound cancels. Interestingly enough, each radio loudspeaker is also a microphone. When the speakers face each other, they "drive" each other, inducing back voltages in each other that reduce the currents in each. Thus energy is diminished but not canceled.

> DEMONSTRATION: Show the reason for speakers mounted in boxed enclosures by producing a bare speaker connected to a music source. The sound is "tinny." State why: that as compressions are produced by one side of the speaker cone, rarefactions are produced by the other. Superposition of these waves results in destructive interference. Then produce a square piece of board (plywood or cardboard) close to a meter on a side with a hole the size of the speaker in its center. Place the speaker at the hole, and let your class hear the difference in the fullness of the sound that results. You have diminished the superposition of waves that previously canceled. The effect is dramatic.

I kid around about my keen ability to completely cancel sound by striking one tuning fork and then the other at precisely the time to produce cancellation. When I do this I quickly grab and release the prongs of the sounding fork while not really making contact with the second. It is especially effective for students who weren't watching carefully. I exclaim that when I'm lucky enough to achieve complete cancellation on the first try, I never repeat it. Is this real science? No, but it's a mood elevator so that my students are receptive to the real science I discuss the remainder of the time.

Beats
Acknowledge you were kidding around before about producing interference with the pair of tuning forks, but now you're for real with them. Strike the slightly different frequency forks and hear the beats. This is even nicer when your students see an oscilloscope trace what they hear.

The Doppler Effect
Introduce the Doppler effect by throwing a ball, perhaps sponge rubber or Styrofoam, around the room. In the ball you first place an electronic whistle that emits a sound of about 3000 Hz. Relate this to the sound of a siren on a fire engine (Figure 8.50) and radar of the highway patrol. (Note that sound requires a medium; radar is an electromagnetic wave and doesn't require a medium.)

Introducing the Electromagnetic Spectrum
If you have already delved into E&M from Chapter 7 with your class, then begin your teaching of the electromagnetic spectrum and properties of light with "Begin 1" that follows. If you're jumping into light without having covered E&M, then jump ahead to "Begin 2."

Begin 1: Electromagnetic Waves
Usually I begin my lecture by asking the class to recall my recent demonstration of charging a rubber rod with cat's fur and how when I brought it near a charged pith ball, I produced action at a distance. When I moved the charged rod, the charged ball moved also. If I gently oscillate the rod, the ball in turn oscillates. State that one can think of this behavior as either action-at-a-distance or the interaction of the ball with the space immediately around it—the electric field of the charged rod. For low frequencies, the ball will swing in rhythm with the shaking rod. But the inertia of the ball and its pendulum configuration make response poor for any vigorous shaking of the rod (that's why it's best not to actually show this, but to only describe it and go through the motions as if the equipment were present—you avoid the "that's the way it would behave" situation). You can easily establish in your students' minds the reasonableness of the ball shaking back and forth in response to the shaking electric field about the shaking rod. Carry this further by considering the ball to be simply a point charge with negligible mass. Now it will respond in synchronous rhythm with the shaking rod. Increase the frequency of the shaking rod, and state that not only is there a shaking electric field about the rod, but because the field is changing, there is also a different kind of field.

> CHECK YOUR NEIGHBOR: What kind of field is induced by the shaking rod? What kind of field, in turn, does this induced field induce? And further in turn, what kind of field does this further induced field induce? And so on.

Begin 2: Electromagnetic Waves
Begin by stating that everybody knows that if you placed the end of a stick in a pond and shook the stick back and forth, you'd generate waves across the water surface. But what everybody doesn't know is that if you shook a charged rod back and forth in free space, you'd generate waves also. Not waves of water, or even waves of the medium in which the stick exists, but waves of electric and magnetic fields. You'd generate *electromagnetic waves*. Shaking the rod at low frequencies generates radio waves. Shaking at a million billion times per second generates waves one could see in the dark, for those waves would be seen as light.

Electromagnetic Spectrum
Continue by stating that, strictly speaking, light is the only thing we see. And to understand what light is, we will first try to understand how it behaves. Call attention to the rainbow of colors that are dispersed by a prism or by raindrops in the sunlight. We know white light can be spread into a spectrum of colors. Ask your students to consider the worldview of little creatures who could see only a tiny portion of the spectrum, creatures who would be color-blind to all the other parts. Their worldview would be very limited. Then state that we are like those little creatures, in that the spectrum of colors we can see are a tiny portion of the *electromagnetic spectrum* (Figure 8.10)—less than a tenth of 1%! We are color-blind to the other parts.

Buckminster Fuller put it well when he stated that 99% of all that is going to affect our tomorrows is being developed by humans using instruments that work in ranges of reality that are nonhumanly sensible. The instruments of science have extended our views of the other parts. These instruments are not microscopes and telescopes, for they enable closer viewing of the part of the spectrum we are familiar with. It is the infrared detecting devices, microwave and radio receivers, that allow us to explore the lower-frequency end of the spectrum, and ultraviolet, x-ray, and gamma-ray detectors that let us "see" the higher-frequency end. What we see with unaided eyes is a tiny part of what's out there in the world around us.

CHECK YOUR NEIGHBOR: Where does sound fit in the electromagnetic spectrum? [It doesn't of course!]

CHECK YOUR NEIGHBOR: A photographer wishes to photograph a lightning bolt and comes up with the idea of having the camera triggered by the sound of thunder. A good idea or a poor idea? [Very poor, for light travels about a million times faster than sound. By the time the sound of thunder arrives, the lightning bolt is long gone!]

CHECK YOUR NEIGHBOR: So the speed of light is finite; does this mean your image in the mirror is always a bit younger or a bit older than you? [Older, but of course not by very much!]

Light Getting Through Glass (or Any Transparent Material)

Recall your earlier demonstration of sound resonance (or if you haven't done this, demonstrate now the resonance of a pair of tuning forks mounted on sounding boxes; see Figure 8.20). The tuning fork demo provides important experience for your students in understanding the interaction of light and matter. In some cases, light strikes a material and rebounds—reflection (next chapter). In cases where light continues through the material, we say the material is *transparent*.

DEMONSTRATION: Show the swinging balls apparatus that is usually used to illustrate momentum and energy conservation. Here you are showing that the energy that cascades through the system of balls is analogous to light energy cascading through transparent matter. Just as the incident ball is not the same ball that emerges, the incident "photon" of light upon glass is not the same photon that emerges through the other side. Although too difficult to see, slight interaction times between balls produces a slight time delay between incidence and emergence of balls, and likewise for light.

(Note that the text does not mention photons in the light-through-glass explanation. Photons aren't introduced until the next chapter.)

Point out the value of *scientific models* in understanding physical phenomena, and hence, incorporate the discussion of cascading balls, tuning forks, and imaginary springs that hold electrons to the nuclei of atoms. A model is not correct or incorrect but is useful or nonuseful. Models must be refined or abandoned whenever they fail to account for various aspects of a phenomenon.

CHECK YOUR NEIGHBOR: Compared to the speed of light in a vacuum, why is the speed of light less in transparent materials such as water or glass? [*Answer:* According to the model treated in the text, there is a time delay between the absorption of light and its reemission. This time delay serves to decrease the average speed of light in a transparent material.]

Another analogy for light traveling through glass is the average speed of a basketball moving down a court. It may fly through the air from player to player at one constant speed, but its average speed down the court depends on the holding time of the players. Carrying the analogy further, different materials have different players, and although the instantaneous speed of light is always the same, the average speed depends on both the number of players encountered and the holding time of each player.

On the subject of glass, it's interesting to note that we see through it for the same reasons we see through water. Despite the appearance of glass, it is really a highly viscous liquid rather than a solid. Its internal structure is not the regular crystalline latticework of most solids but is essentially random, like that of liquids. Whereas conventional liquids have a freezing point at which they become solid, liquid glass gets stiffer as it cools. At room temperature, its rate of flow is so slow that it takes centuries for it to appreciably ooze out of shape. Because of the downward flow due to gravity, windowpanes only several decades old show a lens effect at their bottoms due to the increased thickness there.

Opaque Materials

State that light generally has three possible fates when incident upon a material: (1) it reflects, (2) it is transmitted through the material, or (3) it is absorbed by the material. Usually a combination of all three fates occurs. When absorption occurs, the vibrations given to electrons by incident light are often great enough to last for a relatively long time, during which the vibratory energy is shared by collisions with neighboring atoms. The absorbed energy warms the material.

CHECK YOUR NEIGHBOR: Why, in the sunlight, is a black tar road hotter to the touch than a pane of window glass? [Sunlight is absorbed and turned into internal energy in the road surface but is transmitted through the glass to somewhere else.]

For the record, we say that ultraviolet (UV) light cannot penetrate glass. Hence, you cannot get a sunburn through glass. But *some* ultraviolet light does pass through glass—long wavelength ultraviolet light, which has insufficient energy to cause a sunburn. Most sunlamps aren't made of ordinary glass—they're made of quartz or special UV-transparent glass.

Color Science
What first made Isaac Newton a famous physicist was not his contributions to mechanics, but his contributions to light. He was the first to explain the colors produced by a prism held in the sunlight. White light, after all, is all the colors "smudged" together.

Selective Reflection
Discuss the oscillator model of the atom and the ideas of forced vibration and resonance as they relate to color, as you display different colored objects. A red object, for example, reflects red. It absorbs the other colors. Resonance is *not* occurring for red, by the way, for the resonant frequencies are being *absorbed*. (I was confused about this point for years!)

Selective Transmission
Similarly for colored glass, the resonant frequencies are absorbed and become the internal energy of the transparent material. The frequencies to pass through the glass are those away from the resonant frequencies. Frequencies close to resonance undergo more interactions with the molecules and take longer to travel than frequencies far from resonance. Hence, different colors have different speeds in transparent materials. (If not, no rainbows, as we shall see in the following chapter.)

Reflection
Anybody who has played pool is familiar with the law of reflection—angle of incidence equals angle of rebound. It is likewise for light. Sketch Figure 8.14 on the board and carefully show how image and object distance are the same. You could mention curved mirrors here and stress that the law reigns in whatever small region a light ray strikes and likewise with *diffuse reflection*. Discuss Exercise 10, about the diffuse dry road becoming a "plane mirror" when wet and, hence, the difficulty of seeing the road in a car on a rainy night.

Refraction
Do not fail to emphasize the cause of refraction: a change in the speed of light in going from one medium to another. The analogy of the wheels rolling onto the grass lawn (Figure 8.32) shows that bending of path is the result of this change of speed. This is reinforced in the *Practice Book*.

Cite common examples of refraction: shallow looking pools, distorted viewing in fish tanks, and the operation of lenses, as we shall soon see.

Lenses
The explanation of lenses follows from your demo of light deviating through a prism. Whereas a study of lenses is properly a laboratory activity, all the ray diagrams in the world are of little value unless paired with a hands-on experience with lenses. So if a laboratory experience is not part of your course, I would recommend lenses be treated very briefly if at all in lecture.

Image Formation by a Lens

> DEMONSTRATION: Show examples of converging and diverging lenses. A white light source will do, but a neat source of light is a laser beam that is widened by lenses and then directed through a mask of parallel slits. Then parallel rays of light are incident upon your lenses.

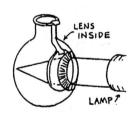

> DEMONSTRATION: Simulate the human eye with a spherical flask filled with water and a bit of fluorescein dye. Paint an "iris" on the flask and position appropriate lenses in back of the iris for normal, farsighted and nearsighted vision. Then show how corrective lenses placed in front of the eye put the light in focus on the retina.

Wave-Particle Duality
Cite the flavor of physics at the turn of the twentieth century when many in the physics community felt that the bulk of physics was in the can and only applications and engineering were left. And then came Einstein and Max Planck, who examined cracks that turned out to be Grand Canyons! Quantum mechanics was born. An intriguing "can't-put-it-down" book that highlights much of this is $E = mc^2$, by David Bodanis, emphasized in the Recommended Reading in the text.

An interesting tidbit concerning Neils Bohr. He dissolved his Nobel Prize gold medal in nitric acid and later the gold was struck as a medal during WWII to keep it from the hands of the Nazis. Bohr was known to be very athletic, and an excellent skier. He was selected for the all-Danish soccer team. Quite a guy!

Here's a quote by Richard Feynman that I wish I had heard during my frustrations with quantum mechanics in graduate school. "I think it is safe to say that no one understands quantum mechanics. Do not keep saying to yourself, if you can possibly avoid it, 'but how can it be like that?' because you will go 'down the drain' into a blind alley from which nobody has yet escaped. Nobody knows how it can be like that."

Integrated Science

There are plenty of ways to weave more subject integration into this chapter. For example, discuss the physics of the eye in advance of the discussion of the eye in Chapter 19 (biology). An interesting tidbit not in the chapter is the explanation for the seemingly luminous eyes of nocturnal animals such as cats and owls at night. It turns out there are reflective membranes located in back of the rods in the animals' eyes, which provide a "second chance" for the animal to perceive light that initially misses the rods. This arrangement, common in night predators, gives excellent night vision and is responsible for the reflection from their eyes when light is shone on them.

Discuss the function of the rods and three types of cones in the retina of the eye, and how color cannot be perceived in dim light, and how the colored stars appear white to us, whereas they show up clearly colored with camera time exposures. (I show a colored slide that I took of the stars, and discuss the curved lines encircling the north star and get into a discussion of how long the camera shutter was held open.)

In discussing color vision, point out that in a bullfight, the bull is angry not at the redness of the cape that is flaunted before him, but because of the darts that have been stuck into him! Whereas a frog is "wired" to see only motion, so it is also on the periphery of human vision. Discuss the fact that we see only motion and no color at the periphery of our vision.

DEMONSTRATION: Stand at a corner of the room and shake brightly colored cards, first turned backward so the color is hidden and students can adjust their head positions (somewhat facing the opposite corner of the room). When they barely see the moving cards, turn them over so the color shows. They'll see the cards but not their colors. Try with different colors. This goes over well and is quite surprising!

Integrated Science—Biology: Sensing Pitch

Explain pitch as well as loudness and sound quality by displaying wave forms on the screen of an oscilloscope. An audio oscillator connected to a loudspeaker and an oscilloscope will demonstrate the relationships between pitch, frequency, and wavelength, and between amplitude and loudness. If you display a decibel meter, show that for mid-range frequencies a decibel is the just-noticeable sound level difference that humans can detect.

The concept of pitch as applied to music is familiar to most. Most students will know a priori that vocal chords produce higher pitched sound by vibrating faster. Expand on this by explaining that you vary pitch by adjusting the tension in your vocal chords. Tension depends on the length of the vocal chords, which can be modified by moving the position of one's larynx (Adam's apple). Moving the larynx higher in the throat produces higher-pitch sounds.

Integrated Science—Biology: Mixing Colored Lights

How many colors are there in the spectrum? Although we commonly group the colors into seven categories (red, orange, yellow, etc.), there are an infinite number of colors. The "in-between" colors are not mixtures of their neighboring colors. The red-orange between red and orange, for example, is not a mixture of red and orange but is a distinct frequency present in sunlight.

DEMONSTRATION: (This is a must!!) Show the overlapping of light from three lamps on your lecture table aimed at a white screen behind you. The variety of colors in the shadows of you are very impressive. And their explanation, by showing only the black shadow from one lamp, then two lamps where the black shadow is now the color of the second lamp, and then three lamps with explanation, is quite satisfying. (If you would like a detailed lecture on the three lamps demo, three pages long, send a note to Paul Hewitt, who will be glad to send it to you.)

As an example of mixing colored light, discuss why water is greenish blue. Water absorbs infrared. It also absorbs visible light up into the red end of the color spectrum. Take away red from white light and you are left with the complementary color—cyan. You can demonstrate this with all three lamps illuminating the white screen. When you turn down the red lamp, the screen turns cyan—the color of the sea! A piece of white paper deep in the water looks cyan. There is no red left in the sunlight to make it white. A red crab and a black crab have the same appearance on the ocean floor.

For another earth science application, discuss why the sky is blue. Compare the molecules in the atmosphere to tiny bells, that when struck, ring with high frequencies. They ring mostly at violet, and next at blue. We're better at hearing blue, so we "hear" a blue sky. On the other hand, bumblebees and other creatures that are good at seeing violet see a violet sky.

LECTURE SKIT, PART 1—Blue sky: Place a variety of six tuning forks at one end of your lecture table, calling their "colors"—a "red" one, "orange" one, "yellow" one, and so forth, to a "violet" one. Ask what "color" sound they would hear if you struck all the tuning forks in unison. Your class should answer, "white." Then suppose you have a mirror device around the forks so that when you "strike"

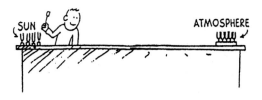

them again, a beam of sound travels down the length of your lecture table. Ask what color they will hear. Several might say "white" again, but state that if there is no medium to scatter the beam, they will hear nothing (unless, of course, the beam is directed toward them). Now place a tray of tuning forks at the opposite end of your lecture table (the tray I use is simply a 2 × 4 piece of wood, about a third of a meter long, with about a dozen holes drilled in it to hold a dozen tuning forks of various sizes). Ask your class to pretend that the ends of your lecture table are 150 million km apart, the distance between the Earth and the sun. State that your tray of assorted tuning forks represents the Earth's atmosphere—point to the tuning forks, calling out their colors: a blue one, a violet one, a blue one, a blue one, a red one, a blue one, a violet one, a blue one, a green one, a blue one, a violet one, and so forth, emphasizing the preponderance of blue and violet forks. Your tray of forks is perpendicular to the imaginary beam from the sun (to simulate a noonish thin atmosphere). Walk to the sun end of the table and again pretend to strike the forks and show how the beam travels down the table and intercepts and scatters from the atmospheric tuning forks in all directions. Ask what color the class hears. Because blue is predominantly scattered, you have a blue sky, especially if they're a bit deficient in hearing violet.

Now, for a final integrated science tie-in: discuss why clouds are white. Small particles scatter high frequencies. Larger molecules and particles also scatter lower frequencies (like larger bells ring at lower frequencies). Very large ones ring in the reds. In a cloud there is a wide assortment of particles of all sizes. They ring with all colors. Ask your class if they have any idea why clouds are white. (Cumulus clouds, composed of droplets, are white because of the multitude of particle sizes, but higher-altitude cirrus clouds are composed of ice crystals, which, like snow, reflect all frequencies.) When drops become too big, they absorb rather than scatter light, and we have a dark rain cloud. (And the rain cleans the sky of particles that make for a whitish sky, and the cleaner sky is a more vivid blue.)

CHECK YOUR NEIGHBOR: Sometimes the sky is not blue, but whitish. Why is it sometimes whitish, and what does your answer have to do with the variety of particle sizes in the atmosphere at these times? [Of course, your double question leads directly to the answer of a wide variety of particle sizes. Question for you: Isn't the question technique preferable than simple statements of fact?]

9   The Atom

A major goal of this chapter is to present atoms and their subatomic particles and thus set the stage for subsequent chapters. Another goal is to show students how conceptual models help us to understand atomic behavior. A simplified conceptual model depicting the atom as a series of concentric shells is presented. This model sets the stage for a deeper understanding of concepts presented in subsequent chapters, such as chemical bonding. The shell model, in its simplified form, is easy for the students to grasp, yet the model is very powerful in its predictive properties. The greatest joy is seeing students impress themselves as they apply the model to suggest chemical insight "all on their own." An example that arises later in the course (Chapter 13) is understanding why elements to the upper right of the periodic table tend to behave as oxidizing agents, while those to the lower left tend to behave as reducing agents. They then realize that chemistry is more about applying conceptual models than it is about memorizing facts.

In the *Practice Book*:
• Subatomic Particles

In *Next-Time Questions*:
• Germanium Capsules
• Neon
• Atomic Size
• Spectroscope

In the *Lab Manual*:
• Thickness of a BB Pancake (experiment)
• Oleic Acid Pancake (experiment)
• Bright Lights (experiment)

Transparencies:
Figures 9.2, 9.4, 9.7, 9.12, 9.28

Suggested Presentation

Begin by posing the situation of breaking a boulder into rocks, rocks into stones, stones into pebbles, pebbles into gravel, gravel into sand, sand into powder, and so forth, until you get to the fundamental building block—the atom. Relate how from the earliest days of science people wondered how far the idea of breaking boulders into stones, pebbles, sand, powder, and so on, would go. Does it ever end? Hundreds of years ago, people had no way of finding out, and they instead carried on with philosophical speculation. Not until "modern" chemistry in the late 1700s did people begin to get indirect evidence of some basic order in the combinations of things. The first real "proof" that there were atoms was given by Einstein in 1905, the same year he published his paper on relativity. He calculated what kind of motion there ought to be in Brownian motion, based on ideas we've considered already, like energy and momentum conservation, and the idea of heat as atomic motion. Many of the "heavies" in physics at that time didn't believe in atoms until Einstein's work.

The Elements

This section contains the first mention of the periodic table. You might consider taking the opportunity to alleviate the fears some, if not many, of your students will have about having to memorize this chart. Of course, it is a good way to test memory skills, but memorizing the periodic table has very little to do with learning physical science. Instead, emphasize to students that through this course they will instead learn how to "read" the periodic table, which is a roadmap to the fundamental ingredients of all that surrounds us.

This section presents the modern definition of an *element*: a substance that contains only one kind of atom. Note how it is that the terms "element" and "atom" are sometimes used interchangeably. Generally, however, "element" is used to indicate a macroscopic sample, while "atom" is used to indicate the fundamental submicroscopic particle of the element.

Elements are the fundamental ingredients of all that surrounds us. Draw an analogy to how it is that food ingredients, such as spices, properly organized in a kitchen, allow a cook to do cooking efficiently. Scientists have looked for a similar way to organize the elements of nature. The end result is the periodic table.

> PRACTICE QUIZ: Go back to a wall-sized periodic table and let students know that atoms of elements to the upper right tend to be the smallest, while the atoms of elements to the lower left tend to be the largest. Now ask the students which is a larger atom: Sulfur, S, or Arsenic, As? Ideally, the class responds that the sulfur atom is larger. Mockingly inquire of the students how they knew the answer, and in the same breath: "Gee, you must have memorized all the properties of all the elements of the periodic table to be able to answer a question like that." Pick two more elements that are on a lower left to upper right diagonal and ask again. Comment on how you are able to pick elements by random and they're *still* able to answer! Your grand finale, of course, is to point out that the periodic table is like a book. We don't memorize books—we learn to read them. Likewise with the periodic table. "As a student of integrated science, you are here to learn how to read the periodic table. Let's begin . . ."

One of the more apparent organizations of the periodic table is by metals, nonmetals and metalloids. Your discussion here will likely be brief. The main intent should be to identify metals, nonmetals, and metalloids by their physical properties. The theme of the periodic table's organization is carried well by pointing out the greater electrical conducting properties of germanium versus silicon.

The text's discussion of the periodic table does not go into sufficient detail to account for the traditional method of numbering the atomic groups (e.g., 1A, 2A, 3B, etc). For this reason, we follow the numbering system recommended by IUPAC (i.e., 1 through 18).

Smallness of Atoms

Give examples to convey the idea of the smallness of the atom, for example, an atom is as many orders of magnitude smaller than a person as an average star is larger than a person, so we stand between the atoms and the stars. The size of an atom is to the size of an apple as the size of an apple is to the size of the Earth. So if you want to imagine an apple full of atoms, think of the Earth, solid-packed with apples.

> CHECK QUESTION: Ask what an atom would "look like" if viewed through a vertical bank of about 40 high-powered optical microscopes stacked one atop the other. [It turns out they wouldn't have an appearance, at least not in the range of frequencies we call light. The atom is smaller than the wavelength of light.]

Recycling of Atoms

State that if you put a drop of ink in a bathtub full of water, you (the students) know that in a short time you can sample any part of the water and find ink in it. The atoms of ink spread out. We can get an idea of how small atoms are from this fact: There are more atoms in a thimbleful of ink than there are thimblefuls of water in the Atlantic Ocean. That means if you throw a thimbleful of ink into the Atlantic Ocean and give it enough years to mix uniformly, and then dip anywhere in the ocean with a thimble, you'll have some atoms of ink in your sample.

Atoms Are Mostly Empty Space

Discuss the Bohr model of the atom and the electrical role of the nucleus and surrounding electrons. Stress the emptiness of the atom and lead into the idea of solid matter being mostly empty space. State how our bodies are 99.999% empty spaces, and how a particle, if tiny enough and not affected by electrical forces, could be shot straight through us without even making a hole! Making a direct hit with an atomic nucleus or an electron is as improbable as making a direct hit with a planet or the sun if you throw a gravity-free dart from outer space at the solar system. Both the solar system and an atom are mostly empty space. Walk through a beam of neutrons and very few if any will interact with your body. Still smaller neutral particles, called neutrinos, the most elusive yet most numerous and fastest of all particles, pass though us every moment. But they do so without consequence, for only very rarely, perhaps once or so per year, do any make a bull's-eye collision with any of our atomic nuclei. They freely pass through the entire Earth with rare interactions.

LECTURE SKIT: Start with a drawing similar to Figure 9.5 on the chalkboard, only indicate electrons as tiny fast-moving specks. State that your drawing is all out of scale. That to be more accurate you need to draw the nucleus much smaller. Erase the nucleus you first drew and replace it with a speck tinier than the electrons. Note that the electrons are actually thousands of times less massive than the atomic nucleus, so it would do far better to just erase them. Erase everything except the tiny speck of a nucleus and, perhaps, leave the perimeter. "Thus it is that we understand that atoms are made mostly of empty space." Finish up by noting that although the atom is mostly empty space, the tiny, tiny subatomic particles it contains have these force fields. It is the electric force of attraction between the electrons and the protons that holds the electrons to the atomic nucleus. Likewise, it is the electric force of repulsion between the electrons of one atom and the electrons of another atom that causes the two atoms to repel. The exception, of course, is when a chemical bond forms between those two atoms, which is a completely different story to be discussed in more detail in Chapter 12.

Point out that the atomic configurations you sketch on the board are simply models, not to be taken as visually correct. For example, if the nuclei were drawn to scale they would be scarcely visible specks. And the electrons don't really "orbit," as your drawings suggest—such terms don't seem to have much meaning at the atomic level. It would be more precise to say they "swarm," or are "smeared," around the central nuclei.

Electrical Forces
Discuss the role of electrical forces in preventing us from oozing into our chairs and so forth. Ask the class to imagine that the lecture table is a large magnet, and that you wear magnetic shoes that are repelled by the table you "stand" on. Ask them to imagine whether or not a sheet of paper could be passed between your shoes and the table. For there is a space there. Then state that on the submicroscopic scale that this is indeed what happens when you walk on any solid surface. Only the repelling force isn't magnetic, it's electric! Discuss the submicroscopic notion of things touching. Acknowledge that under very special circumstances, the nucleus of one atom can physically touch the nucleus of another atom—that this is what happens in a thermonuclear reaction.

Protons and Neutrons
Draw a proton about 2 inches in diameter on the chalkboard or overhead projector. Move the chalk or pen wildly about this proton to indicate an electron whizzing about this proton. End by making a speck some distance from the proton, and let the class know that this represents a crude model of the hydrogen atom. Add a proton, electron, and two neutrons to transform the atom into a helium atom. Continue in this manner building a lithium atom, then a boron atom, and so forth. Point out to students that this is how atoms differ from one another—by the number of subatomic particles they contain. A premise here, of course, is that all electrons are identical to each other, just as all protons are identical and all neutrons are identical. Point out the relationship between the atomic number and the periodic table and how an atom is defined by its atomic number.

Note, when you consider the electrical forces in the atom you're discussing, the implications of Coulomb's law at short distances. Relative distances between charges are important, as later chapters will show.

In discussing isotopes, point out that isotopes are associated with all atoms, not just radioactive ones. Start with the isotopes of hydrogen and then discuss the isotopes of uranium, which will be important in Chapter 10.

Mass Number and Atomic Mass
Which contributes most to an atom's mass, protons or electrons? [Protons, by far.] Which contributes to an atom's size? [Electrons, by far.] Distinguish between mass number and atomic mass. Help students write the chemical symbol for specific elements with atomic numbers and atomic mass numbers.

Identifying Atoms Using the Spectroscope

Cite that a century ago, the chemical composition of the stars was thought to be forever beyond the knowledge of humankind—and now today we know as much about their composition as we do the Earth's. Much more about that will be presented in Chapter 28.

Ideally, you'll have access to some handheld spectrometers (or plain diffraction gratings) for students to use to look at various light sources. Street lights work very well in that they show the discrete emission lines of the elements that are glowing within them. If you don't have gas discharge tubes to share with your students, consider dipping a wet microspatula into various salts, especially strontium chloride or copper chloride. Only after students are well rehearsed at observing the spectra of the overhead lights, direct them to train their spectroscopes onto the flame as you place various salts within the flame. Consider showing and discussing with your students the overhead transparency for Figure 9.12 beforehand.

Cite examples of the uses of spectrometers—how very minute quantities of materials are needed for chemical analysis; how tiny samples of ores are sparked in carbon arcs and the light directed through prisms or diffraction gratings to yield precise chemical composition, and note their use in fields as diverse as chemistry and criminology.

Emphasize the discreteness of the lines from atoms in the gaseous state. Consider going beyond the book treatment and lead into the idea of excitation in an incandescent lamp, where the atoms are in the solid state. Why do we get a continuous spectrum from a solid lamp filament but spectral lines from the same atoms in the gaseous state? The answer is that in the crowded condition, the energy levels interact with one another and produce a smudged distribution of frequencies rather than discrete frequencies characteristic of the gaseous state. It's like the difference between the tone of bells that are struck while packed together in a box, and their tone when suspended apart from one another. The distribution of frequencies of atoms in the solid state make up the standard radiation curve, which you can approximate by sketching a bell-shaped curve on the board. Where the curve peaks indicates the temperature of the source of light hence, the difference between red hot, white hot, and blue hot sources—stars, for example. The peak of the curve is the peak frequency (referred to as average frequency in Chapter 6), which is proportional to the absolute temperature of the source—$f \sim T$. (We'll discuss this again when we explain the greenhouse effect in Chapter 25 and the radiation curves of stars in Chapter 28. The equation tells us that the frequency of light emitted by the hot sun is proportionally higher than the frequency of radiation emitted by the Earth's relatively cool surface. It also explains why stars have different colors—blue stars are hotter than red stars.)

> CHECK YOUR NEIGHBOR: Hold up an obviously broken lightbulb and ask if it is presently emitting electromagnetic energy. [Sure it is, as is everything—its temperature is simply too low for the corresponding frequency to trigger our retinas.]

Get into the idea of the infrared part of the spectrum. Show in a sequence of radiation curves on the board how an increase in temperature brings the curve "sloshing over" into the lower-frequency portion of the visible spectrum—hence, the red hotness of a hot poker. Show how an increase in temperature brings the curve into the visible spectrum producing white light. Show why a hot poker does not become green hot, and how sharp the curve would have to be to produce green without sloshing into the other frequencies to produce white light.

The Quantum Hypothesis

This chapter introduces quantum mechanics by way of the classic wave-particle duality in which light behaves as a wave when it travels in empty space, and lands like a particle when it hits something. It is mistaken to insist it must be both a particle and a wave at the same time. This is not the case. What something *is* and what it *does* are not the same.

Using the Bohr model, explain energy levels with the following analogy: Hold a book above the lecture table and drop it. Then hold it higher and drop it again. State that the potential energy you supplied to the book was converted to kinetic energy and then to sound energy. State that the higher you boost the book before dropping it, the louder the sound. State that a similar thing happens in the case of atoms. Parallel your book example and consider the case of an electron being boosted to a higher orbit in an atom. Just as a screen door that is pushed open against a spring snaps back and produces sound, the displaced electron snaps back to its ground state and produces light. It emits a throbbing spark of light we call a *photon*. Show that when it is boosted to higher levels, it emits a higher-frequency photon upon de-excitation. Introduce the relationship $E \sim f$ for the resulting photons. Discuss the variety of energy-level jumps for a simple atom.

CHECK YOUR NEIGHBOR: Two photons are emitted as a result of the transitions shown on the board. If one photon is red and the other blue, which is which? [Be sure to draw the shorter wavelength for the greater transition, from the second level to ground state, and the longer wavelength for the smaller transition from level one to ground.]

DEMONSTRATION: Show the spectra of gas discharge tubes. Either use a large diffraction grating that you hold in front of the tube, or pass small gratings among the class, so the spectral lines can be observed.

Electron Waves
Like others, de Broglie was in the right place at the right time, for the notion of particles having wave properties was at hand. De Broglie showed Planck's constant again with his formula that relates the wavelength of a "matter wave" with its momentum. So matter, like light, has wave properties. When incident upon a target, its matter nature is evident. We don't ordinarily notice the wave nature of matter only because the wavelength is so extremely small. (Interestingly, de Broglie never did any physics after his one large contribution. He died in 1987.) Electron waves are evident in the electron microscopes, which should be distinguished from the scanning tunneling microscopes.

You will note that the uncertainty principle is not discussed. This is for brevity. You might wish to segue into the uncertainty principle, however, when discussing the probability clouds.

This section treats the matter-wave concept that gives a clearer picture of the electrons that "circle" the atomic nucleus. Instead of picturing them as tiny BBs whirling like planets, the matter-wave concept suggests we see them as smeared standing waves of energy—existing where the waves reinforce, and nonexisting where the waves cancel (Figure 9.21). Electrons form probability clouds (Figure 9.22) and orbitals (Table 9.2) that are distinctly different than the planetary paths of the Bohr atom. The purpose of these models is to enable predictions of atomic behavior—not to provide a picture of "what atoms look like."

DEMONSTRATION: Set up the mechanical vibrator with wire loop shown in Figure 9.21. To drive the mechanical vibrator, you'll need an amplifier (some radios work well) as well as a variable frequency sound generator. You can demonstrate a three-dimensional standing wave by holding a water balloon to the tip of the mechanical vibrator (no loop), which is best set sideways so that you can hold the balloon over a pan in case it breaks. As you vary the frequency, you'll find particular frequencies that establish standing waves within the balloon as evidenced by the stationary bumps that form on the surface. This demo is best for "hands-on," because it is the person holding the balloon that gets the best experience—the bumps are not only seen, they are felt, and it's a bizarre feeling as one set of standing waves gives rise to another as the frequencies are changed.

You may wish to discuss the philosophical implications of quantum mechanics with your students. At minimum, you might warn your class that there are many people who have much to say about quantum mechanics who don't understand it. Quantum mechanics does not come in the neat package that Newtonian mechanics comes in and is not all sewed up like other less complex bodies of knowledge. It is still an incomplete theory. It is a widely respected theory, however, and we should be wary of pseudoscientists who attempt to fit their own theories into the cracks of quantum mechanics and ride on the back of its hard-earned reputation.

Integrated Science—Chemistry, Biology, Earth Science: Physical and Conceptual Models
The fundamental units of matter are so small that hundreds of years ago people had no way of finding out if they existed. Any discussion of the existence of these fundamental units was no more than philosophical speculation. As mentioned in the History of Science feature "The Atomic Hypothesis," not until "modern" chemistry in the late 1700s did people begin to get indirect evidence of some basic order in the combinations of things. The first real "proof" that there were atoms was given by Einstein in 1905.

CALCULATION ASSIGNMENT: The diameter of an atom is about 10^{-10} m. (a) How many atoms make a line a millionth of a meter (10^{-6}) long? (b) How many atoms cover a square a millionth of a meter on a side? (c) How many atoms fill a cube a millionth of a meter on a side? (d) If a dollar were attached to each atom, what could you buy with your line of atoms? With your square of atoms? With your cube of atoms? [Solutions: (a) 10^4 atoms (length 10^{-6} m divided by size 10^{-10} m). (b) 10^8 atoms ($10^4 \times 10^4$). (c) 10^{12} atoms ($10^4 \times 10^4 \times 10^4$). (d) $10,000 buys a small car, for instance. $100 million buys a few jet aircraft and an airport on which to keep them, for instance. $1 trillion buys a medium-sized country, for instance. (Answers limited only by the imagination of the student.)]

Models are not to be judged as being "true" or "mistaken"; models are useful or nonuseful. The particle model of light is useful in making sense of the details of the photoelectric effect, whereas the wave model of light is not useful in understanding these details. Likewise, the wave model of light is useful for understanding the details of interference, whereas the particle model is not useful. The effectiveness of one model over another means simply that one model is more effective than another. This effectiveness doesn't mean that one model is correct and the other invalid. As we gather more data and gain new insights, we refine our models.

Buckminster Fuller put it well when he stated that 99% of all that is going to affect our tomorrows is being developed by humans using instruments that work in ranges of reality that are nonhumanly sensible. The instruments of science have extended our views of the other parts. These instruments are not microscopes and telescopes, for they enable closer viewing of the part of the spectrum we are familiar with. It is the infrared detecting devices, microwave and radio receivers, that allow us to explore the lower-frequency end of the spectrum, and ultraviolet, x-ray, and gamma-ray detectors that let us "see" the higher-frequency end. What we see with unaided eyes is a tiny part of what's out there in the world around us and increasingly, a tiny part of what we can perceive with the aided eye.

Integrated Science—Chemistry: The Shell Model

The big challenge is to convince students that these shells are not meant to represent the Bohr planetary orbits, though they are analogous. Rather, as is explored in the more in-depth text, *Conceptual Chemistry*, each shell consists of a collection of atomic orbitals of similar energy levels. These shells differ from Bohr's planetary model, therefore, in that they are drawn with an understanding of the wave nature of electrons and the quantum mechanics that they follow.

There are many rewards for bringing students to understand the shell model. An in-depth understanding of periodic trends—and thus the glory of the periodic table—is one of these rewards.

10   Nuclear Physics

Begin by asking what is the major source of energy that keeps the Earth's interior molten, that makes volcanoes hot, and hot springs warm? Radioactivity in the Earth's material, from its very beginning, is responsible. Radioactivity is nothing new and is as natural as hot springs and geysers. When electricity was harnessed in the last century, people were fearful of it and its effects on life forms. Now it is commonplace, for its dangers are well understood. We are at a similar stage with regard to anything called nuclear. As scientists, we are all aware of how the medical industry renamed *nuclear magnetic resonance* (NMR) into *magnetic resonance imaging* (MRI). Why? "I don't want *my* Aunt Minnie near any *nuclear* machine!"

Hundreds of thousands of Americans live in houses that have a yearly radiation dose from radon in the ground equal to the dose residents living in the vicinity of Chernobyl received in 1986 when one of its reactors exploded and released radioactive materials into the environment (*Scientific American*, May 1988). This is not to say it is unharmful to live in the vicinity of radon emission, but to say that radioactivity is not a modern problem and not a by-product of science per se. It has been with us since day one.

In the *Practice Book*:
• Radioactivity
• Radioactive Half-Life
• Nuclear Fission and Fusion
• Nuclear Reactions

In *Next-Time Questions*:
• Age of the Earth
• Child's Balloon
• Hot Spring
• Ancient Axe
• Radioactive Cookies

In the *Lab Manual*:
• Get a Half-Life! (activity)
• Chain Reaction (activity)

Transparencies:
Figures 10.3, 10.5, 10.10, 10.11, *Technology* Nuclear fission power plant, 10.26, 10.27, 10.28

Suggested Presentation

Radioactivity
Discuss medical and dental applications of x-rays, citing the newer photographic films now available that permit very short exposures of low intensity and, therefore, safer dosages. Cite also the fact that the eye is the part of the body most prone to radiation damage—something that seems to be ignored by many dentists when making exposures of the teeth (and inadvertently, the eyes). (Why not eye masks as well as chest masks?)

Distinguish between alpha, beta, and gamma rays. Which of the three rays is most like an X-ray? You may wish to review the electromagnetic spectrum so that you may point out how X-rays and gamma rays and visible light are just different frequencies of the same thing: electromagnetic radiation.

As an application of the concept of inertia presented in Chapter 2, ask your students why it is that the alpha particle does not bend in its trajectory as much as the electron does when both pass through the same magnetic field.

Radioactivity Is a Natural Phenomenon

Radiation, like everything else that is both damaging and little understood, is usually seen to be worse than it is. You can alleviate a sense of hopelessness in students about the dangers of radiation by pointing out that radiation is nothing new. It not only goes back before science and technology but before the Earth came to be. It is a part of nature that must be lived with. Radiation is everywhere. However, we can take steps to avoid unnecessary radiation.

Common smoke detectors in the home make use of the very low dose of about 2 microcuries of americium-241, used to make the air in the detector's ionization chamber electrically conductive. When smoke enters the chamber, it inhibits the flow of electricity, which activates the alarm. The lives saved each year by these devices number in the thousands (which dwarfs the numbers seriously harmed by radiation).

Bernard Cohen at the University of Pittsburgh has found from worldwide data that the incidence of cancer is smaller at places with higher than average radiation. His conclusions are that *a radiation dose of 10–20 mSv/year seems to suppress the risk of cancer!* (The SI unit for radiation dose is the *sievert*, Sv.)

Recent studies of survivors of the Nagasaki atomic bomb made by Sohei Kondo (Tokyo) support this conclusion. Kondo found that the probability of getting leukemia, lung cancer, and colon cancer as a function of dose drops at first, has a minimum at about 20–50 mSv, and increases linearly only above 100 mSv. Those people who survived after receiving a modest dose at Hiroshima and Nagasaki lived, on average, 4 years longer than the control population.

Conjecture is that the mass of antibodies that increase in the body as a result of radiation may activate the defense (repair enzyme and antibody production) against oxidative attacks. A small dose may increase the immunity against carcinogens. Apparently, we can defend ourselves biologically against doses below some threshold but cannot against stronger or multiple attacks.

Radioactive Tracers

In Hawaii, the fresh water supply comes from the central mountain regions of each island, which is where moisture-laden clouds collect and condense. In the Halawa valley on Oahu, there is a tunnel that goes deep into the mountains down to where the water table can be found. Pumps pull this water, which is piped to serve the city of Honolulu. I (Suchocki) had the opportunity to take a tour of this tunnel. Eventually, we got to the point where water could be seen dripping from the ceiling. My Board of Water Supply tour guide mentioned that the water passing through at this point was about 50 years old. In other words, it came from rain that passed through the top of the mountains about 50 years ago. "How in the heck was that determined?" I asked. "Radioactive isotopic signatures from nuclear bomb testings," was the reply. Indeed, radioactive isotopes have found numerous applications, some purposely, others more serendipitously.

Tire manufacturers employ radioactive isotopes. Get this: If a known fraction of the carbon atoms used in an automobile tire is radioactive, the amount of rubber left on the road when the car is braked can be estimated through a count of the radioactive atoms.

There are hundreds more examples of the use of radioactive isotopes. The important thing is that this technique provides a way to detect and count atoms in samples of materials too small to be seen with a microscope. Point your students to the problems given at the back of this chapter for some other interesting examples on the use of radioactive isotopes.

The Strong Nuclear Force

This is an important section, and it's important to spend a fair amount of time on it to make sure students have a firm understanding. The basic idea to get across is that there is this constant battle within the atomic nucleus between the repulsive electric force and the attractive strong nuclear force. Neutrons provide sort of a nuclear cement, in that they enhance the strong nuclear forces while not contributing to the electric force. Make the point that although neutrons help to bind the nucleus together, too many neutrons can also lead to instability. The nuclear fragments of fission are radioactive because of their preponderance of neutrons.

To illustrate the stabilizing effect of neutrons, draw a helium nucleus on the board and beneath this draw two columns—one with the header "repulsive electric force" and the second column with the header "attractive strong nuclear force." Place one tick mark in the repulsive force column in reference to the repulsive force between the two protons. Then end up adding six tick marks in the second column in reference to the additional attractions that occur between the protons and neutrons (see Figure 10.11).

Transmutation

Introduce the symbolic way of writing atomic equations. Write some transmutation formulas on the board while your students follow along with their books opened to the periodic table. Repetition and explanation of the reactions shown in the Natural Transmutation section are in order, if you follow up with one or two new ones as check questions. Be sure that your class can comfortably write equations for alpha decay before having them write equations for beta decay, which are more complex because of the negative charge.

Half-Life

Radioactive decay is somewhat like making popcorn. You never know when any individual kernel of popcorn is going to pop. But when it does, it's irreversibly changed. The rate of popping can be described by the time it takes a given amount to pop and likewise with radioactive decay, where we describe decay rate in terms of half-life. Talk of jumping halfway to the wall, then halfway again, then halfway again and so on, and ask how many jumps will get you to the wall. With a sample of radioactivity, there is a time when all the atoms undergo decay. But measuring the decay rate in terms of this occurrence is a poor idea if only because of the small sample of atoms one deals with as the process nears the end of its course. Insurance companies can make accurate predictions of car accidents and the like with large numbers, but not so for small numbers.

Show a list of radioactive isotopes and their half-lives. Use the following data:

Isotope	Half-life
Uranium-238	4.51×10^9 years
Plutonium-239	2.44×10^4 years
Carbon-14	5.73×10^3 years
Lead-210	20.4 years
Bismuth-210	5.0 days
Polonium-214	1.6×10^4 seconds

Ask students which they would rather hold in their hands: a kilogram of uranium-238, or a kilogram of polonium-214. (Neither, of course, but if you had to choose one or the other, the uranium-238 would be a far, far safer choice.)

> CHECK YOUR NEIGHBOR: 1000 grams of substance X has a half-life of 10 years. How much will be left after 10 years? 20 years? 50 years? Will this sample of substance X ever totally disappear? [Answers: 500 grams, 250 grams, 31.25 grams. Yes, the 1000 grams of substance X will totally disappear after the last atom of substance X decays. Point out to students that while the math goes on for infinity, the masses being calculated become less and less until the mass of a single atom is reached. This is the limit.]

Nuclear Fission

The material in the remaining sections of this chapter is of great technological and sociological importance. The public discussion of nuclear power and other applications of nuclear physics are much clouded by fear of all things nuclear. This fear is largely based on a lack of knowledge. To promote rational discussion of nuclear technology, we authors use the appropriate slogan "KNOW NUKES" in our science classes.

It is interesting to note that recent public opinion polls are showing a change in attitude in the United States toward nuclear energy. Be sure also to give your students a global perspective by letting them know that many nations, such as France, have been embracing nuclear energy as a viable alternative to fossil fuels for many years (70% of France's electrical energy is generated at nuclear power plants).

Note that in this text, the energy release from the opposite processes of fission and fusion is approached from the viewpoint of decreased mass rather than the customary treatment of increased binding energy. Hence, the usual binding energy curve is "tipped upside-down" in Figure 10.26 and shows the relationship of the mass per nucleon vs. atomic number. This is conceptually more appealing, for it shows that any reaction involving a decrease in mass releases energy in accordance with mass–energy equivalence.

Briefly discuss the world atmosphere back in the late 1930s when fission was discovered in Germany, and how this information was communicated to U.S. physicists who urged Einstein to write his famous letter urging President Roosevelt to consider its potential in warfare. The importance of the fission reaction was not only the release of enormous energy, but also the ejected neutrons that could stimulate other fissions in a chain reaction.

A piece of uranium or any radioactive material is slightly warmer than ambient temperature because of the thermal activity prodded by radioactive decay. Fission reactions are major nuclear proddings, and the material becomes quite hot—hot enough to boil water and then some. Make clear that a nuclear reactor of any kind is no more than a means to heat water to steam and generate electricity as a fossil fuel plant does. The principle difference is the fuel used to heat the water. You could remark that nuclear fuel is closer to the nature of the Earth than fossil fuels, whose energies come from the sun.

Nuclear Energy Comes from Nuclear Mass and Vice Versa

After group discussions of the graph in Figure 10.25, ask if this plot is a "big deal." The answer is "no," it simply shows that mass increases with the number of nucleons in the nucleus. The reason for this is because of the increased preponderance of neutrons that help hold the larger atomic nuclei together—no surprise.

Distinguish between the mass of a nucleus and the mass of the nucleons that make up a nucleus. Ask what a curve of mass/nucleon vs. atomic number would look like—that is, if you divided the mass of each nucleus by the number of nucleons composing it and compared the value for different atoms. If all nucleons had the same mass in every nuclear configuration, then the graph would be a horizontal line. But this is not the case. Sketch Figure 10.26 to show the reality, which is that the mass of a nucleon depends upon where it is! In a hydrogen nucleus, it has the greatest mass. In an iron nucleus, it has the least mass.

From the curve, you can show that any nuclear reaction that produces products with less mass than before reaction will give off energy. Where did this energy come from? It came from the transformation of matter into energy. Conversely, any reaction in which the mass of the products is increased will require energy. Where did the increased mass come from? It came from the energy. Thus, matter can be converted into energy, and vice versa. This is all in accordance with Einstein's famous equation $E = mc^2$.

> CHECK YOUR NEIGHBOR: Will the process of fission or fusion release energy from atoms of lead? Gold? Carbon? Neon? [Be careful in selecting atoms too near atomic number 26 in this exercise—for example, elements slightly beyond 26 when fissioned will have more massive products that extend "up the hydrogen hill"; elements near 26 when fused will combine to elements "up the uranium hill." Acknowledging this point, however, may only serve to complicate the picture.]

State how the graph can be viewed as a pair of "energy hills," that to progress "down" the hill is a reaction with less mass per nucleon and therefore a gain in energy.

Nuclear Fusion

By way of the energy hill idea, there are two hills to go down. Going from hydrogen down to iron is even steeper—more mass "defect" in combining light nuclei than splitting heavy ones. This combining atomic nuclei is nuclear fusion—the energy releasing process of the sun and the stars.

> CHECK YOUR NEIGHBOR: Will the process of fission or fusion release energy from the nucleus of iron? [Neither! Iron is the nuclear sink; either process results in "going up the hill," gaining rather than losing mass.]

A discussion of the prospects of fusion power is most fascinating. With all the inputs students get from the prophets of doom, it is well to balance some of this negativity with some of our positive prospects. Abundant energy from controlled fusion is one such positive prospect, which should concern not only scientists, but economists, political scientists, sociologists, ecologists, psychologists, and the everyday person on the street. Particularly exciting is the prospect of the fusion torch, which may provide a means of recycling material and alleviate the scarcity of raw material—not to mention the sink it could provide for wastes and pollutants. Ideally, all unwanted wastes could be dumped into a plasma hot torch emanating from the side of a fusion reactor and thus be vaporized. Atoms could be separated into respective bins by being beamed through giant mass spectrographs.

Point out that the fusion torch may never come to be—not because technology won't progress to such a point, but because it most likely will progress further. If the past is any guide, something even better will make the intriguing idea of a fusion torch obsolete. Whether or not the fusion torch is around the corner, the more important question to consider is how this or comparable achievements will affect the lives of people. How will people interact with one another in a world of relatively abundant energy and material? Admittedly, abundant energy and material will not solve all the major problems but will mark an end to the scarcity that has always been a condition affecting governance of past and the present civilization—a scarcity that has shaped the institutions governing the respective civilizations. Just as the Industrial Revolution reshaped yesterday's world, and cyberspace affects our world today, the abundance of energy and materials will surely affect the institutions of tomorrow's world. Conversely, an age of scarcity of fuel and materials is a possibility as well. Discuss the diminution of fossil fuels and mineral resources and the need for new sources of these resources just to maintain today's standard of living.

This is a time of transition—an exciting time to be alive, particularly for those who are participating in the transition, for those who have not lost nerve and retreated from knowledge into irrationality in its many generally respected forms. Ask your students: How many would prefer living in the past?

Integrated Science—Biology: Doses of Radiation
Relevant to this discussion is Section 16.9 on genetic mutations. If your students have sufficient biology background, have them read the Integrated Science feature, "How Radioactivity Causes Genetic Mutations." Besides birth defects, excess radiation is also linked to cancer, as is well known. For this reason, you may wish to preview Section 16.10: Cancer—Genes Gone Awry, and the Integrated Science feature *Environmental Causes of Cancer* at this point as well.

Integrated Science—Biology, Earth Science: Isotopic Dating
You may find it useful to draw a diagram on the chalkboard depicting a cow eating grass with the sun up in the sky. Show neutrons coming in from outer space (from the sun) and colliding with a nitrogen atom in the atmosphere producing carbon-14 (as per the equations given in the feature). Draw curved arrows that show this carbon-14 transforming into carbon dioxide and being incorporated by the photosynthesizing grass (or a pretty flower). The grass is thus radioactive. A cow comes along and eats the plant, and the cow is thus now radioactive. Draw a hungry-looking cowboy (with fork and knife), and then discuss how it is that the human thus becomes radioactive.

Pose the *Check Yourself* question from the text after explaining the nitrogen–carbon–nitrogen cycle.

11 Investigating Matter

Part 2, Chemistry, touches lightly on the risks of technology vs. its benefits. If you and your class want to delve deeper into science, technology, and society (STS) issues, you can easily work it into this part of the program. Chemistry is linked with life-saving medicines, food safety, the materials science revolution underlying electronics and computing, and other benefits. Yet, toxic waste, ozone depletion, air and water pollution, and global warming also derive from society's application of chemistry. Because there are such clear technological risks and benefits associated with chemistry, this subject segues naturally into STS discussions.

Integrated science differs from dedicated science, technology, and society courses in that there's more emphasis here on the nuts and bolts of learning science concepts, plus more concepts are covered. However, just as a command of integrated science sets a student up for later scientific coursework, it also can serve as a foundation for STS-oriented coursework including environmental education, history of science, philosophy of science, and so forth.

This chapter serves as an introduction to the language of chemistry and its submicroscopic perspectives. It promotes visualizing the realm of the submicroscopic and is designed to set the foundation for all subsequent chemistry chapters.

In the *Practice Book*:
• Change of Phase
• Melting Points of the Elements
• Densities of the Elements
• The Submicroscopic
• Physical and Chemical Changes

In *Next-Time Questions*:
• Open Structure in Ice
• Rusting
• Chemical or Physical Change?
• Solvent in Solution

In the *Lab Manual*:
• Chemical Personalities (experiment)
• Mystery Powders (experiment)

Transparencies:
Figures 11.5, 11.8, 11.9, 11.12, 11.21, 11.24

Suggested Presentation

Chemistry: The Central Science

Ask students if they would prefer to live without medicines, an abundant and safe food supply, or anything made of plastic or metal. Yes, there are numerous problems we encounter living in this modern age, but the many benefits we enjoy should not be ignored. Emphasize that we solve our current problems not by retreating to our past, to those "simpler" times. Rather, why not embrace all that we have learned and apply this knowledge with as much wisdom and foresight as we can muster?

You can weave STS into this chapter by emphasizing Section 11.1 and the Science and Society feature: Chemistry and Public Policy. Discuss the Responsible Care emblem, perhaps inviting students to debate its merits. There are several ways to structure debate in class. You can break students into small groups and assign each group a position, give time for each group to prepare their arguments, then let the debate begin! Another technique is to have students write down their positions pre-debate. Then hold the debate and have students write a follow-up paragraph explaining how the debate modified their initial opinion.

Besides facilitating debate, you can bring STS into your class by researching case studies. Use material from this book, for example, the information on global warming in Chapter 25 or the information on ozone depletion in Chapter 13. You can find other issues to frame as case studies readily on the Internet. Sample topics that you could easily tie into the science presented in this book are the storage of nuclear waste at Yucca mountain, the banning of MTBE in California, the Kyoto agreement, offshore oil drilling, nuclear power, genetic modification of crops, and so forth. Students can write papers or give oral presentations or multimedia presentations summarizing their research findings.

Chemistry, as the central science, plays a foundational role in integrated science. Be sure to discuss where chemistry stands relative to other sciences. Ask your students: "Which is the most complex science: physics, chemistry, earth science, astronomy, or biology?" The answer, of course, is *biology*, for it involves the application of chemistry to living organisms—highly complex systems, indeed. Chemistry is not only a foundation of biology but underlies the earth sciences and astronomy as well (as the IS feature in this chapter, The Origin of the Moon, indicates) Chemistry, in turn, involves the application of physics. In this sense, chemistry is the "Central Science" situated between physics and biology, the earth sciences, and astronomy. Go to any biology lab and you'll see chemistry on the chalkboard. Go to any chemistry lab and you'll see physics on the chalkboard. (What might you see on the chalkboard of a physics laboratory?)

The Submicroscopic World

This section is a good opportunity to introduce (or reintroduce) the idea that the materials around us are made of these incredibly small particles called atoms and molecules. Go back to Chapter 9 and review the feature, *History of Science: The Atomic Hypothesis*. Also review Sections 9.1–9.3 if your students need to be reminded of the basic features of atoms. You can do this by leafing through these sections, calling attention to important figures and discussing them. The technology feature, the *Scanning Tunneling Microscope*, is especially relevant here.

Phases of Matter

Extend your description of the submicroscopic world to phases of matter. Consider using your hands as an analogy: Particles of a solid are fixed and can only vibrate relative to one another (hold your two fists together while giving them a vibrating motion). Particles in a liquid, on the other hand, are able to tumble over one another much like a bunch of marbles in a plastic bag (tumble your fists over each other). Particles in the gaseous phase are moving so rapidly that they separate from one another altogether. (Rapidly bring your two fists together and bounce them off each other.)

> DEMONSTRATION: Refer to Figure 11.6. Show how gases occupy much more volume than do solids or liquids by crushing some dry ice and using a powder funnel to add about a tablespoon to a 9-inch balloon. Place the expanding balloon in a tub of warm water for a more rapid effect. In talking about phase changes, you may find that the water directly beneath the dry ice containing balloon has frozen. Be sure to identify the dry ice as solidified carbon dioxide having nothing in common with water ice except for its solid phase. (Note how the dry ice "sublimes" directly from the solid to gaseous phase. Snow does the same thing, especially high on mountaintops where it is sunny and dry. Mention this now, but explain that you will be talking about phases change in greater depth in the following section.)

Model the gaseous phase by filling a punching balloon with little plastic beads. Blow the punching balloon to full size, and then, holding the balloon firmly with the palms of your hands, shake vigorously. This is certainly a "hands-on" activity, as only the person performing the activity can feel the many pulses of beads hitting against the hands. This is nicely analogous to what happens inside the hot-water balloon demonstration as described below. Pass the bead-containing balloon around for some student testimonials.

Phase and Change of Phase

Relate heat transfer to change of phase. Ask if it is possible to heat a substance without raising its temperature, and why a steam burn is more damaging than a burn from boiling water at the same temperature. After citing examples of changes of phase where energy is absorbed, cite examples where energy is released—like raining and snowing. People sometimes say that it is too cold to snow. Explain that this statement arises from the fact that the process of snowing warms the air!

Begin by citing the familiar case of leaving the water when bathing and feeling chilly in the air, especially when it is windy. Explain the cooling of a liquid from an atomic point of view, and reinforce the idea of temperature being a measure of the average molecular kinetic energy, and acknowledge molecules that move faster and slower than the average.

Sketch a bell-shaped distribution curve on the board to represent the wide array of molecular speeds in a container of water. The peak of the curve represents the speeds that correspond to the temperature of the water. Stress the many lower and higher speeds to the left and right of the peak of your curve at any moment in the water. Which molecules evaporate? The fast ones, which you clip from the right hand tail of your curve. What is the result? A shift toward the left of the peak of the curve—a lowering of temperature. [Actually, this approach is highly exaggerated, for the molecules that do penetrate the surface and escape into the air have energies that correspond to 3400K! See Paul Hewitt's article on page 492 of *The Physics Teacher*, October 1981.]

Be sure to make clear just what is cooling when evaporation occurs. To say that one thing cools most often means that another warms. When a hot cup of coffee cools by evaporation, the surrounding air is warmed. Conservation of energy reigns!

Make the point that a change of state from liquid to gas or vice versa is not merely one or the other. Condensation occurs while evaporation occurs and vice versa. The net effect is usually what is spoken about. The following demonstration shows this.

DEMONSTRATION: Pour 2 teaspoons of water into a 9-inch rubber balloon. Squeeze out as much air as you can, and knot the balloon. Put the balloon in the microwave oven and cook at full power for however many seconds it takes for boiling to begin, which is indicated by a rapid growth in the size of the balloon. It may take only about 10 seconds for the balloon to reach full size once it starts expanding. (The balloon will pop if you add too much water or if you cook it for too long.) Remove the heated balloon with the oven mitt, shake the balloon around, and listen for the return of the liquid phase. You should be able to hear it raining inside the balloon. A marble hitting your hand pushes against your hand. In a similar fashion, a gaseous water molecule hitting the inside of the balloon pushes against the balloon. The force of a single water molecule is not that great, but the combined forces of the billions and billions of them in this activity are sufficient to inflate the balloon as the liquid water evaporates to the gaseous phase. Thus, you saw how the gaseous phase occupies much more volume than the liquid phase. If you observed the balloon carefully, you noticed it continues to inflate (although not so rapidly) after all the water has been converted to water vapor. This occurs because the microwaves continue to heat the gaseous water molecules, making them move faster and faster, pushing harder and harder against the balloon's inner surface.

After you take the balloon out of the microwave, the balloon is in contact with air molecules, that, being cooler, move more slowly than the water molecules. Gaseous water molecules colliding with the inner surface of the balloon pass their kinetic energy to the slower air molecules, and the air molecules get warmer because their kinetic energy increases. (This is similar to how the kinetic energy of a hammer pounding a nail into a flimsy wall can be transferred to a picture frame hanging on the opposite side of the wall.) You can feel this warming by holding your hand close to the balloon. As the gaseous water molecules lose kinetic energy, they begin to condense into the liquid phase, a noisy process amplified by the balloon (listen carefully).

Now, you may want to discuss boiling and the roles of adding heat and pressure in the boiling process. A tactic we use throughout our teaching is to ask the class members to pretend they are having a one-to-one conversation with a friend about the ideas of physics. Suppose a friend is skeptical about the idea of boiling being a cooling process. We tell our class just what to say to convince the friend of what is going on. We tell them to first point out the distinction between heating and boiling. If the friend knows that the temperature of boiling water remains at 100°C regardless of the amount of heat applied, point out that this is so because the water is cooling by boiling as fast as it is being warmed by heating. Then if this still is not convincing, ask the friend to hold his or her hands above a pot of boiling water—in the steam. Your friend knows the hands will be burned. But burned by what? By the steam. And where did the steam get its energy? From the boiling water; so energy is leaving the water—that's what we mean by cooling! Bring in the role of pressure on boiling, and illustrate this with the pressure cooker.

CHECK QUESTIONS: In bringing water to a boil in high mountains, is the time required to bring the water to a boil longer or shorter than at sea level? Is the time required for cooking longer or shorter? (Preface this second question with the statement that you are posing a different question, for any confusion about this is most likely due to failing to distinguish between the two questions.)

Physical and Chemical Properties

The main difference between a physical and chemical change is that only a chemical change involves the production of a new material. Distinguishing between the two in the laboratory, however, is not easy, because in both cases, there are changes in physical attributes.

Because physical and chemical properties are such broad concepts, almost any chemistry demonstration can be performed within their context. Here are some favorites.

DEMONSTRATIONS: Demonstrate the physical properties of liquid nitrogen by quick freezing flowers, balloons, and so forth. Here's an interesting aside: solidify liquid nitrogen by placing about 100 mL inside a bell jar and reducing the pressure with a good vacuum pump. Demonstrate the physical properties of metallic sodium (can be cut with a knife), then drop a small amount (less than a pea-size) into some phenolphthalein-containing water to demonstrate chemical change. (Metallic sodium is very hazardous, as it reacts violently with water to form sodium hydroxide and combustible hydrogen gas. It should be stored under mineral oil or kerosene.) Flash paper from your local magician's shop also works well for demonstrating chemical change. A crowd favorite is to blow soap bubbles using methane gas. Because methane is less dense than air (a physical property), the bubbles rise. Dim the lights and ignite one of the bubbles (a chemical property) with a butane lighter. CAUTION: Only ignite bubbles that are still relatively far from the ceiling. If your natural gas soap bubbles persistently fall rather than rise, they contain not methane but propane, which I've not so ignited before and so cannot recommend, except to say that, perhaps, such a demo would be more dangerous.

DEMONSTRATION: React baking soda and vinegar in a tall drinking glass. Let the mixture settle. Because the carbon dioxide is heavier than the air, it remains within the glass. Dip a lighted match within the carbon-dioxide-containing glass to demonstrate that chemical property of carbon dioxide.

DEMONSTRATION: React a 3% hydrogen peroxide solution with bakers yeast in a bowl. Poke the resulting bubbles with a red-hot wood splint to demonstrate the formation of oxygen. This is a repeat of the activity: Oxygen Bubble Bursts.

DEMONSTRATION: For distinguishing between a physical and chemical change, a favorite demonstration is the comparison of what happens upon the heating of potassium chromate vs. the heating of ammonium dichromate. Unfortunately, the potassium chromate is a known carcinogen, while the ammonium dichromate is classified as an explosive, which means extra precautions must be taken on the handling of these compounds. The potassium chromate can be recycled. The ammonium dichromate, however, transforms into chromium oxide (a common component of green paint), along with ammonia and water vapor.

Organization of the Periodic Table

The periodic table was introduced in Chapter 9, where the chemical elements were first discussed. The material picks up here with a brief review and then delves into the organization of the periodic table.

A good way to enhance your lectures is to bring to class many samples of different elements. Or better yet, make it an assignment for your students to bring to class as many elements as they can find within their households. Examples would include aluminum (aluminum foil), carbon (graphite from pencil), helium (from helium balloon), nitrogen and oxygen (from the air we breathe), iron (nails), nickel (the 5-cent piece, though this is actually an alloy containing little nickel), copper (copper penny), silver (silverware), iodine (disinfectant swab), gold (jewelry), mercury (old fashion thermometer—careful!), and lead (fishing line sinker).

Continue with atomic group discussions and demonstrations:

Group 1: Exercise extra caution when adding a group 1 metal, especially potassium and higher, to water. Hydrogen gas is produced, which is often ignited by the heat of reaction. Sodium hydroxide, which turns the solution alkaline, is also produced. These metals must be stored under kerosene or mineral oil. Wear protective clothing, latex gloves, and safety glasses. For your demonstration, drop a small amount of a group 1 metal (less than a pea-size) into a beaker of fresh water containing phenolphthalein pH indicator to demonstrate its reactivity. Contrast the reactivity of sodium with two other group 1 elements, lithium and potassium.

If your students will not be performing flame tests of group 1 and 2 elements in the laboratory, you might consider demonstrating these flame tests. Chloride or nitrate salts of lithium (scarlet), sodium (yellow), potassium (purple), strontium (red), and barium (green) are most impressive. These materials give the color to fireworks. Interestingly, fireworks had little or no color prior to the discovery of these compounds in the late 1800s. The world really was black and white back then!

Group 2: In a plastic weigh boat (5" times 5"), mix 10 grams of sand with 3.33 grams of lime (calcium oxide). Stir in 5 mL of water to create a thick paste of brick mortar. Use universal pH paper to note its alkalinity. Measure its weight and ask the class to predict whether the mortar will weigh more or less after it hardens. [Hardening cement mortar gains mass as it absorbs carbon dioxide from the air. Chemically, the calcium oxide reacts with water to form calcium hydroxide (slaked lime). This material, in turn, absorbs carbon dioxide to form calcium carbonate, limestone, which is reinforced by sand particles. As CO_2 is absorbed, water is lost. Because carbon dioxide is more massive than water, the mortar gains weight. Protective clothing and safety glasses should be worn, as calcium oxide is a powerful dehydrating agent and is irritating to skin. Avoid breathing any calcium oxide dust. Calcium hydroxide is very caustic and should be handled with care. Interestingly, calcium hydroxide is the active ingredient of many hair removal products.]

It is always interesting to burn a small ribbon of magnesium. The brightness of the flame is impressive. If you can find some "Magicube" flash bulbs, this reaction can be used to demonstrate the conservation of mass principle. First demonstrate how the magnesium strip is "consumed" as it burns. Ask students if matter was destroyed. Point out the magnesium strips inside one of the flash bulbs and ask whether the bulb should weigh more or less after being ignited. Weigh the bulb before and after igniting it with a 9-V battery and wire leads. Despite the intense heat, the bulbs are thick enough to contain all the reactants and products.

Groups 3–10: Transition elements: Compare various transition elements in their metallic state to some of the highly colored compounds they form. Search your stockroom for examples such as iron III nitrate, $Fe(NO_3)_3$ (orange); cobalt II nitrate, $Co(NO_3)_2$ (purple); nickel II nitrate, $Ni(NO_3)_2$ (green). Many pigments consist of transition element compounds.

Groups 13 and 14: Students should recognize that elements in the same group don't always share similar properties. With groups 13 and 14, for example, upper elements are nonmetallic while lower elements are metallic. The statement that elements in the same group often share many properties is a broad generalization with numerous exceptions.

Aluminum is commonly thought of as an inert metal. In fact, aluminum is quite reactive, especially in a powdered form. The reaction between powdered aluminum and ammonium perchlorate, NH_4ClO_4, for example, is used to lift the space shuttle into orbit. Aluminum also reacts rapidly with atmospheric oxygen to form relatively inert aluminum oxide, Al_2O_3. Interestingly, you do not touch aluminum. Instead, you touch a very thin, transparent, and protective coating of aluminum oxide. Tear a piece of aluminum foil and the freshly exposed aluminum immediately transforms into aluminum oxide. A piece of aluminum foil ground up in a sealed container lacking oxygen—in a vacuum, for example—will burn spontaneously as it is exposed to atmospheric oxygen. Sodium chloride is able to "eat through" aluminum's thin protecting coat. This can be demonstrated by submerging a small sheet of aluminum foil in a shallow dilute solution of copper (II) sulfate. Sprinkle some salt onto the aluminum. Where the salt contacts, it exposes the aluminum, which is then able to react with the copper ions to form copper metal. The reaction can release enough heat to cause the water within the vicinity of the salt to boil. Look for small bubble formations.

Place a sample of the group 13 element gallium, Ga, in a sealed vial and pass it around the class. The warmth from students' hands will cause this intriguing metal to melt (m.p. 30°C). Interestingly enough, gallium, like water, is one of those rare materials that expands upon freezing. Also, the compound gallium arsenide, GaAs, is a remarkable semiconductor used to make integrated circuits that operate up to five times faster than silicon circuits. Gallium arsenide, however, is relatively expensive to produce.

Display molecular models of graphite, diamond, and buckminsterfullerene. Mention how carbon is unique from all other elements in that it is able to bond with itself repeatedly. An astounding variety of materials can be produced when carbon also forms bonds to elements such as hydrogen, oxygen, and nitrogen. These are the organic compounds discussed in Chapter 14.

Group 15: Comment to your students that you need not bring nitrogen to class, for it's already there—air is almost 80% nitrogen. As an exciting alternative (if you haven't done so already), bring in a Dewar of liquid nitrogen. The last element in group 15 is bismuth, Bi, which is the heaviest of the nonradioactive elements. Crystals of bismuth are iridescent and quite beautiful. Bismuth salts make the active ingredient of Pepto-Bismol. The great atomic mass of these salts assists in their ability to "soothe and coat" the digestive tract.

Group 16: Along with showing the properties of liquid nitrogen, you might demonstrate the properties of liquid oxygen. The boiling point of oxygen (183°C) is higher than that of nitrogen (196°C). So, liquid oxygen can be generated by flowing gaseous oxygen into a container immersed in liquid nitrogen. Clamp a large test tube and immerse it into about a liter of liquid nitrogen in a Dewar flask. Connect one end of rubber tubing to the valve of an oxygen tank and the other end to about 30 cm of glass tubing. Place the free end of the glass tubing into the test tube, and open the valve to allow a gentle flow of oxygen. In a few minutes, about 20–30 mL of liquid oxygen can be collected. Transfer the liquid oxygen to an unsilvered Dewar flask to show its pale blue color (water quickly condenses on the outside of the test tube, obscuring the oxygen from view). To show the effects of high concentrations of oxygen, pour several milliliters of the liquid into a 250-mL beaker and then quickly toss in a smoldering wood splint. The splint will rapidly catch fire. Substances that do not combust under ordinary conditions, such as clothing, can be quite flammable in such high concentrations of oxygen. Open flames, therefore, are particularly dangerous, and extreme caution should be exercised.

Sulfur has the elemental formula S_8. The chemical structure of the most stable allotrope of sulfur is that of an eight-membered ring, which has the shape of a crown. Heat several grams of sulfur in a crucible over a Bunsen burner flame. At 119°C, the sulfur will melt. Then, as the temperatures rises above 150°C, the ring structure breaks apart, and the melt becomes viscous due to tangling of the sulfur chains. The chains recombine upon cooling. Pour the viscous melt into water, and the sulfur will appear back in its original form. (If you've saved this demo for Chapter 17, you should ask your students whether it is a physical or chemical change.) Note how elemental sulfur is not the same as hydrogen sulfide, which is a compound that gives the smell of rotten eggs. As was discussed earlier, compounds are uniquely different from the elements from which they are composed.

Group 17: The halogens iodine and bromine may be shown for their different phases. Keep them in sealed containers. The sublimation and deposition of iodine may be presented as a demonstration (but only under a fume hood!).

Group 18: Blow soap bubbles using various noble gases. The rate at which noble gases heavier than helium fall is directly proportional to their masses. If you don't have any argon available, it is interesting to note that carbon dioxide is only 4 amu more massive than is argon. You may also choose to demonstrate several noble gas-containing discharge tubes.

Elements to Compounds
This section explains the concept of the elemental formula. Ask the following question.

CHECK YOUR NEIGHBOR: The oxygen we breathe, O_2, is converted to ozone, O_3, in the presence of an electric spark. Is this a physical or chemical change? [Oxygen, O_2, and ozone, O_3, are both elemental forms of oxygen, much in the same way that diamond and graphite are elemental forms of carbon. Oxygen, O_2, and ozone, O_3, however, are fundamentally different materials, because they differ in the way the atoms are bonded together. The change, therefore, is a chemical change.]

A *compound* results when different types of atoms bond to one another. It should be emphasized that a compound is uniquely different from the elements from which it is made. Sodium and chlorine, for example, are toxic, but sodium chloride is essential for good health. The reason that a compound is uniquely different from the elements from which it is made is because of a different arrangement of atoms. You might stress to your class that it is the arrangement of atoms within a material that defines its identity as judged by its physical and chemical properties. That a new material is formed when atoms connect differently is exactly what gives rise to the great diversity of materials around us. Many different compounds can be produced out of a smaller variety of elements.

A most effective way of illustrating the point of how a compound is uniquely different from the elements from which it is made is as follows:

> DEMONSTRATION: Hold up samples of copper, sulfur, and oxygen. Rather than pulling out a genuine tank of oxygen, merely scoop up some air into a transparent plastic canister and then cap it before your students. Ask them what the properties of a compound formed from copper, sulfur, and oxygen might be. Perhaps, a combination of all the various properties of copper, sulfur and oxygen? Surprise them by showing some large blue crystals of copper sulfate pentahydrate, though you need not mention the pentahydrate part. In short, there is really no way to predict what the properties of the compound might be. A compound is uniquely different from the elements from which it is made.

Integrated Science—Astronomy: The Origin of the Moon
This feature examines the role chemistry has played in establishing the Giant Impact Theory of the Moon's formation. This example serves to illustrate one of the points of Section 11.1; namely, that chemistry underlies astronomy. If you want to give students more context for the Giant Impact Theory, turn to Chapter 27, The Solar System. Students need no more background than they have at this point to understand Section 27.2, The Nebular Theory. The nebular theory explains the origin of the solar system and explains why it was that large chunks of debris orbited the Sun during Earth's early history. Note that an integrated science feature "The Chemical Composition of the Solar System" immediately follows Section 27.2 on the nebular theory. If you invite your students into that material as well, you will be starting off your study of chemistry with very strong integration with astronomy.

Integrated Science—Physics and Biology: Evaporation Cools You Off, Condensation Warms You Up
Ask, If evaporation is a cooling process, what kind of process would the opposite of evaporation be? This is condensation, which is a warming process.

> CHECK YOUR NEIGHBOR: Why is it that many people after taking a shower will begin drying in the shower stall before getting outside? (While still in the shower region, appreciable condensation offsets the cooling by evaporation.)

It's fun and easy to think of everyday examples of condensation as a warming process and evaporation as a cooling process. Brainstorm examples with the class. For subject integration with biology, discuss perspiration as a means of cooling through evaporation. Experiments conducted in Death Valley, California, showed that humans can lose over 3 gallons of water a day if they are given water to drink and salt pills to replace lost fluids and salts. Your students will appreciate this shows how hard their sweat glands work to keep them cool. In movies, and even in real life, people sweating profusely may be seen to have drops of sweat actually dripping off their bodies. Ask your students whether this form of perspiration is effective in cooling. The answer is that it's not—it's evaporation of perspiration that cools, because evaporating sweat absorbs heat (actually *latent heat*, Chapter 6) from its surroundings (the skin). While rivulets of perspiration may look impressive, perspiration that drips off the body does little to cool it.

12   The Nature of Chemical Bonds

A central theme for this chapter is how the periodic table can be used to gain insight into the nature of chemical bonding. Students who are familiar with the shell model of Chapters 9 and 10 will have an added advantage.

In the *Practice Book*:
- Losing Valence Electrons
- Drawing Shells
- Atomic Size
- Effective Nuclear Charge
- Solutions
- Pure Mathematics
- Chemical Bonds
- Shells and the Covalent Bond
- Bond Polarity
- Atoms to Molecules

In *Next-Time Questions*:
- Carbon
- The Weight of Rust
- Atomic Transformation I
- Atomic Transformation II
- Sugar Water
- Oxygen in Water
- Bending Stream
- Ionic Bond
- Rain Spots on Car

In the *Lab Manual*:
- Dot to Dot: Electron-Dot Diagrams (activity)
- Repulsive Dots: VSEPR Theory (activity)
- Molecules by Acme (experiment)
- Salt and Sand (experiment)
- Sugar Soft (experiment)
- Bubble Round-Up (activity)
- Circular Rainbows (activity)
- Pure Sweetness (activity)

Transparencies:
Figures 12.1, 12.4, 12.6, 12.16, 12.22

Suggested Presentation

Electron Shells and Chemical Bonding
You might wish to show students how to draw a shell model using the following steps. Not all students, however, will catch on. Thus, you should also announce that a series of concentric circles works just as well. (The shell model was introduced in Chapter 9.)

1. Draw a diagonal guideline in pencil. Then, draw a series of seven semicircles. Note how the ends of the semicircles are not perpendicular to the guideline. Instead, they are parallel to the length of the page (Figure A).

2. Connect the ends of each semicircle with another semicircle such that a series of concentric hearts is drawn. The ends of these new semicircles should be drawn perpendicular to the ends of the previously drawn semicircles (Figure B).

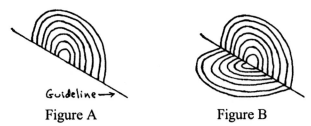

Guideline →

Figure A   Figure B

3. Now the hard part. Draw a portion of a circle that connects the apex of the largest vertical and horizontal semicircles as in Figure C.

4. Now the fun part. Erase the pencil guideline drawn in Step 1, then add the internal lines, as shown in Figure D, that create a series of concentric shells.

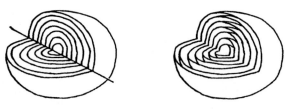

Figure C   Figure D

Point out the various electron capacities of each shell and how this corresponds to the organization of the periodic table. Define valence electrons.

Remind your students that shells do not refer to the electron orbits of Bohr's planetary model.

A very good extension is to get to periodic trends, using the concepts of inner-shell shielding and effective nuclear charge. For brevity, these concepts are addressed lightly in the textbook. *Inner shell shielding* is the process of inner shell electrons weakening the attraction between outer shell electrons and the nucleus. The result of inner shell shielding is that outer shell's electrons don't experience the full charge of the nucleus. The outer shell electron of a lithium atom, for example, doesn't experience a +3 nucleus, because this nucleus is "shielded" by two inner shell electrons. The diminished nuclear charge that the outer shell electron experiences is referred to as the *effective nuclear charge*. Accordingly, the effective nuclear charge for lithium's outer shell electron is around +1.

From left to right across any row of the periodic table, the atomic diameters get *smaller*. Let's look at this trend from the point of view of effective nuclear charge. Consider lithium's outermost electron, which experiences an effective nuclear charge of +1. Then look across period 2 to neon, where each outermost electron experiences an effective nuclear charge of +8. Because the outer-shell neon electrons experience a greater attraction to the nucleus, they are pulled in closer to it than is the outer-shell electron in lithium. So neon, although nearly three times as massive as lithium, has a considerably smaller diameter. In general, across any period from left to right, atomic diameters become smaller because of an increase in effective nuclear charge.

Moving down a group, atomic diameters get larger because of an increasing number of occupied shells. Whereas lithium has a small diameter because it has only two occupied shells, francium has a much larger diameter, because it has seven occupied shells.

Ionic Bonds

Discuss the sodium, Na^+, and chloride, Cl^-, ions. Point out how these two oppositely charged ions are attracted to one another—there is an electrical force of attraction based upon the principle that opposite signs attract. We give this force a name. We call it the *ionic bond*. Define what is meant by an *ionic compound*.

> CHECK YOUR NEIGHBOR: Can a sodium ion be attracted to two chloride ions? [Some students may believe that the charges of two bonded ions cancel each other, and so each sodium ion can only be attracted to one chloride ion. A good follow-up demonstration is to hold a bar magnet up to the

class. Attach a second magnet to the tip of this magnet and ask if it would be possible to attach a third. How about a fourth? A fifth?]

A sodium ion can be attracted to a second chloride ion provided that the second chloride ion approaches from another angle. Draw the second chlorine ion on the opposite side of the sodium ion already drawn. Ask students if any additional chloride ions may be attracted to this sodium ion. As they answer "yes," draw chlorine ions above and below the sodium ion. You should mention that electric fields are three-dimensional, so chloride ions may also approach from outside the plane of the board. Ask then how sodium ions might feel about all these chloride ions. *Answer*: Pretty good! Oppositely charged ions packed together in such an orderly three-dimensional fashion form an *ionic crystal*. Interestingly, the macroscopic dimensions of a crystal are the consequence of this ionic packing. Sodium and chlorine ions pack in a cubic orientation, hence, table salt crystals are cubic. (Salt manufacturers have discovered that under the proper conditions, cubic salt crystals will coalesce into the shape of a hollow pyramid. This dietetic "flaked" salt occupies greater volume so that less salt is used per shake. Also, flaked salt is thought to be more easily tasted by the tongue, because it has a greater surface area per crystal.)

An important consideration is that the ions of any ionic bond must balance each other electrically—every electron lost by one atom is gained by another. For example, if one ion carries a double charge and the second ion carries a single charge, then the ratio of ions can no longer be 1:1. Rather, there will need to be twice as many of the singly charged ion. There is a Conceptual Integrated Science Practice Book page covering this concept.

Metallic Bonds

The metallic bond, according to the "sea of electrons" model, is fairly easy for students to understand. Where it gets sticky is in our trying to classify the products that are formed. Whereas ionic and covalent bonds give rise to chemical compounds, metallic bonds give rise to mixtures. The primary distinction between a compound and a mixture, therefore, is that within a compound, the component atoms are held in fixed orientations relative to one another. The components of a mixture, on the other hand, are free to change their relative orientations. It is the "fluid" nature of the metallic bond, therefore, that prompts us to classify an alloy of metal atoms as a mixture rather than a compound. That the proportions of metal atoms within an alloy can vary is also important.

Covalent Bonds

Illustrate how two kids may be held together by their mutual attraction for toys they share. In this analogy, the kids represent protons, and the toys represent electrons. To keep it accurate, the kids should be nasty to each other (protons repel protons) and each have one toy (bonding electron) to share. Show how the analogy relates to the hydrogen molecule. Point out that in a covalent bond there are no ions involved, but that the force holding the two atoms together is still electrical. This level of understanding satisfies most students. You may be asked, however, how it is that two repelling electrons can be squeezed together in between two hydrogen atoms. To answer this question, you might refer the student to the shell model and note how it is that electrons tend to form electron pairs. In such a case, the paired electrons are actually spinning about their axes (like the Earth spins on its axis) in opposite directions. This provides for oppositely aligned magnetic fields that allow the electrons to "tolerate" each other. A more accurate (and more detailed) explanation would require that you introduce the concept of quantum numbers.

Point out that covalent bonds primarily involve those elements toward the upper right-hand side of the periodic table, with the exception of the noble gases. These are the elements with greatest electronegativities. Also address the unique feature of multiple covalent bonds. The term *molecule* should then be introduced as a group of atoms held together by covalent bonds. Check to see who was listening by announcing the following question:

CHECK YOUR NEIGHBOR: Are atoms made of molecules or are molecules made of atoms?

The term "molecule" was introduced in the early 1800s by the French chemist Gay-Lussac in his work with the principle of combining volumes, which is not addressed in this textbook. During this time, very few believed in the existence of atoms, and even fewer in the existence of groups of atoms—molecules. Ask students if it's possible to see a single molecule. Note that a diamond is an example of a *macromolecule*. Show the molecular model of a diamond. A large model (>1 dm^3) built from miniature pieces can be placed on the overhead projector and twirled for a dramatic effect. Note the "tunnels" as they appear on screen.

Polar Covalent Bonds

The applications of bond polarity are far reaching. See the Conceptual Integrated Science Practice Page entitled "Bond Polarity and the Shell Model." This practice page was developed out of a lecture skit that you may wish to apply here. You may or may not involve the shell model in your presentation. The two key points to address are as follows:

1. Different atoms have different "pulling powers." This pulling power, also known as electronegativity, is a function of how strongly the atomic nucleus is able to pull on the valence electrons. The greater the pulling power of an atom, the greater its ability to pull bonding electrons closer to itself.

2. An atom that pulls electrons closer to itself will be slightly negative in charge because of the greater amount of time that electrons spend on that side of the bond.

Wrap up your discussion of covalent bond polarity by comparing it to the ionic bond. That all ionic bonds have some covalent character and that all polar covalent bonds have some ionic character is a useful unifying concept. Covalent bonds and ionic bonds are just two extremes of the same thing: atoms held together by some distribution of electrons.

Molecular Polarity

A good order of examples to choose is as described in the text: carbon dioxide, CO_2, followed by water, H_2O.

The presentation assumes that students understand the concept of boiling. Be sure they do by presenting the following peer instruction question:

> CHECK YOUR NEIGHBOR: When water boils, water molecules
> (a) break down into hydrogen and oxygen.
> (b) separate from one another.
> (c) become lighter in mass.
> (d) All of the above.

Interparticle Attractions

Start by distinguishing between a chemical bond and a molecular attraction. Both involve electrical forces of attraction, but chemical bonds are over 100-fold stronger. Be careful with some semantics: "what holds a molecule together" and "what holds molecules together" may be easily confused. Review the concept of the molecular dipole to be sure your students understand it before going further. Use water as an example.

For the ion–dipole attraction, explain that ionic bonds are broken as an ionic compound dissolves in water. When a covalent compound, such as sugar, dissolves in water, however, the covalent bonds remain intact.

Discuss the dipole–dipole attraction, which is fairly straightforward—if students know what a dipole is, then they should understand how two dipoles may be attracted to each other. Note how the hydrogen bond is simply a relatively strong dipole–dipole attraction.

> DEMONSTRATION: Fill two burets, one with 50.00 mL of water, and the other with 50.00 mL of 95% ethanol. Ask the students what volume will be obtained when the two liquids are combined. Drain the two liquids simultaneously into a 100-mL volumetric flask (use a permanent marker to calibrate the last three milliliters). A total of only 98.0 mL will be obtained. Tell the students to "ask their neighbor" for an explanation. [One half of an answer (by analogy): At a dance hall, 50 men by themselves and 50 women by themselves occupy a given amount of floor space. Bring the men and women together, however, and they occupy a total floor space that is less than the sum of the floor space they occupied while by themselves. Similarly, water and ethanol molecules are attracted to one another, hence, they are able to contract into a volume less than the sum of their volumes alone. The second half of an answer: The molecules are able to pack into a smaller combined volume. By analogy, the combination of 50 mL of marbles and 50 mL of sand does NOT result in 100 mL of mixture.]

Induced Dipoles

Electrons in a molecule are not static. Instead they are continually moving around. In a polar molecule, the electrons, on average, are found closer to one side. In a nonpolar molecule, the electrons, on average, are distributed evenly across the whole molecule. Because the electrons in a nonpolar molecule are not held in place, they can be shuffled to one side or the other upon the application of an electric force. Draw Figure 12.23 on the chalkboard to show how the permanent dipole of a water molecule induces a temporary dipole in an oxygen molecule. Point out how the oxygen dipole exists only so long as the water is present. It is the dipole-induced dipole attraction that permits small quantities of nonpolar substances such as oxygen and carbon dioxide to dissolve in water.

> CHECK YOUR NEIGHBOR: There are dipole-induced dipole forces of attraction between oil and water molecules. So, why don't the two mix? [Answer: They do mix, but like oxygen and carbon dioxide, only to a very small extent, because water molecules have such a great preference for other water molecules.]

Here is an analogy you might use to explain why oil and water form two different phases. Say, at a party there are two kinds of people, those who like to talk and share ideas and those who are stone-faced and would rather say nothing. Mix these two types of people together and soon the talkative people are on one side and the stone-faced people on the other. It's not that there is a repulsion between the talkative people, and the stone-faced people. In fact, there may be a weak attraction—some people need to be *induced* into a conversation. There is, nonetheless, a greater force of attraction between talkative people, and this is what pulls them together to the point that they exclude most of the stone-faced people. Similarly, water is too attracted to itself by the stronger dipole–dipole attractions to the point that it excludes most of the oil molecules.

> CHECK YOUR NEIGHBOR: Due to ion–dipole attractions, a thin stream of water bends toward a charge balloon. Will a thin stream of hexanes, a nonpolar organic solvent, also bend toward the charged balloon? [Answer: Yes, and it does so by way of ion-induced dipole attractions. This demonstration makes for a good follow-up to the demo where you show how a thin stream of water can be bent by a statically charged balloon.]

A fourth type of molecular attraction is the induced dipole-induced dipole attraction. Omitted from the text for brevity, discuss it here if you are getting into interparticle attractions in depth. On the average, electrons in a nonpolar molecule or atom are distributed evenly. But electrons are perpetually moving around and at times more may be grouped to one side. This is the nature of a "momentary" dipole. A momentary dipole, albeit weak, is able to induce dipoles in neighboring molecules or atoms just as a permanent dipole can. The induced dipole can then, in turn, induce dipoles in other molecules or atoms. Because all the molecules or atoms are nonpolar, it is unclear as to who induced whom first. So, the interaction is simply called "induced dipole-induced dipole," rather than "momentary dipole-induced dipole."

The less volume electrons occupy in an atom, the less of a tendency they will have to congregate to one side of the atom because of greater electrical repulsions. This means that smaller atoms, such as fluorine, exhibit weaker induced dipole-induced dipole attractions than do larger atoms, such as iodine. This explains why very few things stick to Teflon. It also explains why iodine, I_2, which is very nonpolar, is a solid at room temperature.

Solutions
Explain that matter does not cease to occupy volume even when it's dissolved. To make this point, the following demonstration is simple, yet highly effective.

> DEMONSTRATION: Before lecture, fill a 500-mL graduated cylinder to the 500-mL mark, then find out how much sugar must be added so that the volume of solution reaches the brim of the cylinder. For this demonstration, add 500 mL of warm water to the graduated cylinder. Tell the students that you are going to dissolve some sugar in this water. Ask them to think about whether the volume should increase, decrease, or remain the same. Pour the water into a dry beaker (make a fuss about how it is that the beaker is bone dry and that you are not going to spill a drop of the water in your transfers). Mix in the sugar until it dissolves. Pour the solution back into the graduated cylinder. Slow down as you approach the 500-mL mark. Many students will be surprised as you reach the 500-mL mark. More surprise comes when you fill it exactly to the brim.

Solubility
The emphasis for this section should be on how the solubility of a solute depends upon the molecular attractions occurring between the solute and solvent. The more significant the molecular attractions, the greater the solubility. The old saying that "like dissolves like" arises from the fact that if two materials exert the same sorts of molecular attractions, then they are likely to mix together very finely, down to the level of molecules, which means that a solution will form.

> DEMONSTRATION: Float a Styrofoam coffee cup in a petri dish full of acetone placed on the overhead projector. Flippantly ask the students if they can see the Styrofoam cup melting. Ask the question again and again until they realize it's not melting at all. So cried the Wicked Witch of the East, "I'm dissolving! I'm dissolving!" For the pure humor of it, cut out a small circle of yellow paper and place it in the middle of the remaining deformed Styrofoam. Use a spatula to place the "fried egg" on a paper towel while saying: "Chemistry is aiming to serve. How would you like your egg? Sunny side up?"

You could discuss soap in this section if you wish. Draw soap molecules surrounding grime to illustrate how soap works. Point out the induced dipole-induced dipole attractions between the nonpolar tail of soap and the grime, and the ion–dipole attractions between the polar head of soap and water. Note that your drawing is a cross section of a spherical conglomeration, also known as a *micelle*. Time permitting, you might take this a step further and draw a lipid bilayer in the shape of a circle. Note that this is a cross section of a three-dimensional conglomeration known as a *cell*. Point out the aqueous inner chamber. Add proteins to the bilayer and call it a membrane. Throw in a cellular nucleus and some organelles and call it living tissue.

Integrated Science—Biology and Earth Science: Mixtures

In nature, it's rare that elements or compounds are found in a "purified state." Instead we find them mixed together. Challenge your students to think of a material that is NOT actually a mixture of elements, compounds, or both. Consider listing their replies in columns on the chalkboard. Be lenient with them and allow items such as aluminum foil, or diamond, to be listed in the nonmixture column. Then start getting nitpicky and point out how aluminum foil is hardly pure, consisting of small amounts of magnesium, with a coating of aluminum oxide. Or how it is that diamond's "color" (not refraction of light) results from the impurities it contains. Tell your students that you'll be getting into the technical definition of "pure" in this chapter, then proceed to discuss how it is that the air we breathe and the water we drink are examples of mixtures and why.

If you want to get into mixtures in more depth than in the text, you can explain that the components of a mixture can be separated ("purified") based upon differences in physical properties. Some demonstrations help here.

DEMONSTRATION: Hold out a cup of water and add to it a piece of chalk. Announce that you have just created a mixture. Ask students how you might separate the components of this mixture. As you pour the water through your fingers, alert students to the fact that you are separating based upon differences in physical properties—at room temperature, water is a liquid while chalk is a solid. Show how this same principle applies to a distillation setup. Distilling water away from food coloring works well.

DEMONSTRATION: Pour liquid nitrogen into an empty soda can held up by a clamp. The oxygen in the surrounding air will condense along the sides of the soda can much as water vapor condenses along the sides of a filled soda can just removed from the refrigerator. Ask your students what evidence they see that the drips off of the liquid nitrogen filled soda can are *not* drips of water. Note that the drips are most visible only upon close inspection. Otherwise, the vapor they leave upon falling can be seen from farther back. Notably, as the drips strike a tabletop they make an audible sound.

DEMONSTRATION: Post-1982 pennies can be heated to separate the internal zinc from the copper coating. Heat the penny over a Bunsen burner or propane torch until blistering occurs, and then "shake" the internally melted zinc into a crucible. After it cools, the sample should be passed around the class.

DEMONSTRATION: Before lecture, boil down a large glass of tap water in a clean beaker. Scrape the residual contents from the bottom of the beaker into a small vial. During lecture, hold out the vial and describe what you did. Encourage students to do the same at home using kitchenware. Ask them if the contents represent "concentrated water" or "not concentrated water." A successful answer is: "That's not water at all. That's the material that was *in* the water. Ew!" You might label your vial as "[Your state's] drinking water," for example, "California drinking water." Suggest to students the possibility of selling such vials abroad with the directions "Just add distilled water."

Integrated Science—Biology: How Geckos Walk on Walls—The Adhesive Force

This is a fun topic with many everyday life applications in addition to the gecko. Try this simple hands-on activity to compare the adhesive force acting between various substances and wax paper. Take a strip of waxed paper and hold it at an angle (for example, by taping it to a book and then elevating one end of the book). Spill a drop of each of these liquids at the high side of the waxed paper: corn oil, tap water, soapy water, or alcohol. Compare the trail left by each liquid as it falls to the bottom of the sheet. Adhesion is greatest between oil and waxed paper, as can be seen by the streak it leaves on the paper. Adhesion is least for the water; it leaves no trail on the waxed paper at all.

Integrated Science—Biology: Fish Depend on Dissolved Oxygen

Perform the following demonstration to show that tap water does indeed contain dissolved gases.

DEMONSTRATION: Fill a large beaker with warm tap water and let it stand at room temperature while you lecture. Note the bubbles that adhere to the inner sides of the beaker. Ask the students where the bubbles came from and what they contain. For further experimentation, perform the same demonstration in two beakers side by side. In one beaker, use warm water from the faucet. In the second beaker, use boiled water that has cooled down to the same temperature. The process of boiling *deaerates* the water, that is, removes the atmospheric gases. Chemists sometimes need to use deaerated water, which is made simply by allowing boiled water to cool in a sealed container. Ask your students, why don't fish live very long in deaerated water? Then read the Integrated Science feature for a complete answer.

13   Chemical Reactions

Welcome students to this important chapter, which covers many concepts that are at the heart of chemistry.

In the *Practice Book*:
- Balancing Chemical Equations
- Exothermic and Endothermic Reactions
- Donating and Accepting Hydrogen Ions
- Loss and Gain of Electrons

In *Next-Time Questions*:
- Neutral Solution
- Ionic Compound
- Gasoline and Fuel

In the *Lab Manual*:
- Sensing pH (extracting and using red cabbage pH indicator) (activity)
- Upset Stomach (experiment)
- Tubular Rust (activity)

Transparencies:
Figures 13.3, 13.4, 13.7, 13.8, 13.11, 13.14, 13.15, 13.27, 13.29

Suggested Presentation

Chemical Equations
The chemical equation is used to depict the chemical reaction. Significant features of the chemical equation are presented in this section. The importance of having a balanced chemical equation should be related back to the conservation of mass principle.

A good way to keep the art of balancing chemical equations low key in your quizzes and exams is to present an equation and simply ask whether or not it is balanced. Learning how to balance chemical equations is good mental exercise, but it is not a prerequisite for subsequent chapters.

A methodology explored in one of the Practice Pages is as follows:

1. Focus on balancing only one element at a time. Start with the left-most element, and modify the coefficients such that this element appears on both sides of the arrow the same number of times.

2. Move to the next element, and modify the coefficients so as to balance this element. Do not worry if you incidentally unbalance the previous element. You will come back to it in subsequent steps.

3. Continue from left to right balancing each element individually.

4. Repeat Steps 1–3 until all elements are balanced.

Seven reasonable equations you might try balancing with your class—reviewing techniques as you go along—are as follows:

$3 \, O_2 \rightarrow 2 \, O_3$
$4 \, Cr + 3 \, O_2 \rightarrow 2 \, Cr_2O_3$
$2 \, SO_2 + O_2 \rightarrow 2 \, SO_3$
$2 \, N_2O \rightarrow 2 \, N_2 + O_2$
$2 \, NO + O_2 \rightarrow 2 \, NO_2$
$3 \, HNO_2 \rightarrow HNO_3 + 2 \, NO + H_2O$
$2 \, N_2H_4O_3 \rightarrow 2 \, N_2 + O_2 + 4 \, H_2O$

When dealing with odd and even subscripts, as in $O_2 \rightarrow O_3$, it's useful to "borrow the opposite subscript as the coefficient." In this manner, the subscript of O_3 is used as the coefficient of O_2, and vice versa. Alternatively, an extra oxygen atom might simply be added to the left side: $O + O_2 \rightarrow O_3$. This is illegal, however, because it alters the identity of the reactants (O is not O_2). A way around this is to use a fraction of a coefficient, such as $\frac{1}{2}$, which gives $\frac{1}{2} \, O_2 + O_2 \rightarrow O_3$, which can also be written as $\frac{3}{2} \, O_2 \rightarrow O_3$. The fraction of oxygen can be corrected by multiplying every term by 2, which gives: $2(\frac{3}{2}) \, O_2 \times 2(O_3)$, which equals: $3 \, O_2 \rightarrow 2 \, O_3$.

Acid–Base Reactions

Begin by discussing the many commercial applications of acids and bases. Point out how economists judge the economic strength of nations based upon the quantities of these materials produced.

FYI, emphasis is placed on the Bronsted–Lowry definition of acids and bases. This definition is more general than is the Arrhenius definition, though not as general as the Lewis definition. The acronym BAAD is a useful tool for many students: "Bases Accept, Acids Donate."

My thinking (Suchocki) is that it is best not to say that a chemical *is* an acid or that it *is* a base. Students may get confused when they find that in one instance a chemical, such as water, is an acid, and in another it is a base. It is far better to say that a chemical *behaves* as an acid, or that it *behaves* as a base. When a chemical donates a hydrogen ion, it behaves as an acid; when the same chemical accepts a hydrogen ion, it behaves as a base.

On the chalkboard, it is useful to show the movement of the hydrogen ion from one molecule to the other. Draw the symbol for hydrogen on a piece of paper, which may be taped to the board. Show how the acid donates the hydrogen ion by transferring the paper between reactants. Likewise, note how the base accepts the hydrogen ion. For example,

Before   **After**

This visualization helps students to recognize which chemicals in an equation are behaving as acids and which are behaving as bases. Also, students get the sense that products are, in fact, made from the reactants, despite that they are both seen at once in the chemical equation. The reversibility of acid/base reactions can be visualized by using two pieces of paper containing the symbol for hydrogen. For example,

Salts

Define the chemist's use of the terms "salt" and "neutralization reaction." Draw an illustration such as the following on the chalkboard while emphasizing how it is that, upon neutralization, negative and positive atoms come together.

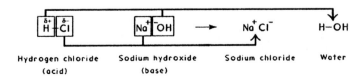

Hydrogen chloride (acid)   Sodium hydroxide (base)   Sodium chloride   Water

Solutions: Acidic, Basic, or Neutral

Water is such a weak acid and weak base that the concentration of hydronium and hydroxide ions in "pure" water is very small, about 10^{-7} M. Although the concentration of these ions is very small, what students can be brought to understand is that, in pure water, for each hydroxide ion that forms, there will be one hydronium ion that forms. It's analogous to a room full of people with one hat each. If suddenly a number of the people gave their hats to someone with one hat, the consequence would be that the number of people with no hat would be equal to the number of people with two hats. For water, the hydrogen ion is the hat—for each hydronium ion that gets formed from the donation of a hydronium ion, there will also be a hydroxide ion that gets formed. Thus, in pure water, the concentration of hydronium and hydroxide ions are the same. Once this concept is established, you can define a neutral solution as one in which the hydronium and hydroxide ion concentrations are equal. When an acid is added, the hydronium ion concentration will be greater than the hydroxide ion concentration, and this makes for an acidic solution. Likewise, when a base is added, the hydroxide ion concentration will be greater than the hydronium ion concentration, and this makes for a basic (or alkaline) solution.

The pH Scale

Spend a few minutes reviewing the logarithm. Most students wince at the sight of the log function on the chalkboard. Turn this around and have fun by stating that "logs are dirt easy." Declare that logs are so easy that you can teach them logs in 45 seconds. Boast a pretend previous record and then the bet is on! Wait for the second hand on the clock to get to a 12, 3, 6, or 9, then begin. "When one is asking for the log of a number, they are really asking 'to what power is ten raised?' Thus, if one wanted to know the log of 10^3 as in $\log 10^3 = ?$, you would simply ask 'To what power is 10 raised?' We see here plainly that the answer is 3. So, if I've really taught you about logs, you should be able to answer this: 'What is the log of 10^2?'" Then solicit the response of "2" from the students, whereupon you can speedily look to the clock and declare victory . . . in record time! The follow-up is to show them how it is that the log of 100 also equals 2. Then draw a table on the chalkboard that shows the relationship between the power of ten and the decimal value. For example,

$$10^3 = 1000 \text{ (three zeros)}$$
$$10^2 = 100 \text{ (two zeros)}$$
$$10^1 = 10 \text{ (one zero)}$$
$$10^0 = 1 \text{ (zero zeros)}$$
$$10^{-1} = 0.1 \text{ (one zero to the left)}$$
$$10^{-2} = 0.01 \text{ (two zeros to the left)}$$
$$10^{-3} = 0.001 \text{ (three zeros to the left)}$$

The hydronium ion concentrations we usually deal with are very small. This means taking the log of negative exponents. Chemists use the negative sign in the definition of pH to change these negative numbers to positive numbers. It is then helpful to show students what's happening when they press their [log] button on their calculators, and how calculators are very useful for concentrations that don't begin with the numeral 1.

> CHECK YOUR NEIGHBOR: What's the pH of a 0.5 M solution of HCl? How about a 1.0 M solution? A 2.0 M solution? [Answers: 0.301; 0; −0.310. Students may be surprised that negative pH values are possible. The lower limit of pH depends on the solubility of acid. A saturated solution of hydrochloric acid is 12.0 M, which corresponds to a pH of −1.08.]

Many chemicals change color with pH. These chemicals, which are usually organic, can serve as pH indicators. You'll note that pH indicators are not discussed in the text. The stage is set, however, to present pH indicators as a demonstration, such as the red cabbage.

Some dyes used to make color paper are also pH sensitive. Certain brands of goldenrod colored paper, for example, turn bright red when dipped in a solution of sodium hydroxide.

> DEMONSTRATION: Submerge a pH electrode in a glass of water, and then using a straw, blow bubbles into the water. The carbon dioxide of your breath will bring the water to a pH of 5. Ask the class whether they think you really have acid breath. While the pH meter is set up, be sure to submerge the electrode in a glass of cola. Another favorite is to stir campfire ashes into water and see the pH rise to above 10. Alkaline ashes were once used to make soap. Note that the term alkaline is derived from the Arabic term for ashes: *al-qali*.

The Rates of Chemical Reactions

This section is based upon kinetic-molecular theory, which tells us that in order for two chemicals to react they must first come together. The rate of chemical reactions has importance in atmospheric chemistry as well as biology. Specifically, the concept of the catalyst will be revisited in Chapter 25 when ozone depletion is discussed, as well as in biology. You could preview those applications here. If you do, you could do the following demonstration to show how chlorine atoms catalyze the destruction of atmospheric ozone. Be sure to distinguish ozone depletion from global warming.

DEMONSTRATION: Dip a hot platinum wire into a 3% solution of hydrogen peroxide. The platinum will catalyze the decomposition of the hydrogen peroxide. With greater concentrations of hydrogen peroxide, enough heat can be released to cause the water to boil. If you have no platinum available to you, consider returning to the Oxygen Bubble Bursts activity, in which baker's yeast is used to catalyze the decomposition of consumer-grade hydrogen peroxide.

Exothermic and Endothermic Reactions

It takes energy to break a chemical bond, and energy is released when a chemical bond is formed. The analogy with magnets is quite useful. Students easily recognize that it takes energy to pull two magnets apart. Similarly, they can be led to understand that energy is released when two magnets come together (in the form of kinetic energy or heat from the collision). Holding with the principle of the conservation of energy, the amount of energy required to break a bond is equal to the amount of energy released when a bond is formed.

Show how there is a net release of energy when water is produced from hydrogen and oxygen. Write the equation on the board using chemical structures rather than chemical formulas. This makes for a conceptual presentation, because students can actually see the bonds that are to be broken and the ones that are to be formed. Summarize the data of Table 13.2.

Show how energy is a product in an exothermic reaction and a reactant in an endothermic reaction. Cite examples of both.

DEMONSTRATION: Show how the formation of crystals is an exothermic reaction. Sporting goods stores and science supply companies sell hand-warmers (instant hot packs) that typically consist of a supersaturated solution of sodium acetate. The bending of a small metal disk inside the plastic pouch initiates crystallization with the production of heat.

Concerning an explanation of the chemical hot pack: Particles set loose from the bent metal disk initiate the formation of anhydrous sodium acetate, $C_2H_3O^-Na^+(s)$. Interestingly, this step is endothermic, requiring about 16 kJ/mole. This may seem odd, because there is the ionic bond *forming* between the sodium and acetate ions. This bond forms, however, at the expense of *breaking* the many ion–dipole attractions that hold the sodium and acetate ions in solution. In the second step, water molecules pull toward the solidifying anhydrous salt to form the hydrate complex. During the rapid crystallization, the water seems to vanish, being replaced by crystals. Students may wonder where the water went. The answer is that the water is now organized within the crystal lattice such that there are three water molecules for every unit of sodium acetate, $C_2H_3O^-Na^+ \cdot 3\ H_2O(s)$. The formation of sodium acetate trihydrate from anhydrous sodium acetate releases about 37 kJ/mole. The total amount of energy released from this reaction, therefore, is about 21 kJ/mole.

	ΔH formation
$C_2H_3O^-(aq) + Na^+(aq) \rightarrow C_2H_3O^-Na^+(s)$	+16 kJ/mole
$C_2H_3O^-Na^+(s) + 3\ H_2O(\ell) \rightarrow C_2H_3O^-Na^+ \cdot 3\ H_2O(s)$	−37 kJ/mole
NET: $C_2H_3O^-(aq) + Na^+(aq) \rightarrow C_2H_3O^-Na^+ \cdot 3\ H_2O(s)$	−21 kJ/mole

Pedagogically, there are at least three approaches to telling your students what is happening. The first approach is most demanding: Review the explanation given above. The second approach is more basic: Crystallization is an exothermic process, because it involves the formation of bonds among molecules or ions (the bonds are formed as the molecules or ions pack together). The third approach is a twist of the truth: Tell students that energy is released upon the formation of ionic bonds. Present the following equation:

$$C_2H_3O^-(aq) + Na^+(aq) \rightarrow C_2H_3O^-Na^+(s) + ENERGY$$

Strictly speaking, this is true only when the reactants are in a gaseous phase. Ignoring the effects of water, however, helps students to focus on the main concept—that energy is always released upon the formation of a chemical bond.

CHECK YOUR NEIGHBOR: Is the hot pack reusable? How so? [Answer: Yes, the hot pack is reusable, provided energy is put back into the system to separate the chemical bonds. This is done by placing the solidified hot pack in boiling water. Point out that the heat being felt by the hot pack today is the heat that was added to it the previous night while on the stove. The hot pack does not create energy—it simply stores energy for later use.]

Some endothermic reactions can absorb energy from their immediate surroundings. (If students don't believe there's a lot of heat available at room temperature, ask them to compare it to the amount of heat available in a room kept at a temperature of $-10°C$). The dissolution of many salts provides good examples. The driving force for these reactions is the increase in entropy.

DEMONSTRATION: Fill two clear plastic cups halfway with warm water. Pour the water back and forth between cups. Ask students why you are doing this while you do it. (Your answer: Just the kind of thing they might expect a chemist to do. Hmm?) Then ask them if they would believe that the water in each of the cups was at the same temperature. (Sure, because of the mixing.) Ask a student volunteer to verify this fact. Show on the chalkboard that an endothermic reaction occurs when sodium nitrate dissolves in water, because it is separated into sodium and nitrate ions (note the breaking of the ionic bond):

$$Energy + NaNO_3 \rightarrow Na^+(aq) + NO_3^-(aq)$$

Ask a student volunteer to close his or her eyes as you mix several scoops of sodium nitrate into one of the cups. (Dry the outsides of the cups.) Carefully hand the two cups to the eyes-closed volunteer, and ask him or her to judge to which one the sodium nitrate had been added. The student will choose the colder cup. The saltpeter used to make homemade ice cream is a mixture of sodium nitrate and potassium nitrate. Potassium nitrate has a greater enthalpy of dissolution (gets colder) than sodium nitrate, but its solubility in water is significantly less. Commercial cold packs use ammonium nitrate, because it's cheaper and much more soluble in water. Its enthalpy of dissolution is greater than that of sodium nitrate but less than that of potassium nitrate. Ammonium nitrate can be used in this demonstration, however, as a solid, it is a powerful oxidizing agent and forms explosive mixtures with chloride salts. Aqueous solutions of ammonium nitrate are relatively safe to handle, except that they can irritate the skin.

CHECK YOUR NEIGHBOR: Salt lowers the melting point of ice, but at the same time, the temperature of the ice

  a. increases.   b. decreases.   c. remains the same.

[Answer: The melting point of ice decreases because salt ions interfere with the packing of water molecules. The temperature of the ice, however, decreases as it loses energy to the breaking of ionic bonds in salt.]

Integrated Science—Earth Science: Acid Rain
Students should have little difficulty in understanding and appreciating this environmentally oriented section. The following demonstration serves as a nice introduction. After showing how your breath is acidic because of the CO_2 it contains, students will appreciate how the atmosphere is acidic for the same reasons.

DEMONSTRATION: Add a drop of phenolphthalein to a few milliliters of water in a test tube. Make the solution slightly alkaline by adding a small amount of sodium carbonate, Na_2CO_3. The solution will turn pink. Point out that by adding an acid, the pH drops, and the pink color will disappear (phenolphthalein indicator changes color at about a pH of 7). Demonstrate by adding a drop of acid, such as hydrochloric acid or vinegar. Repeat the same procedure in a second test tube, this time using a straw to blow in carbon dioxide from your breath.

Integrated Science—Physics, Biology, and Earth Science: The Effect of Temperature on Reaction Rate
This feature makes the connection between chemical reactions that maintain body temperature in an ectotherm and the environmental temperature. Figure 13.28, the photo of the "frozen" alligator, proves the point that chemical reactions proceed faster at higher temperatures. You can use this photo to emphasize the point. Also, this feature introduces the concept of activation energy. Watch for students to possibly confuse bond energy with activation energy. Emphasize that bond energy is the energy released as a bond is formed (equal to the energy absorbed as that bond breaks); activation energy is the energy needed to initiate a chemical reaction. Once catalysts are understood (next section), explain that cells rely on catalysts that lower the activation energy of reactions, so that biochemical reactions can happen as quickly as they are needed. Catalysts in cells are large, complex proteins called *enzymes*. Enzymes are discussed in greater length in Chapter 15.

14   Organic Chemistry

The structures of organic compounds and their physical and chemical properties are introduced in this chapter. Much of the chapter is descriptive; however, you will also find the application of previously learned concepts such as molecular attractions and acid/base chemistry.

That carbon atoms are able to bond with themselves repeatedly can be related to the strength of the carbon–carbon single bond. The C—C bond energy is 347 kJ/mole. Compare this to the bond energies of N—N (293 kJ/mole), O—O (138 kJ/mole), S—S (213 kJ/mole), and Si—Si (176 kJ/mole). Another vital characteristic of carbon is its ability to form four covalent bonds. Point out to students how this is a "peak" in terms of the periodic trend of valence—neon forms zero bonds, fluorine forms 1, oxygen forms 2, nitrogen forms 3, carbon forms 4, boron forms 3, and so on.

Using a molecular modeling kit, show the wide variety of structures possible from six carbon atoms alone. (Leave out the hydrogen atoms to facilitate switching between structures.) Note how each configuration has a different set of physical and chemical properties. Introduce an oxygen atom to show an even greater variety of compounds. That carbon forms strong covalent bonds with "heteroatoms" is another important aspect of carbon's versatility. The number of possible carbon-based compounds is truly endless.

With organic chemicals, carbon and hydrogen atoms provide a relatively inert framework to which more reactive atoms, such as nitrogen and oxygen, may attach. These added atoms give the organic chemical much of its character—much like ornaments on a tree. We begin by studying the carbon–hydrogen framework.

In the *Practice Book*:
• Structures of Organic Compounds
• Polymers

In *Next-Time Questions*:
• Aspirin

In the *Lab Manual*:
• Smells Great! (activity)
• Name That Recyclable (activity)

Transparencies:
Figures 14.3, 14.6, 14.7, 14.14; Table 14.1

Suggested Presentation

Hydrocarbons
Hydrocarbons come in all three phases. Blow some soap bubbles using methane (or propane) to demonstrate the gaseous phase (methane bubbles will rise, but propane bubbles will sink). Bring in some hexanes or gasoline to show the liquid phase. The solid phase is seen with plastics such as high- or low-density polyethylene, polypropylene, or polystyrene. The phase of a hydrocarbon is a function of its molecular mass. Consider creating a handout or an overhead transparency of the following "Properties of Hydrocarbons" table:

Properties of Hydrocarbons

Molecular Formula	Name	Melting Point (°C)	Boiling Point (°C)	Phase at Room Temperature
CH_4	Methane	−184	−161	
C_2H_6	Ethane	−183	−88	Gas
C_3H_8	Propane	−188	−42	
n-Butane	n-Butane	−138	−0.5	
C_5H_{12}	n-Pentane	−130	36	
C_6H_{14}	n-Hexane	−94	69	
C_7H_{16}	n-Heptane	−91	98	Liquid
C_8H_{18}	n-Octane	−57	126	
$C_{16}H_{34}$	n-Hexadecane	18	288	
$C_{17}H_{36}$	n-Heptadecane	23	303	
$C_{18}H_{38}$	n-Octadecane	28	317	Solid
$C_{2000}H_{4002}$*	Polyethylene	136	dec.**	

* The number of carbon atoms per molecule in polyethylene varies greatly but is generally a large number not more than 100,000.
** Decomposes before boiling.

Show what is meant by a structural isomer. Introduce the term *conformation* and contrast it to what is meant by *configuration*, which refers to how the atoms are connected. Use the human body as an analogy. The configuration of the arm is such that the wrist bone is connected to the ulna bone, the ulna bone is connected to the elbow bone, and so forth. The conformation refers to how the bonds are oriented within a particular configuration. Again, using the human body as an analogy, the whole arm is one configuration, which can have a wide variety of different conformations (extend your arm and twist it about). Go through examples so that students can recognize when two structures are either different configurations or different conformations of the same configuration.

> CHECK YOUR NEIGHBOR: How many different configurations are shown below? Which ones, if any, are different conformations of the same configuration?

A   B   C   D

Unsaturated Hydrocarbons

When students hear the term "unsaturated," they are likely to think of unsaturated fats. "Saturated" means that a carbon atom is saturated with hydrogen atoms, that is, bonded to a maximum number. Only single covalent bonds appear in saturated hydrocarbons. The hydrocarbons discussed in the previous section are all saturated. "Unsaturated" means that there are fewer than a maximum number of hydrogen atoms bonded to carbon. This occurs when double or triple bonds are present. Relating this to one's diet, the hydrocarbon portions of saturated fat molecules consist of only single bonds. The hydrocarbon portions of unsaturated fats, however, contain multiple bonds, usually one or more double bond. One reason unsaturated fats may be better for our health is that double bonds are more chemically reactive, hence, easier to metabolize. You might tell your students that the double bond is like a handle that the body grabs to help move the molecule through the digestion process. In general, the better an organic molecule flows through your body, the less harmful it is.

Consider the review article by Gary Taubes in the March 30, 2001, issue of *Science*. This article, entitled "The Soft Science of Dietary Fat," points out that there is little to no evidence correlating dietary saturated fats to coronary heart disease. The article explores in depth the history of how we have come to assume that saturated fats are necessarily bad and ought to be avoided at all expense. It makes for an interesting exposé on what happens when science and politics come together. If not available through your library, it may be found on the Web at the AAAS:

www.sciencemag.org/content/vol291/issue5513/index.shtml#newsfocus.

Functional Groups

Heteroatom is the common term used by organic chemists to describe nitrogen, oxygen, chlorine, or any other noncarbon/nonhydrogen atoms in an organic molecule. In introducing the various heteroatom containing functional groups, you might wish to emphasize that these structures are presented as a display of the diversity of carbon, more than for memorization.

In society, the words "alcohol" and "ethanol" are used interchangeably. From a chemical point of view, however, alcohols are a class of organic compounds, of which ethanol is one example. Define the alcohol as an organic molecule containing the hydroxyl functional group.

> CHECK YOUR NEIGHBOR: Because water consists of a hydroxyl group bonded to a hydrogen atom, can it be classified as an alcohol? [No. Alcohols are organic molecules, which by definition contain carbon. Because there is no carbon in water, it cannot be classified as an alcohol.]

Alcohol molecules are attracted to one another primarily by the dipole–dipole attractions between hydroxyl groups. The more hydroxyl groups in an alcohol, the greater the molecular attractions.

> DEMONSTRATION: Write on the chalkboard the chemical structures for ethanol, ethylene glycol, and glycerol. Ask students to predict the order of boiling points. Then produce three unlabeled glass vials, each containing one of the above alcohols. Ask students to identify them. Point out how viscosity is also a function of the strengths of molecular attractions.

Show how ethers are structurally related to alcohols. You might do this with a molecular modeling kit. It is interesting to note that a new class of compounds is produced simply by changing the arrangement of atoms. Because they lack the oxygen–hydrogen dipole, ethers are much less soluble in water, and their boiling points are lower.

> DEMONSTRATION: Contrast the miscibility of ethanol and diethyl ether with water. First define miscibility as the ability of two substances to form a single phase. Pour equal amounts of water into two graduated cylinders. Have the class note the volume levels. Mix in a drop of water-soluble food coloring. Pour the same quantity of ethanol to one of the containers and the same quantity of diethyl ether to the other. Cover the tops with parafilm and shake. (You will note a pressure buildup as you mix the water and ether.) The water and ethanol form a single liquid phase. The water and ether, however, form two liquid phases. Note the volume level of the water in the water/ether cylinder, and ask the class to explain any discrepancies. That some of the ether has dissolved in the water can be demonstrated by pouring the two phases into a separatory funnel and collecting the lower aqueous phase. Have a student volunteer note the odor of this ether-containing water.

Low molecular mass amines have a characteristic bad odor. Inform your students that this is why you have not brought any samples to show them. Higher molecular mass amines, however, do not have such characteristic odors.

> CHECK YOUR NEIGHBOR: Higher molecular mass amines do not give off the characteristic bad odor released by lower molecular mass amines. Why not? [We can only smell that which reaches our nose. In order for a scent to reach our nose, it must be in a gaseous phase. Lower molecular mass amines have fewer molecular attractions, hence, they are more volatile, which means that the molecules readily escape into the gaseous phase. Higher molecular mass amines, on the other hand, have strong molecular attractions that hold the molecules to the solid or liquid phases, which we cannot smell.]

Show how amines can act as bases by accepting the hydrogen ion. The hydrogen ion is attracted to the lone pair of electrons on the nitrogen atom. You might show where these electrons come from by drawing the shell model for nitrogen.

> DEMONSTRATION: Show how to extract caffeine from coffee. Pour a strong cup of coffee into a separatory funnel. Bring the coffee to a pH of about 9 or 10 by adding drops of a solution of sodium hydroxide. Pour some diethyl ether (about a third the volume of the coffee) into the funnel. Stopper the funnel, invert it, and open the stopcock to release any pressure. Close the stopcock, and shake the contents. After the two layers settle, collect the lower aqueous layer in a beaker. Collect the ether layer in a second beaker. Add some anhydrous sodium sulfate to the ether to absorb any water. Decant some of the ether into a watch glass and let it evaporate. The residues left behind contain caffeine. Be careful not to let too many of the ether fumes migrate toward the students. If possible, perform this demo in a fume hood, or at least cover the open beaker containing the ether layer with parafilm or with a larger beaker inverted over it. If not much residue is collected, consider rotovapping an ether layer prior to the class so that you can show what the residue looks like after all of the ether is evaporated. Brewed coffee

contains from 18 to 15 milligrams of caffeine per ounce. Decaffeinated coffee is made by extracting whole coffee beans with organic solvents, usually supercritical carbon dioxide. The beans are then roasted to bring out flavor.

DEMONSTRATION: Bring to class samples of some of the more pleasantly fragrant aldehydes such as the ones listed in Figure 14.17.

CHECK YOUR NEIGHBOR: Most of the aspirin consumed today is synthetically produced from crude oil. How is this aspirin different from aspirin derived from the willow tree? [There is no difference. They are exactly the same. Neither one is either better or worse.]

DEMONSTRATION: In the event your students are not performing the Smells Great! lab activity, add a couple grams of salicylic acid to a watch glass. State how this material is a precursor to aspirin, then ask for a volunteer to attest to the fact that it doesn't have much of an odor. Dissolve the salicyclic acid in a couple milliliters of methanol. Follow up by adding a couple drops of concentrated sulfuric acid. Stir, and set it aside to evaporate. Alternatively, set it atop an overhead projector. The heat of the projector lamp will speed up the evaporation, and the shadows of the crystal formations can be seen on the projection screen. Note that crystal formation upon the evaporation of the methanol is sometimes quite beautiful. After the methanol has evaporated, ask for a volunteer to attest to the fact that wintergreen (methyl salicylate) has been formed. Show the equation for the reaction on the board. FYI: The sulfuric acid helps this reaction move forward by making it easier for the oxygen of the methanol molecule to attack the carbon of the carbonyl. It does so by donating a hydrogen to the oxygen of the carbonyl. This, in turn, makes the carbon of the carbonyl more positive in character, which makes it susceptible to an attack by the lone pair on the oxygen of the methanol molecule.

Polymers

A good theme to carry through this section is how the physical properties of a polymer are a consequence of the chemical structure of its component monomers. Properties to focus on include density, hardness, and melting point. (*Note*: Glass transition temperature is not defined.)

You should touch upon the idea of biopolymers, such as starches, proteins, and nucleic acids. These are the polymers that we eat and of which our bodies are made. With an understanding of the synthetic polymers discussed in this chapter, students will have a good handle for understanding biopolymers in their life science courses.

Addition Polymers

Show the formation of polyethylene as per Figure 14.22. You can then use this same transparency to show the formation of other addition polymers. Using a transparency marker, simply write in $-CH_3$ groups on every other carbon, or benzene groups on every other carbon, to show the formation of polypropylene and polystyrene, respectively. These are different monomer starting materials, but the chemistry is the same. Let students in on the excitement that early polymer developers must have experienced—all they had to do was play around with the starting materials and, voilá, a wide variety of different polymers could be formed with applications limited only by our imaginations.

Condensation Polymers

Discuss the formation of Nylon through Figure 14.26. If possible, perform the synthesis of Nylon for your students. It is an unforgettable experience for them. As with all demos, be sure to experiment with the conditions on your own before performing in front of the group.

DEMONSTRATION: Here is a procedure for the synthesis of Nylon. Prior to class, prepare two solutions as follows:

Solution A: Place 5.81 g of hexamethylenediamine (1,6-diaminohexane) in a beaker. Warm until it melts, and dilute to 100 mL with 0.5 M NaOH (20 g NaOH per liter).

Solution B: Dilute 4.58 g of adipoyl chloride with cyclohexane to a volume of 100 mL. Caution, the adipoyl chloride is corrosive, releasing hydrogen chloride fumes. Prepare in a fume hood.

During class, place about 5 mL of Solution A in a 50-mL beaker. Slowly add the same quantity of Solution B to the same beaker. Beware of the hydrogen chloride fumes that form upon the reaction. The role of the sodium hydroxide in Solution A is to react with this HCl, but some still invariably escapes as fumes. Hold some litmus paper to the fumes to show the students the formation of this gas. A film will form at the interface of the two solutions. Do not stir this mixture. Instead, wearing gloves, carefully hook the film with a paper clip bent at the tip, and pull the film from the beaker. It works well to hold the beaker at a slight angle and pull the Nylon off the wet lip of the beaker. Carefully guide the Nylon out of the beaker. Continue pulling until the solutions are exhausted. The Nylon can be spooled around a large beaker. Pop any bubbles that formed during the pulling process. Rinse the Nylon thoroughly before passing it around for the class to examine more closely.

Students will comment on how "weak" the strand of Nylon is. In other words, it is fairly easy to break. You might bring out some fine Nylon rope. Pull it apart carefully so as to collect some single strands. Note that "yes" these single strands are weak, but that together they form a very strong rope.

Attitudes About Plastics Have Changed

After a brief discussion on the virtues of recycling plastics, take the issue a step further by surveying the students on what they believe to be the top three problems/concerns currently faced by the human race. Human population growth is usually a popular choice, but it's not likely that it will be voted unanimously by students as the number one problem or concern facing us. The follow-up of showing them how most all other problems hinge on this one is not difficult.

There is cause for hope. Remarkable treatments for diseases such as AIDS have been developed, and drug companies are doing what they can to provide these medicines to those who can't afford them. Chlorofluorocarbon concentrations are coming down. Many nations have established zero population growth, and many developing nations have shown dramatic drops in their population growths. Air pollution control measures do work to give us cleaner air to breathe. Sustainable energy resource technologies are being embraced by developing nations. The list of optimistic notes goes on. Perhaps most significant, however, is the integration occurring as more and more people from different nations become connected to one another by electronic media, telecommunications, and the World Wide Web. Perhaps by these global communications, exploits of nations and peoples over other nations and peoples will diminish. The power of human voices speaking in unison is not to be underestimated. A major concern is that these voices be voices of both compassion and reason. We are not born with compassion or reason—these are traits that develop as we mature. As teachers, helping our students mature in these traits is perhaps our greatest service.

Integrated Science—Biology: Drug Action and Discovery

To illustrate the lock-and-key model, take a piece of paper and crumple it up. The resulting wad will have numerous nooks and crannies. Explain to students how these nooks and crannies are analogous to certain regions of their bodies, especially on the surface of cells. Show how it is that a piece of chalk, or similar prop, is able to fit within one of these nooks and crannies. As the chalk is nestled into the nook, show how it is that the paper is not static. Rather, it may contort when the paper binds to its site. The contortion of the paper wad opens up other nooks that other molecules might be able to fit into. This is the essence of the lock-and-key model of drug action: A drug works as it bonds to some receptor site in the cell. As it binds, it causes the surface to contort, which then influences other receptor sites and, hence, other biochemical reactions that might be occurring in the body.

In explaining the similar actions of morphine, codeine, and heroin, it is very useful to have their molecular models on hand. One suffices. Simply change the functional groups accordingly to transform from one compound to the next. Although the functional groups change, the overall shape of the molecules are the same. This helps us to visualize the important relationship between the structure of a drug molecule and its biological effect.

Be sure not to miss the opportunity to stress yet another reason that the world's tropical forests should be preserved. Plants are often in mortal combat against other plants, insects, fungi, and animals. From this combat arises a multitude of biologically active compounds that serve the plant some evolutionary advantage. These compounds are the very ones that chemists look for in the search for new medicines.

15   The Basic Unit of Life—The Cell

Demonstration Equipment

Diverse images of cells

Large models of cells

A candle

Pairs of distinctly colored socks

This first biology chapter begins with a discussion of what characterizes living things. It then moves on to describe the cell, the basic unit that makes up all living things (with the possible exception of viruses, which are considered living by some biologists and nonliving by other biologists). Cell structure is described in both prokaryotic and eukaryotic cells. Following this, the discussion moves on to how cells accomplish basic functions—how they control transport, reproduce, run chemical reactions, photosynthesize, and obtain energy. The chapter ends with a consideration of why certain cells have a limited life span, whereas others are potentially able to continue to divide forever.

In the *Practice Book*:
• Features of Prokaryotic and Eukaryotic Cells
• Transport In and Out of Cells
• Photosynthesis and Cellular Respiration

In *Next-Time Questions*:
• Active and passive transport across the cell membrane
• Caramel apples (surface areas and volumes)
• The cell cycle and mitosis
• Where does oxygen come from?

In the *Lab Manual*:
• Magnifying Microscopes (experiment)
• In and Out (experiment)

Transparencies:
Figures 15.7, 15.13, 15.14, 15.25, 15.32, 15.36

Suggested Presentation

Characteristics of Life
What is a living thing? We can generally say with some confidence what's living and what isn't—although sometimes, we might be fooled. Think about corals, clouds, fire—might any of these things fool us? Why? Try this class activity—have students imagine themselves as space explorers searching for extraterrestrial life

on an unexplored planet. How would they look for living things? What cues would they look for? Have students discuss this with their neighbors and make a list of potentially useful cues. After going through these lists briefly, have students work with their neighbors to make a list of characteristics of living things on Earth. Compare what students come up with with the list in the text of some traits of living things. Which traits characterize all living things, and which traits have exceptions?

Macromolecules Needed For Life

Why is carbon the basis of life? The fact that life on Earth is carbon-based is not arbitrary—carbon is uniquely able to form strong bonds with as many as four other atoms at a time, allowing it to serve as the basis for highly complex molecules. (You might note in passing that some science fiction writers have dreamed up imaginary worlds with life forms based on silicon—silicon too can form bonds with as many as four other molecules. However, these bonds are generally weaker than the ones carbon can form, with the result that silicon-based molecules are more fragile, perhaps too fragile to be used in living organisms.)

Four types of macromolecules make up living things—proteins, carbohydrates, lipids, and nucleic acids. Each type of macromolecule has a distinct chemical structure and a distinct set of functions. Students may be most familiar with proteins, carbohydrates, and lipids (fats and oils) as components of the foods they eat, so that might be a good way to introduce the topic.

Cell Types: Prokaryotic and Eukaryotic

A good way to begin the discussion of cells is to bring up Robert Hooke's discovery of them when he looked at a piece of cork under a microscope—a reproduction of Hooke's original illustration is provided in the text. Hooke also gave cells their name, naming them for the monk cells (tiny, bare rooms) they reminded him of.

From here, it would be great to show a photo gallery of diverse cells, including bacteria, microorganisms, plant cells, and a variety of cells of the human body. Be sure to keep students fascinated by offering a little of the natural history of whatever you find to show—for example, where do these bacteria and microorganisms live? Do they make their own food using energy from sunlight, the way plants do? If not, what do they eat? Are they able to move? If so, how? Bacteria and microorganisms that cause human diseases might be a subset of particular interest. As for human cells, focus on what their function is in the body. You can show muscle cells, red blood cells, immune cells, neurons, skin cells, sperm and eggs, and so on.

Once you have wowed students with the range of cell diversity, you can tell them that, despite all that diversity, all cells have a number of things in common. There are two different types of cells in the world today—prokaryotic and eukaryotic. Distinguish between these, explaining that prokaryotic cells evolved long before the earliest eukaryotic cells. Diagrams of prokaryotic and eukaryotic cells showing the relative size and complexity of the cells are a must, and physical models, if available, can be very helpful too. True multicellularity is found only in eukaryotes.

Integrated Science—Physics: The Microscope

Our knowledge of cells has gone hand in hand with our ability to see inside of them. You can combine a brief description of the history of our knowledge of cells (see the History of Science feature "Cell Theory") with a description of advances in microscopy. This is another opportunity to show some wonderful images, including electron microscope images as well as fluorescently tagged images (such as the one of telomeres in the last section).

Tour of a Eukaryotic Cell

This is a challenging section, as there is a lot of new terminology and information to master. To help reinforce content, an activity you might consider is dividing students into groups and assigning each group a single component of the eukaryotic cell (the membrane, the nucleus, the cytoskeleton, and each of the organelles). Have each group present the function of their organelle. What would happen to the cell if it lacked that cell component?

Cell Membrane: Structure and Function

Focus on the structure and function of each of the three components of the cell membrane—phospholipids, membrane proteins, and short carbohydrates. The fluid mosaic model might be compared to a swimming pool filled with floating balls and other objects—the phospholipids and many (but not all) of the proteins can slide around freely as those objects slide around the surface of a pool.

Transport Mechanisms

A fundamental task of the cell membrane is to control what moves in and out of cells. Some things can cross the cell membrane directly, but most things cannot.

Many molecules move in and out of cells through diffusion. Diffusion occurs all around us—smells from the kitchen diffuse through the entire house, so that we smell spaghetti and meatballs on the stove. Cooking spaghetti works because of diffusion—water molecules diffuse into the dried pasta, making it softer and thicker. A simple classroom demonstration of diffusion can be performed by lighting and then blowing out a candle. When you blow out the candle, a puff of white smoke appears. Wouldn't it be strange if the puff of smoke just hung there, over the extinguished candle, forever? Instead, what happens is that it spreads away from the candle, becoming invisible as it diffuses through the room. (Be sure to note that if you wave the smoke molecules away by fanning the air, this is not diffusion, but another process—convection.)

Diffusion requires no energy and is a consequence of the random motion of molecules. Its effect is to move molecules from an area of high concentration to an area of low concentration, that is, down a concentration gradient. Emphasize that an individual molecule may move in the opposite way—from low concentration to high—but that the net movement is always from high concentration to low. A variety of metaphors could be helpful here, including the behavior of objects that either move or appear to move randomly—say, a dense pack of active puppies enclosed within a fence. You take away the fence and what happens?

Carrier proteins might be compared to gates in the cell membrane that are very specifically shaped—say one that is exactly the size and shape of a Hershey's kiss (insert your own favorite mass-produced snack food here). Carrier proteins are involved in two different processes—facilitated diffusion (no energy required) and active transport (energy required). Facilitated diffusion occurs if molecules move down a concentration gradient. Active transport occurs if molecules move up a concentration gradient. An example of facilitated diffusion is the movement of glucose into red blood cells. Examples of active transport include the sodium-potassium pump, discussed in detail in the Integrated Science feature "Chemical Reactions in Cells," and the transport of digested nutrients (such as glucose) from the small intestine into the bloodstream (see Chapter 20).

Exocytosis and endocytosis can also be used to move materials in and out of cells. To understand exactly how exocytosis and endocytosis work, it often helps to draw the steps—have students do this in class. You may also be able to find some good images of the two processes.

Math Connection: Why Does Diffusion Limit the Size of Cells?

A good way to think about surface area to volume ratios is to think about caramel apples. The volume of a caramel apple is basically the amount of apple, and the surface area of a caramel apple is basically the amount of caramel. As the size of your caramel apple increases, the volume increases (there's more apple) and the surface area increases (there's more caramel). However, the surface area to volume ratio decreases. (The ratio of caramel to apple decreases—another way to say this is that the amount of apple increases faster than the amount of caramel as caramel apples get bigger.)

Cellular Communication

For good examples of cellular communication via the lock-and-key fit of molecules and receptors, it may be worthwhile to look ahead to our senses of taste and smell, discussed in Chapter 19. Or, introduce the chemical synapse between neurons (also described in Chapter 19) for an example of communication between cells. (Discussing the chemical synapse will also give you an opportunity to bring up exocytosis again!)

How Cells Reproduce

Good diagrams of the cell cycle and mitosis are a must. These can be complemented with photos of actual dividing cells. One of the best ways to learn about mitosis is by drawing the phases out by hand. Encourage the students to do this with you during class, using distinctly sized chromosomes. Or, prepare a more hands-on model using pairs of socks as duplicated chromosomes and follow them through the cell cycle and mitosis.

How Cells Use Energy

Review the chemistry concepts of activation energy and catalysts with students before introducing enzymes. You can make enzymes seem more real to students by discussing some of the numerous conditions and human diseases that result from a faulty or insufficient amount of enzyme for a particular chemical reaction. For example, lactose intolerance is caused by insufficient amounts of lactase, an enzyme normally made in the small intestine that breaks down lactose, the predominant sugar found in milk. (Instead, the lactose continues on to the large intestine, where it is broken down [feasted upon] by bacteria residing there, producing the digestive symptoms associated with lactose intolerance.)

Integrated Science—Chemistry: Chemical Reactions in Cells

The fact that ATP is used by cells to run chemical reactions can seem pretty abstract to students. Explicit examples of how it does this—such as the one in the text regarding the sodium-potassium pump (in which the transfer of a phosphate molecule from ATP to the carrier protein causes it to change shape)—help make the idea more concrete.

Photosynthesis

Photosynthesis is the basis of life as we know it, both because photosynthetic organisms form the base of the food chain in just about every habitat on Earth and because photosynthesis produces the oxygen we breathe. Start with the overall equation for photosynthesis, discussing where each reactant in the equation comes from—how do plants get carbon dioxide, water, and sunlight? (You can consult Chapter 18 for more information.) Then, move on to discussing the light-dependent and light-independent reactions. When is each product of photosynthesis made? (When is oxygen made? When is glucose made?) Finally, what becomes of all that glucose? Glucose is used to make all the organic macromolecules that make up living things. For example, cellulose, the carbohydrate found in plant cell walls (and the most abundant organic molecule on Earth) is made up of linked glucose subunits.

Cellular Respiration

Cellular respiration is the process cells use to break down glucose (and sometimes other organic molecules) to make ATP. Cellular respiration should be distinguished clearly from digestion—digestion breaks down the food we eat into molecules that can be used by cells in the body. These molecules are then broken down by cells in the process of cellular respiration. Digestion occurs in the digestive system, whereas cellular respiration occurs in all our cells (with a few odd exceptions, such as red blood cells). In order to give students a handle on the process, it may be helpful to use a diagram of the cell that shows where each of the different steps take place (glycolysis in the cytoplasm, Krebs cycle and electron transport in the mitochondria).

Be sure to point out that plants use cellular respiration as well! Yes, they perform photosynthesis as well as cellular respiration, and they have mitochondria, too. Plants use photosynthesis to build glucose molecules, and then they break them down again to make ATP.

Your discussion of alcoholic fermentation and lactic acid fermentation can emphasize the importance of these processes in human lives. Alcoholic fermentation is used in wine-making, beer-brewing, and bread-baking. Lactic acid fermentation occurs in our bodies, powering our muscles when we need more oxygen than the body is taking in. Lactic acid fermentation is also used in our red blood cells, which, in order to be small enough to move easily through the circulatory system, have lost the nucleus and mitochondria.

The Life Spans of Cells

The idea that telomeres control cellular life spans is of particular interest because of its implications for aging and cancer. Students may enjoy hearing about some current research. For example, some scientists wonder if lengthening telomeres (by somehow activating the enzyme telomerase, for example) can help slow aging. This research is in its early stages, and many are skeptical. As for cancer—cancer cells typically have activated telomerase (otherwise they would not be able to divide indefinitely the way they do). Because of this, some researchers are attempting to fight tumors by interfering with telomerase activity. But this, of course, could harm those cells in our body that also use telomerase and are able to divide indefinitely—germ cells such as sperm and eggs, as well as the blood-forming stem cells that make our red blood cells and immune cells. In addition, some cancer cells appear to be able to maintain telomeres through a mechanism that doesn't involve telomerase.

16   Genetics

Demonstration Equipment

Images of different human karyotypes

Socks, in "pairs" that are the same size but differently colored, cut and prepared as described below

Images of dominant and recessive human traits

All living things have genes. We begin by asking what genes are and then move on to describe the structure of the genetic material. We will talk about chromosomes, the structures that contain our DNA, and then learn about the famous "double helix" structure of DNA. From there, we will describe how DNA is used to build proteins through the two-step process of transcription and translation. Armed with an understanding of how genes work on the molecular level, our attention will then turn to inheritance, beginning with a discussion of how meiosis allows sexually reproducing organisms to make an almost infinite variety of different gametes. We will then consider patterns of inheritance in more detail, beginning with Mendel's experiments and moving on to more complex patterns of inheritance. We will then cover the topic of genetic mutations, the ultimate source of all biological diversity. Finally, we will discuss what is known about the human genome as well as how genetic mutations produce cancer.

In the *Practice Book*:
• DNA Replication, Transcription, and Translation
• Meiosis
• Inheritance

In *Next-Time Questions*:
• What do hens study in college?
• Freckles or no freckles?
• Who's the father?
• Nonsense

In the *Lab Manual*:
• Ufroom Pollywoggles (activity)
• Real-Life Inheritance (activity)

Transparencies:
Figures 16.3, 16.9, 16.10, 16.15, 16.16

Suggested Presentation

What Is a Gene?
One way to begin a discussion of genetics is to talk about how much it appears in the news. Much of this has to do with advances in biotechnology—a number of examples are provided in the feature "Big News in

Biology Today—Biotech." The bit on getting spider silk from goat milk is extremely striking and likely to captivate most audiences. Other genetics-related topics are in the news because they are controversial—cloning and genetically modified foods are good examples. In addition, there are often news items on the discovery of genes related to human diseases, and continued debate on whether certain human characteristics—such as homosexual behavior—are genetic or environmental in origin.

All this sets the stage for describing what genes actually are—sequences of DNA that code for protein products. Be sure to explain why so many of our traits depend on proteins, emphasizing that the enzymes that allow chemical reactions in cells to happen are proteins.

Chromosomes: Packages of Genetic Information
Our genetic material is found in structures called chromosomes. Describe the structure of chromosomes, explaining that in sexually reproducing organisms, they come in pairs. Show karyotypes of human chromosomes, perhaps mentioning techniques such as amniocentesis and chorionic villus sampling. What can you learn from looking at human chromosomes at this (very rough) level of detail? You can learn a human being's sex, for one thing. You can also see phenomena such as trisomies and translocations, some of which are implicated in disease (such as Down syndrome).

Integrated Science—Chemistry: The Structure of DNA
DNA is frequently described as a spiraling ladder, a very helpful metaphor for understanding its structure. Using this metaphor, explain what the sides of the ladder are and what the rungs are. Also explain how the two strands of DNA can be separated. Emphasize the base-pairing rules. As with the rest of this chapter, it is crucial to work out examples on paper. So, give students a list of bases on one strand of DNA and have them work out the sequence of bases on the other strand. They can check their answers with a neighbor.

DNA Replication
An understanding of the structure of DNA makes the topic of DNA replication a snap. Show students how the base-pairing rules permit each strand to serve as a template for building a new strand. Again, a very helpful exercise is to have students draw a stretch of DNA with the strands separated and then to fill in the new bases following base-pairing rules. Are both new strands identical to the original? Sure enough! And, this also makes it clear that each new DNA molecule consists of one old strand and one new strand.

Transcription and Translation
Proteins are made from DNA through the two-step process of transcription and translation. Begin by introducing RNA, describing its structure. Emphasize RNA's similarity to DNA as well as differences between the two nucleic acids.

The metaphor of a cell's DNA as a book—perhaps an encyclopedia—can be useful. The transcription of a gene can be compared to copying out a single article from that encyclopedia. If you do use this metaphor, be sure to note the difference between literal copying and what happens during mRNA transcription. In mRNA transcription, the product is not an exact copy of the DNA. Rather, it is a transcript based on base pairing. Again, you should have students work out examples in class—provide a sequence of DNA to be transcribed, and let them work out the transcript and check their answers with their neighbors.

Following transcription is the processing phase, which is fairly straightforward. If you wish to continue the book metaphor, you might explain that the transcript of your encyclopedia article contains (for a reason that continues to remain elusive) blocks of text that have no relevance to the topic—these have to be removed (see the *Hamlet* example in the text).

Scientists do not yet have a good explanation for why introns exist. You might mention alternative splicing, however, noting that sections of DNA sometimes contain the instructions for making multiple proteins. These different protein products are made by cutting out different sections of bases from the mRNA transcript (different introns) and, therefore, leaving different exons behind. Interestingly, scientists involved in the Human Genome Project concluded that alternative splicing turns out to be quite common and accounts in part for why there are only some 30,000 genes in the human genome, rather than the 100,000 previously estimated.

The next step in building a protein is translation. The mechanics of how translation occurs is somewhat complicated and should be described using good, clear figures. Conceptually, translation is similar to translating between different languages. Specifically, three-letter "words" in mRNA are translated to single amino acids. Again, allow students to work multiple examples that will make them comfortable with using the genetic code table and with the translation process.

Meiosis: Genetic Diversity

Drawing out the steps of meiosis is the best way to master how it occurs. Meiosis has a great deal in common with mitosis (covered in Chapter 15), so much of your time may be spent emphasizing the differences. In mitosis, the chromosomes line up individually at metaphase. In meiosis, chromosomes line up with their homologues and crossing over occurs. Crossing over should be explained by carefully following colored chromosomes. You can also use a sock model, employing differently colored but same-sized socks to represent homologous chromosomes. To show the effects of crossing over, you can cut off the feet of the socks and have them exchange parts. Diagrams can also be used to show how independent assortment makes for a dizzyingly huge number of possibilities when sperm and eggs are made during meiosis.

Mendelian Genetics

With this section, we begin the study of inheritance. There is a lot of important new terminology—alleles, homozygote, heterozygote, dominant, recessive. You can review these concepts in a way that students will enjoy by having them go through a series of dominant and recessive human traits (a list appears below). Ideally, you should provide images of the more obscure traits for students to consult. (Note that figuring out whether freckles are a dominant or recessive trait appears as a Next-Time Question, so you may wish to avoid using that if you plan to use the question in class.)

Ask students to figure out if they are homozygotes or heterozygotes and whether they have dominant or recessive alleles. (Some of them will be able to say for sure, based on their traits and what they know of their parents' traits; however, for other students, it may be impossible to say with certainty.) Be sure to emphasize the distinction between genotype and phenotype. For a twist, you can list the traits but not tell them which are dominant and which are recessive. By considering their own traits and their parents' traits, they may (particularly as a class) be able to figure some of this out.

Dominant Human Traits	Recessive Human Traits
No cleft in chin	Cleft in chin
Widow's peak hairline	Straight hairline
Broad eyebrow	Slender eyebrow
Separated eyebrow	Joined eyebrow
Dimples	No dimples
Free earlobes	Attached earlobes
Almond-shaped eyes	Round eyes
Freckles	No freckles
Able to roll tongue into U shape	Unable to roll tongue into U shape
Straight thumb	"Hitchhiker" thumb (curved thumb)

Working many exercises will help ensure mastery of this material, so give students lots of problems, such as: Can two dimpled parents produced a nondimpled child? If Io has dimples, does her brother Pico necessarily have dimples too? If Io has almond-shaped eyes and her mother has almond-shaped eyes, what can you say about her father's eye shape? And so on.

Inheritance: Beyond Mendelian Genetics

Inheritance is not always—in fact, it is not usually!—as simple as dominant and recessive. This section includes numerous examples of additional wrinkles, such as incomplete dominance, codominance, polygenic traits, pleiotropy, and sex-linked traits. Again, have students work on inheritance problems alone or in pairs or small groups. Many good problems can be asked about the inheritance of blood type and sex-linked traits. (For example, can two parents with types A and B blood, respectively, have a child with type O blood? Or, if a boy is born with hemophilia, what can you say about his mother's genotype and phenotype? His father's genotype and phenotype?) Students may also be interested in drawing a pedigree showing blood types in their families.

The Human Genome

The Human Genome Project, completed in 2003, sequenced the entire human genome, which turns out to contain over 3 billion base pairs and about 30,000 genes. Of particular ongoing interest are the 3 million or so SNPs (single nucleotide polymorphisms) that have been identified. Scientists believe that these SNPs will allow them eventually to identify genes associated with a variety of human diseases, including cancer, diabetes, Alzheimer's disease, and heart disease. More information about the history and results of the Human Genome Project, as well as ethical, legal, and social issues surrounding the project, is available at the United States Department of Energy's Human Genome Project Web site at

www.ornl.gov/sci/techresources/Human_Genome/home.shtml.

Genetic Mutations

Genetic mutations are changes in the nucleotide sequence of an organism's DNA. Emphasize that genetic mutations occur all the time—for example, as a result of mistakes made when DNA is copied for cell division or of exposure to mutation-causing agents in the environment. In fact, the slow accumulation of mutations is believed to be responsible for many of the effects of aging, as well as the disease cancer. Explain why a mutation in sperm or eggs is particularly significant—this type of mutation can be passed to offspring and affect every cell in the body, so it can have more impact than a mutation that affects only a single cell somewhere in the body.

Explain the different types of mutations—point mutations, nonsense mutations, and frameshift mutations—and the effects these can have on proteins. You may wish to go back to the metaphor of a gene as a sequence of words in order to help students appreciate the effects of different types of mutations (see Figure 16.21). As with so many other topics in this chapter, working problems relating to mutations can be extremely helpful. Show students a DNA sequence and a variety of potential mutations, working out the effects of each on the protein assembled.

Integrated Science—Physics: How Radioactivity Causes Genetic Mutations

Radioactivity may be far from the experience of most students, so you may wish to discuss related topics such as lab uses of radioactive isotopes, radiation therapy for cancer, x-rays, or another topic that they may be more familiar with. If you cover radiation therapy for cancer, you can describe how radiation kills cancer cells, common side effects of the therapy, and what physicians do to try to maximize effectiveness against tumor cells while minimizing damage to healthy tissues.

Cancer—Genes Gone Awry

Cancer results from sets of mutations that cause cells to divide out of control and, eventually, to migrate around the body and give rise to secondary tumors. You may wish to cover this topic in more detail, describing the wide array of genes (and therefore their functions) that are affected in advanced cancers (these include genes that contribute to unchecked cell division, as well as genes related to obtaining a plentiful blood supply for tumor cells, as well as genes that allow cells to slip into the bloodstream where they can migrate to new locations and start secondary growths). Looking ahead to Chapter 17, you might point out that at all stages in the disease, natural selection operates to "select for" the diseased cells that are best at dividing rapidly, at further infiltrating tissues, and at surviving radiation therapy and chemotherapy, causing ever more damaging cells to become more common. This is why cancer progresses.

Integrated Science—Earth Science: Environmental Causes of Cancer

Genetic and environmental effects both contribute to cancer. Examples abound. You can discuss the well-known roles of cigarette smoking in lung cancer, asbestos in mesothelioma, and ultraviolet light in skin cancer as examples of environmental risk factors. You can also discuss cancers that are caused by pathogens, including the role of *Helicobacter pylori* in stomach cancer and human papillomavirus (HPV) in cervical cancer. For genetic risk factors, you can discuss the BRCA genes that are associated with aggressive, early-onset breast cancer, the disease retinoblastoma, and the relevance of the APC gene in colon cancer.

17 The Evolution of Life

Demonstration Equipment

Images of potential bacteria fossils found in Martian meteorite

Images of organisms and their interesting adaptations (the bioluminescent lures of deep-sea anglers, mating behavior of praying mantises, and symbiotic relationship of ants and acacia trees are possible examples, but you may have others you wish to use)

Images of camouflaged peppered moths

The subject of this chapter is the origin and evolution of life. We begin with the origin of life, a subject on which there is still little consensus, though there are many ideas and many intriguing clues. We then discuss some of the major events in the history of life, including the origin of autotrophs, an oxygen-rich atmosphere, and eukaryotic cells. From there, our focus shifts to evolution. We begin with a brief history of evolutionary theory, discussing the ideas of Aristotle, Lamarck, and Darwin. Darwin's influences, including the voyage of the *Beagle* and the work of Charles Lyell and Thomas Malthus, are covered. We then delve into how natural selection actually works, focusing on how natural selection results in the evolution of adaptation. This is followed by a case study of the famous peppered moth population in industrial England. We then discuss speciation, the process through which new species arise. This is followed by a consideration of the wide-ranging evidence supporting evolutionary theory. There is a brief discussion of punctuated equilibrium and then a synopsis of the evolution of our own species, *Homo sapiens*.

In the *Practice Book*:
• Natural Selection
• Adaptation
• Speciation

In *Next-Time Questions*:
• Heritable or variable?
• Fish evolution
• Meadowlarks
• Big floppy ears

In the *Lab Manual*:
• Understanding Darwin (activity)
• Investigating Evolution (activity)

Transparencies:
Figures 17.18, 17.25, 17.37, 17.39, 17.44

Suggested Presentation

The Origin of Life

Spontaneous generation may seem like a bizarre idea to students, and so it will fascinate them that it survived for so long. The careful work required to disprove spontaneous generation is an excellent example of the scientific method. You may wish to describe both how the spontaneous generation of large-sized organisms, such as flies, and that of microscopic organisms was disproved to people's satisfaction.

You can then move on to discuss current ideas about how life originated. This issue, which for a long time seemed "settled" by the Miller and Urey experiment, is now very controversial, with arguments from those supporting a Miller–Urey-like model, an extraterrestrial (meteorite) model, and a hydrothermal vent model. This is a welcome opportunity to show students that vibrant debate is a crucial part of the scientific endeavor. Don't miss the Integrated Science feature on the possible bacterial fossils on Mars!

Integrated Science—Astronomy: Did Life on Earth Originate on Mars?

The idea that life on Earth might have come from Mars is a thrilling and audacious idea. It is, of course, highly controversial, with most scientists probably falling on the side that the evidence is not quite compelling enough, at least at present, to get too excited about. Images of the supposed fossils would certainly be helpful here.

Again, this is a good opportunity to highlight the vibrant nature of scientific research and debate. You may wish to bring up planned NASA missions to Mars and how they will continue the search for evidence that life once existed on the Red Planet.

Early Life on Earth

In this section, we review some of the important events early in the history of life. One of these is the origin of autotrophs. Emphasize that all life is ultimately dependent on autotrophs, which form the basis of food chains in all biological communities.

Another key event discussed is the origin of oxygen in Earth's atmosphere. This event is hypothesized to have caused a massive die-out of living organisms that were unable to withstand the presence of oxygen. Interestingly, there are many living organisms today that cannot survive in the presence of oxygen. These organisms are known as obligate anaerobes and include the bacteria that cause botulism and tetanus.

The First Eukaryotic Cells

The origin of the eukaryotic cell via endosymbiosis is now broadly accepted. You should outline the evidence for the theory. It may also be interesting to note in passing that the endosymbiosis of cyanobacteria to form chloroplasts may have occurred multiple times, once in the ancestor of green algae and plants, and another time in the red algae. (This is the type of seaweed used to make the Japanese delicacy *nori*.)

In addition, a small number of photosynthetic organisms today appear to have obtained their photosynthetic machinery not by engulfing cyanobacteria, but by engulfing photosynthetic eukaryotes—this is evident from the fact that the endosymbionts retain evidence of a nucleus. Finally, you may wish to point out that a wide variety of heterotrophs today harbor autotrophs in their bodies in order to take advantage of nutrients obtained via photosynthesis. These include corals (their symbiotic relationship with autotrophic dinoflagellates is described in detail in Chapter 18) and certain clams, such as giant clams.

Charles Darwin and *The Origin of Species*

For a long time, species were believed to be static and unchanging. Lamarck had considerable impact as one of the first scientists to argue strongly in favor of evolution—change over generations—and to provide a hypothesis for its mechanism. You can explain Lamarck's theory of the inheritance of acquired characteristics with the classic example of the giraffe's long neck. You may wish to ask your students, who already know something of genetics, whether that knowledge bears on whether Lamarck's argument is plausible.

The story of Darwin's voyage on the *Beagle* is a fascinating one and can be told in greater detail if time allows. Emphasize as well the roles of Lyell and Malthus in leading Darwin to his great idea. You may also wish to tell the story of Alfred Russell Wallace, who hit upon an idea similar to Darwin's idea of natural selection. In fact, it was reading a draft of Wallace's paper on the subject that finally convinced Darwin to wrap up his own work and publish. In the end, Darwin receives most of the credit for coming up with the theory of evolution both because he had the idea first and because he thought broadly and carefully about all the evidence for and implications of natural selection.

How Natural Selection Works
This section presents the meat and bones of how natural selection works. You can begin by discussing any of a number of examples that will interest students—pesticide resistance, warfarin and rats, antibiotic resistance, beak evolution in Galápagos finches during drought, or, as in the text, myxoma virus and Australian rabbits.

Natural selection should be presented carefully, step by step: variation, heritability, selection. Making drawings of the process (see, for example, Figure 17.18) is likely to be helpful for students.

Students will be very interested in the section on adaptation, which gives you the opportunity to provide as examples any of a number of organismal traits that can only be described as amazing. How about the way certain female anglers (a type of deep-sea fish) grow a glow-in-the-dark lure on their heads to attract prey (the lure contains luminescent bacteria)? Or the well-known fate of mating male praying mantises? (This example also underlines the point that it all comes down to reproduction and that, from the point of view of natural selection, survival is only a stepping stone to reproduction.) Or discuss the relationship acacia trees have evolved with ants that protect them from herbivores and competing plants (see Chapter 21 for more details on this amazing symbiosis). Use good images to really grab student attention. The possibilities are endless—and a great deal of fun to learn about!

Cover the three modes of selection—directional, stabilizing, and diversifying selection—using graphs showing how the distribution of traits in a population changes over time. There are some good real-life examples of each of these in the text.

The section on the Modern Synthesis details mutation pressure, genetic drift, and migration. Of these, genetic drift is the most conceptually difficult. Emphasize that there are many chance events in life (the cheetah doesn't always catch the slowest gazelle) and that these sometimes produce a bias that has no real "cause." The fact that flipping coins does not always yield exactly 50% heads and 50% tails is a good metaphor. (To begin with, what if you flip a coin an odd number of times? There's simply no way to get exactly 50% heads and 50% tails!)

The peppered moth is a wonderful story both of adaptation and scientific controversy. Good images will help students appreciate the importance of camouflage.

Integrated Science—Physics: Animal Adaptations to Heat and Cold
You can review surface area to volume ratios by going back to the caramel apple analogy of Chapter 15. Most students will probably be familiar with their fingers, toes, and noses getting most cold when it's chilly out, so that's a good place to start the discussion of the importance of limb length in heat regulation.

How Species Form
Countless speciation events have produced the diversity of species found on Earth. Introduce this topic by defining species and discussing many of the possible barriers to reproduction that might evolve, using examples from the text or elsewhere. Some barriers to reproduction are pre-zygotic, whereas others are post-zygotic. Emphasize that most speciation is allopatric—that is, occurs after the introduction of a geographic barrier that separates a single population into two isolated populations. Discussion and description of a few pairs of recently speciated organisms (these tend to be similar but to have evolved a distinct reproductive barrier) may help students with the concept. Examples in the text include snapping shrimp and treefrogs, among others.

Evidence of Evolution
This section provides some of the evidence supporting the idea that evolution is responsible for the diversity of life on Earth today. Examples are provided of natural selection in action; artificial selection imposed by humans; similarities in the anatomy, molecules, development, and DNA sequences of related species; the existence of anatomical intermediaries in the fossil record; and biogeographical patterns of distribution on Earth.

Integrated Science—Earth Science: Earth's Tangible Evidence of Evolution
This integrated science feature describes evidence of evolution from the fossil record and from biogeography. The intermediaries captured in the fossil record are particularly fascinating. Whales with nostrils instead of a blowhole? Birds with teeth and bony tails? Amazing! (You might add, at this point, snakes with vestigial legs—but wait! You don't have to go to the fossil record for this! Boas have little "spurs" on the underside of their bodies that are actually vestigial legs.)

Does Evolution Occur Gradually or in Spurts?
The theory of punctuated equilibrium argues that most evolutionary change occurs very rapidly and during speciation. It neither requires nor proposes a mechanism outside of Darwin's theory of evolution by natural

selection. Remember that tens of thousands of years can pass like the blink of an eye in geologic time, and processes that look sudden in the fossil record may have unfolded over quite a number of years.

The Evolution of Humans

What could be more interesting than the evolution of our own species? Use a timeline of hominid evolution to help frame the discussion of the major species. Consider discussing recent discoveries in detail, such as the discovery of *Homo floresiensis* fossils (mentioned briefly in the text) or the discovery of a nearly toothless *Homo erectus* skull—taken by some as evidence that the old and infirm were cared for—even 1.75 million years ago!

18   Biological Diversity

Demonstration Equipment

Living organisms of all types—or perhaps preserved museum specimens—to show in class, as available

Many photos of organisms

Photos or specimens of pollen, seeds, flowers

Videos on plant and animal natural history

This chapter chronicles biological diversity. A section on biological classification opens the chapter and is followed by an enjoyable introduction to all the major groups of living things—bacteria, archaea, protists, plants, fungi, and animals. Finally, attention is given to infectious agents such as viruses, viroids, and prions.

In the *Practice Book*:
• Classification
• Biological Diversity I (Bacteria, Archaea, Protists)
• Biological Diversity II (Plants, Fungi, Animals)

In *Next-Time Questions*:
• Interpreting cladograms
• Ferns
• Flatworm, roundworm, or annelid?
• The lightest and heaviest flying birds

In the *Lab Manual*:
• What Is It—Bacterium? Protist? Fungus?
• All Plants Are Not Created Equal

Transparencies:
Figures 18.2, 18.4, 18.13, 18.15, 18.34

Suggested Presentation

Classifying Living Things
This is the most conceptually challenging section in the chapter. A description of Aristotle's Chain of Being is followed by discussions of Linnaean and cladistic classification.

You may begin by describing some of the motivation for classifying organisms. It comes naturally to us to say things such as "I saw a butterfly" or "I saw a bird." Or, "There are ants in my house." The fact that these words—butterfly, bird, ant—are in common use is proof positive that these categories are useful to us. (You might ask your students to ponder, in an aside, why we go to the zoo and report "We saw a bird" or "We saw a frog" yet tend to be so much more specific about the mammals we saw—"We saw an elephant," "We saw a giraffe," etc. Interesting, isn't it?)

Biological classification carries this process further. Describe Linnaean classification, emphasizing its hierarchical nature. That is, two species that belong in the same family are always also in the same order, the same class, the same phylum, the same kingdom, and the same domain. Spend some time going over the Linnaean levels of classification, looking at several examples. You might point out to students that whereas species are objectively "real" entities (populations of interbreeding organisms, as we saw in Chapter 17), all biological groups larger than species are, to some extent, arbitrary in that we have named them because having these names is useful to us (or at least to some biologist somewhere).

Once Linnaean classification is well understood, point out some of the problems with it. For example, the "shared similarity" upon which Linnaean classification is based is to some degree arbitrary. Who's to say that a dolphin is more similar to dogs, shrews, humans, and other mammals than it is to salmon and bass and tuna? Another way in which Linnaean classification is arbitrary is in the assignment of levels to biological groups. Why should mammals be a class rather than an order? Why should frogs be an order rather than a family?

Linnaean classification is most problematic, however, insofar as it sometimes obscures the evolutionary relationships among species. This leads us into the discussion of cladistic classification.

Cladistics is a method of biological classification that groups species together based on evolution. Begin by introducing the notion of an evolutionary tree and explaining how it relates to past speciation events. Show students how a tree can be used to determine whether certain species are more closely related to one another than to other species, and how this is used as the basis of classification.

If you wish, you can mention that, as with all scientific revolutions, there was some controversy surrounding cladistic classification when it first was proposed. (It is now generally widely accepted.) The specific example of birds as reptiles and birds as dinosaurs (used in the text) was particularly contentious. Many people really couldn't stand to associate those warm-blooded feathery things with those scaly creatures. (Do you think it has something to do with we mammals being warm-blooded and covered with hair?) Anyhow, certain ornithologists were vocal in their opposition to birds being considered reptiles. And dinosaur-lovers too, tend not to appreciate the argument that birds are dinosaurs. Anyway, there is now lots of research aimed at reconstructing the evolutionary relationships of different groups of living organisms.

The Three Domains of Life
The three domains of life are the bacteria, the archaea, and the eukarya. A key point to take away is that certain prokaryotes—the archaea—are more closely related to eukaryotes (that's right, to onions and mushrooms and human beings) than they are to bacteria, odd as that may seem at first glance.

Bacteria
Many students are probably most familiar with bacteria as disease-causing organisms. So, a major goal here should be to emphasize the diverse roles bacteria play in ecosystems.

Archaea
Archaea are fascinating for many reasons. The extremophiles are found in really unusual Earth environments— hot hydrothermal vents, hot springs, salty pools—and are hypothesized to have retained these habits from when the Earth was relatively young. For this reason, scientists are looking to them for clues on the origin of life. Hydrothermal vent archaea are of particular interest now that hydrothermal vents have been pinpointed as a potential origination site for life (Chapter 17).

Protists
Protist classification is an ongoing effort. This group contains a wide variety of organisms, all eukaryotes. Emphasize the diversity within the group—there are autotrophs and heterotrophs, many unicellular species and some multicellular ones as well. Within the group, the closest relatives of plants and animals have been identified.

You may wish to spend some time on slime molds, which will probably be new to most students. These creatures are particularly interesting because they can move between single-celled and multicellular over the course of their lives. In cellular slime molds, single-celled individuals exist independently most of the time. When conditions become unfavorable, however, individual cells come together to form a multicellular aggregation that looks and moves like a large slug. The slug then develops a reproductive structure that consists of a stalk and a cap, and the cap releases spores that later "hatch" into independent slime mold cells. Scientists have shown that there is fierce competition among aggregating cells to become the cap cells in the reproductive structure, which reproduce, rather than the stalk cells, which do not. The cost of this competition in the multicellular slug may explain why the vast majority of multicellular organisms, including humans, are clonal—that is, all our cells have the exact same DNA, because we all develop from a single cell. This makes the fierce competition among cells to pass on genes unnecessary. Lucky for us!

Plants

Students will be pretty familiar with plants, so the emphasis is on explaining the basics of plant anatomy, discussing how plants "make their living" (that is, obtain what they need for photosynthesis), and describing the major groups of plants.

Understanding alternation of generations is essential to understanding how plants reproduce. This topic is fairly complex, with the alternation between haploid and diploid, gametophyte and sporophyte. The subject is further complicated by the fact that each of the major groups of plants has its own unique version of this life cycle. Spend some time comparing the life cycles of mosses, ferns, and seed plants.

Emphasize the tremendous diversity of seed plants and, particularly, flowering plants, discussing the adaptations (pollen and seeds in all seed plants, flowers and fruit in flowering plants only) that have made their success possible. Emphasize the importance of insects and other animal pollinators in the life cycle of many flowering plants. A discussion of the coevolution of plants and pollinators can be extremely illuminating about how evolution and adaptation occur. The relationship between plant and pollinator may appear to be, on the one hand, a mutualism that benefits both species, and yet, at the same time, an arms race in which each member of the interaction tries to gain an advantage over the other. Examples of plants that appear to have gotten the better of their pollinators include the dragon orchid, which mimics the appearance and "smell" (pheromones) of female wasps in order to attract male wasp pollinators, and the dead horse arum lily (described briefly in the text), which attracts flies with its foul odor and them traps them with stiff guard hairs before dusting them with pollen and then releasing them. Amazing stuff!

Students are also likely to enjoy a brief discussion of parasitic plants—plants that parasitize other plants—as well as those fascinating insect-catching plants. Again, good pictures are a must.

Finally, you might consider showing a nature documentary focusing on plant life. Consider David Attenborough's PBS series "The Private Life of Plants."

Fungi

Students are likely to have some familiarity with fungi, primarily, perhaps, in their experiences with mold on food. Mushrooms, of course, will also be familiar. Emphasize that fungi are heterotrophs. Instead of moving after their food, as so many animals do, fungi grow over their food, or make spores that search out food and then eat it when they find it. Be sure to point out how fascinating it is that these two groups of heterotrophs, fungi and animals, have evolved such different ways of obtaining food.

Students may be also interested to know that there are actually some actively predatory fungi! No, they won't chase *you* down baring teeth. Some predatory fungi secrete sticky substances that they use to trap small worms or insects. Perhaps more interesting are the fungi that produce small "nooses"—loops of tissue that rapidly swell when their inner surfaces are brushed by passing roundworms, which are then caught and digested.

Animals

Animals are a very diverse group. Begin by emphasizing the traits all animals have in common—multicellularity and a heterotrophic feeding strategy. Then describe each of the major groups of animals, focusing on basic anatomy and feeding strategy. Bring in organisms to show if available, or direct students to local zoos or aquaria. There are also a huge number of interesting nature documentaries that focus on the natural history of animals. Consider in particular David Attenborough's PBS series "The Life of Birds" and "The Life of Mammals."

Integrated Science—Earth Science: Coral Bleaching

Coral bleaching is expected to become more common and more devastating as Earth warms. This feature integrates biology with climate, explaining bleaching as the result of toxins that build up during photosynthesis when seawater temperatures are unusually high. This is also an opportunity to explore in greater detail the remarkable mutualistic relationship between corals and photosynthetic dinoflagellates and to consider the effects of global warming on one particular ecosystem. (See the text for descriptions of how coral habitats may need to shift and grow, and how the composition of species may change if warming continues.)

There are also opportunities here for relating science to society, because mass coral bleachings are the result of global warming. Emphasize the importance of coral reefs—not only are they home to over a million species, but they also bring substantial economic benefits to many people through fisheries, tourism, and recreation and help protect coastal areas against waves, storms, and floods.

Integrated Science—Physics: How Birds Fly

This feature looks at the physics of flying. You may wish to show videos of flying birds, perhaps comparing and contrasting the abilities of small birds (such as hummingbirds) with large ones (such as eagles and vultures)—the latter, in fact, often spend the bulk of their time soaring.

Viruses and Infectious Molecules

Viruses are probably the only entities on Earth that aren't definitely either living or nonliving. It's not a matter of collecting more information about them—it's just that they really do sit on the fence. Viruses have genes, made either of DNA or RNA, and they evolve. But they are not made of cells, and they can only reproduce inside a host cell. So far as is known, viruses are never good for their hosts.

You will likely want to describe a few viruses. The AIDS virus is an obvious one, because of the great impact that disease continues to have on the world.

Viroids are simpler than viruses in that they are just molecules of RNA. They cause diseases in plants, spreading through pollen or seeds.

Prions are misfolded proteins. They are responsible for "mad cow" disease and its related human version, Creutzfeldt–Jakob disease. The idea that a protein could cause disease was controversial when first proposed—how can anything reproduce without a genome? It turns out that prions can make copies of themselves by converting normally folded proteins to the misfolded, prion variety—a Dr. Jekyll to Mr. Hyde transformation, if there ever was one. In addition to mad cow disease and Creutzfeldt–Jakob disease, prions are believed to be responsible for scrapie, a disease in sheep first seen in Iceland in the 18th century, and kuru, a disease affecting cannibalistic human societies in New Guinea. A Nobel prize was awarded in 1997 to Stanley Prusiner for his discovery of prions and his work on them.

19   Human Biology I—Control and Development

Demonstration Equipment

Models of sense organs, particularly the eye and ear

Models of human reproductive systems

Models of the human body, showing the skeleton and/or muscles

This chapter covers control and development of the human body. After introducing the concepts of tissues, organs, and organ systems, five major body systems are covered. These are the nervous system, sensory systems, endocrine system, reproductive systems, and musculoskeletal system.

In the *Practice Book*:
• The Nervous System
• Senses
• Skeleton and Muscles

In *Next-Time Questions*:
• What time is it?
• The action potential
• Looking for faint stars
• Events in muscle contraction

In the *Lab Manual*:
• The Amazing Senses
• Muscles and Bones

Transparencies:
Figures 19.3, 19.7, 19.14, 19.19, 19.30

Suggested Presentation

Organization of the Human Body
Introduce the concepts of tissues, organs, and organ systems, using several examples from the human body. Tissues include things like skin, muscle, and nervous tissue. Organs include the heart, lungs, liver, pancreas, and so forth. Organ systems are those that are considered in this and the following chapter—nervous, endocrine, reproductive, sensory, musculoskeletal, circulatory, respiratory, digestive, excretory, and immune systems.

Homeostasis
Remind students that maintaining a relatively stable internal environment is one of the key features of living things. Water balance is a good example to use in class. Students have no doubt noticed that sometimes they feel thirsty—the body's signal that it needs more water. Students are also likely to have noticed that the color of their urine varies. You can explain that this is because we excrete a more watery, dilute urine when our bodies have excess water to get rid of, and a darker, more concentrated urine when our bodies need to conserve water.

Temperature regulation is another good example to discuss in class. Everyone knows about 98.6, and all have no doubt experienced shivering, sweating, and the desire to put on or remove clothes. You can also discuss changing patterns of blood flow, which account for cold fingers, toes, and nose tips, as well as warm, red faces.

The Brain
A good way to begin is with the story of Phineas Gage, which is perhaps one of the most famous stories in medicine. Gage was a 26-year-old railroad worker, thoughtful, intelligent, and well-liked by everyone. A workplace explosion drove a 3-foot-long iron rod through his left cheekbone and out his skull. Miraculously, Gage survived. His memory was intact, as were his motor and language skills. However, he emerged from the accident an entirely different man—his friends described him as "no longer himself." Gage became rude when he was formerly polite, often failed to observe social conventions, and seemed unable to think ahead or formulate plans. It turned out that Gage had injured the very front part of his brain.

Injuries to the brain—through accidents as well as strokes and other conditions—have helped us gain knowledge about the roles of different parts of the brain. These days, techniques such as functional magnetic resonance imaging (see technology box on this topic) allow for even more precise experiments.

Describe the different parts of the brain and the functions that each is responsible for. You may wish to assign groups of students different parts of the brain and have them think about which bodily activities would be impaired by damage to that part of the brain.

The Nervous System
This section introduces the different parts of the nervous system. There is a fair amount of new terminology. You can help motivate students by providing examples of different activities (seeing a stop sign, kicking a ball, tasting a strawberry, etc.) and having them think about what parts of the nervous system are involved, and how. Are sensory neurons involved? Or motor neurons? If motor neurons, do they belong to the somatic or autonomic nervous systems? If autonomic, are they part of the sympathetic or parasympathetic divisions?

How Neurons Work
This is a comparatively challenging section describing how neurons fire and how neuronal signals are propagated. Begin by explaining basic facts about action potentials—they are electric signals, and they are all-or-nothing events. Neurons can convey the intensity of a particular signal by firing frequently, however.

Then, describe the membrane potential of a neuron, and carefully outline the sequence of events in an action potential. You may wish to review the sodium-potassium pump, which was described in Chapter 15, and remind students that some membrane proteins act as carrier proteins for molecules that cannot move directly across the cell membrane—including ions. Some students may find it useful to trace the events that occur during an action potential using a graph of membrane potential over time.

After students have grasped how action potentials work, you can move on to how action potentials are propagated along axons. The metaphor of a row of dominoes may be useful—the axon is like a row of dominoes, and the action potential begins at one end, moving along the axon toward its end the way a falling domino knocks over the next domino, which knocks over the next, and so forth, until the entire row of dominoes has fallen.

Discuss the role of myelin sheaths in speeding axonal propagation.

Describe the two types of synapses, focusing on the advantages and disadvantages of each. Explain that most synapses in the nervous system are chemical synapses. These topics will allow you to review some cell structures and processes covered in Chapter 15. Electric synapses make use of gap junctions between cells. Chemical synapses make use of vesicles containing neurotransmitters that are released through the process of exocytosis. The neurotransmitters bind to receptors, a classic instance of cell signaling.

Integrated Science—Physics: How Fast Can Action Potentials Travel?
This feature uses physics to explain why action potentials travel faster through thicker axons than thinner ones, as well as why myelin sheaths allow action potentials to travel more quickly. Those without the necessary physics background will, nevertheless, be able to appreciate the repeated evolution of giant axons in numerous independent lineages, as well as the fact that myelin and giant axons are two evolutionary solutions to the same "problem."

Integrated Science—Chemistry: Endorphins
This is a fun feature on endorphins, the body's natural opiates.

The Senses
All the senses do the same thing—translate stimuli from the environment into action potentials that the brain can understand. Each sense does this in a different way.

For your discussion of vision and the eyes, a large model of the parts of the eye may be useful. If this is not available, it is useful to draw a model on the board and have students draw along as well. Describe the path of light and the function of each part of the eye. Describe the sensory cells of the eyes, the rods and the cones. You can quiz students on what types of visual activity make use of rods and which make use of cones.

Students may also be interested in a little comparative anatomy of the eye. Why are the retinas of nocturnal animals made up exclusively of rods? (This has evolved to maximize their ability to see in dim light.) Why do cats have that distinctive cat's-eye pupil shape? (Again, this is related to their nocturnal habits—their irises open like curtains sliding apart at night in order to let in as much light as possible.) Why do many birds have so many more cones per unit area than humans? (It is probably related to the need for sharp vision in a flying animal. Predatory birds such as hawks, which detect tiny prey from high in the air, have a particularly high cone density.)

For your discussion of the ear, again focus on tracing the path of sound describing the function of each part of the ear. Again, a little comparative anatomy may be interesting. For example, mammals are the only group of vertebrates that have three middle ear bones. Other terrestrial vertebrates have only the stirrup. Amazingly enough, the hammer and anvil of mammals evolved from jaw bones!

Smell and taste are examples of chemoreception. You will want to point out parallels between chemoreception and the general model of receptor-based signaling (of which neurotransmitters were a recently discussed example). Humans have a relatively weak sense of smell compared to most mammals—the superiority of the dog (think of bloodhounds, drug-sniffing dogs at airports, truffle-hunting dogs, etc.) is probably familiar to most people.

Students will probably be familiar with "touch" as one of the five senses but may not have thought carefully about what this sense is. You can describe pressure, temperature, and pain receptors in body tissues.

The proprioceptors are something students may not have heard of and probably take for granted! Have them touch their noses with their eyes shut or tie their shoes with their eyes shut. Impressive, isn't it?

The vestibular senses, which tell us whether we are rotating or accelerating, are also ones students may not realize they have. However, they no doubt are familiar with what happens when they turn quickly around and around and around—dizziness is a consequence of the vestibular sense. Basically, the sense organs tell the brain that we're still moving when we've already stopped, with the result that we feel dizzy.

Hormones
Testosterone may be a good topic with which to introduce the subject of hormones. It is a hormone most students will have heard of, with both physical and behavioral effects. In human males, there are a number of testosterone bursts during life—a prenatal burst causes the development of male genitalia, an early infancy burst has still unknown effects but is hypothesized by some to be associated with "brain masculinization," and another burst occurs during puberty. Testosterone is associated with aggressive behavior in numerous species. In addition, you can discuss anabolic steroids, which are synthetic forms of testosterone used by some athletes to build muscle mass.

Describe the differences between protein hormones and steroid hormones, emphasizing differences in chemical structure and mode of function.

Finally, you can describe major endocrine organs and the hormones they produce. Emphasize the role hormones play in homeostasis, noting how they are often found in pairs with opposing effects. Insulin and glucagon provide an ideal example for examining how this works.

Reproduction and Development
You may wish to begin by reviewing the role of meiosis in producing haploid gametes: eggs in women and sperm in men. Describe female reproductive anatomy, the menstrual cycle, and ovulation, and then move on to male reproductive anatomy and spermatogenesis. Describe the events surrounding fertilization and early development, and outline the major events of pregnancy.

If you have time to cover supplementary topics, students may be interested in hearing about advances in reproductive technology, such as the nuts and bolts of in vitro fertilization.

The Skeleton and Muscles
The primary functions of the skeleton are support and protection. Give students multiple examples of each. Also describe how the muscles and skeleton work together to allow us to move.

Spend some time going over muscle contraction, a topic that is sometimes challenging for students. As with teaching about action potentials, list and illustrate the steps one at a time.

20   Human Biology II—Care and Maintenance

Demonstration Equipment

Model of the heart or of the heart and lungs

Working model of the lungs made from three balloons and some tubing (see respiration section below)

Model of the digestive system

This chapter continues our coverage of the human body, examining circulation, respiration, digestion, excretion, and defense.

In the *Practice Book*:
- Circulatory System
- Respiration, Digestion
- Excretory System, Immune System

In *Next-Time Questions*:
- Four chambers
- A hole in the thoracic cavity
- How the filtrate moves through the excretory system
- "Y" are antibodies so good at defending the body from pathogens?

In the *Lab Manual*:
- Keep Pumping
- Breathe In, Breathe Out

Transparencies:
Figures 20.4, 20.9, 20.20, 20.22.

Suggested Presentation

Integration of Body Systems
You can demonstrate how almost any activity of the body requires the integrated effort of multiple body systems. Almost any activity, for example, relies on nervous system control, oxygen from the circulatory and respiratory systems, and energy obtained through digestion.

One of the most impressive examples of body system integration comes from temperature regulation. In humans, this is the maintenance of a high, stable body temperature somewhere around 98.6 degrees Fahrenheit. This is our body temperature whether it's the peak of summer and 110 degrees outside or the middle of winter and −5 degrees outside—a remarkable instance of homeostasis. How does the body do it? With the help of lots of different body systems. The muscles shiver when we're cold, releasing heat to warm us up. The skin sweats when we're hot, allowing us to lose heat through evaporation. The circulatory system is a major player—it sends blood to different parts of the body depending on whether we need to save heat or shed it. When we're cold, less blood goes to the extremities, which lose heat faster than the core of the body. (This is why fingers and toes are most prone to frostbite.) When we're hot, more blood goes to the extremities and to the face, which is good at shedding heat (this is why our faces get red in hot weather). Stress hormones from the adrenal gland and thyroid hormones increase body temperature by increasing our metabolic rate. Finally, there are all our behavioral reactions, the conscious activities discomfort drives us to—wrapping our arms around our body when we're cold, fanning ourselves when we're hot, putting on or taking off clothes, seeking shade or cover—these actions require the cooperation of the senses, the nervous system, and the muscles and skeleton. And, of course, it's the senses that tell us if we're cold or hot in the first place, and the nervous system that coordinates all the body's responses.

The Circulatory System

You can begin your discussion of the circulatory system with the heart. Describe the heart's ceaseless activity—it's stunning how quickly the number of heartbeats adds up—over 100,000 in a single day! Have your students clench their fists and relax, clench and relax, over and over again, and imagine doing that nonstop for 80 years—that's what the heart does! You can also have students feel their pulses and measure their heart rates. Describe the anatomy of the heart, using a model if available. You can have students think about the advantages of a four-chambered heart. Why do you need atria at all? (It's more efficient if blood can continue to flow in and be collected in the heart while the previous load is being pumped.) What is the advantage of having separate left and right ventricles? (The deoxygenated blood returning from the body doesn't mix with the oxygenated blood returning from the lungs.) A bit of comparative anatomy could be useful here—is it a coincidence that only the endotherms (birds and mammals) evolved four-chambered hearts? Might it have something to do with their rapid metabolism, which makes efficient circulation of oxygen essential?

Describe the different types of blood vessels and the path of blood flow around the body. Note the anatomical differences between the different types of blood vessels and how each type is suited to its function.

Describe the content of blood, including both its cellular and noncellular components. Describe how blood clotting occurs.

If you have time to cover supplementary topics, consider talking about heart disease—still the #1 killer in the United States. You can describe what happens during a heart attack and talk about treatments such as bypass surgeries, angioplasty, and so forth.

Integrated Science—Chemistry: Hemoglobin

This integrated science feature describes the chemical structure of hemoglobin. It also delves into some of the ways hemoglobin is particularly well suited to transporting oxygen to body tissues. Many students will be amazed to learn that the molecule actually changes in adaptive ways under different environmental conditions.

Respiration

Begin by emphasizing the importance of respiration. Four minutes without oxygen, and the brain, which is dependent on the continuous breakdown of glucose for ATP, suffers irreparable damage. This is what CPR and the Heimlich maneuver are all about—ways for people to intervene before the four minutes are up, and often before professional help is able to arrive. Learn these techniques and maybe one day you'll save a life!

You can then describe the anatomy of the respiratory system, focusing on the pathway of air into and out of the body. You can also build a very simple model of how inhalation and exhalation work by connecting two balloons (representing lungs) to some tubing (representing trachea and bronchi). These are placed in a plastic cylinder with the top sealed except for the exiting "trachea." A third balloon is stretched over the bottom of the cylinder and represents the diaphragm. Pulling down on the diaphragm-balloon causes the "lungs" to inflate. Letting go of the diaphragm-balloon is akin to the relaxation of the diaphragm and causes the lungs to deflate.

Digestion

You might consider beginning your discussion of the digestive system by describing the work of William Beaumont, sometimes called the "Father of Gastric Physiology." Beaumont learned a great deal about digestion from his work on Alexis St. Martin, a man who had been shot accidentally in the stomach and who defied expectation by surviving. After recovering, St. Martin retained a permanent hole in his stomach. Beaumont conducted experiments in digestion by tying pieces of food to strings and inserting them into St. Martin's stomach. He could then remove the food and make observations on their digestion. Beaumont also collected gastric acid from St. Martin's stomach and watched it digest food *in vitro*.

Describe the path of food through the digestive system, explaining what happens at each step. One way to help students engage actively with this material is to have them discuss what they would find if they took samples at various points along the digestive tract.

110

Nutrition, Exercise, and Health

This brief discussion of nutrition, exercise, and health describes some of the nutrients humans require and provides suggestions for a healthy diet and lifestyle.

You might open this topic with descriptions of scurvy, a horrific disease that at one time killed sailors with great frequency. Symptoms of scurvy include skin bruises, spongy gums, joint pain, and weakness. It is caused by a deficiency of vitamin C. Once the connection between scurvy and vitamin C was clear, long-lasting lemons and limes became a feature of every sea voyage. (This last fact apparently explains the origin of the word "limey" to describe sailors.)

The importance of vitamin A to vision (among many other body functions) may also be interesting to students, who have probably heard all their lives that "carrots are good for the eyes." The importance of adequate vitamin A intake also explains why it is frequently added to milk, something your students will likely remember when you bring it up. You may also wish to tell students that in the developing world, as many as half a million children go blind each year because of inadequate vitamin A intake. If you have time, you can also describe the development of "golden rice," a strain of rice genetically engineered to provide vitamin A to these populations. As a genetically modified food, golden rice continues to be mired in controversy.

Integrated Science—Physics and Chemistry: Low-Carb Versus Low-Cal Diets

This integrated science feature takes on the topic of low carb diets, still very much in vogue today. The material is interesting and relatively straightforward. Students will learn what low-carb diets are, that they are, in fact, helpful for many people who are trying to lose weight, and some of the potential pitfalls of these diets.

Excretion and Water Balance

The kidneys are remarkable organs. They filter blood nonstop, removing wastes and returning valuable substances to the bloodstream. Your focus should be on how the filtrate moves through the nephron—how blood plasma goes in and urine comes out. Describe the structure and function of each part of the nephron. How water reabsorption occurs in the loop of Henle and collecting duct is probably the most challenging part of the process to understand and should be described with some care. This may require a quick review of osmosis and diffusion.

If you have enough time, you might mention kidney disease and dialysis. The complexity of dialysis should give students a great appreciation for what the kidney does.

Keeping the Body Safe: Defense Systems

The body has a diverse array of defenses against potential pathogens. A possible way to begin this section is to talk about AIDS, a disease that has had, and continues to have, a terrible impact on the world. By weakening the immune-system, the HIV virus makes the body vulnerable to a wide variety of infections it would normally fight off easily, as well as to many types of tumors. Other immune-system-related diseases, including well-known autoimmune diseases such as lupus, Type I diabetes, rheumatoid arthritis, and multiple sclerosis, may also be interesting to students.

In your discussion of the immune system, begin with the distinction between innate and acquired immunity. List the major players in each type of immunity and describe their functions in protecting the body from disease. Then focus on differences between innate and acquired immunity.

Spend some time describing how vaccines work, a topic which most students will enjoy. You can begin by telling the story of smallpox. After describing the disease and its devastating effects (including in the Americas, where it killed huge numbers of Native Americans after being introduced by explorers), you can discuss the history of strategies for dealing with the disease. First came the technique of variolation, in which healthy people were inoculated with pus from people who had suffered mild cases of smallpox. They typically developed a relatively mild form of the disease, with much lower death rates than those who acquired smallpox in the usual way (by inhalation). Then, the physician Edward Jenner made use of the widely known fact that milkmaids who caught cowpox, a mild related disease, appeared to be immune to smallpox (in fact, the word "vaccine" comes from the Latin word for cow, *vacca*). Later vaccines made use not of cowpox, but of a different virus (probably a very weakened form of the smallpox virus itself)—however, the concept remains the same. The availability of an effective vaccine eventually allowed smallpox to be eliminated from the world—although it still exists in a few scientific laboratories.

21   **Ecosystems and Environment**

Demonstration Equipment

Photos of world biomes

This chapter describes the interactions of organisms with their environments—that is, the study of ecology. The chapter opens with an introduction to the different levels of ecological study—individuals, populations, communities, and ecosystems. Then, a section on species interactions covers the most important types of interactions between species—food chains, competition, and symbiosis. We then move on to the energetics of ecosystems, tracing the flow of energy up trophic levels. This is followed by descriptions of the major types of terrestrial and aquatic ecosystems on Earth. Biogeochemical cycles are covered, with an emphasis on water, carbon, and nitrogen. A section on ecological succession discusses primary succession, secondary succession, and the relationship between habitat disturbance and biodiversity. Finally, population studies are introduced. We look at exponential and logistic models of population growth, different life history strategies in different populations of organisms, and the history of human population growth.

In the *Practice Book*:
* Species Interactions
* Ecosystems
* Populations

In *Next-Time Questions*:
* Starlings
* Female-mimicking orchids and their pollinators
* Pesky pests and endangered species
* Survivorship curves

In the *Lab Manual*:
* Prey Versus Predators
* Ecological Footprints

Transparencies:
Figures 21.4, 21.24, 21.28, 21.33, 21.36

Suggested Presentation

Organisms and Their Environment
Give students some idea of the huge breadth of things involved when we refer to an organism's environment. Define abiotic and biotic, and have them describe some of the abiotic and biotic features of their own environment. Biotic features include other people, obviously, but also dogs, birds, worms, mold, mosquitoes, and pathogenic bacteria and viruses.

Then introduce the various levels of study within ecology—the individual, population, community, and ecosystem levels. Provide abundant examples of each. In order to reinforce these concepts, you might consider breaking students into small groups and having them devise research questions (perhaps pertaining to local fauna and flora) at each of these levels.

Species Interactions

Species interactions are interactions between members of *different* species—not interactions between members of the *same* species. (This may be particularly confusing when discussing competition. Competition, of course, occurs between members of the same species as well—in fact, this intraspecific form of competition is usually much stronger than interspecific competition and often drives evolution and natural selection.)

The first type of species interaction covered concerns who eats whom. A good class exercise is to diagram some part of the human food chain. What do we eat? A variety of fruits and vegetables, as well as animals such as chickens and cows and various fishes. What do these organisms eat? Students will enjoy helping you construct this food chain in class. Once you have diagrammed the food chain, you can bring in trophic levels, describing producers, primary consumers, secondary consumers, and so forth. You will want to point out that humans actually eat at many different trophic levels.

The second type of species interaction discussed is competition. Be sure to point out in your discussion that species compete with one another any time they use the same limited resource. Direct interactions are not required. For example, a nocturnal seed-eater and a diurnal seed-eater may never encounter one another because of their different schedules. However, one species' dining reduces the amount of food that is available to the other species, and so they are in competition.

The third type of species interaction considered is symbiosis, a close relationship between two species. There are spectacular examples of parasitism and mutualism in the world. Here is your chance to wow students with natural history.

Some interesting examples of parasitism that you might consider describing in detail include tapeworms, which parasitize vertebrates, and *Rafflesia,* a flowering plant that makes gigantic flowers as large as a meter across. Another aspect of parasitism that is likely to fascinate students is that some parasites actually affect the behavior of their hosts in a way that helps them move through their life cycle. This is particularly true in parasites that require multiple hosts. For example, a parasitic fluke that uses fish as an intermediate host makes the fish jump around, so that it is more noticeable to the fish-eating birds that are the parasite's final host. Or, another fluke that uses an ant as an intermediate host causes the ant to crawl up a blade of grass and attach itself there, so that it is more likely to be eaten by a cow, the fluke's final host. Of course, we are all familiar with pathogens (which are also parasites) that cause us to spread them through coughing, sneezing, and diarrhea.

As for mutualism, consider telling the ant–acacia story in detail. Or, describe the mutualistic relationship between certain species of ants and caterpillars. The caterpillars produce a "honeydew" that the ants eat. In return, the ants protect the caterpillars from parasites.

Energy Flow in Ecosystems

This section covers the flow of energy in ecosystems. Energy comes from the sun, is converted to biomass by producers during photosynthesis, and then moves up the food chain. Emphasize the loss of energy as you move up trophic levels. This is due to the fact that not all the organisms at one trophic level get eaten by organisms at the next trophic level, and to the fact that energy is also lost to feces or used as maintenance. Only what remains after those things take their share is converted to biomass via growth and reproduction.

You can make this more concrete for students by asking them how much food they eat—how many pounds a day, between breakfast, lunch, and dinner? What happens to all that food? If they eat 20 pounds of food in a week, do they gain 20 pounds of weight? Does eating 8 pounds of food allow you to produce an 8-pound baby? In both cases, decidedly not! A lot of the energy is lost as heat, something we will discuss further in the integrated science feature "Energy Leaks Where Trophic Levels Meet." Some of the energy is used to fuel activity—breathing, circulation, excretion, walking to class, taking notes, thinking, seeing, and so forth. Some of it is lost in feces. And perhaps some does go to building biomass in the form of weight gain or reproduction, but not always.

Integrated Science—Physics: Energy Leaks Where Trophic Levels Meet

This integrated science feature looks more closely at energy leakage between trophic levels. The Second Law of Thermodynamics states that natural systems tend to move from organized energy states to disorganized energy states—that is, useful energy dissipates to unusable energy. This explains why so much of the energy organisms obtain from food is lost as heat. The example of breaking down glucose to make ATP is used to emphasize the point. You may want to add that endotherms need a lot more food than ectotherms, because they need constant fuel to burn in order to release the heat that maintains their high body temperatures. Anyone who has kept both an endotherm (such as a dog or a cat) and an ectotherm (such as a lizard or a frog) as a pet will know this well.

Kinds of Ecosystems
This section goes through major types of terrestrial and aquatic ecosystems one by one. Students may find this material overwhelming because of the large number of ecosystems. Stick to the most important features of each type of ecosystem, including, perhaps, climate and rainfall regime, major types or features of plant life, and level of biodiversity. Showing photographs of the same biome in different parts of the world (for example, Southeast Asian rain forest and South American rain forest) will help students appreciate the convergent evolution of similar types of life forms in completely different parts of the world.

Integrated Science—Earth Science: Materials Cycling in Ecosystems
This integrated science topic covers biogeochemical cycles. Begin by describing what all biogeochemical cycles have in common—the cycling between biotic and abiotic reservoirs. Then, cover each cycle in detail. Be sure students know how water, carbon, and nitrogen each move from the abiotic world to the biotic world and back. You may wish to spend time discussing fossil fuels, the carbon cycle, and global warming.

Change in an Ecosystem
Krakatoa is a wonderful story of ecological succession that can be told in detail in class. Emphasize the order in which species successfully colonized the island and the time it took for Krakatoa to return to its climax community of tropical forest. Define primary and secondary succession, and provide generalities regarding early vs. late colonizers of a disturbed habitat. Explain the intermediate disturbance hypothesis.

Population Studies
Some students may find this section on population studies challenging. In several places, it requires the ability to interpret graphs. Begin by reviewing the concept of a population. Then discuss population growth, emphasizing that exponential and logistic growth are useful models only. Not all populations will grow in ways that resemble these models. Describe circumstances under which exponential growth and logistic growth are expected to occur. Discuss the text's examples of each type of growth or offer other examples, using graphs of population size over time. It may be useful for students to think of exponential growth as corresponding to a J-shaped curve and logistic growth as corresponding to an S-shaped curve. Appendix D in the text offers additional information on exponential growth that you may find useful in explaining the concept.

In order to show students that many other types of population growth are possible, consider showing graphs of lynx–rabbit oscillations.

Students will be very interested in the strategies of r-selected vs. K-selected organisms. A variety of examples are possible. If you wish, you can use examples in birds, discussing differences between the clutch sizes of precocial species such as ducks and altricial species such as songbirds. Or, you can give particular attention to species that raise a very small number of chicks each year. These include penguins and albatrosses. What factors might play into small clutch size in those species? In your examples, emphasize how different reproductive strategies are advantageous to different organisms.

When you discuss survivorship curves, you may wish to use graphs of human survivorship curves in different countries or at different times. These illustrate the tremendous impact of modern medicine on death rates, particularly early in life. An example is shown in the exercises section at the end of the chapter in the text. Did humans always have a Type I survivorship curve?

Human Population Growth
Human population growth is an exciting topic these days, particularly because of the recent realization that human population is no longer growing exponentially. It is believed that human population will never double again and will settle in at somewhere around 10 billion soon after the year 2050. Remarkable!

22 Plate Tectonics

Demonstration Equipment

Slinky®

Hot water bottle or inflatable mattress

Students will easily see that the theory of plate tectonics rests on a firm foundation of physics. Integration is inevitable. Physics concepts are reviewed here (or if less than completely reviewed, they are referenced). Your class can, therefore, begin the study of plate tectonics at any time, independent of how much physics you have covered previously.

Plate tectonics can impart a conception of the Earth as a large but simple system. It's fascinating to see concepts of physics—from convection to density to gravity—playing out on this big ball we all live on. We hope that your students will grasp this overall picture of the Earth, as a dynamic physical system that is ever demonstrating physical laws in action. Of secondary importance are the details of plate tectonics (which are quite marvelous in their own right) and the extensive history of science this chapter entails.

This chapter develops the theory of plate tectonics semi-historically. Plate tectonics lends itself to a historical treatment, because the underlying concepts trend from simple to complex in a roughly chronological sequence. We present seismic waves and the turn-of-the-century pioneers of seismology first, then move on to continental drift and Alfred Wegener, then World War II–era Harry Hess and seafloor spreading, then finally we discuss the confirming studies of magnetic striping, and the articulation of a cohesive theory of plate tectonics in the 1960s.

In the *Practice Book*:
• Faults
• Structural Geology
• Plate Boundaries
• Seafloor Spreading
• Plate Boundaries and Magma Generation

In *Next-Time Questions*:
• Natural Hot Spring
• Continental Crust Thickness

Transparencies:
Figures 22.6, 22.16, 22.17, 22.22, 22.23, 22.24, 22.32

Suggested Presentation

Earth Science Before the Twentieth Century

Acquaint your students with highlights in the history of earth science with this introductory section. In reading Section 22.1, students will get a first look at the diversity of earth science topics. This would be a good time to explain how broad a field earth science is. Name some of its many subdisciplines: geology, geochemistry, geophysics, meteorology, mineralogy, petrolology, atmospheric physics and chemistry, geography, geomorphology, paleontology, and so forth. Tell your students they will get a taste of each of these in their studies of *Conceptual Integrated Science*.

To whet students' interest for earth science, you might write a chart on the chalkboard with two headings: *What I Know About Earth Science* and *Things I Want to Know About Earth Science*. Brainstorm entries to the chart. Or ask students to write their own chart and fill it out themselves. Discuss charts in small groups or as an entire group. Then follow through by addressing students' questions as you teach this unit. Students will appreciate you being responsive to their needs! If you can't answer all the questions students have in the course of your teaching, try to direct the students to the resources that will.

The salient point of Section 22.1 is how recent our knowledge of Earth's interior is. Call students' attention to the insight exclaiming that there were cars and a baseball world series before we knew the Earth has layers. It is remarkable how far our understanding of the Earth's interior has come in a hundred years—thanks to plate tectonics. And plate tectonics—"the theory that explains much"— rests upon seismology. On to seismology, then!

Using Seismology to Look Inside the Earth

In your lectures, you may want to review Chapter 8 material on the properties of waves (refraction and wave speed, particularly) as well as the characteristics of transverse and longitudinal waves. Figure 22.1 helps students visualize body waves and surface waves of different kinds. There is an overhead transparency of this figure. While the characteristsics of different seismic waves are presented for interest, we feel it is enough for students to come away from this section with three objectives met: (1) students are able to distinguish body waves from surface waves; (2) students recognize that P- and S-waves are both body waves; and (3) students understand that P-waves are longitudinal ("push–pull") and S-waves transverse ("side-to-side").

If your students know their physics, they will appreciate the material explaining how seismic waves were used to uncover the Earth's interior structure. The inability of longitudinal waves (S-waves) to transmit through liquids as well as the change of a wave's speed as it passes through media of different density (producing refraction) are physics concepts used to great effect by seismologists. Remind students of the characteristics of longitudinal and transverse waves with this demonstration.

> DEMONSTRATION: To demonstrate how P-waves propagate through Earth's interior, have a volunteer hold one end of a Slinky. Stand far enough away to stretch the Slinky, and then give the Slinky a push so it compresses and expands as the longitudinal (or *compressional*) wave travels along its length. The wave's speed depends on the spring's resistance to being compressed. Show S-waves similarly, but now generate the wave by moving one end of the Slinky up and down. If students focus on a particular part of the Slinky, they will see it moves up and down as the wave moves in a perpendicular direction. This is a transverse (or shear) wave. The speed of this wave is related to the spring's rigidity.

Most kids learn the picture of Earth shown in Figure 22.2 in grade school. Likewise, the analogy of Earth as a boiled egg is well known. These concepts should be well understood *a priori* and are an essential foundation. Check to be sure all students understand this basic picture of the earth. Remediate as needed.

Similarly, check to be sure all students are clear on the application of seismology discussed in this section with the following "safety-net" check question:

> CHECK YOUR NEIGHBOR: Except for the observations in deep mines, how do we know any details about the Earth's interior? [Answer: How we know about the details of the Earth's interior is not altogether different than how a bat knows about the details of a dark cave or the ocean floor. We analyze the speed and direction of waves propagating through the medium. To do this, we observe how the waves are transmitted, reflected, and refracted.]

Add a little subject integration here by mentioning that not only does a bat know details of caves it can't see, dolphins sense the details of the dark ocean bottom using feedback from sound waves. In a similar way, earth scientists probe the Earth's interior with seismic waves. Here you make the point that seismic waves are quite like sound waves.

An interesting aside is that earth scientists learned much about the Earth's interior during the Cold War. During the height of the Cold War, numerous underground tests conducted by the former Soviet Union were of great concern to the United States, and vice versa. To more closely monitor these tests, an extensive network of sensitive seismographs were installed around the world. The seismograms from all this monitoring allowed a closer examination of the Earth's interior—a boon to earth scientists.

Earth's Internal Layers

The relative positions and the nature of each of the internal layers are the important take-home messages of this section. Details, such as the actual thicknesses or depths of each layer, can always be looked up in reference tables.

The Core The core-forming process has a dramatic name: "the iron catastrophe." The story goes like this: The planets formed when many stony and metallic meteorites, gases, dust, and so forth, clumped together due to gravitational attraction. Heat from the impacts and radioactive decay initiated melting. Molten rock and molten metal are largely immiscible, so the Earth's own gravity resulted in the very quick (in geologic terms) migration of denser molten metal toward the center of the planet. This formation of Earth's layers due to gravity is called *differentiation*. The iron catastrophe is believed to have occurred approximately 4.3 billion years ago. This information on the origin of Earth's layers is discussed in Section 23.1. Discuss differentiation and the "iron catastrophe" here if your students are becoming curious about the origin of Earth's layers and just can't wait to get to Chapter 23.

After completing this section, students should know three things: (1) the lithosphere is a brittle surface layer including crust and upper mantle; (2) the asthenosphere is a portion of the mantle underlying the lithosphere; and (3) all rock has some degree of plasticity, but asthenosphere is more plastic than surrounding rock. It flows markedly over geologic time as a result of convection. Flowing asthenosphere carries lithosphere with it, something like rafts on an ocean (to use a simple analogy).

Convection in the mantle over the eons is intimately linked with the motion of Earth's plates—plate tectonics. Also, the mantle is "a jewelry store's best friend," because all natural gem-quality diamonds are formed in the intense pressure environment of the mantle. The diamonds are later brought near the Earth's surface by rare, explosive volcanic eruptions called *kimberlite pipes*. More on diamonds and other gems will be presented in Chapter 23.

The Crust The crustal surface is where we are able to directly observe the dynamics of our planet. The crust is the thinnest and, more than likely, the most chemically heterogeneous of Earth's layers. The crust is composed of the end products of partial melting of the mantle. The thicker continental crust is further "refined" than the thin oceanic crust. As students will learn in Chapter 23, fractional crystallization of the magma produced from partially melted mantle rock has given rise to the great variety of igneous rocks that make up the continental crust.

> CHECK YOUR NEIGHBOR: If you wish to drill a hole through the Earth's crust to the mantle, where would you drill so that you have the shortest hole? [The ocean floor.]

Continental Drift—An Idea Before Its Time

Begin this section with a question to pique interest in continental drift.

> CHECK YOUR NEIGHBOR: We understand that coal deposits are the remains of ancient swamp vegetation. And we find coal deposits in Antarctica, a place too cold for swamps supporting such vegetation. How can coal deposits exist in cold Antarctica? [Antarctica wasn't always at the South Pole. It was at one time far from the pole, where the climate was warm enough for vast vegetated regions. The stage is now set to study continental drift.]

Emphasize the strong evidence Alfred Wegener offered in support of continental drift, calling attention to Figure 22.11. The fact that such evidence was so readily dismissed by Wegener's contemporaries reveals much about how the practice of science plays out in the larger social context. Wegener was not actually the first scientist to suggest that the continents are mobile. American geologist Frank Bursley Taylor put forth the idea in 1908, but he didn't offer supporting evidence. His prescient suggestions thus made not a dent in the prevailing geological doctrine of fixed continents. Perhaps Wegener was inspired by Taylor, or he may have developed the idea of continental drift on his own. In any case, Wegener first articulated his theory in the book he published in 1912 called *The Origins of Continents and Oceans*. This book went largely unnoticed, partly because it was published during World War I. Three years later, Wegener published his ideas in another expanded volume, which *did* attract attention—negative attention. Before Wegener's ideas were dismissed, they were discredited. A couple of social factors probably played a role in the scientific community's resistance to Wegener's work. For one thing, Wegener was not a geologist but a meteorologist (really he was a little bit of everything—an integrated scientist before his time). Further, he was German at a time when Germany had just lost the war. It was a bit of heresy for a German nongeologist to question the main tenets of geological science. Consider the following.

In 1955, Albert Einstein wrote a praise-filled forward to a book by geologist Charles Hapgood entitled *Earth's Shifting Crust: A Key to Some Basic Problems of Earth Science*. The intent of this book was to demolish the idea that continents moved as Wegener described. Hapgood said that a few misguided investigators had noticed "an apparent correspondence in shape between certain continents." He continued, "it is even claimed that rock formations on opposite side of the Atlantic match." Hapgood thus ignored extensive fieldwork by geologists supporting Wegener's original findings of matching rock strata. Even as late as in 1964, the *Encyclopædia Britannica* described Wegener's theory as full of "numerous grave theoretical difficulties." Ironically, while academics generally scoffed at continental drift, oil company geologists knew such movement occurred and factored it into their searches for oil deposits. How can this industry–academic disconnect be explained? Oil geologists generally don't develop comprehensive scientific theories or write academic papers. Tie all this back to Chapter 1 and the idea that the practice of science requires openness to new ideas. The Wegener episode, some would say, is an example of the scientific community going beyond a healthy intellectual skepticism. Bring in some science and society here: Ask your students to weigh in on the question:

> DISCUSSION QUESTION: Was the scientific community too resistant to Wegener's theory of continental drift, or is such resistance a vital part of the search for truth?

A Mechanism for Continental Drift

The conveyor belt analogy is the key pedagogical tool for teaching seafloor spreading. Students should acquire the basic picture that lithosphere is created at mid-ocean ridges and then moves toward and is destroyed at ocean trenches in a conveyor-belt fashion. Simple and elegant. Be sure to make use of Figure 22.16.

> CHECK YOUR NEIGHBOR: If lithosphere is continually created at mid-ocean ridges, why isn't the Earth expanding—or is it? [Answer: No, it's not expanding. Lithosphere is destroyed about as fast as it is created, by "recycling" at ocean trenches, that is, subduction zones. (We'll refine this picture when we discuss subduction in the section on convergent boundaries.)]

Magnetic stripes show that the seafloor is youngest at the rift and oldest near the trenches. Thus, they are evidence that the seafloor does move away from mid-ocean rifts, and this provides a mechanism for continental drift. Note that seafloor spreading is a mechanism for continental drift though not a driving force. For more on the driving forces that move plates and, thus, continents, turn to the Integrated Science feature, *What Forces Drive the Plates?*. To be sure students grasp the essential features of magnetic striping, ask the following:

> CHECK YOUR NEIGHBOR: What do magnetite crystals in lava reveal about Earth's magnetic field? [Answer: In lava, a fluid, the magnetite crystals turn so as to align with the magnetic field. Thus, the crystals show the polarity of the field when the lava cooled. Poles wander, and the crystals also show the direction from the lava to the pole when it cooled.]

> CHECK YOUR NEIGHBOR: What information does the pattern of magnetic stripes in the seafloor provide? [It tells the age of different parts of the seafloor and the rate at which they are moving away from the rift.]

Conclude the section by stating that we no longer need to rely on the clever scientific deductions, careful evidence gathering, or the sanctions of the geoscientific establishment to know that the continents move. We can directly observe it. Thus, continental drift has moved from the realm of theory to one of fact (though it is still generally called the "theory" of continental drift). A standard definition of a scientific fact is *an observation that all competent observers can agree to be true*. With the help of global positioning systems (GPSs) and very long baseline interferometry (VLBI), continental drift is now an observable fact.

The Theory of Plate Tectonics

Stress the newness of the theory of plate tectonics as well as its far-reaching consequences. It is truly the theory that explains much. Ask students for examples of such unifying theories in other branches of science. (The theory of universal gravitation, the theory of biological evolution, the nebular theory of solar system foundation, and the cellular theory are some examples.) When referring to Figure 22.18, emphasize that the plate boundaries do not define continents.

There are many analogies you can use when describing tectonic plates and their relative motions. Here are a few:
- Rafts drifting on a lake
- Islands of soap suds in the tub, combining and separating in various configurations
- Bumper cars crashing and moving apart
- Puzzle pieces shifting

Plate Boundaries

H. H. Hess showed that the seafloor spreads at *divergent* boundaries. Later work by others hinted at subduction zones (*convergent* boundaries). Because mid-ocean ridges are quite long, and because they are on a sphere, spreading cannot occur at equal rates along the whole ridge. Hence, the ridge becomes "offset" and segmented. *Faults at transform plate boundaries* provide the mechanism that accommodates the different spreading rates by transferring motion among ridge segments.

The formation of new lithosphere, including oceanic crust, at divergent boundaries can be a confusing topic. Once students understand that partial melting of the asthenosphere produces the magma that eventually erupts to form oceanic crust, try asking this question:

> CHECK YOUR NEIGHBOR: How does the mantle portion of the lithosphere form? Is it erupted as lava like in the oceanic crust? [The simple truth is that the lithospheric mantle is just cooled-down (and thus more rigid) asthenosphere. More below.]

As pointed out by University of California, Santa Barbara, geophysicist Tanya Atwater, divergent boundaries can be thought of as passive cracks in the lithosphere. They form because the plates they separate are drifting apart. As the plates move apart, asthenosphere upwells to fill the gap. The upwelling reduces pressure, so the asthenosphere partially melts. The upwelling asthenosphere is part of a convection cell that moves laterally away from the divergent boundary after it reaches the surface. The magma erupts as lava and forms a cap on top of the moving asthenosphere. The asthenosphere underlying the new oceanic crust cools to become the lithospheric mantle. Presto!

Earthquakes

Begin this section with this question:

> CHECK YOUR NEIGHBOR: Okay, so the continents drifted long ago. How do we know whether or not they are still drifting? [Ask people who live along the plate boundaries, where earthquakes are quite common, if the plates are still moving.]

Earthquakes are not only dramatic, they also illustrate plate tectonics concepts quite nicely. There are many film and Internet resources on the topic. Don't miss the opportunity to discuss any earthquakes in the news or earthquakes of historical importance in your area.

Use the expression "rock blocks stick and slip" as a shorthand summary for the process that creates earthquakes. It makes a good mantra. Review the concept of elastic potential energy and the idea that springs store such energy when stressed or compressed. Point out how similar this is to the storing of elastic potential energy in strained rock.

Here are a couple of vocabulary points: Note that *stress* is a force applied to rock, while *strain* is the response (deformation) to that stress. And if your students are getting the terms *epicenter* and *focus* mixed up, explain that the Latin prefix *epi* means "over." So, epicenter literally means "over the center." The focus, on the other hand, is the actual location of the disturbance.

Here is an interesting development: As we know, when an earthquake occurs, P-waves are detected by seismic instruments just before the arrival of the slower S-waves and surface waves. It is the S-waves and surface waves that typically produce the strongest ground motions and cause the most damage. Two scientists, R. M. Allen and H. Kanamori, have developed an early-warning system for southern California that uses the frequency content of the P-wave arrivals to determine the earthquake's magnitude and thus the strength of the impending surface waves. The determination is made about 3 to 10 seconds before the strong ground motion begins. Such early warnings could be used to automatically halt mass transit systems or industrial operations. For more details, see

Allen, R. M., and H. Kanamori. The potential for earthquake early warning in Southern California. *Science* 300 (May 2, 2003):786–789. Abstract available at http://www.sciencemag.org/cgi/content/abstract/300/5620/786.

Integrated Science—Physics: Isostasy

Many people like to use the analogy of a floating iceberg to describe how the crust is buoyantly supported by the mantle. This is especially true for the thick continental crust that characterizes mountain ranges. The idea of "floating" mountains goes only so far, so be sure to use caveats if you use this analogy. As explained in the text, the crust does not sink below the mantle–crust interface; it simply depresses the interface. So the crust isn't truly floating in the mantle. Use a water bed as an analogy; it closely resembles the geometry of the mantle–crust relationship. The water bed is the mantle, and the person sitting on it is the crust. The crust pushes down and sinks into the mantle without being immersed in it. A heavy person sinks low in the water bed; a light person doesn't depress the mantle much. And so it is with oceanic and continental crust achieving *isostatic equilibrium*. Note that a water bed rebounds as the weight upon it is reduced—excellent analogy for *isostatic adjustment*.

DEMONSTRATION: In addition to discussing isostasy in terms of a water bed, use a hot water bottle or inflatable mattress as a model for the mantle, like a water bed. Demonstrate isostatic equilibrium by showing that the depth to which the "mantle" (mattress) sinks depends on how dense the overlying body is. Demonstrate isostatic adjustment by showing that the hot water bottle or mattress springs back when the weight upon it is reduced.

Integrated Science—Physics: What Forces Drive the Plates?

While the mantle convection model is still the most popular cause given for plate motion, slab-pull and ridge-push are gaining adherents. Probably all three explanations play a role. The advantage of the mantle convection model pedagogically is that it ties two indisputable facts together—convection in the mantle and movement of the plates. The true picture is not as neat as this, but for a first course in plate tectonics, the mantle convection model is a good basic picture that can be refined.

Integrated Science—Biology: Life in the Trenches

This feature focuses mainly on life in hydrothermal vents, which occur many places in the seafloor besides the trenches. There is more information on the biology of hydrothermal vents in Chapters 17 and 18.

Integrated Science—Physics: Anatomy of a Tsunami

Time permitting, have students research the Boxer Day Tsunami to get the latest information on the disaster and recovery efforts. Share with the class. This gives you the opportunity to conclude the chapter with a plug for plate tectonics: The more we learn about plate tectonics, the more able we will be to prepare for earthquakes, tsunami, and other such devastating geologic events.

23   Rocks and Minerals

Demonstration Equipment

Movie projector

Stream table

Mixture of fine sand, coarse sand, small pebbles, and crushed chalk

Pennies

Calcite

Hammer

Safety glasses

Hand lens

Samples of various rocks and minerals you wish to discuss in class (for example, halite, garnet, quartzes, biotite, granite, marble, slate, calcite)

Rock-hounds notwithstanding, this chapter may be challenging to some students because of the small-scale and, therefore, abstract nature of the study of minerals. Many students are more interested in big-picture earth science, especially how it relates to the environment and geological disasters. Still, Earth is mostly made of rock and, therefore, mostly made of minerals. In a comprehensive study of earth science, there can be no getting around these topics. That said, there is more than enough material here for an introductory course, so this would be a good chapter to skim lightly if you are pressed for time. Consider omitting 23.4, *The Formation of Minerals,* and 23.5, *Classifying Minerals.*

We have tied the study of rocks and minerals to everyday life, consumer, and ecological issues as much as possible to sustain students' interest. While many students come to class thinking of rocks as rather dirty, drab, utterly inert, and pedestrian lumps, it is our hope that all students will leave with a sense that rocks and minerals are the stuff of which the Earth is made. They have a fascinating, hidden "life history" that plays out over a time scale we cannot perceive—geologic time.

The study of rocks and minerals is much integrated with chemistry and physics. This part of earth science clearly rests on chemistry (e.g., composition of minerals), and these chemistry concepts conspicuously hearken back to physics (e.g., pressure and temperature). Don't miss the opportunity to point this out and pat your students on the back for building an increasingly integrated body of scientific knowledge.

We emphasize process over vocabulary in this chapter. Nevertheless, there is new vocabulary for the study of minerals. The specialized vocabulary may prompt some students to memorize all the new terms—not a good way to build a strong conceptual framework. So, we'd like to suggest that memorization be kept to a minimum (open-book exams promote this).

In the *Practice Book*:
- Chemical Structure and Formulas of Minerals
- The Rock Cycle

In *Next-Time Questions*:
- What is the fundamental difference between a rock and a mineral?
- Igneous minerals form when magma cools
- Which type of rock do petroleum geologists search for?
- Permeability and Porosity of rocks

In the *Lab Manual*:
- Crystal Growth
- What's that Mineral?
- What's that Rock?
- Rock Hunt

Transparencies:
Figures 23.1, 23.2, 23.7, 23.32, 23.36, 23.37

Suggested Presentation

Materials of the Earth

To begin the chapter, we address a question that may have first occurred to students in Chapter 22: How did Earth's layers form? The process, differentiation, is described. You could skip ahead to Chapter 27 to discuss the nebular theory or to Chapter 26 to discuss Earth's formation in more depth if you like. Tell students they can go to those chapters for more context regarding differentiation right away. Notice that the subject of differentiation depends on an understanding of density. Density was introduced in Chapter 2 and was important in the discussion of isostasy in Chapter 22. Here it is again; it's a unifying concept. This would be a good time to remind students that density is an important concept they should be sure to understand. Remind them density is defined as an object's mass divided by its volume—verbally, it's a measure of the compactness of matter.

Call attention to Figure 23.2. Discuss the large amounts of silicon and oxygen in earth's crust. Ask:

> CHECK YOUR NEIGHBOR: What two elements would you predict would be most common in Earth's rocks? [Answer: Silicon and oxygen]

What Is a Mineral?

You are now launching into the core material of the chapter—the nature of minerals and how they come together to make up rocks. Review definitions from physics and chemistry (e.g., atom; element and compound; solid, liquid, and gas; ionic and covalent bonds; density; pressure; and temperature). Tell students they will need these concepts to grasp the story of how minerals form rocks. The two main topics presented in this section, the definition of a mineral and the nature of crystallization, are prerequisite for understanding the rest of the chapter, so check carefully that students master these.

The definition of a mineral will be straightforward—except to students looking for high precision. The definition of a mineral has two caveats, as indicated by the footnotes. Don't emphasize these caveats—the naming and terminology regarding varieties of minerals is not always consistent, and it's best not to get mired in these potentially confusing (and not conceptually important) areas. In this chapter, students may begin to notice a major difference between physics and earth science: earth science is far less precise than physics and a bit of a hodgepodge. Exceptions to general rules abound. You don't find this much in physics. Perhaps warn your students that this is the nature of many earth science subjects—particularly mineralology and petrology. Look for the main ideas.

Crystalline structure is easy at the level it is treated in this chapter. It would be possible to launch into involved discussions of crystallography, lattice structures, symmetries, and more—but that would take you into a specialized realm. Just refer back to the material on phase changes presented in Section 11.4, and point out that most solids are crystalline. Think Tinker Toys. Contrast crystalline solids with amorphous solids, and point out the Insight on this topic for a bit of humor. The lab on Crystal Growth is a good supplement to the text material in this section. The lab can be done by student groups or, if need be, as an instructor demonstration.

Mineral Properties

Time for some sensory learning! Make the material as sensory an experience as possible. Bring in minerals, and display their intriguing properties. Assign some Web surfing to supplement in-class experiences. There are some outstanding Web sites. A particularly fascinating and beautiful page describes the property of fluorescence: http://mineral.galleries.com/minerals/property/fluoresc.htm. This page is part of the Mineral Gallery Web site—a don't miss experience. Here's the home page: http://mineral.galleries.com/default.htm. While such pictures of well-formed minerals delight the viewer and clearly show the form, luster, and other properties we will study, most minerals are actually irregular blobs in rocks—an important point.

Note that, in the text, we focus on the properties of minerals that have a direct connection to atomic structure and bonds. Although properties like hardness and cleavage can be used for mineral identification, other properties (e.g., luster) that can be used for identification purposes are not discussed in the text. Discuss such properties in the lab portion of the course, if you can. Involve your students in the discussion of cleavage with this calcite demonstration.

> DEMONSTRATION: Check the cleavage properties of calcite, which exhibits perfect cleavage in three directions. Align a screwdriver in the direction of a cleavage plane, and hit the calcite with a hammer. The calcite should break into two pieces, each piece displaying rhombohedral cleavage planes. Then wrap one piece of calcite in cloth or newspaper. Hit it with a hammer. Unwrap and show the numerous pieces, each displaying the rhombohedral cleavage planes. Be careful not to hit the calcite too hard, for calcite will crumble.

While discussing precious minerals, distinguish between 10 and 24 karat gold. The proportion of pure gold in an alloy is thus: Pure gold is 24 karat; 10 karat is 10/24 pure, or 10 parts pure gold by weight and 14 parts of another metal. The specific gravity of gold alloys increases as gold content increases.

> DEMONSTRATION: Pennies made after 1982 contain both copper and zinc. Pennies made before this date are pure copper. Zinc is less dense than copper, so post-1982 pennies are less dense and have less mass than pre-1982 pennies. Have your students dig into their penny collections and find 20 pre-1982 and 20 post-1982 pennies. Have a few students measure their penny masses on a sensitive scale, such as a home postage scale. Alternatively, have your students hold their pennies in opposite hands to see if they can feel the difference in their masses. Ask them to see how few pennies they can hold and still feel the difference. Then have them try holding single pennies on their left and right index fingers. Can they tell the difference with their eyes closed?

Classifying Minerals

Silicate minerals are divided into two groups based on the abundance of iron and magnesium. Minerals containing high proportions of iron or magnesium in their structures are referred to as ferromagnesian silicates, whereas minerals with a low proportion of iron or magnesium are simply referred to as nonferromagnesian silicates. Here we describe some minerals that would be of interest to students. If you can, bring in samples to class, and share the following background information.

Ferromagnesian Silicates   Olivine and garnet are the two chief groups of silicates built of isolated tetrahedra. Olivine, predominant in basaltic rocks of the oceanic crust and rocks of the upper mantle, is olive-green to yellowish brown in color, has a glassy luster, and a conchoidal fracture. Garnet, characteristically found in metamorphic rocks of the continental crust, is most often brown to deep red in color. Both have a glassy luster and conchoidal fracture.

Pyroxenes and amphiboles are silicates made of continuous chains of silicate tetrahedra. Pyroxenes are built from single chains; amphiboles are built of double chains. Most are dark green to black in color and have good cleavage parallel to the silicate chain. The bonds are weaker across these surfaces than the bond between silicon and oxygen. The two differ in cleavage angle; pyroxenes cleave at a 90° angle, and amphiboles at 60° and 120° angles. Pyroxene is dominant in dark–colored igneous rocks formed by basaltic lavas and intrusions. Pyroxene commonly alters to amphibole during late stages of crystallization of igneous rocks and during metamorphism.

Biotite, a member of the mica family, has a sheet-like silicate tetrahedra as a basic building unit. The bond between the sheets is weaker than the bond holding the tetrahedra together within the sheet. Hence, biotite, like other micas, has excellent cleavage in one direction. Biotite is black due to its iron content and occurs in a variety of geologic environments. Biotite is a characteristic mineral in igneous rocks such as granite and granitic pegmatites.

Nonferromagnesian Silicates   Muscovite, also a member of the mica family, has the same sheet-like structure of biotite but has a lighter color. Muscovite occurs in a variety of geologic environments from igneous, metamorphic, and sedimentary. It is a common to abundant mineral in almost every type of metamorphic schist.

Quartz is the only mineral consisting entirely of silicon and oxygen. Quartz belongs to a network in which all the oxygen atoms in each SiO_4 tetrahedron are shared with neighboring tetrahedra, producing a stable, strongly bonded structure. As a result, quartz is hard, resistant to weathering, and displays no cleavage—quartz has a conchoidal fracture. Generally colorless unless affected by impurities, quartz characteristically forms six-sided, hexagonal, crystals. Quartz is a common and abundant mineral occurring in a great variety of geological environments. It is present in many igneous and metamorphic rocks, where it is a major constituent of granitic pegmatites. In sedimentary rocks, quartz is the major constituent of sandstone.

Feldspar is the most common mineral in the Earth's crust. It accounts for about 60% of all minerals in the continental crust and, together with quartz, comprises about 75% of the volume of the continental crust. The structure of feldspar is similar to the shared oxygen network found in quartz, except that some silicon atoms are replaced by aluminum atoms. Feldspars are relatively hard, have two planes of cleavage meeting at 90° angles, and vary in composition. There are two types of feldspars, alkali-feldspars ($KAlSi_3O_8$ to $NaAlSi_3O_8$) and plagioclase-feldspars ($NaAlSi_3O_8$ to $CaAlSi_3O_8$). Members of both of these groups are given individual names. Most alkali-feldspars are light in color (for example, the alkali-feldspar orthoclase is usually light to salmon pink in color). Most plagioclase feldspars range in color from white to gray. The only sure way to distinguish between the two types of feldspars is to look for parallel lines, striations, on the cleavage faces. Only plagioclase feldspar has striations. As rock-forming minerals, feldspars are widely distributed and very abundant. They are found in igneous, metamorphic, and, more rarely, in sedimentary rocks.

Rocks

Point out that the igneous, metamorphic, and sedimentary rock classifications are not mutually exclusive, because, over long periods of time, the same material may be subjected repeatedly to all the different processes.

Briefly discuss the broad circumstances under which different rock types form. For example, when magma cools or erupts as lava, we get igneous rocks. After weathering and the processes of erosion, we have deposition of sediments and then sedimentary rocks—rocks that blanket the Earth's surface. Metamorphic rocks are the direct result of huge tectonic stresses within the Earth, stresses so intense that preexisting rocks transform into rocks with new crystal structures.

Igneous Rock

In discussing sedimentary rocks, consider showing the 20-minute educational film *Fire Under the Sea*. This film features the first scenes ever filmed of undersea lava activity.

Many students will be surprised to learn that rocks can contain water. Water increases the melting point of rock, so water-containing rocks require higher temperatures to melt. To make this point, ask this question:

> CHECK YOUR NEIGHBOR: Granite rock has a high water content. Can buildings constructed of granite be called fireproof? Why or why not? [No. Granite does not ignite like wood, but because granite has a high water content, it weakens and crumbles once heat evaporates away the moisture in it.]

Refer back to Chapter 10, and discuss the radioactivity in Earth's mantle and core as the main source of Earth's heat. Radioactive decay keeps the Earth's interior very hot and gives rise to the geothermal gradient. Explain that many people who know about the geothermal gradient think that at a certain depth rocks cannot remain solid. Also, many people think that, because there are volcanic eruptions, the Earth's interior must be molten. In fact, the only part of the Earth that is molten is the outer core—and it is not rock. The core of the Earth is mostly iron and nickel.

Increased pressure is the main reason Earth remains solid at depth. After a certain depth, temperatures are higher than the melting point of rock. The immense weight of the rock above acts like a pressure cooker. Boiling and freezing points are raised as pressure increases. As a result, the principal magma generation mechanism is decompression melting.

Sedimentary Rock

The takeaway point for students is that Earth's surface is mostly covered by sedimentary rock, and that surface is forever changing as erosion, transportation, deposition, and lithification alter that rock. Discuss the biological weathering of rock to emphasize integration. Explain that biological weathering is caused by roots of plants that work their way into cracks in rocks then wedge the rock apart. Burrowing animals produce biological weathering by digging, which exposes surfaces to rain and wind for further mechanical and chemical weathering.

DEMONSTRATION: To enhance your discussion of erosion and deposition, bring a stream table to class. Place a wedge under the table so it tilts and direct overflow into a sink. Place a mixture of different materials with different grain sizes (coarse sand, fine sand, small pebbles, and ground chalk) on the table. Let the water drip into the mixture. Meanwhile, write the following questions on the chalkboard, and use them to frame the demonstration:

1. Erosion
   - Are the water channels that form straight, or do they meander?
   - Do channels, once formed, change? If so, how?
   - How does the slope of the table and the flow rate of the water affect erosion?
   - What size particles are eroded first? Last?

2. Deposition
   - Where are the transported particles deposited?
   - Where on the table do the "streams" flow quickly? Where do they flow slowly?
   - Is the speed of water related to the sizes of deposited particles?

Fossils will be discussed further in Chapter 26. Remind students that fossils are found in sedimentary rock with this question:

CHECK YOUR NEIGHBOR: Why are fossils found in sedimentary rock but not igneous or metamorphic rock? [Answer: Sedimentary rock formation doesn't require heating. By contrast, the high heats and pressures that are needed to form igneous and metamorphic rock would melt of crushed fossils.]

Metamorphic Rock

Figure 23.36 sums up the main ideas relating to metamorphic rock. If students understand rocks as consisting of minerals with unique crystalline structures (Section 23.1), they will understand how temperature and pressure make new minerals out of old by altering those crystal structures. Pass around a piece of marble as an example of nonfoliated metamorphic rock and gneiss as an example of a foliated metamorphic rock.

The Rock Cycle

Discuss Figure 23.37 as an overhead transparency. It provides a view of the rock cycle and is also a good point of departure for a review of the entire chapter. Review the definition of minerals, the relationship of minerals to rock, and the three major rock types. Or, review the chapter by way of the following question, which should stimulate a cascade of answers:

DISCUSSION QUESTION: Your friend says rocks are inert, dull, boring, and all the same. Do you agree? Why or why not? [Open ended]

Integrated Science—Chemistry: The Silicate Tetrahedron

The two most abundant elements, oxygen and silicon, combine with other cations to form the most common mineral group, the silicates. The silicon-oxygen (SiO_4) tetrahedron is the common building block of the silicates. It has four oxygen atoms (O^{2-}) with a single silicon atom (Si^{4+}) at the center. The tetrahedron has an excess charge of -4 and is not stable. To satisfy the charges, the tetrahedron acts as a simple anion ($-$) and forms a bond to a cation ($+$). Another way to satisfy the negative oxygen charge is by polymerization, the linking of tetrahedra to form chains, sheets, and various network patterns.

Asbestos is mentioned in this feature. For enrichment along illustrating the interface between science and society, discuss the public misunderstanding of the asbestos minerals. People have been ingesting asbestos since time zero. It has always been in the air and water, the amounts being little different today than centuries ago. What is not popularly appreciated is that there are two common kinds of asbestos—one harmless and one harmful. The most prevalent form of asbestos is relatively harmless chrysotile. The dangerous form of asbestos is amphibole crocidolite.

The two minerals differ in composition, color, shape, solubility, and persistence in human tissue. Chrysotile, $Mg_6Si_4O_{10}(OH)_8$, is a white serpentine mineral that tends to be soluble and disappears in tissue. Crocidolite, $Na_2(Fe^{3+})_2(Fe^{2+})_3SiO_{22}(OH)_2$, is blue in color, relatively insoluble, and persists in tissue. Only about 5% of the asbestos in use in the United States is crocidolite. Much of North American asbestos comes from chrysotile mines in Quebec, which have been operating since before 1900 and have produced about 40 million tons of chrysotile. Lax mining practices resulted in large amounts of chrysotile dust in the surrounding air. Wives of miners who lived near the mines were heavily exposed. But four epidemiological studies of Quebec chrysotile mining localities show that lifelong exposure of women to dust from nearby mines caused no statistically significant excesses in asbestos-related disease. The panic to remove all types of asbestos reflects an absence of science. Crocidolite, meanwhile, causes asbestosis, a form of lung cancer.

Amazingly enough, a multibillion-dollar asbestos removal program is in full swing in the United States that is dedicated to removing or containing both forms of asbestos—harmless and harmful alike. Clearly, there wasn't an accurate assessment of the problem initially nor has there been timely corrective action. You can find out more about this in the March 1990 *Science* editorial, "The Asbestos Removal Fiasco," the October 1995 *Environmental Geology* article, "The Schoolroom Asbestos Abatement Program," and the July 1997 *Scientific American* article, "Asbestos Revisited."

24 Earth's Surface—Land and Water

This chapter is an amalgam of several earth science subjects—geomorphology, hydrology, surface geology, and even a little geography. In a course as wide ranging as introductory integrated science, the plow cannot be set too deep. To teach a wide variety of topics in a short time, we try to stick to the big ideas and minimize details (unless the details are simply too fascinating to pass up!) This chapter exemplifies this approach more than any other in the book. It's a work of fusion, and it aims to sketch a picture of the earth as it is today in broad strokes.

Demonstration Equipment

Throw rug

3 feet of 6-inch diameter nonporous, flexible, plastic tubing

Coarse sand

In the *Practice Book*:
• Groundwater Flow and Contaminant Transport
• Aquifer Hydraulics
• Stream Flow
• Stream Velocity
• Glacial Movement

In *Next-Time Questions*:
• Folded rock layers
• Faulting of rock layers
• Why don't ponds and lakes seep away?
• Permeability and Porosity
• Does groundwater flow into streams or does stream-water flow into the ground?
• Floodplain
• Delta
• Density of seawater
• Evaporation and precipitations over the ocean

In the *Lab Manual*:
• Walking on Water (experiment)

Transparencies:
Figures 24.4, 24.5, 24.7, 24.8, 24.9, 24.17, 24.18, 24.24, 24.25

Suggested Presentation

A Survey of the Earth
This section is intended to be a quick and enjoyable read to set the context and motivate interest. Supplement the reading with a slide show of the diverse landforms of Earth. Copy pictures from the Web or other source, and narrate as you go. There is no need to restrict yourself to the landforms mentioned in this section. Consider including all of the following landforms or structures in your show, and tell students they will learn all about them in the coming chapter: plains, abyssal plains, aquifers; ocean trench; mid-ocean ridge; continental

margins; deltas; divides; caves; sinkholes; seamounts; plateaus; glaciers; faults (dip-slip, strike-slip, and oblique); fold; mountain (folded, fault-block, and upwarped); volcanoes; watersheds; water tables; moraines; dikes; batholiths; glaciers. Make your presentation interactive by asking students to name these geologic features before you do.

Folds and Faults

Physics comes into play in regard to compression forces (reverse faults and folds), tension (normal faults), and shearing forces (strike-slip faults). Be sure to enact the rug example given in the text as a quick demonstration of folding in rock.

> DEMONSTRATION: Put a small throw rug on a table top or the floor. Ask a volunteer to stand at one end of the rug. Push the rug toward your friend while keeping it on the floor. Notice a series of ripples, or *folds,* develop in the rug. Explain to students that this is similar to what happens to the Earth's crust when it is subjected to compressive stress. Explain that if the compressive force overcomes the mechanical strength of the rock, thrust or reverse faults form to accommodate the compression.

Earth's Water

Call students' attention to Figure 24.17, the water cycle. Familiar since grade school, this concept can be covered quickly. Remind students that water is a finite resource, and that most freshwater resides underground. No new water has entered Earth's natural systems since the planet formed (except for tiny amounts from comets and comet dust). Earth's water simply is cycled and recycled. The text describes the ocean floor as a zone of much topographical variation with its soaring underwater mountain ranges and deep ocean trenches. It is fascinating that most of the relief on Earth is actually underwater. The deepest part of the ocean is much deeper than the tallest mountain. Still, the bumpiness of the ocean and Earth as a whole is all a matter of perspective. Your students may be interested in the following analogy: A pool cue ball, if magnified to the same scale as the Earth, would show more relief than the visible surface of the Earth. Incredibly, compared with its radius, the "bumps" on the Earth are insignificant. Indeed, it's a matter of perspective.

Appendix E, "The Physics of Fluids," discusses pressure in a liquid. This has some bearing on the flow of subsurface water, so refer students to that appendix as needed. Begin discussing subsurface water and drainage with the following questions:

> DISCUSSION QUESTION: If you dig a hole in the ground and then fill it with water, the water soon seeps into the ground and is gone. Now consider a lake or pond. Why doesn't water in these similarly seep into the ground? What's going on—Is there plastic or something beneath the bottom that prevents draining?

State that these questions are not correctly answered by most people—who are only vaguely aware of what groundwater and water tables are all about. A knowledge of water tables tells us that the interesting reason that lakes don't (ordinarily) drain, and a hole dug in the ground that is then filled with water (ordinarily) does, is that the pond or lake intersects the water table. When you dig a hole in the ground that is above the water table, of course, the water soon drains downward until it can go no further, for example, when it meets the water table. Many students will find the subject of groundwater fascinating, because we rely so heavily on this hidden resource. Groundwater can be found just about anywhere below the Earth's surface. Point out that all underground water is not groundwater. In the unsaturated zone (sometimes called the *vadose* zone), water is called *soil moisture.* Try the following question:

> CHECK YOUR NEIGHBOR: Why aren't soil moisture and deep groundwater available as a freshwater resource? [Answer: Soil moisture resides in the unsaturated zone under negative pressure (i.e., less than atmospheric pressure). If a pump were operating in the unsaturated zone it would pump only air. Deep groundwater is simply too expensive to bring to the surface (due to pumping costs). It is cheaper to get water from other sources.]

Surface Processes

The work done by groundwater discussed in the text focuses on land subsidence and the development of carbonate dissolution features. Many students have probably visited picturesque caves and caverns. You can use such familiar experiences to generate student interest. As needed, discuss solubility (Section 12.8) and acids (Section 13.2). The chemistry "refresher" will provide some insight into cave formation.

Land subsidence related to water supply and agriculture is a problem in many places throughout the world. Imagine the shock people felt when they realized the seemingly unlimited groundwater supply they'd been tapping for irrigation turned out to make their land sink! The photo illustrating the impact of land subsidence in the San Joaquin Valley of California is particularly striking. Examples such as the Leaning Tower of Pisa and Mexico City highlight the impact on humanity that land subsidence can have.

25   Weather

The Earth is powered by the radiant energy of the sun. For more than 4.5 billion years, the sun's radiant energy has traveled across space to Earth, where a small portion of its solar output is intercepted. Because of Earth's curvature, the energy at the top of the atmosphere is unevenly distributed, creating an imbalance of energy from the equator to the poles. This unevenness of energy generates circulations in the atmosphere and on the surface below. Because of the Earth's tilt and corresponding uneven distribution of energy during the year, our planet undergoes seasonal change.

Filtering harmful UV radiation, charged particles, and space debris from reaching the Earth's surface, the atmosphere protects our planet as it balances the amount of energy the Earth receives. The atmosphere also affects our everyday activities directly, for as the text states, the state of the atmosphere at any place and time is the *weather*!

The chapter is structured so that weather is introduced in terms of six variables (atmospheric pressure, temperature, wind, precipitation, cloudiness, and humidity), and then each of these is discussed in turn. Changing weather, storms, and global climate change complete the chapter.

In the *Practice Book*:
• The Earth's Seasons
• Short and Long Wavelengths
• Driving Forces of Air Motion
• Air Temperature and Pressure Patterns
• Surface Weather Maps
• Chilly Winds

In *Next-Time Questions*:
• Ozone depletion
• Coriolis Effect
• Why don't all the water droplets in a cloud fall to the ground?
• Which is more dense: dry air or humid air?
• Evaporation
• Foggy sunglasses (summer)
• Foggy sunglasses (winter)
• Flat-bottom clouds
• Why airlines have pressurized cabins

In the *Lab Manual*:
• Solar Power I (experiment)
• Solar Power II (experiment)
• Indoor Clouds (activity)

Transparencies:
Figures 25.4, 25.5, 25.6, 25.16, 25.17, 25.31, 25.32, 25.37

Suggested Presentation

Solar Energy and Temperature

Do the flashlight demonstration suggested in the text. Take the demonstration one step further by bringing in a globe and showing the wide distribution of light at the poles and the concentration of light at the equator. Relate seasons to the Earth's tilt. New Englanders who revel in the fall foliage and others who enjoy the seasonal cycle can be thankful that the polar axis is inclined at 23.5 degrees to the orbit plane (the ecliptic). Refer students to Figure 25.5 or draw the sketch on your blackboard, first with only the two positions of the Earth at the far left and far right. Ask which of these two positions represents the Northern Hemisphere's winter months and which represents summer months. Encourage neighbor discussion.

Once it is clear that winter is at the right, show the position of the Earth in autumn and in spring. Shift the position of the sun closer to the Earth in winter, for this is actually the case. From your drawing, your class can see why Northern Hemisphere types enjoy an extra week of spring and summer! Southern Hemisphere types are compensated by a somewhat milder climate year round due to the greater amount of ocean in the Southern Hemisphere (80% as compared to about 60% for the Northern Hemisphere).

Discuss temperature inversion and the role it plays in air pollution, or at least in confining air pollution. On the matter of pollution, we find now that even rain is polluted. Acid rain has wreaked havoc with the environment in many parts of the world. Interestingly enough, pure rain water is naturally acidic. Ever-present carbon dioxide dissolves in water vapor to form carbonic acid. Decomposing organic matter, volcanoes, and geysers can release sulfur dioxides that form sulfuric acid. Lightning storms can cause nitric acid formation. The environmental problem of acid rain, however, is not the small amount caused by natural sources. Fossil fuel combustion is the largest single source of acid-producing compounds. Interestingly enough, it isn't the destruction of vast forests or poisoning of wildlife that has evoked the loudest public outcry—acid rain dulls the high-tech finishes on automobiles, and *that*, for John Q. Public, is going too far!

The Structure of the Atmosphere

If we make a tall stack of foam-rubber bricks, the bricks at the bottom will be more squashed than the bricks at the top. So it is with the atmosphere. The densest part of the atmosphere is at the Earth's surface (or in mines below). Most of the atmosphere is near the Earth's surface because of gravity. So, it is the force of gravity on molecules of air that holds most of the atmosphere from going off into space. (If gravity were less, like on the moon, molecular speed caused by solar energy would be greater than escape velocity, and no atmosphere would be maintained.) The atmosphere thins with altitude and ultimately becomes indistinguishable from the background gas in space. So there is no upper "surface" of the "ocean of air" like there is on the ocean of water.

> CHECK YOUR NEIGHBOR: When a helium-filled balloon is released in the air, how high does it go? Does it leave the Earth's atmosphere? [It doesn't get very high before it bursts, usually within sight. Why does it burst? Because surrounding air pressure decreases with height, allowing the balloon to grow until it ruptures. Special balloons for high-altitude measurements can achieve altitudes into the stratosphere without bursting—another story.]

Wind and Ocean Currents

Consider a nonspinning world with a uniform surface and without clouds. Then you have a world with very little air and water movement and a world without weather. The unequal heating of the Earth's surface produces the fluctuations in the atmosphere. Give the world a spin, and you'll get meandering waves moving west to east just below the poles. You now have a world with jet streams.

The processes of the pressure gradient force, Coriolis effect, and frictional force operate on the atmosphere as well as the ocean. Emphasize the connections between these two fluids—what affects one affects the other. Atmospheric circulation assists in the important transfers of energy and mass on Earth. Together, Earth's atmospheric and oceanic circulations represent a vast heat engine powered by the sun.

Humidity

Use the following material for a discussion that integrates physics. The textbook discusses the energy release that accompanies the condensation of water in the atmosphere. It doesn't discuss the mechanism for this energy release. Interestingly enough, H_2O molecules simply give most of their KE to the air during their last collision before condensation. The details are shown in the sequence of sketches below.

Consider two pairs of molecules, say with equal KEs before collision (Sketch 1). After collision, individual KEs may be quite unequal, for molecules that transfer much of their KE to others are left with correspondingly less KE of their own (Sketch 2). So far, there is no change in the air's total KE score. But if the slower

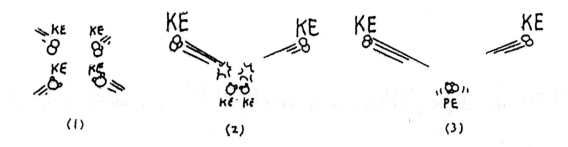

(1) (2) (3)

molecules happen to be H_2O, they are candidates for condensation if their next collisions are with other H_2Os that have similarly just given most of their KE to neighboring molecules (Sketch 3). Upon condensation of the slow-moving H_2Os, other molecules remaining in the air have an increase in average KE. Voila! *H_2O molecules transfer KE to the surrounding air during their last collision while in the gaseous phase*—the collision that immediately precedes condensation. The energy gained by the air is the well-known heat of vaporization—about 540 calories per gram of condensed H_2O for an ambient temperature of 100°C. It's greater for lower temperatures (molecules bopped to high speeds in a low-speed environment gain more energy than molecules bopped to the same high speeds in higher-speed environments). All things being equal, a rainy day really is warmer than a cloudy day.

An interesting way to present the condensation of water vapor to droplets is the following: Ask why a glass containing an iced drink becomes wet on the outside, and why a ring of moisture is left on the table. You can inject a bit of humor here and state that the reason has to do with—make an underline—then pause and write a big 25.24 on the board. Then ask why the walls of the classroom would become wet if the temperature of the room were suddenly reduced. State that the answer is—then underline your 25.24. Ask why dew forms on the morning grass, and state the answer is—another underline for 25.24. Ask why fog forms, and how the clouds form, and back to your 25.24. By now, your class is wondering about the significance of 25.24. Announce you're discussing Figure 25.24, and with class attention and interest, show the overhead transparency of this figure and then go on to discuss the formation of fog and clouds, and even rain, hail, and snow. (Snow crystallizes from vapor; hail is rain that freezes when tossed upward, often repeatedly, by strong updrafts.)

Condensation is enhanced by the presence of ions, dust, or tiny particles that act as the nuclei of droplets. London became much foggier when coal burning provided more particles in the air to initiate condensation.

Integrate condensation in the atmosphere with what students learned in Section 11.4 about heat transfer and change of phase by explaining how frost forms on materials that are poor conductors of thermal energy. Grass, wood, and straw are poor conductors and that is why on very chilly (not yet freezing temperature) mornings we can see frost-covered lawns and fields. On these particular mornings, we do not see frost form on the sidewalks—concrete (like metal and stone materials) is a good conductor of thermal energy.

Evaporation
In discussing evaporation in the atmosphere, consider the effects of phase changes. Phase change infers a corresponding energy change. Interesting examples are the following:
- Cooling produced by an air conditioner
- Warming produced by a heat pump (an air conditioner "turned backward")
- Spraying of crops when frost threatens
- Freeze-dried products (including coffee)

> CHECK YOUR NEIGHBOR: Is evaporation greater over warm water or cold water? [Evaporation is greater above warm water, for greater molecular motion pops more of them from the water. Thus, evaporation is greater over oceans in warm regions (warm air holds more moisture than cool air) than over oceans in cold polar regions (which is also one reason why there is little snowfall in the polar regions).]

Precipitation
It is interesting to note that raindrops evaporate as they fall toward the Earth's surface, so they need to be relatively large in order to reach the Earth's surface. If they are not large enough, they evaporate in the atmosphere, forming *virga* (streams seen under clouds).

There are two interesting effects of energy transfer in rainfall. The key concept is that energy is absorbed by something that changes phase from solid to liquid to gas, and energy is released by something that changes

131

the other way, from gas to liquid to solid. Consider water vapor condensing to form raindrops. Energy is released by the H_2O, tending to warm the air. But when rain falls, considerable evaporation occurs. If drops evaporate entirely on the way down, then no net energy transfer occurs.

CHECK YOUR NEIGHBOR: When rainfall does reach the ground, which wins, cooling or warming? [For rain that reaches the ground, the net effect is warming—until it again evaporates. Interesting material!]

Integrate condensation, evaporation, and rainfall with the following diagram:

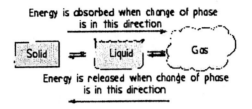

Whenever a substance changes phase, a transfer of energy occurs. Energy must be added to melt ice into water or vaporize water into steam. Energy must be removed to condense steam back into water or freeze water into ice. In general, a solid absorbs energy turning into a liquid, and a liquid absorbs energy turning into a gas. When the phase change is from a gas to a liquid, energy is released.

Clouds
Air expands as it rises and, therefore, cools. What happens to the water molecules in the air that cools? Condensation! If it happens high up in the sky, it's called a cloud. If it happens down near the ground, it's called fog. So remember the three Cs—Cools, Condenses, Clouds.

CHECK YOUR NEIGHBOR: Why does cooling air condense? [Recall that water molecules are polar, which makes them tend to stick to one another, as seen when water drops bead on a surface. In warm air, they are moving too fast to stick when they collide. Like a couple of magnets thrown at each other, they fly off in different directions when they bounce. But toss the magnets slowly and they'll stick when they meet. Likewise for H_2O molecules in the air. Slow-moving water molecules stick—condensation.]

CHECK YOUR NEIGHBOR: Why are clouds predominantly over mountain ranges, rather than above adjoining valleys? [Any moist air that blows against the mountains is swept upward, and then it's the three Cs!]

CHECK YOUR NEIGHBOR: Why are clouds so prevalent over islands—even those without mountains to provide updrafts? [When exposed to sunshine, land warms more than water (recall water's high specific heat capacity). So moist air blowing over the relatively warm land is heated. When it warms, it expands and becomes buoyant and rises. Then it's the three Cs!]

(Hey, three questions in a row—by now you've likely noticed that some of your most successful lectures occur when you pose intriguing questions instead of professing! Most of the questions you pose pop up spontaneously, and those appearing here are merely samples.)

Air Masses
The Earth's atmosphere and weather is very much influenced by the ground surface. The Earth's surface is heated unequally, with some areas being better absorbers of energy than other areas. Once again, refer back to Section 6.10, on the absorption of radiant energy. As the air touches areas that are "good" absorbers of energy, the air is warmed by contact. As the air touches areas that are "poor" absorbers of energy, the air is cooled by the contact. When those areas are large and extensive, and those areas greatly impact the air, the air is termed an "air mass." The air picks up the characterization of the ground surface—polar maritime or tropical continental. Hey, this gets back to Newton's third law, "You cannot touch without being touched." Connections are everywhere!

Storms
Violent weather is a newsmaker. Rare is the day that some sort of violent weather is not occurring somewhere on Earth. In this section, we discuss the three major types of storms: thunderstorms; tornadoes, and hurricanes. But violent weather is not limited to these three types of storms. Expand your coverage of violent weather according to what is going on in the news of the day. Fire storms from intense heat waves, drought, blizzards, and floods can all be discussed. Weather conditions change on a daily basis. The text gives your

students a foundation to build upon—atmospheric moisture, air pressure, temperature, density, absorption of radiant energy, and the different types of air masses. With a basic foundation, this section of the chapter can be made relevant by examining the "storms" of the day.

Conclude this section with your best photos (and perhaps your students' photos) of major storms—thunderstorms, tornadoes, hurricanes, the works!

Integrated Science—Physics: The Greenhouse Effect

Compare the window glass of the florist's greenhouses to the water vapor and carbon-dioxide window glass of the Earth's atmosphere. Relate the section on solar and terrestrial radiation back to concepts covered in physics (Chapter 6 and Chapter 8). Short waves easily penetrate the Earth's atmosphere, whereas long waves do not. (They are reflected back to the Earth, and thus, they warm the Earth.) Emphasize that among the atmospheric gases, water vapor plays the largest role in confining the Earth's heat.

State that terrestrial radiation rather than solar radiation is directly responsible for the warmth of the air around us. Air is primarily warmed by the Earth, which is an important reason we don't freeze at night when we're not in the sun's light. Three cheers for terrestrial radiation!

Interesting point: The Earth is always "in equilibrium," whether it is overheating or not. At a higher temperature, as global warming produces, the Earth simply radiates more terrestrial radiation. Income and outgo match in any case; the important consideration is the temperature at which this income and outgo match.

Demonstration Equipment

230-sheet toilet paper roll

Marker pens (that do not bleed)

It has been said that children can't really appreciate history, because their own experience of time is too limited for them to appreciate long time scales. A fully conscious insect with a few-hour life span similarly would have no idea that the plant or tree it feeds upon has a "short" life cycle that fits in the life cycles of other life forms that utilize trees. "Short" to us, that is. Upon casual observation, even we are not fully aware of the actions of plants and trees. Because their activities are in "slow motion." we do not see that vegetation is every bit as violent as animals in maintaining their hierarchical positions in the food chain. Even slower and more violent are the Earth's geological processes. Like the insect with the few-hour life span, we are not aware of long-term changes, unless we study our surroundings very carefully, which is what this chapter is about.

In the *Practice Book*:
• Relative Time—What Came First?
• Age Relationships
• Unconformities and Age Relationships
• Radiometric Dating
• Our Earth's Hot Interior

In *Next-Time Questions*:
• The age of the Earth is most accurately determined by . . .

In the *Lab Manual*:
• Reading the Rock Record (activity)
• Geologic Time Scale and Relative Dating (activity)

Transparencies:
Figures *History of Science: Uniformitarianism versus Catastrophism* Delaware Water Gap, 26.2, 26.3, 26.5

Suggested Presentation
Two hundred years ago, humans had only a vague idea of how old the Earth was, and virtually had no reliable method for determining the age of any rock, fossil, geologic feature, or geologic event. By the early 1800s, however, observation of sedimentary rock records led to the formulation of some basic geologic concepts. With these basic concepts, a relative succession of geologic events for a particular region could be worked out. With more work and further observations, by the end of the 19th century, a relative time scale was constructed that could be applied to most parts of the world.

Early (European) Thoughts About Geologic History

Before ~1500 (pre-Renaissance): strictly biblical

~1500   **DaVinci** (Italy): Questioned the flood as the cause of fossils

~1670   **Nicolaus Steno:** Superposition, Original Horizontality, Lateral Continuity

Robert Hooke: Looked at fossils with a microscope; suggested fixed life span for species; questioned flood

~1785   **James Hutton/John Playfair** (Scotland): Uniformitarianism

~1800   **William Smith** (England): Nickname William "Strata" Smith; map completed in 1815, plus table of strata; general ideas about correlation of fossils

~1800   **W. Smith/G. Cuvier** (France): Principle of faunal succession (oldest fossils are in lowest strata); principle of faunal assemblages (strata with similar fossils are similar age)

Concepts led to principles. And the basic principles, plus lots of detailed descriptive work, led to the Relative Time Scale (which is always in the process of being revised).

Early Attempts at Establishing Absolute Time Scale

1654   Archbishop **Ussher** (Ireland): Added up life spans of Old Testament characters; Earth was created in 4004 B.C., on October 26 at 9 a.m. (apparently he wasn't into significant figures!); very influential for about 150 years, and is still cited

~1760   **Buffon:** 75,000 years based on cooling rate of Earth's iron core

~1850   **Kelvin** (Scotland): 20–40 million years, based on cooling of Earth

Kelvin ~18 million years, and **Helmholtz** 20–40 million years, both based on radiation from the Sun, assuming energy from gravitational contraction

~1893   **Walcott** ~75 million years, based on total thickness of strata

1899   **Joly** ~90–100 million years, based on salt accumulation in the ocean

The discovery of radioactivity in the late 1800s led to radiometric dating. Early in the 1900s, attempts to measure decay rates of various unstable isotopes provided geologists with the ability to fit numbers into the already established relative time scale. By the mid-1900s, measurement techniques became significantly improved, which provided much more precise dating information. Thus, the modern numerical time scale was established.

- Radioactivity discovered by Becquerel (France)
- X-rays by Roentgen (Germany)
- Isolation of radium by Curie (France)
- In 1905, Rutherford suggested the use of radioactivity for dating
- In 1950, Libby (United States) developed C-14 dating

Geologic Time

There are many ways to have your students visualize Geologic Time.

In the Classroom Draw a long line on the chalkboard. Then segment the line into 12 equal pieces to represent the months of the year, going from January to December. In the various sections, mark off the time for the different events. Some of the dates used are not known with great precision (especially early dates). Provided are the dates used in developing this time line.

Jan 1—the origin of the Earth (4.5 billion years ago)

Feb 26—earliest Earth rocks (3.8 billion)

Mar 23—first simple life and photosynthesis (3.5 billion)

July 22—free oxygen begins to accumulate in the atmosphere (2.0 billion)

Sept 1—first green algae and organisms with a nucleus (1.5 billion)

Nov 17—the proliferation of life; the beginning of the Paleozoic Era (544 million)

Nov 21—first fish; the first vertebrate (505 million; Cambrian–Ordovician boundary)

Nov 27—life on land (plants) (423 million; mid-Silurian)

Dec 2—amphibians move to land (360 million; Devonian–Carboniferous boundary)

Dec 13—first mammals (226 million; mid-Triassic)

Dec 14–Dec 26—the age of the dinosaur (215 to 65 million; mid-Triassic to end of Cretaceous)

Dec 31 at 11:49 p.m.—humans emerge (90,000 years ago)

Dec 31, 14 seconds before midnight—the birth of Christ (33 B.C.)

Dec 31, 2 seconds before midnight—the Declaration of Independence (1776)

Dec 31, about 1 second before midnight—the start of the Industrial Revolution (1800)

Follow this up with the analogy: If the age of the Earth is the length of the Golden Gate Bridge (about 6000 ft long), then 600 years of civilization is 0.1 inch (about the thickness of a car key)! Whereas most fields of study are concerned with no more than the car key, geologists are concerned with the whole bridge! (Or carrying this further, cosmologists are concerned with the bridge and its more than 2-mile-long on-ramp!)

Outside, on Campus Geologic Time on a Toilet Paper Roll: With a 230-sheet roll of toilet paper, mark the following dates onto the roll. You will begin with recent dates and work backwards. *To save class time, do this ahead of time and use tape to reinforce the toilet paper.*

Sheets	Event
	Geological time (Number of years before present)
0.00	Present
	0
0.0005	Modern man
	10,000
0.01	Neanderthal man
	100,000
0.03	First use of fire
	500,000
0.06	Worldwide glaciation
	1,100,000
0.07	*Homo erectus*
	1,300,000
0.08	Linking of North and South America
	1,500,000
0.08	Oldest stone tools
	1,600,000
1.15	**Beginning of Quaternary period (end of Tertiary/Neogene)**
	23,000,000
0.15	Australopithecus
	3,000,000
0.50	Beginning of Antarctic ice caps
	10,000,000

Sheets	Event
0.50	Opening of Red Sea
	10,000,000
0.75	Formation of Himalayan Mountains
	15,000,000
1.25	First evidence of ice at the poles
	25,000,000
2.00	Collision of India with Asia
	40,000,000
2.50	Early horses
	50,000,000
2.50	Separation of Australia and Antarctica
	50,000,000
3.00	Early primates
	60,000,000
3.00	Swiss Alps form
	60,000,000
3.25	Beginning of Tertiary
	65,000,000
3.25	**Beginning of Cenozoic Era**
	65,000,000 "recent life"
3.25	Cretaceous Period, Mesozoic Era end
	65,000,000
3.25	Dinosaurs became extinct
	65,000,000
4.00	Rocky Mountains form
	80,000,000
7.00	Cretaceous Period begins (Jurassic ends)
	144,000,000
7.50	Early flowering plants
	150,000,000
9.00	Early birds and mammals
	180,000,000
10.40	Jurassic Period begins (end of Triassic)
	208,000,000
11.00	Opening of Atlantic Ocean
	220,000,000
12.25	Triassic Period begins
	245,000,000

(Continued)

Sheets	Event
12.25	**Beginning of Mesozoic Era (end of Paleozoic)**
	245,000,000 "middle life"
14.00	Final assembly of Pangaea
	280,000,000
14.50	Beginning of Permian period (end of Carboniferous/Pennsylvanian)
	286,000,000
16.25	First reptiles
	325,000,000
16.15	Beginning of Carboniferous/Pennsylvanian period (end of Mississippian)
	325,000,000
18.15	Early trees, formation of coal deposits
	360,000,000
18.15	Beginning of Carboniferous/Mississippian period (end of Devonian)
	360,000,000
20.45	Beginning of Devonian period (end of Silurian)
	410,000,000
21.50	Early land plants
	430,000,000
21.95	Beginning of Silurian period (end of Ordovician)
	440,000,000
24.50	Early fish
	490,000,000
25.50	Beginning of Ordovician period (end of Cambrian)
	505,000,000
28.50	Early shelled organisms
	570,000,000
28.50	Beginning of Cambrian period (end of Precambrian time)
	544,000,000 rise of multicellular animals
28.50	**Beginning of Paleozoic Era**
	544,000,000 "ancient life"
35.0	Early multicelled organisms
	700,000,000
40.0	Breakup of early supercontinent
	800,000,000
70.0	Formation of early supercontinent
	1,400,000,000
60.0	First known animals
	1,200,000,000
135	Buildup of free oxygen in atmosphere
	2,700,000,000

138

Sheets	Event
170	Early bacteria and algae
	3,400,000,000
190	Oldest known Earth rocks
	3,800,000,000
230	**Precambrian time begins**
	4,500,000,000
230	Origin of Earth
	4,500,000,000

Doing one or the other geologic time scale demonstrations will really help your students visualize the immensity of geologic time. If you decide on the toilet paper demonstration, it promises to be a demo never to be forgotten!

Radiometric Dating

Radiometric dating gives us the absolute age of a mineral. Radiometric dating is a refinement of relative time. This section can be tied to earlier material on radioactivity (Chapter 10). Point out that the age of the Earth is not estimated by analyzing rocks that formed 4.5 billion years ago. Instead, scientists have dated certain meteorites, which presumably coalesced at the same time as the Earth. The processes of erosion, volcanism, and plate tectonics have effectively obliterated all traces of the Earth's early history.

> CHECK YOUR NEIGHBOR: The Earth is some 4.5 billion years old, yet the oldest rocks only date back to 3.8 billion years. Why don't we find rocks dated at 4.5 billion years? [The material that may have formed any rocks 4.5 billion years ago has been mixed back into the rock-cycle stew. The oldest mineral found thus far is 4.4 billion years old, but it was found in a sedimentary rock, not the original igneous rock.]

Precambrian Time

The Precambrian comprises over 85% of Earth's history. In this time, Earth's surface cooled, which allowed the formation of lithospheric plates. The development of photosynthesis generated free oxygen and the beginning of primordial life forms.

> CHECK YOUR NEIGHBOR: From where did the oxygen that makes a large part of the Earth's early atmosphere originate? [Mainly from the waste products of plant life.]

The Paleozoic Era

The Paleozoic Era marks the first abundant fossil evidence of life. The significant occurrences of the Paleozoic include the emergence of many diverse life forms and the formation of the supercontinent of Pangaea.

The Mesozoic Era

The Mesozoic Era is the age of the reptile. The main discussion points of the Mesozoic Era include the rise and fall of the dinosaurs, the appearance of the first mammals, and the breakup of Pangaea.

The Cenozoic Era

The Cenozoic Era is the age of the mammals and is the era in which humans evolved. Point out that humans, like other species from previous geologic times, adapt to the environment to survive. But humans do more than adapt, they also change the environment. Humans can be a geologic force as discussed in the text. Relate your discussion about the Pleistocene to the effects of glacial erosion.

Point out that there have been several glacial and interglacial periods in the present ice age. Many people do not realize that we are still in an ice age (see box in text). An ice age can be defined as a time period when continental scale glaciers (such as the polar ice caps) are present. You may remark about the Little Ice Age — the period of cold between the 15th and 19th centuries. The Little Ice Age is depicted in the paintings of ice skaters by Flemish artists. Point out that significant glacial advances are accompanied by a drop in sea level, due to water taken up by glacial ice.

27   The Solar System

Demonstration Equipment

Dark-colored ball with one half painted white (simulated moon phases)

This is the time to bring your class to a planetarium, if possible. Or give a slide show, and invite your colleagues in astronomy to give an illustrated guest lecture with their best slides. If you are lucky enough to have one or two portable telescopes and the time in the evening, you might consider a class "star party" and discuss the universe out of doors. Some teachers do this with telescopes, hot dogs, and soft drinks.

The International Space Station (ISS), like many other satellites, is occasionally bright enough in the night sky to be seen by the naked eye. One reason for its visibility is sunlight glinting off its large solar wings. The ISS is in one of the lowest orbits possible, about 242 miles overhead. The ideal viewing time is immediately before dawn or after sunset, when the observer is in the dark and the satellite is in the sunlight. Circling the globe in somewhat different orbits 15 times a day, the ISS passes over most of the Earth in a 24-hour period. One Web site that tells you when the ISS will pass over your location is www.heavens-above.com. Because the ISS travels at nearly 8 km/s, it isn't likely to be over your location for more than 10 minutes. Happy hunting!

A superior 10-minute film that makes an excellent tie-in from the solar system, galaxies, and the universe to the atom—comparing sizes as powers of ten—is the oldie-but-goody *Powers of Ten,* by Charles and Ray Eames, and narrated by Philip Morrison (Pyramid Films, 1978).

A worthwhile class activity to consider is constructing a sundial.

The instructor notes for this chapter feature numerous supplemental topics that go beyond the text. We hope you can utilize these with the text material as a foundation.

In the *Practice Book*:
• Earth–Moon–Sun Alignment
• Pinhole Image Formation

In Next-Time Questions:
• Measure Sun's diameter
• Earth-Rise from the Moon
• Lunar eclipse

In the *Lab Manual*:
• Sunballs (experiment)
• Ellipses (activity)
• Reckoning Latitude (experiment)
• Tracking Mars (activity)

Transparencies:
Figures 27.5, 27.11, 27.20, 27.24, 27.25, 27.30, 27.31

Suggested Presentation

Overview and Origin of the Solar System

You could begin the chapter with an overview of the solar system to acquaint your students with what it contains. The definition of the solar system as the collection of bodies gravitationally bound to the Sun is particularly edifying. How many people, though familiar with the solar system in broad outline, appreciate that it is defined so neatly in terms of the gravitational force?

It's a natural progression from Section 27.1 to Section 27.2. Section 27.1 explains what's in the solar system, and Section 27.2 explains how it all got there. The nebular theory, like universal gravitation, the atomic theory, the cell theory, plate tectonics, and biological evolution, is an elegant tool—so simple, yet so powerful. By this time in the course, students may be able to see the parallels between these great unifying theories of science.

Stress to your students how lucky they are to be living in a time when such knowledge of the solar system is readily available. The human desire to know what heavenly bodies occupy space and how they got there reaches back to prehistory. Today, it's presented to us on the silver platter of full-color books, films, and Web sites!

History of Science: Eratosthenes Measures the Diameter of the Earth in 235 B.C.

To make the point that state-of-the-art astronomical knowledge rests on a foundation built up over thousands of years, you may wish to digress a bit here with the story of how Eratosthenes measured the size of the Earth in 235 B.C. I (Hewitt) have used this material over the years and have found it to be an interest-grabber.

Begin by challenging your class to give convincing information to support the notion that the world is not flat, but round. Students "know" the Earth is round and in motion around the sun, but how many are prepared to defend these beliefs? Their belief is usually based on faith in a teacher, in a book, in an astronomer, or in programs they have watched on TV—but rarely upon evidence. Interestingly, there is much evidence that the Earth is flat and not in motion at all!

What is the direct evidence for a round Earth? Does it appear round when you drive across the country? Does it appear round from a high-flying plane? And how does one know whether or not pictures taken from space are authentic? How does one know whether or not the space ventures by astronauts were not "Hollywood"?

Enter Eratosthenes. Earth's size was first measured in Egypt by the geographer and mathematician Eratosthenes about 235 B.C. Eratosthenes calculated the circumference of the Earth in the following way. He knew that the sun is highest in the sky at noon on the summer solstice (which is June 22 on modern calendars). At this time, a vertical stick casts its shortest shadow. If the sun is directly overhead, a vertical stick casts no shadow at all. This was known to occur in Syene, a city south of Alexandria (where the Aswan High Dam stands today). Eratosthenes learned that the sun was directly overhead in Syene at the summer solstice from library information, which reported that, at this unique time, sunlight shines directly down a deep well in Syene and is reflected back up again. Eratosthenes reasoned that, if the sun's rays were extended into the Earth at this point, they would pass through the center. Likewise, a vertical line extended into the Earth at Alexandria (or anywhere else) would also pass through the Earth's center.

At noon on the summer solstice, Eratosthenes measured the shadow cast by a vertical pillar in Alexandria and found it to be one-eighth the height of the pillar (see figure). This corresponds to a 7.2-degree angle between the sun's rays and the vertical pillar. Because 7.2° is 7.2/360, or one-fiftieth of a circle, Eratosthenes reasoned that the distance between Alexandria and Syene must be one-fiftieth the circumference of the Earth. Thus, the circumference of the Earth becomes 50 times the distance between these two cities. This distance, quite flat and frequently traveled, was measured by surveyors to be 5000 stadia (800 kilometers). So Eratosthenes calculated the Earth's circumference to be 50 × 5000 stadia = 250,000 stadia. This is within 5% of the currently accepted value of the Earth's circumference.

We can get the same result by bypassing degrees altogether and comparing the length of the shadow cast by the pillar to the height of the pillar. Geometrical reasoning shows that, to a close approximation, the ratio shadow length/pillar height is the same as the ratio distance between Alexandria and Syene/Earth's radius. So, just as the pillar is eight times greater than its shadow, the radius of the earth must be eight times greater than the distance between Alexandria and Syene.

Because the circumference of a circle is 2π times its radius ($c = 2\pi r$), the Earth's radius is simply its circumference divided by 2π. In modern units, the Earth's radius is 6370 kilometers, and its circumference is 40,000 km.

The Moon

Don't be disheartened if you find that there are students in your class who don't know that the Moon can be seen in the daytime. Suggest they look for it during the daytime near the first or third quarter. Ask on which side of the Moon they should look for the sun at these times. Be sure all your students make observations of the Moon for several weeks. Observations night after night will show that at the same time each evening, the Moon is farther to the east among the stars.

Phases of the Moon

Be prepared to find out (if you haven't already) that many students in your class think the crescent moon is due to the Earth's shadow on it. A survey before the chapter is covered may reveal this. (If the survey shows the same students believing this after you have covered the chapter, then . . . egad!)

DEMONSTRATION: Play flashlight tag. Suspend a large ball above your lecture table, turn off the lights, and illuminate the ball with a flashlight from different parts of the room. Phases of the ball are easily seen, and the phases of the Moon forever understood by those who disappointed you on your survey. Learning has occurred! Or toss Styrofoam balls, about 6 cm in diameter or larger, to your class. Let them move the balls around their heads to see the changing phases as you shine the light on them.

DEMONSTRATION: An easier way to show Moon phases is to display a large ball (perhaps a basketball or beach ball) with one half painted white and the other half very dark. The white side represents the hemisphere of the Moon that is always in sunlight (except during a lunar eclipse). You can hold the ball up, turn it, and ask where the Sun would have to be located for the lit part they see. After showing full, quarter, and new Moons, show them a view where the crescent they see is tipped from the vertical. When tipped so the lit side points at an angle downward, ask if this is a Moon in the daytime or nighttime. Aha, you have a handle on how they grasp the idea. Tip it the other way and ask again. After this or the preceding demo, your students should from now on see the moon differently.

Cratering is a notable feature of the lunar surface. Point out that the craters are often many times larger than the meteorites that caused them. A unit of energy from a munitions explosion causes the same size crater as the same unit of kinetic energy from a falling object. If you toss a baseball into mud, you'll produce crater shapes not unlike those seen on the Moon. Different impact speeds will produce different shaped craters, with depth-to-width ratios much the same as those produced by meteorites. Of course, the many craters made on the Earth when the Moon's were occurring have long since been obliterated by weathering and other geologic processes.

Eclipses—The Shadows of the Earth and the Moon

A solar eclipse occurs when the relatively tiny Moon covers the enormous sun in the sky. The diameter of the sun is four hundred times that of the Moon, but the Sun is also four hundred times farther away. So just as your thumb at arm's length can block the view of a far-off mountain, the Moon blots out the Sun. Use Figures 27.30 and 27.31 to explain eclipses. Stress the idea that like everything in the sunshine, a shadow is cast. Imagining the shadow cast by the huge Earth will be challenging to many students. Those in a total solar eclipse experience the shadow of the Moon firsthand. The shadow of the Earth is seen on the Moon during a lunar eclipse. Interesting lesson!

Color of the Moon

In discussing moon color, the question often arises about the "Blue Moon." The term "Blue Moon," for what it's worth, is the name given to the second full moon that appears in a calendar month. Since the lunar cycle is 29.5 days and the average month is 30 days, there will be times when the 29.5-day cycle fits within a calendar month. This happens every 2.7 years, on the average. The blue moon has little to do with physics or astronomy. However, the term "Blue Moon" also refers to a different phenomenon that involves physics: That's when the moon's disk appears bluish, which occurs when the Earth's atmosphere contains particles 0.8 to 1.8 microns in diameter, slightly larger than the wavelength of visible light. Such particles, produced by forest fires or volcanoes, scatter red light while allowing the blue through (just the opposite of red getting through blue, scattering to produce red sunsets).

The Sun

Sunspots are dark, because they are cooler than the surrounding regions. Their darkness has to do with the contrast of hotter regions. If you put a 75-watt light bulb and a 100-watt lightbulb at the ends of your lecture table, they both look rather bright. Bring them together, and the 75-watt bulb looks darker when held in front of the brighter 100-watt bulb. (In a similar way, the black you see on a TV screen is actually no blacker than the "gray" face when not lit up. It looks black in contrast to the brightness of the illuminated part.)

Consider scaling the solar system down to the size of a football field, where the sun is on the goal line and Earth on the 2-yard line (leaving some room for Mercury and Venus). Mercury would then be on the 2-foot line and Venus on the 4-foot line. Beyond Earth, Mars would be on the 3-yard line, Jupiter on the 10-yard line, Saturn on the 20-yard line, Uranus on the 40-yard line, Neptune on the 60-yard line, and Pluto on the 80-yard line. On this scale, the nearest star would be 1000 miles away!

Planets of the Solar System

ACTIVITY: Integrate planetary sizes and distances into the student's experience by scaling 1 foot = one million miles. Then the Sun is close to the size of a basketball. The planets are small objects that can be held in the hand. Calculate the sizes and distances of one or two planets with your students, and let them calculate others. The Earth, for example, would be 93 feet away from the basketball, easy to set off as paces. Ask for a volunteer for each of the other planets. Whoever volunteers for Pluto (average distance some 3800 million miles) will have to pace 3800 feet away across town!

The Inner Planets—Mercury, Venus, Earth, and Mars

People who talk about visiting Mars usually have no idea of how far away it is. They may remember that it is supposed to take 2 years to reach it, but how far away is it? It is not a short hop away on a spaceship. Scaling of the solar system is a worthwhile activity.

The space probe *Mars Odyssey* reached Mars in October 2002, and discovered via its gamma ray spectrometer enough ice lurking under the Martian surface to fill Lake Michigan twice over. This indicates the planet could have supported life in a wetter past. Mars continues to intrigue us.

The Outer Planets—Jupiter, Saturn, Uranus, and Neptune

Uranus is barely perceptible to the naked eye in a clean dark sky. In ancient times, without photographic film and time exposures that betray movement in the skies, Uranus went unnoticed as a planet. Nobody noticed that it wandered. Photographic time exposures were one of the first boons to astronomy.

Since *Voyager 2* flew past Neptune in 1989, astronomers claim to have found three additional moons about Neptune. This brings its number to 11 moons. Confirmation awaits.

Pluto

Rather than being the pipsqueak of planets, Pluto is now recognized by the scientific community as being the king of the Kuiper belt. Perhaps for sentimental reasons, we should still regard Pluto as a planet. But then in fairness, many other similar bodies should enjoy the same status. One such body in the Kuiper belt was discovered in 2002—Quaoar, which like Pluto, has a moon. So what is it—eight planets or more than a couple of dozen new planets?

Asteroids, Meteoroids, and Comets

Meteorites

How have scientists established the age of the Earth as 4.5 billion years? By rock samples? No, any rocks that existed in early Earth have long ago subducted to magma and become part of the rock cycle (Chapter 23). We date the Earth not by dating Earth rocks, but by dating meteors, which presumably coalesced at the same time as the Earth. Geologists love meteors!

Meteor showers dump an estimated 360 to 6000 tons of cosmic dust on the Earth each year. Annual meteor showers occur when the Earth passes through streams of material formed from the outgassing of a comet's nucleus as it nears perihelion. Micrometeorites do not incandesce like larger meteorites, because their large surface area to mass ratio allows them to radiate heat very rapidly. They pass through the atmosphere relatively unchanged. It turns out the Earth appears to be under a constant rain of micrometeorites. Collecting them can be done by placing the sticky side of ordinary Scotch tape upon a rooftop exposed to the clear sky. Investigation of the tape after several hours of exposure can be done by microscope, where the tape is sandwiched between microscope slides. At a magnification of about 100, airborne dust, pollen, and various types of industrial pollution are evident on the tape. Micrometeorites appear as metallic nickel–iron spheres. You'll need to be proficient at identifying nickel–iron compounds to increase the likelihood of extraterrestrial origin. More of these should be found, of course, during times of meteor showers.

How long does a comet live? Answer: Until it runs out of gas. The text states that the orbits of comets extend far beyond the orbit of Pluto. This is true for most comets, but not the shorter periodic comets like Halley's (76 years), which orbits the sun well within the solar system. The majority of comets discovered each year are the long-period comets that take 100,000 to 1 million years to complete a solar orbit. Most of their times are beyond the orbit of Pluto, at distances of 40,000 to 50,000 AU from the sun—about one-fifth the way to the nearest star.

Integrated Science—Physics: Why One Side of the Moon Always Faces Us

The moon's gravitational lock on Earth such that one side always faces us may need further explanation, for Figure 27.28 cites two concepts not covered earlier in the text: torque and center of mass. The center of mass of the moon is in its geometric center (assuming symmetrical structure). The center of gravity, with respect to the Earth, is displaced toward the Earth from its center of mass. This is because the nearer side of the moon interacts with more force than the far part—it "weighs" more. Like a compass, any off-axis orientation with the force field produces a torque that tends to line it on-axis. (Torque is treated in Appendix B.)

This chapter provides the important facts and findings of astronomy and cosmology. However, astronomy and cosmology involve unfathomable distances and time sequences. You might utilize films and other media in an effort to convey processes occurring over great time spans and distances. For example:

- NASA's film "Flight of Apollo 11" (29 minutes) shows the dynamics of the solar system, star systems, and galaxies.
- NASA's "Space Shuttle: A Remarkable Flying Machine" (31 minutes) illustrates Kepler's and Newton's laws.
- TV tape from the Nova series "Lives of the Stars" (60 minutes) presents stellar evolution in supercompressed time, with characteristics of the sun, white dwarfs, neutron stars, and black holes.
- A great little book with many teaching tips is *West's Great Ideas for Teaching Astronomy,* by West Publishing Company, 1989. Some of the ideas in the suggested lecture below come from this dandy book.

In the *Practice Book*:
- Stellar Parallax

In *Next-Time Questions*:
- Solar Black Hole
- Olbers's Paradox

Transparencies:
Figures 28.2, 28.8, 28.9, 28.11, 28.21, 28.22, 28.23

Suggested Presentation

Begin by relating the statement by the French philosopher Auguste Compte in the early 1800s: that humankind, despite advances in science, would never know much about the distant stars—certainly not their chemical compositions. Considering the information available to Compte and his contemporaries at that time, the conjecture was reasonable, for the great distance of the stars seemed certainly to put information about them out of reach. What Compte didn't realize, however, is that the light emitted by those stars, quite within reach, contained much information about their makeup. Starlight betrays the elements that emit it, as the soon-to-come science of spectroscopy showed. That we know so much about stars is incredible—and the present time is the golden age for astronomers, who are presently finding more about them each decade than was ever known previously. Gone are the eyepieces on telescopes that once viewed only the visible part of the spectrum. In their place are receptors for the nonvisible parts of the spectrum—from radio waves to X-rays. The field of astronomy is bursting with excitement these days.

The Constellations

An interesting quote by Jeans on the constellations is "The division of the stars into constellations tells us very little about the stars, but a great deal about the minds of the earliest civilizations and of the mediaeval astronomers."

Discuss the constellations, the Big Dipper in particular, and Polaris. Every student in the northern hemisphere should be able to locate Polaris in the night sky. Explain why Polaris is directly overhead only at the pole, and how and why it is seen lower in the sky the closer one gets to the equator.

CHECK QUESTION: Polaris is stationary above the Earth's north pole and is a guide to all in the northern hemisphere. Why are there no "stationary stars" above [your city]?

Ask your class to pretend they are on a merry-go-round in motion, viewing lamps on the stationary ceiling overhead. Further suppose they took time-exposure photographs of the lamps above. What would the photos look like?

Confronting Astrology

To confront astrology, better than lecturing in an authoritarian manner, do as Stephen Pompea of the University of Arizona does and try the following experiment: Ask students not to consult a horoscope for three days. During this period, students keep a daily diary of their feelings and moods. They may also make note of how their financial and love lives are going, because this is a major aspect of horoscopic predictions. In class, distribute the 36 horoscopes of the three-day period, but with the sun signs removed and the order scrambled. Students must then find the three that best describe their days. Then, a comparison between their answers and the "correct" horoscopes is made to see if the predictive power of astrology is significant.

Interestingly enough, due to precession of the Earth about its axis, with a period of 26,000 years, the sun is about one and a half astrological signs off those of 3000 years ago, when astrology was born. During the last 3000 years, the Earth has wobbled about 1.5 constellations along the zodiac.

Astrology was an important stepping stone to science. It went beyond physical speculations and certainly emphasized observation, progressed to processes of experimentation, and to logical reasoning, which are now cornerstones of science. Interestingly, science advanced faster in Western rather than Eastern cultures, largely because of the different social and political climates. While early Greeks in an era of experimental democracy and free thinking were questioning their speculations about the world about them, their counterparts in eastern parts of the world were largely occupied in absorbing the knowledge of their forebears. Absorbing this knowledge was the key to personal success. This may explain why the progress in science in regions like China were without the period of questioning that accelerated the scientific advances of Europe and Eurasia.

I (Hewitt) like the position of my good friend Will Maynez who believes in astrology in the sense that we're all connected somehow in a cosmic way. What he adamantly doesn't believe in is astrologers!

Birth of Stars

Just as a child cannot see the aging of friends from babies to adults, the astronomer cannot see stellar evolution directly. But the child can see the various ages of other children, adults, and elderly people, even though seeing the transition for any one person is not possible. The direction of time is evident. Just as a baby in no way resembles its form as an elderly person, changes in a star throughout its lifetime are similar. Young stars do not resemble mature stars, and in no way do they resemble dead stars.

Stellar Distances—Parallax

How do we know the distances to stars? We know by parallax, which you may want to explain, though this is not covered in the text for the sake of brevity. Begin by having students hold a finger at arm's length in front of their faces and look with one eye at the position of the finger with respect to the background. Then have them switch eyes. Parallax! The parallax is easily seen, because the finger is relatively close to the eye. The parallax of more distant objects is more difficult to see, as can be seen by judging the distance of something a few meters distant, and then something many meters distant. Cite the importance of the distance between one's eyes—the baseline. At any given moment, the largest baseline for finding parallax among the stars is the Earth's diameter. Stars viewed from one side of the Earth can be compared to the same stars viewed at the opposite side of the Earth. A still larger baseline that takes a 6-month interval to utilize is the diameter of the Earth's orbit about the sun. Have your students do the Practice Page on parallax at this point.

Ever wonder why a chicken or pigeon bobs its head while it walks? Ronald Stoner of Bowling Green University ties the chicken walk to stellar parallax. Here's how: While the chicken's body moves forward, the head remains momentarily fixed as if anchored in space. This is because a chicken's eyes are on the sides of its head, not suited for parallax viewing. Vision for the chicken is monocular. So the chicken gauges distances to objects in its sight by the shifts of the objects against the background with succeeding steps. Images on the retina of the chicken are compared when the head moves through a standard difference (one step). Astronomers, likewise, measure distances to the stars by noting shifts of images of stars on photographic plates when the telescope moves through a standard difference (one-half Earth orbit around the sun). Just as a chicken compares the image of something in the foreground with the background between steps, an astronomer does much the same with foreground and background stars between 6-month intervals.

Life and Evolution of Stars

Chris Impey at the University of Arizona points out that the composition of humans is quite different from the composition of the universe as a whole. Of every 10,000 atoms in the sun, 7400 are H, 2440 are He, only 3 are C, 2 are N, 5 are O, and 150 all other elements. But of the same 10,000 atoms in a child's body, or anyone's body, 6500 are H, 2 are He, 2000 are C, 500 are N, 900 are O, and 100 all other elements. Our bodies are cinders formed in the residue of stellar collapses in a universe that is overwhelmingly H and He. It is important to stress that the cinders came from previous generations of stars—before the sun formed.

Stars, like all parts of nature, eventually run their course. Even the sun will burn out in 5 million more years. In its death throes, it will expand to become a red giant, swallowing the Earth. Will humans be on Earth awaiting this fate? Speculation says no—we'll have reached our end by then or be somewhere more hospitable.

The bigger they are, the harder they fall. This is the plight of the giant stars when they become supernovae. Supernovae are of particular interest to us, because they are the source of all atoms heavier than iron. The heavy elements consume energy when fused, so they don't get manufactured in normal stellar fusion. These elements are formed when giant stars explode. These are the supernovae.

Stellar Masses—Binary Stars

Binary stars offer the astronomer a direct means of determining the mass of a star. About half the stars in the sky are binaries. Do as Gene Maynard of Radford University does and attach a pair of Styrofoam balls of different diameters (and masses) with plastic sticks to model binary star systems. Balance on a finger to illustrate the center of mass, and the center about which the stars circle each other. The relative sizes of orbit about the center of mass are easily seen to relate to the relative masses.

Black Holes

When you toss garbage into a garbage disposal without putting the lid on, much material goes into the drain, but some pieces come flying out considerably faster than they went in. It is similar for matter that encounters a black hole. The death of a giant star is the birth of a black hole. Recent findings of gamma-ray bursts of radiation indicate the birth of black holes. One theory is that jets of radiation from a forming black hole generate a supernova in the process. Black holes are a fascinating topic to students.

Galaxies

Invite your students to make their own model of a spiral galaxy the next time they have a cup of coffee, as Stephen Pompea at the University of Arizona does with his students. Simply stir the coffee before adding a little cream—the cream will take a shape not unlike a spiral galaxy. Fluid flow in a cup of coffee approximates the flow on a much larger scale, just as wind tunnel tests on tiny airplanes predict the behavior of larger ones in larger air flows. (There is more on this in P. Stevens's book, *Patterns in Nature*.)

We think of stars as motionless in the sky. Actually, most are orbiting galactic centers, in a way similar to the planets orbiting the sun. If a planet ever stopped in its tracks, it would simply fall into the sun. This situation is similar to that with stars that orbit galactic centers. When they don't have sufficient tangential velocities, they do fall into the galactic centers, usually black holes. Stars, like planets, are always on the move.

The Big Bang

Most astrophysicists subscribe to the Big Bang theory, called the "standard model." Present estimates are of a universe some 13.7 billion years old, with 4% ordinary matter, 23% invisible stuff called dark matter, and 73% so-called dark energy. Point out that this model doesn't picture an explosion *in* space at a time in the past, like a giant firecracker going off, but rather *an explosion of space and time*. This is heavy stuff—and intriguing stuff. More intriguing is recent evidence that the universe is accelerating in its expansion—which challenges the simple model of a universe that blows up like a firecracker in space, with remnants slowing with time. Presently, there are many more questions than answers, so encourage your students to make hypotheses about some of the questions in astronomy, and incorporate news articles and video clips of cutting-edge discoveries about cosmology and the universe.

Appendix B Linear and Rotational Motion

Advanced Concepts of Motion
Circular Motion
Torque
Angular Momentum
Conservation of Angular Momentum

This material extends the brief treatment of linear motion in Chapter 2. It shows in detail the results of Galileo's inclined plane experiment, where acceleration is evident. The derivation of the relationship of distance and time is shown on page B-1. A look at the pair of tracks made by Chelcie Liu on page B-2 should alone make this appendix appealing to the instructor. You'll have fun with this in your class!

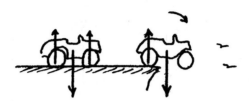

Torques are covered here, mentioned briefly in Chapter 27 when the gravity lock of the Moon is described. The fact that a torque accounts for a change in rotation is nicely illustrated with a chalkboard explanation of why a vehicle rotates after driving off a cliff.

Circular motion is briefly treated. Tangential speed is directly proportional to rotational speed; $v = r\omega$, where r is the radial distance from the center of circular motion, and ω is the rotational (angular) speed in radians per second. When proportionalities are used, you can say RPMs (rotations per minute), a more common expression for rotational speed.

What would be the likely path of a person lost in the woods who has one leg shorter than the other? The path would likely be circular. The longer leg goes farther than the shorter one with each step. So it is that a railroad train executes turns on curved tracks.

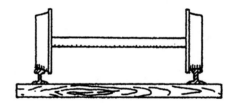

The wheels are slightly beveled, with the inside slightly wider than the outside. In accord with $v = r\omega$, the wider part travels faster and farther than the narrower part. The wheels of trains are rigidly attached (no differential like on many other vehicles). Both wheels rotate with the same ω. But when one wheel rides on the wide part of the beveled surface, it moves faster and farther than the opposite wheel that rides on its narrow part (smaller r). Rolling a tapered cup shows this. Tape a pair of cups together at their mouths, and you'll be able to roll the pair along a pair of parallel metersticks. (Note this in the Next-Time Question on Rolling Cups.) They won't roll off the tracks. When they start to, the wide part goes faster and self-corrects, and likewise with a train. After a train rounds a curve, the passengers feel the train swaying to and fro a bit. The wheels are self-correcting and stay on the track.

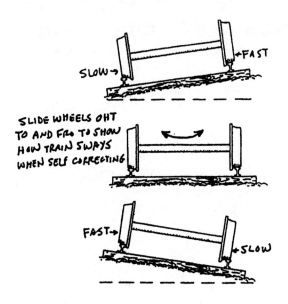

SLOW→   →FAST

SLIDE WHEELS OUT
TO AND FRO TO SHOW
HOW TRAIN SWAYS
WHEN SELF CORRECTING

FAST→   ←SLOW

Angular momentum and its conservation are treated here. Both are mentioned in Chapter 27 with respect to the nebular theory.

In the *Practice Book*:
• Mobile Torques
• Torques and See-Saws

In *Next-Time Questions*:
• Greatest Average Speed
• Torque pull
• Speed involves distance and time
• Path of object on rotating disk
• Rolling cups
• Advanced concepts of motion
• Circular motion
• Torque
• Angular momentum
• Conservation of angular momentum

Appendix C   Vectors

Adding Vectors
Finding Components of Vectors
The Polarization of Light—An Application of Vector Components

There are two impressive applications of vectors in elementary physics. One is the method of sailboats tacking into the wind, and the other is the explanation for light traversing a pair of crossed Polaroids sandwiching another. Both are treated in this appendix, and the sailboat treatment is in the Practice Book. If you're going to go beyond a minimal treatment of vectors, these two applications are a must.

In the *Practice Book*:
• Vectors and Sailboats

In *Next-Time Questions*:
• Sailing on a windy day
• Sail impact
• Plane of polarization
• Polaroids overlap
• Air speed relative to ground speed

Appendix D Exponential Growth and Doubling Time

This material, adapted from papers written by Al Bartlett, makes a fine lecture. The material is not only very important but is fascinating—and very wide in scope. It can nicely follow discussions of population growth, global warming, and continued industrial growth. Or it can be coupled to a discussion of exponential decay—as in discharging a capacitor, cooling a vessel of water, or radioactive disintegration—and radioactive half-life as treated in Chapter 10. Although not part of any chapter, it can be treated in any break—following an exam, perhaps, or on any day that lends itself to a departure from chapter material.

The concept of growth rate can be expressed in simple steps:

Step 1: (new amount) = (old amount) + k times (old amount).

Step 2: (new amount) becomes (old amount).

Step 3: Keep repeating. That's it. The mathematics is just arithmetic. Use positive k for growth, and negative k for decay.

A beginning application is a simple 10% annual interest on each dollar in a savings account. At the end of the first year, $A = 1 + 0.10(1)$; second year, $A = 1.10 + 0.10(1.10)$; third year, $A = 1.21 + 0.10(1.21)$; and so on. Suppose your savings are silver dollars, and the bank charges 10% annual storage fee.

	INTEREST		RENTAL	
Year	Change	Amount	Change	Amount
0		1.00		1.00
1	+0.100	1.10	−0.100	0.90
2	+0.110	1.21	−0.090	0.81
3	+0.121	1.33	−0.081	0.73
4	+0.133	1.46	−0.073	0.66
5	+0.146	1.61	−0.066	0.59
6	+0.161	1.77	−0.059	0.53
7	+0.177	1.95	−0.053	0.48
8	+0.195	2.14	−0.048	0.43
9	+0.214	2.36	−0.043	0.39
10	+0.236	2.59	−0.039	0.35
20	+0.612	6.73	−0.014	0.12

Note that in 7 years at a 10% rate, the amount just about doubles for positive k and just about halves for negative k.

It is customary to use the decay halving time (half-life) of processes such as radioactive decay as a property of the decaying elements. There is nothing special about doubling–halving time. Tripling–thirding or 3/2ing–2/3ing, or any factor and its reciprocal could be used. As the number of time intervals increases, the process approaches continuity, which leads to the exponential, e^{kt}.

The formula for doubling time in the text appears without derivation, which is likely beyond the scope of your class. Its derivation is as follows: Exponential growth may be described by the equation

$$A = A_o e^{kt}$$

where k is the rate of increase of the quantity A_o. Reexpress this for a time T when $A = 2A_o$,

$$2A_o = A_o e^{kT}$$

If we take the natural logarithm of each side, we get

$$\ln 2 = kT \text{ where } T = \frac{\ln 2}{k} = \frac{0.693}{k}$$

If k is expressed in percent, then

$$T = \frac{69.3}{\%} \sim \frac{70}{\%}$$

When percentage figures are given for things such as interest rates, population growth, or consumption of nonrenewable resources, conversion to doubling time greatly enhances the meaning of these figures.

In *Next-Time Questions*:
- Beanstalk
- Paper Fold

Answers to Appendix D Problems

1. The pond was half-covered on the 29th day, and one-quarter–covered on the 28th day.

2. A dollar loses 1/2 its value in one doubling time of the inflationary economy; this is 70/7% = 10 years. If the dollar is loaned at 7% compound interest, it loses nothing.

3. At a steady inflation rate of 7%, the doubling time is 70/7% = 10 years; so every 10 years, the prices of these items will double. This means the $20 theater ticket in 10 years will cost $40, in 20 years will cost $80, in 30 years will cost $160, in 40 years will cost $320, and in 50 years will cost $640. The $200 suit of clothes will similarly jump each decade to $400, $800, $1600, $3,200, and $6,400. For a $20,000 car, the decade jumps will be $40,000, $80,000, $160,000, $320,000, and $640,000. For a $200,000 home, the decade jumps in price are $400,000, $800,000, $1600,000, $3,200,000, and $6,400,000! Inflation often increases earnings more than prices, so we'll be able to pay for these things, and more.

4. For a 5% growth rate, 42 years is three doubling times (70/5% = 14 years; 42/14 = 3). Three doubling times is an eightfold increase. So in 42 years, the city would have to have eight sewerage treatment plants to remain as presently loaded; more than eight if load per plant is to be reduced while servicing eight times as many people.

5. All things being equal, doubling of food for twice the number of people simply means that twice as many people will be eating, and twice as many will be starving as are starving now!

6. Doubling one penny for 30 days yields a total of $10,737,418.23! On the 30th day, your wages will be $5,368,709.12, which is one penny more than the $5,368,709.11 total from all the preceding days.

Answers to *Conceptual Integrated Science* End-of-Chapter Questions

Chapter 1: About Science

Answers to Chapter 1 Review Questions

1. The era of modern science in the 16th century was launched when Galileo Galilei revived the Copernican view of the heliocentric universe, using experiments to study nature's behavior.

2. In *Conceptual Integrated Science*, we believe that focusing on math too early is a poor substitute for concepts.

3. We mean that it must be capable of being proved wrong.

4. Nonscientific hypotheses may be perfectly reasonable; they are nonscientific only because they are not falsifiable—there is no test for possible wrongness.

5. Galileo showed the falseness of Aristotle's claim with a single experiment—dropping heavy and light objects from the Leaning Tower of Pisa.

6. A scientific fact is something that competent observers can observe and agree to be true; a hypothesis is an explanation or answer that is capable of being proved wrong; a law is a hypothesis that has been tested over and over and not contradicted; a theory is a synthesis of facts and well-tested hypotheses.

7. In everyday speech, a theory is the same as a hypothesis—a statement that hasn't been tested.

8. Theories grow stronger and more precise as they evolve to include new information.

9. The term *supernatural* literally means "above nature." Science works within nature, not above it.

10. They rely on subjective personal experience and do not lead to testable hypotheses. They lie outside the realm of science.

11. Science, art, and religion can work very well together; like strings on a guitar, when played together, the chord they produce can be a chord of profound richness.

12. Science is concerned with gathering knowledge and organizing it. Technology lets humans use that knowledge for practical purposes, and it provides the instruments scientists need to conduct their investigations.

13. Chemistry builds on physics by telling us how matter is put together, how atoms combine to form molecules, and how the molecules combine to make the materials around us. Biology is more complex than physical science (physics and chemistry), because it involves matter that is alive and, therefore, engaged in complex biochemical processes.

14. Integrated science is valuable because the real-life phenomena we are interested in typically involve principles from more than one branch of science; put another way, we study integrated science because the world is integrated.

Answers to Chapter 1 Integrated Science Concepts

Chemistry and Biology: An Investigation of Sea Butterflies

1. The disciplines of biology and chemistry are needed to understand the behavior of the Antarctic amphipod.

2. The control used in the investigation was the pellets fed to the predator fish that were not treated with sea-butterfly extracts. The control was needed to see whether the chemical deterrent isolated from the sea butterfly deterred the predator fish.

3. McClintock and Baker's hypothesis was that amphipods carry sea butterflies because sea butterflies produce a chemical that deters a predator of the amphipod. This is a scientific hypothesis because it would be proven wrong if the secreted chemical were found to not deter amphipod predators.

Answers to Chapter 1 Exercises

1. Are the various branches of science separate or do they overlap? Give several examples to support your answer.

   The various branches of science overlap as we see by the existence of these hybrid fields: astrobiology; biochemistry; biophysics; ecology (biology and earth science); geochemistry, etc.

2. What do science, art, and religion have in common? How are they different?

   Science, art, and religion are all searches for deeper understanding of the world. The differences can be summed up as follows: science asks *how*, art asks *who*, and religion asks *why*. The most important difference between religion and science is that religion asks *why* and science asks *how*.

3. Can a person's religious beliefs be proven wrong? Can a person's understanding of a particular scientific concept be proven wrong ?

   No; religion is a subjective area of study so that it cannot be wrong in the sense of being provably false. However, religions that do claim to be based on a factual knowledge of the physical world that is provably false can be said to be logically flawed. A person can certainly be wrong in their understanding of scientific concepts—experiments and observation often can correct such misunderstandings.

4. In what sense is science grand and breathtaking? In what sense is it dull and painstaking?

   Science is grand and breathtaking in its remarkable insights into the mechanisms of the universe; it is dull and painstaking in that careful, disciplined, and sometimes even tedious research is needed to reach those conclusions.

5. How is the printing press like the Internet in terms of the history of science?

   The printing press greatly accelerated the progress of science by facilitating communication—suddenly practitioners of science could collaborate across distance. The Internet takes communication to a new level because it is so fast, open, and accessible.

Solutions to Chapter 1 Problems

1. The more candy bars you add to your diet per day, the more weight you gain (all other factors such as the amount of exercise you get being equal). Is this an example of a direct proportion or an inverse proportion?

   Direct proportion

2. State the above relation in mathematical form. (*Hint*: Don't forget to use a proportionality constant with appropriate units.)

   We set W = weight gain/week and C = candy bars eaten/week. Then the more candy bars you add to your diet per week, the more weight you gain per week is expressed like this: $W = \alpha C$, where α is the proportionality constant. Because W has units of lb/week and C has units of candy bars/week, $\alpha = W/C$ has units of lb/candy bars. Given values for W and C, one can solve for the numerical value of α. For example, if eating seven candy bars per week results in a 1-lb per week weight gain, $\alpha = 1/7$ lb/candy bars.

3. What is an example of an inverse proportion that you have observed in your daily life? Express it in mathematical form.

   Sample answer: The more you practice shooting a basketball (P), the fewer shots you miss (m); $P = k/m$.

Chapter 2: Describing Motion

Answers to Chapter 2 Review Questions

1. Aristotle classified motion into two kinds: *natural motion* and *violent motion.*

2. Aristotle believed forces were necessary. It was Galileo who later refuted this idea and established the concept of inertia.

3. Galileo discredited the idea that heavy objects fall faster than light ones, and that a force is necessary to maintain motion.

4. Experiment. In conducting experiments, Galileo ushered in the age of modern science.

5. Inertia.

6. Weight depends on gravity, while mass does not.

7. Your weight is greater on the Earth because of its stronger gravity. Your mass is the same at all locations.

8. Newtons for weight, kilograms for mass.

9. Less.

10. Any amount of water has the same density.

11. The net force on the box is 10 N to the right.

12. Both magnitude and direction.

13. Tension.

14. 20 N.

15. $\Sigma F = 0$ means that the vector sum of all the forces that act on an object in equilibrium equal zero. Forces cancel.

16. Because it acts at right angles to the surface. Normal is another term for "right angle."

17. The same. You actually read the support force by the scale, which is the same as your weight when the scale is stationary.

18. It is in equilibrium if its velocity is not changing.

19. Because it slides in equilibrium (constant velocity), we know the friction must be equal and opposite to our push. That way, they cancel, and the crate slides without changing speed.

20. Opposite, always.

21. To the left.

22. Yes, opposite to your push, just enough so that $\Sigma F = 0$.

23. speed = distance/time

24. Velocity involves both magnitude (speed) and direction. Speed involves only magnitude.

25. Instantaneous speed.

26. You can be at rest relative to the Earth but moving at 100,000 km/h relative to the sun.

27. acceleration = change in velocity/time interval

28. Acceleration is zero, and the net force is therefore zero.

29. It appears once for the unit of velocity, and again for the time during which velocity changes.

30. It decreases by 10 m/s each second.

Answers to Chapter 2 Multiple-Choice Questions

1c, 2d, 3b, 4a, 5a

Answers to Chapter 2 Integrated Science Concepts

Biology: Friction Is Universal

1. Synovial fluid is a lubricant. It protects the bones against the wearing effects of friction—bones rub against the lubricating synovial fluid instead of against each other.

2. Possible examples include physics–air resistance; chemistry–lubricants; biology–fingerprints; earth science–earthquakes; atronomy–meteors.

3. One might argue that friction prevents earthquakes in the sense that large blocks of rock are held still because of the friction between them. However, friction truly is implicated as a cause of earthquakes because if there were no friction, the blocks of rock could move along one another smoothly, never building up the strain that is released violently and suddenly in an earthquake.

Biology: Hang Time

1. Your speed is zero at the top of your jump.

2. Length of legs and strength of leg muscles.

Answers to Exercises

1. A bowling ball rolling along a lane gradually slows as it rolls. How would Aristotle interpret this observation? How would Galileo interpret it?

   Aristotle would likely say the ball slows to reach its natural state. Galileo would say the ball is encountering friction, an unbalanced force that slows it.

2. What Aristotelian idea did Galileo discredit in his fabled Leaning Tower of Pisa experiment? With his inclined plane experiments?

   The Leaning Tower experiment discredited the idea that heavy things fall proportionally faster. The incline plane experiments discredited the idea that a force was needed for motion.

3. What physical quantity is a measure of how much inertia an object has?

   Mass.

4. Does a dieting person more accurately lose mass or lose weight?

   Mass. To lose weight, the person could go to the top of a mountain where gravity is less. But the amount of matter would be the same.

5. One cm^3 of lead has a mass of 11.3 g. What is its density? Two grams of aluminum has a mass of 5.4 g. What is the density of aluminum?

   The density of lead is 11.3 g/cm^3. The density of aluminum is 5.4 g/2 cm^3 = 2.7 g/cm^3.

6. Which has the greater density—5 kg of lead or 10 kg of aluminum?

   Density is a ratio of weight or mass per volume, and this ratio is greater for any amount of lead than for any amount of aluminum, so 5 kg of lead has a greater density than 10 g of aluminum.

7. Consider a pair of forces, one with a magnitude of 25 N, and the other 15 N. What maximum net force is possible for these two forces? What is the minimum net force possible?

   Maximum, 25 N + 15 N = 40 N. Minimum, 25 N − 15 N = 10 N.

8. The sketch shows painter's scaffold in mechanical equilibrium. The person in the middle weighs 250 N, and the tensions in each rope are 200 N. What is the weight of the scaffold?

   From $\Sigma F = 0$, the upward forces are 400 N and the downward forces are 250 N + weight of the scaffold. The scaffold must weigh 150 N.

9. A different scaffold that weighs 300 N supports two painters, one 250 N and the other 300 N. The reading in the left scale is 400 N. What is the reading in the right scale?

   From $\Sigma F = 0$, the upward forces are 400 N + tension in right scale. This sum must equal the downward forces of 250 N + 300 N + 300 N. Arithmetic shows the reading on the right scale is 450 N.

10. Can an object be in mechanical equilibrium when only a single force acts on it? Explain.

    No, not unless the force is zero. A net force will accelerate the object.

11. Nellie Newton hangs at rest from the ends of the rope, as shown. How does the reading on the scale compare to her weight?

    Each scale shows half her weight.

12. Harry the painter swings year after year from his bosun's chair. His weight is 500 N, and the rope, unknown to him, has a breaking point of 300 N. Why doesn't the rope break when he is supported? One day Harry is painting near a flagpole, and, for a change, he ties the free end of the rope to the flagpole instead of to his chair as shown to the right. Why did Harry end up taking his vacation early?

    In the left figure, Harry is supported by two strands of rope that share his weight (like the little girl in the previous exercise). So, each strand supports only 250 N, below the breaking point. Total force up supplied by ropes equals weight acting downward, giving a net force of zero and no acceleration. In the right figure, Harry is now supported by one strand, which for Harry's well-being requires that the tension be 500 N. Because this is above the breaking point of the rope, it breaks. The net force on Harry is then only his weight, giving him a downward acceleration of g. The sudden return to zero velocity changes his vacation plans.

13. Consider the two forces acting on the person who stands still, namely, the downward pull of gravity and the upward support of the floor. Are these forces equal and opposite?

    Yes, the forces are equal and opposite and cancel to zero putting the person in equilibrium.

14. Can we accurately say that if something moves at constant velocity that there are no forces acting on it? Explain.

    No, we cannot, for there may well be forces that cancel to zero. We can say no net force acts on it.

15. At the moment an object tossed upward into the air reaches its highest point, is it in equilibrium? Defend your answer.

    No, for the force of gravity acts on the object. Its motion is undergoing change, as a moment later should be evident.

16. If you push horizontally on a crate and it slides across the floor, slightly gaining speed, how does the friction acting on the crate compare with your push?

    If the crate speeds up, then your force is greater than the force of friction.

17. What is the impact speed when a car moving at 100 km/h bumps into the rear of another car traveling in the same direction at 98 km/h?

    Relative speed is 2 km/h.

18. Harry Hotshot can paddle a canoe in still water at 8 km/h. How successful will he be at canoeing upstream in a river that flows at 8 km/h?

    Not very, for his speed will be zero relative to the land.

19. A destination of 120 miles is posted on a highway sign, and the speed limit is 60 miles/hour. If you drive at the posted speed, can you reach the destination in 2 hours? Or more than 2 hours?

    More than 2 hours, for you cannot maintain an average speed of 60 miles/hour without exceeding the speed limit. You begin at zero, and end at zero, so even if there's no slowing down along the way you'll have to exceed 60 mi/h to average 60 mi/h. So it will take you more than 2 hours.

20. Suppose that a freely falling object were somehow equipped with a speedometer. By how much would its speed reading increase with each second of fall?

    10 m/s.

21. Suppose that the freely falling object in the preceding exercise were also equipped with an odometer. Would the readings of distance fallen each second indicate equal or unequal distances of fall for successive seconds? Explain.

    Distance increases as the square of the time, so each successive distance covered is greater than the preceding distance covered.

22. When a ball player throws a ball straight up, by how much does the speed of the ball decrease each second while ascending? In the absence of air resistance, by how much does it increase each second while descending? How much time is required for rising compared to falling?

    The ball slows by 10 m/s each second and gains 10 m/s when descending. The time up equals the time down if air resistance is nil.

23. Someone standing at the edge of a cliff (as in Figure 2.24) throws a ball straight up at a certain speed and another ball straight down with the same initial speed. If air resistance is negligible, which ball has the greater speed when it strikes the ground below?

Both hit the ground with the same speed (but not in the same time).

24. For a freely falling object dropped from rest, what is its acceleration at the end of the 5th second of fall? The 10th second? Defend your answer (and distinguish between velocity and acceleration).

Acceleration is 10 m/s^2, constant, all the way down. (Velocity, however, is 50 m/s at 5 seconds, and 100 m/s at 10 seconds.)

25. Two balls, A and B, are released simultaneously from rest at the left end of the equal-length tracks A and B as shown. Which ball will reach the end of its track first?

The ball on B finishes first, for its average speed along the lower part as well as the down and up slopes is greater than the average speed of the ball along track A.

26. Refer to the tracks. (a) Does ball B roll faster along the lower part of track B than ball A rolls along track A? (b) Is the speed gained by ball B going down the extra dip the same as the speed it loses going up near the right-hand end—and doesn't this mean the speed of balls A and B will be the same at the ends of both tracks? (c) On track B, won't the average speed dipping down and up be greater than the average speed of ball A during the same time? (d) So overall, does ball A or ball B have the greater average speed? (Do you wish to change your answer to the previous exercise?)

(a) Average speed is greater for the ball on track B. (b) The instantaneous speed at the ends of the tracks is the same, because the speed gained on the down-ramp for B is equal to the speed lost on the up-ramp side. (Many people get the wrong answer for Exercise 25, because they assume that because the balls end up with the same speed that they roll for the same time. Not so.)

Solutions to Chapter 2 Problems

1. Find the net force produced by a 30-N force and a 20-N force in each of the following cases:

   (a) Both forces act in the same direction.

   (b) The two act in opposite directions.

   (a) 30 N + 20 N = 50 N.   (b) 30 N − 20 N = 10 N.

2. A horizontal force of 100 N is required to push a box across a floor at constant velocity.

   (a) What is the net force acting on the box?

   (b) How much is the friction force that acts on the box?

   (a) Net force is zero (because velocity is constant!).   (b) Friction = −100 N.

3. A firefighter with a mass of 100 kg slides down a vertical pole at constant speed. What is the force of friction provided by the pole?

   From ΣF = 0, friction equals weight, *mg*, = (100 kg)(9.8 m/s^2) = 980 N.

4. The ocean's level is currently rising at about 1.5 mm per year. At this rate, in how many years will sea level be 3 meters higher than now?

$$\text{From } v = \frac{d}{t}, t = \frac{d}{v}.$$

We convert 3 m to 3000 mm, and $t = \dfrac{3000 \text{ mm}}{1.5 \text{ mm/year}} = 2000$ years.

5. A vehicle changes its velocity from 90 km/h to a dead stop in 10 s. Show that its acceleration in doing so is −2.5 m/s^2.

$$a = \frac{\textit{change in velocity}}{\textit{time interval}} = \frac{-90 \text{ km/h}}{10 \text{ s}} = -2.5 \text{ km/h} \cdot \text{s}.$$

   (The vehicle decelerates at 2.5 km/h·s.)

6. A ball is thrown straight up with an initial speed of 40 m/s. (a) Show that its time in the air is about 8 seconds. (b) Show that its maximum height, neglecting air resistance, is about 80 m.

Because it starts going up at 40 m/s and loses 10 m/s each second, its time going up is 4 seconds. Its time returning is also 4 seconds, so it's in the air for a total of 8 seconds. Distance up (or down) is $1/2\, gt^2 = 5 \times 4^2 = 80$ m. Or from $d = vt$, where average velocity is $(40 + 0)/2 = 20$ m/s, and time is 4 seconds, we also get $d = 20$ m/s $\times$ 4 s = 80 m.

7. Extend Table 2.2 (which gives values of from 0 to 5 s) to 0 to 10 s, assuming no air resistance.

Time (in seconds)	Velocity (in meters/second)	Distance (in meters)
0	0	0
1	10	5
2	20	20
3	30	45
4	40	80
5	50	125
6	60	180
7	70	245
8	80	320
9	90	405
10	100	500

8. A ball is thrown with enough speed straight up so that it is in the air several seconds. (a) What is the velocity of the ball when it reaches its highest point? (b) What is its velocity 1 s before it reaches its highest point? (c) What is the change in its velocity during this 1-s interval? (d) What is its velocity 1 s after it reaches its highest point? (e) What is the change in velocity during this 1-s interval? (f) What is the change in velocity during the 2-s interval? (Caution: velocity, not speed!) (g) What is the acceleration of the ball during any of these time intervals and at the moment the ball has zero velocity?

(a) The velocity of the ball at the top of its vertical trajectory is instantaneously zero.

(b) One second before reaching its top, its velocity is 10 m/s.

(c) The amount of change in velocity is 10 m/s during this 1-second interval (or any other 1-second interval).

(d) One second after reaching its top its, velocity is −10 m/s—equal in magnitude but oppositely directed to its value 1 second before reaching the top.

(e) The amount of change in velocity during this (or any) 1-second interval is 10 m/s.

(f) In 2 seconds, the amount of change in velocity, from 10 m/s up to 10 m/s down, is 20 m/s (not zero!)

(g) The acceleration of the ball is 10 m/s^2 before reaching the top, when reaching the top, and after reaching the top. In all cases, acceleration is downward, toward the Earth.

Chapter 3: Newton's Laws of Motion

Answers to Chapter 3 Review Questions

1. Every object continues in a state of rest, or in a state of motion in a straight line at constant speed, unless it is compelled to change that state by forces exerted upon it.

2. Straight line.

3. The acceleration produced by a net force on an object is directly proportional to the net force, is in the same direction as the net force, and is inversely proportional to the mass of the object.

4. Acceleration is directly proportional to force. As an example, if the net force on a body is doubled, the acceleration doubles also.

5. No change in acceleration.

6. 10 m/s^2.

7. When in free fall, the ratio of weight/mass is the same for all objects.

8. Zero.

9. Air resistance depends on speed and surface area.

10. The greater weight of the heavier person compared to air drag produces a greater acceleration until terminal velocity is reached.

11. Two.

12. When you push on the wall, the wall pushes on you. It is the force of the wall on your fingers that bends them.

13. He can't exert any more force on the tissue paper than the tissue paper can exert on him. The tissue paper has insufficient inertia for a great force.

14. Whenever one object exerts a force on a second object, the second object exerts an equal and opposite force on the first.

15. Ball against the bat.

16. Simultaneously.

17. Each of the equal forces acts on different masses.

18. An external force is needed to accelerate a system.

19. Force, velocity, and acceleration are vector quantities. Time, speed, and volume are scalar quantities.

20. The resultant is $\sqrt{2}$ times greater than each of the equal-length, right-angled vectors.

21. The diagonal represents the resultant vector.

22. (a) Yes. (b) Yes.

Answers to Chapter 3 Multiple-Choice Questions

1d, 2b, 3a, 4c, 5d

Answers to Chapter 3 Integrated Science Concepts

Biology: Gliding

1. Gliding describes a mode of locomotion in which animals move through the air in a controlled fall.

2. The more air resistance an animal encounters, the slower and more controllable its fall. And, the amount of air resistance a falling object encounters depends on the object's surface area.

3. "Flying" squirrels have large flaps of skin between their front and hind legs; Draco lizards have long extendable ribs that support large gliding membranes; "flying" frogs have very long toes with extensive webbing between them; gliding geckos have skin flaps along their sides and tails in addition to webbed toes.

Biology: Animal Locomotion

1. In animal locomotion, an animal typically pushes against some medium (the ground, water, or air) that pushes back on it, providing the force needed for the animal to accelerate.

2. Newton's third law: the squid pushes the water, the water pushes the squid.

3. The force of friction between your back foot and the floor pushes you forward.

4. The slippery surface cannot provide a large reaction force to the duck's push against it.

Answers to Chapter 3 Exercises

1. In the orbiting space shuttle, you are handed two identical closed boxes, one filled with sand and the other filled with feathers. How can you tell which is which without opening the boxes?

   Poke or kick the boxes. The one that more greatly resists a change in motion is the one with the greater mass—the one filled with sand.

2. Your empty hand is not hurt when it bangs lightly against a wall. Why is it hurt if it is carrying a heavy load? Which of Newton's laws is most applicable here?

   Mainly the first law, for the bag in motion tends to continue in motion, which results in a squashed hand.

3. Each of the chain of bones forming your spine is separated from its neighbors by disks of elastic tissue. What happens, then, when you jump heavily on your feet from an elevated position? Can you think of a reason why you are a little taller in the morning than in the night? (*Hint:* Think about how Newton's first law of motion applies in this case.)

   Newton's first law again—when you jump, you tighten the disks. This is similar to how you can tighten a hammerhead by banging it against a surface. The greater inertia of the massive hammerhead makes it harder to stop than the less massive hammer handle. Similarly, when you jump you tighten your vertebrae. This effect also explains why you're shorter at the end of the day. At night, while lying prone, relaxation undoes the compression and you're taller!

4. As you stand on a floor, does the floor exert an upward force against your feet? How much force does it exert? Why are you not moved upward by this force?

   Yes, an upward support force acts on you while standing on a floor, which is equal and opposite to the force of gravity on you—your weight. You are not moved upward by this force, because it is only one of two vertical forces acting on you, making the net force zero.

5. To pull a wagon across a lawn with constant velocity, you have to exert a steady force. Reconcile this fact with Newton's first law, which says that motion with constant velocity indicates no force.

   You exert a force to overcome the force of friction. This makes the net force zero, which is why the wagon moves without acceleration. If you pull harder, then net force will be greater than zero, and acceleration will occur.

6. A rocket becomes progressively easier to accelerate as it travels through space. Why is this so? (*Hint:* About 90% of the mass of a newly launched rocket is fuel.)

   Let Newton's second law guide the answer to this: $a = F/m$. As m gets less (much the mass of the fuel), acceleration a increases for a constant force.

7. As you are leaping upward from the ground, how does the force that you exert on the ground compare with your weight?

   The force that you exert on the ground is greater than your weight, for you momentarily accelerate upward. Then the ground simultaneously pushes upward on you with the same amount of force.

8. A common saying goes, "It's not the fall that hurts you; it's the sudden stop." Translate this into Newton's laws of motion.

   The sudden stop involves a large acceleration. So in accord with $a = F/m$, a large a means a large F. Ouch!

9. On which of these hills does the ball roll down with increasing speed and decreasing acceleration along the path? (Use this example if you wish to explain to someone the difference between speed and acceleration.)

   Only on hill B does the acceleration along the path decrease with time, for the hill becomes less steep as motion progresses. When the hill levels off, acceleration will be zero. On hill A, acceleration is constant. On hill C, acceleration increases as the hill becomes steeper. In all three cases, speed increases.

10. Neglecting air resistance, if you drop an object, its acceleration toward the ground is 10 m/s^2. If you throw it down instead, would its acceleration after throwing be greater than 10 m/s^2? Why or why not?

    When air resistance affects motion, the ball thrown upward returns to its starting level with less speed than its initial speed, and also less speed than the ball tossed downward. The downward thrown ball hits the ground below with a greater speed.

11. In the preceding exercise, can you think of a reason why the acceleration of the object thrown downward through the air would actually be less than 10 m/s^2?

Air resistance on the thrown object decreases the net force on it ($mg - R$), making its acceleration less than that of free fall.

12. You hold an apple over your head. (a) Identify all the forces acting on the apple and their reaction forces. (b) When you drop the apple, identify all the forces acting on it as it falls and the corresponding reaction forces.

(a) Two force pairs act; Earth's pull on the apple (action), and the apple's pull on the Earth (reaction). Hand pushes apple upward (action), and apple pushes hand downward (reaction). (b) If air drag can be neglected, one force pair acts; Earth's pull on apple, and apple's pull on Earth. If air drag counts, then air pushes upward on apple (action), and apple pushes downward on air (reaction).

13. Does a stick of dynamite contain force? Defend your answer.

Neither a stick of dynamite nor anything else "contains" force. We will see later that a stick of dynamite contains *energy*, which is capable of producing forces when an interaction of some kind occurs.

14. Can a dog wag its tail without the tail, in turn, "wagging the dog"? (Consider a dog with a relatively massive tail.)

No, for in action–reaction fashion, the tail also wags the dog. How much depends on the relative masses of the dog and its tail.

15. If the Earth exerts a gravitational force of 1000 N on an orbiting communications satellite, how much force does the satellite exert on the Earth?

1000 N.

16. If you exert a horizontal force of 200 N to slide a crate across a factory floor at constant velocity, how much friction is exerted by the floor on the crate? Is the force of friction equal and oppositely directed to your 200-N push? Does the force of friction make up the reaction force to your push? Why not?

The friction on the crate is 200 N, which cancels your 200-N push on the crate to yield the zero net force that accounts for the constant velocity (zero acceleration). Although the friction force is equal and oppositely directed to the applied force, the two do *not* make an action–reaction pair of forces. That's because both forces *do* act on the same object—the crate. The reaction to your push on the crate is the crate's push back on you. The reaction to the frictional force of the floor on the crate is the opposite friction force of the crate on the floor.

17. If a Mack truck and motorcycle have a head-on collision, upon which vehicle is the impact force greater? Which vehicle undergoes the greater change in its motion? Explain your answers.

In accord with Newton's third law, the force on each will be of the same magnitude. But the effect of the force (acceleration) will be different for each because of the different mass. The more massive truck undergoes less change in motion than the motorcycle.

18. Two people of equal mass attempt a tug-of-war with a 12-m rope while standing on frictionless ice. When they pull on the rope, they each slide toward each other. How do their accelerations compare, and how far does each person slide before they meet?

The forces on each are the same in magnitude, and their masses are the same, so their accelerations will be the same. They will slide equal distances of 6 meters to meet at the midpoint.

19. Suppose in the preceding exercise that one person has twice the mass of the other. How far does each person slide before they meet?

The person with twice the mass slides half as far as the twice-as-massive person. That means the lighter one slides 4 feet, and the heavier one slides 8 feet (for a total of 12 feet).

20. Which team wins in a tug-of-war; the team that pulls harder on the rope, or the team that pushes harder against the ground? Explain.

The winning team pushes harder against the ground. The ground then pushes harder on them, producing a net force in their favor.

21. The photo shows Steve Hewitt and his daughter Gretchen touching. Is Steve touching Gretchen, or is Gretchen touching Steve? Explain.

In accord with Newton's third law, Steve and Gretchen are touching each other. One may initiate the touch, but the physical interaction can't occur without contact between both Steve and Gretchen. Indeed, you cannot touch without being touched!

22. When your hand turns the handle of a faucet, water comes out. Does your push on the handle and the water coming out comprise an action–reaction pair? Defend your answer.

No. The reaction to the force of your hand on the handle is the force of the handle on your hand. A on B, action; B on A, reaction (not C on A!).

23. Why is it that a cat that falls from the top of a 50-story building will hit the ground no faster than if it fell from the 20th story?

The terminal speed attained by the falling cat is the same whether it falls from 50 stories or 20 stories. Once terminal speed is reached, falling extra distance does not affect the speed. (The low terminal velocities of small creatures enable them to fall without harm from heights that would kill larger creatures.)

24. Free fall is motion in which gravity is the only force acting. (a) Is a sky diver who has reached terminal speed in free fall? (b) Is a satellite circling the Earth above the atmosphere in free fall?

(a) A skydiver encountering no air resistance is in free fall. One at terminal velocity does encounter air resistance and is not in free fall. (b) The only force acting on a satellite is that due to gravity, so a satellite is in free fall (much more about this in Chapter 5).

25. How does the weight of a falling body compare to the air resistance it encounters just before it reaches terminal velocity? After?

Before reaching terminal velocity, weight is greater than air resistance. After reaching terminal velocity, both weight and air resistance are of the same magnitude. Then the net force and acceleration are both zero.

26. You tell your friend that the acceleration of a skydiver decreases as falling progresses. Your friend then asks if this means the skydiver is slowing down. What is your response?

Your friend is correct; the skydiver is, in fact, slowing down as acceleration decreases in a dive. Eventually the acceleration will become zero, in which case the diver has reached terminal velocity.

27. If and when Galileo dropped two balls from the top of the Leaning Tower of Pisa, air resistance was not really negligible. Assuming both balls were the same size yet one much heavier than the other, which ball struck the ground first? Why?

Air resistance is not really negligible for so high a drop, so the heavier ball does strike the ground first. But although a twice-as-heavy ball strikes first, it falls only a little faster, and not twice as fast, which is what followers of Aristotle believed. Galileo recognized that the small difference is due to friction and would not be present if there were no friction.

28. If you simultaneously drop a pair of tennis balls from the top of a building, they will strike the ground at the same time. If one of the tennis balls is filled with lead pellets, will it fall faster and hit the ground first? Which of the two will encounter more air resistance? Defend your answers.

The heavier tennis ball will strike the ground first for the same reason the heavier parachutist in Figure 3.10 strikes the ground first. Note that although the air resistance on the heavier ball is smaller relative to the weight of the ball, it is actually greater than the air resistance that acts on the other ball. Why? Because the heavier ball falls faster, and air resistance is greater for greater speed.

29. Which is more likely to break, the ropes supporting a hammock stretched tightly between a pair of trees or one that sags more when you sit on it? Defend your answer.

A hammock stretched tightly has more tension in the supporting ropes than one that sags. The tightly stretched ropes are more likely to break.

30. A stone is shown at rest on the ground. (a) The vector shows the weight of the stone. Complete the vector diagram showing another vector that results in zero net force on the stone. (b) What is the conventional name of the vector you have drawn?

(a) The other vector is upward as shown. (b) It is called the normal force.

31. Here a stone is suspended at rest by a string. (a) Draw force vectors for all the forces that act on the stone. (b) Should your vectors have a zero resultant? (c) Why, or why not?

(a) As shown.

(b) Yes.

(c) Because the stone is in equilibrium.

32. Here the same stone is being accelerated vertically upward. (a) Draw force vectors to some suitable scale showing relative forces acting on the stone. (b) Which is the longer vector, and why?

(a) As shown.

(b) Upward tension force is greater to result in upward net force.

33. Suppose the string in the preceding exercise breaks, and the stone slows in its upward motion. Draw a force vector diagram of the stone when it reaches the top of its path.

It would be the same except that the upward vector would be absent. Only the downward *mg* vector acts.

34. What is the net force on the stone in the preceding exercise at the top of its path? Its instantaneous velocity? Its acceleration?

The acceleration of the stone at the top of its path, or anywhere where the net force on the stone is *mg*, is *g*.

35. Here is the stone sliding down a friction-free incline. (a) Identify the forces that act on it and draw appropriate force vectors.

(b) By the parallelogram rule, construct the resultant force on the stone (carefully showing it has a direction parallel to the incline—the same direction as the stone's acceleration).

(a) Weight and normal force only.   (b) As shown.

36. Here is the stone at rest, interacting with both the surface of the incline and the block. (a) Identify all the forces that act on the stone, and draw appropriate force vectors. (b) Show that the net force on the stone is zero. (*Hint 1*: There are two normal forces *on* the stone. *Hint 2*: Be sure the vectors you draw are for forces that act on the stone, not *by* the stone on the surfaces.)

(a) As shown.

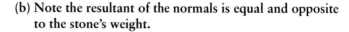

(b) Note the resultant of the normals is equal and opposite to the stone's weight.

Solutions to Chapter 3 Problems

1. A 400-kg bear grasping a vertical tree slides down at constant velocity. Show that the friction that acts on the bear is about 4000 N.

   Constant velocity means zero acceleration and, therefore, zero net force. So the friction force must be equal to the bear's weight, *mg*.

2. When two horizontal forces are exerted on a cart, 600 N forward and 400 N backward, the cart undergoes acceleration. Show that the additional force needed to produce nonaccelerated motion is 200 N.

   The given pair of forces produce a net force of 200 N forward, which accelerates the cart. To make the net force zero, a force of 200 N backward must be exerted on the cart.

3. You push with 20-N horizontal force on a 2-kg mass on a horizontal surface against a horizontal friction force of 12 N. Show that the acceleration is 4 m/s^2.

   Acceleration $a = F_{net}/m = (20\ N - 12\ N)/2\ kg = 8\ N/2\ kg = 4\ m/s^2$.

4. You push with 40-N horizontal force on a 4-kg mass on a horizontal surface. The horizontal friction force is 12 N. Show that the acceleration is 7 m/s^2.

   Acceleration $a = F_{net}/m = (40\ N - 24\ N)/4\ kg = 16\ N/4\ kg = 4\ m/s^2$.

5. A cart of mass 1 kg is accelerated 1 m/s^2 by a force of 1 N. Show that a 2-kg cart pushed with a 2-N force would also accelerate at 1 m/s^2.

   Acceleration $a = F_{net}/m = 2\ N/2\ kg = 1\ m/s^2$, the same.

6. A rocket of mass 100,000 kg undergoes an acceleration of 2 m/s^2. Show that the force developed by the rocket engines is 200,000 N.

   $F = ma = (100{,}000\ kg)(2\ m/s^2) = 200{,}000\ N$.

7. A 747 jumbo jet of mass 30,000 kg experiences a 30,000-N thrust for each of its engines during take-off. Show that its acceleration is 4 m/s^2.

   Acceleration $a = F_{net}/m = (4 \times 30{,}000\ N)/30{,}000\ kg = 4\ m/s^2$.

8. Suppose the jumbo jet in the previous problem flies against an air resistance of 90,000 N while the thrust of all four engines is 100,000 N. Show that its acceleration will be about 0.3 m/s2. What will the acceleration be when air resistance builds up to 100,00 N?

   air resistance = 90,000 N
   thrust = 100,000 N

   $$a = \frac{F_{net}}{m} = \frac{100{,}000\ N - 90{,}000\ N}{30{,}000\ kg} = \frac{10{,}000\ N}{30{,}000\ kg} = 0.33\ m/s^2$$

   When air resistance equals 100,000 N it will equal the forward thrust force. The net force will be zero, as will acceleration.

9. A boxer punches a sheet of paper in midair, bringing it from rest to a speed of 25 m/s in 0.05 second. If the mass of the paper is 0.003 kg, show that the force the boxer exerts on it is only 1.5 N.

   $F = ma = m\ \Delta v/\Delta t = 0.003\ kg \times [(25\ m/s)/0.05\ s] = 1.5\ N$.

10. Suppose that you are standing on a skateboard near a wall and that you push on the wall with a force of 30 N. (a) How hard does the wall push on you? (b) Show that if your mass is 60 kg your acceleration while pushing will be 0.5 m/s^2.

    The wall pushes as much on you, 30 N. Acceleration $a = F_{net}/m = 30\ N/60\ kg = 0.5\ m/s^2$.

11. If raindrops fall vertically at a speed of 3 m/s and you are running horizontally at 4 m/s, show that the drops will hit your face at a speed of 5 m/s.

    By the Pythagorean theorem, $V = \sqrt{[(3m/s)^2 + (4\ m/s)^2]} = 5\ m/s$.

12. Horizontal forces of 3 N and 4 N act at right angles on a block of mass 5 kg. Show that the resulting acceleration will be 1 m/s^2.

Acceleration $a = F_{net}/m = \sqrt{[(3.0\ N)^2 + (4.0\ N)^2]}/5\ kg = 1.0\ m/s^2$.

13. Suzie Skydiver with her parachute has a mass of 50 kg. (a) Before opening her chute, show that the force of air resistance she encounters when reaching terminal velocity is about 500 N. (b) After her chute is open and she again reaches a smaller terminal velocity, show that the force of air resistance she encounters is also about 500 N. (c) Discuss why your answers are the same.

(a) **Force of air resistance will be equal to her weight, *mg*, or 500 N.**

(b) **She'll reach the same air resistance, but at a slower speed, 500 N.**

(c) **The answers are the same, but for different speeds. In each case, she attains equilibrium (no acceleration).**

14. An airplane with an air speed of 120 km/h encounters a 90-km/h crosswind. Show that its groundspeed is 150 km/h.

By the Pythagorean theorem, $V = \sqrt{[(120\ m/s)^2 + (90\ m/s)^2]} = 150\ m/s$.

Chapter 4: Momentum and Energy

Answers to Chapter 4 Review Questions

1. Moving skateboard; anything at rest has *no* momentum.

2. Enormous momentum due to huge mass.

3. Force is a push or pull, while impulse is the product of force and time.

4. By increasing force, or increasing the time the force is exerted.

5. A cannonball will have more momentum coming from the long cannon due to the force acting over a longer time.

6. (3) (Twice the change occurs if speed thrown is the same as speed caught.)

7. (3) (Twice if speed thrown is the same as speed caught.)

8. No because, although you produce impulse on the car, the car produces an equal and opposite impulse on you, so the sum of the impulses equals zero net impulse.

9. That it remains unchanged in a process.

10. An elastic collision is a collision in which colliding objects rebound without lasting deformation or the generation of heat; an inelastic collision is a collision in which the colliding objects become distorted, generate heat, and possibly stick together. Momentum is conserved during elastic collisions.

11. Has the same initial speed of A.

12. Half speed.

13. When it undergoes a change—as when being transferred or transformed.

14. *Work*, which changes *energy*.

15. Joules.

16. True.

17. Four watts.

18. Twice.

19. Twice.

20. Four times as much.

21. Whether or not it experiences a change in energy.

22. 16 times as much work to stop the car.

23. With no external work input or output, the energy of a system doesn't change. Energy cannot be created or destroyed.

24. The source of energy is sunlight that evaporated water from the ocean, which ended up as rain in mountains and trapped behind dams.

25. Yes. Yes. No! (There is no way to increase energy without doing work.)

26. Twice the force through half the distance.

27. No way! If that is done, new physics is afoot! Such would violate the conservation of energy.

Answers to Chapter 4 Multiple-Choice Questions

1c, 2c, 3a, 4b, 5a

Answers to Chapter 4 Integrated Science Concepts

Biology: The Impulse–Momentum Relationship in Sports

1. (a) An extended hand has room to move backward when the ball is caught. This stretches the time, resulting in less force. (b) The force of impact will be less if momentum changes over a long time. By making t long, F will be smaller. (c) The shorter time is accompanied by a greater force when the momentum of the arm is reduced.

2. In accord with Newton's third law, the forces are equal. Only the resilience of the human hand and the training she has undergone to toughen her hand allow her to perform this without breaking any bones.

3. The impulse will be greater if her hand bounces from the bricks. If the time of contact is not increased, a greater force is then exerted on the bricks (and on her hand).

Biology and Chemistry: Glucose—Energy for Life

1. The "burning" that goes on in cells differs from the burning or combustion of a log on a campfire in that the cellular process is much slower and more controlled.

2. You are powered by solar energy in the sense that the energy you use to perform the biochemical and physical processes needed to sustain life comes from your food which stores chemical energy. This chemical energy is solar energy that has been transformed by photosynthesizing organisms.

Answers to Chapter 4 Exercises

1. What is the purpose of a "crumple zone" (which has been manufactured to collapse steadily in a crash) in the front section of an automobile?

   A steady collapse in a crash extends the time that the seat belt and air bags slow the passengers less violently.

2. To bring a supertanker to a stop, its engines are typically cut off about 25 kg from port. Why is it so difficult to stop or turn a supertanker?

   Supertankers are so massive, that even at modest speeds, their motional inertia, or *momenta*, are enormous. This means enormous impulses are needed for changing motion. How can large impulses be produced with modest forces? By applying modest forces over long periods of time. Hence, the force of the water resistance over the time it takes to coast 25 kilometers sufficiently reduces the momentum.

3. Why might a wine glass survive a fall onto a carpeted floor but not onto a concrete floor?

   The time during which momentum decreases is lengthened, thereby decreasing the force that brings the wine glass to rest. Less force means less chance of breaking.

4. If you throw an egg against a wall, the egg will break. If you throw an egg at the same speed into a sagging sheet, it won't break. Why?

   When the moving egg makes contact with a sagging sheet, the time it takes to stop it is extended. More time means less force, and a less-likely broken egg.

5. Why is a punch more forceful with a bare fist than with a boxing glove?

Impact with a boxing glove extends the time during which momentum of the fist is reduced and lessens the force. A punch with a bare fist involves less time and, therefore, more force.

6. A boxer can punch a heavy bag for more than an hour without tiring but will tire quickly when boxing with an opponent for a few minutes. Why? (*Hint*: When the boxer's punches are aimed at the bag, what supplies the impulse to stop them? When aimed at the opponent, what (or who) supplies the impulse to stop the punches that are missed?)

When a boxer hits his or her opponent, the opponent contributes to the impulse that changes the momentum of the punch. When punches miss, no impulse is supplied by the opponent—all effort that goes into reducing the momentum of the punches is supplied by the boxer. This tires the boxer. This is very evident to a boxer who can punch a heavy bag in the gym for hours and not tire, but who finds by contrast that a few minutes in the ring with an opponent is a tiring experience.

7. Railroad cars are loosely coupled so that there is a noticeable time delay from the time the first car is moved and the time the last cars are moved from rest by the locomotive. Discuss the advisability of this loose coupling and slack between cars from an impulse–momentum point of view.

Without this slack, a locomotive might simply sit still and spin its wheels. The loose coupling enables a longer time for the entire train to gain momentum, requiring less force of the locomotive wheels against the track. In this way, the overall required impulse is broken into a series of smaller impulses. (This loose coupling can be very important for braking as well.)

8. A fully dressed person is at rest in the middle of a pond on perfectly frictionless ice and must reach the shore. How can this be accomplished?

To get to shore, the person may throw keys or coins or an item of clothing. The momentum of what is thrown will be accompanied by the thrower's oppositely directed momentum. In this way, one can recoil toward shore. (One can also inhale facing the shore and exhale facing away from the shore.)

9. A high-speed bus and an innocent bug have a head-on collision. The sudden change in momentum of the bus is greater, less, or the same as the change in momentum of the unfortunate bug?

The momentum of both bug and bus change by the same amount, because the amount of force and the time and, therefore, the amount of impulse, are the same on each. Momentum is conserved. Speed is another story. Because of the huge mass of the bus, its reduction of speed is very tiny—too small for the passengers to notice.

10. Why is it difficult for a firefighter to hold a hose that ejects large quantities of water at a high speed?

The large momentum of the spurting water is met by a recoil that makes the hose difficult to hold, just as a shotgun is difficult to hold when it fires birdshot.

11. You're on a small raft next to a dock and jump from the raft only to fall into the water. What physics principle did you fail to take into account?

Oops, the conservation of momentum was overlooked. Your momentum forward equals (approximately) the momentum of the recoiling raft.

12. Your friend says the conservation of momentum is violated when you step off a chair and gain momentum as you fall. What do you say?

Whether or not momentum is conserved depends on the system. If the system in question is you as you fall, then there is an external force acting on you (gravity), and momentum increases and is, therefore, not conserved. But if you enlarge the system to be you and the Earth that pulls you, then momentum is conserved, for the force of gravity on you is internal to the system. Your momentum of fall is balanced by the equal but opposite momentum of the Earth coming up to meet you!

13. If a Mack truck and a Honda Civic have a head-on collision, which vehicle will experience the greater force of impact? The greater impulse? The greater change in its momentum? The greater acceleration?

The magnitude of force, impulse, and change in momentum will be the same for each. The Civic undergoes the greater acceleration, because its mass is less.

14. Would a head-on collision between two cars be more damaging to the occupants if the cars stuck together or if the cars rebounded upon impact?

Cars brought to a rapid halt experience a change in momentum and a corresponding impulse. But greater momentum change occurs if the cars bounce, with correspondingly greater impulse and, therefore, greater damage. Less damage results if the cars stick upon impact than if they bounce apart.

15. In Chapter 3, rocket propulsion was explained in terms of Newton's third law. That is, the force that propels a rocket is from the exhaust gases pushing against the rocket, the reaction to the force the rocket exerts on the exhaust gases. Explain rocket propulsion in terms of momentum conservation.

If the rocket and its exhaust gases are treated as a single system, the forces between rocket and exhaust gases are internal, and momentum in the rocket–gases system is conserved. Any momentum given to the gases is equal and opposite to momentum given to the rocket. A rocket attains momentum by giving momentum to the exhaust gases.

16. Suppose there are three astronauts outside a spaceship, and two of them decide to play catch with the third man. All the astronauts weigh the same on Earth and are equally strong. The first astronaut throws the second one toward the third one and the game begins. Describe the motion of the astronauts as the game proceeds. In terms of the number of throws, how long will the game last?

We assume the equal strengths of the astronauts means that each throws with the same speed. Because the masses are equal, when the first throws the second, both the first and second move away from each other at equal speeds. Say the astronaut moves to the right with velocity V, and the first recoils with velocity $-V$. When the third makes the catch, both she and the second move to the right at velocity $V/2$ (twice the mass moving at half the speed, like the freight cars in Figure 4.11). When the third makes her throw, she recoils at velocity V (the same speed she imparts to the thrown astronaut) which is added to the $V/2$ she acquired in the catch. So, her velocity is $V + V/2 = 3V/2$, to the right—too fast to stay in the game. Why? Because the velocity of the second astronaut is $V/2 - V = -V/2$, to the left—too slow to catch up with the first astronaut who is still moving at $-V$. The game is over. Both the first and the third got to throw to the second astronaut only once!

17. How is it possible that a flock of birds in flight can have a momentum of zero, but not have zero kinetic energy?

They may fly in opposite directions wherein the momenta cancel to zero. But if moving, there is no way kinetic energy can cancel. Hence, the difference between a vector quantity (momentum) and a scalar quantity (kinetic energy).

18. When a cannon with a long barrel is fired, the force of expanding gases acts on the cannonball for a longer distance. What effect does this have on the velocity of the emerging cannonball?

When a cannon with a long barrel is fired, more work is done as the cannonball is pushed through the longer distance. A greater KE is the result of the greater work, so of course, the cannonball emerges with a greater velocity. (It might be mentioned that the force acting on the bullet is not constant but decreases with increasing distance inside the barrel.)

19. You and a flight attendant toss a ball back and forth in an airplane in flight. Does the KE of the ball depend on the speed of the airplane? Carefully explain.

The KE of the tossed ball relative to occupants in the airplane does not depend on the speed of the airplane. The KE of the ball relative to observers on the ground below, however, is a different matter. KE, like velocity, is relative.

20. Can something have energy without having momentum? Explain. Can something have momentum without having energy? Defend your answer.

If an object has KE, then it must have momentum—for it is moving. But it can have potential energy without being in motion and, therefore, without having momentum. And every object has "energy of being"— stated in the celebrated equation $E = mc^2$. Whether an object moves or not, it has some form of energy. If it has KE, then with respect to the frame of reference in which its KE is measured, it also has momentum.

21. To combat wasteful habits, we often urge others to "conserve energy" by turning off lights when they are not in use, for example, or by setting thermostats at a moderate level. In this chapter, we also speak of "energy conservation." Distinguish between these two usages.

168

In the physical science sense, energy cannot be created or destroyed. When consuming energy, however, we can use more than we need and be wasteful. So we speak of saving energy, using it more wisely, and not in the science sense of conserving it.

22. An inefficient machine is said to "waste energy." Does this mean that energy is actually lost? Explain.

    Energy is dissipated into nonuseful forms in an inefficient machine and is "lost" only in the loose sense of the word. In the strict sense, it can be accounted for and is therefore not lost.

23. A child can throw a baseball at 20 mph. Some professional ball players can throw a baseball 100 mph, five times as fast. How much more energy does the pro ball player give to the faster ball?

    Twenty-five times as much energy (as speed is squared for kinetic energy).

24. If a golf ball and a Ping-Pong ball both move with the same kinetic energy, can you say which has the greater speed? Explain in terms of KE. Similarly, in a gaseous mixture of massive molecules and light molecules with the same average KE, can you say which have the greater speed?

    If KEs are the same but masses differ, then the ball with smaller mass has the greater speed. That is, $1/2\ Mv^2 = 1/2\ mV^2$, and likewise with molecules, where lighter ones move faster on the average than more massive ones. (We will see in Chapter 6 that temperature is a measure of average molecular KE—lighter molecules in a gas move faster than same-temperature heavier molecules.)

25. Consider a pendulum swinging to and fro. At what point in its motion is the KE of the pendulum bob at a maximum? At what point is its PE at a maximum? When its KE is half its maximum value, how much PE does it have?

    The KE of a pendulum bob is maximum where it moves fastest, at the lowest point; PE is maximum at the uppermost points. When the pendulum bob swings by the point that marks half its maximum height, it has half its maximum KE, and its PE is halfway between its minimum and maximum values. If we define PE = 0 at the bottom of the swing, the place where KE is half its maximum value is also the place where PE is half its maximum value, and KE = PE at this point. (In accordance with energy conservation: total energy = KE + PE.)

26. A physics instructor demonstrates energy conservation by releasing a heavy pendulum bob, as shown in the sketch, allowing it to swing to and fro. What would happen if in his exuberance he gave the bob a slight shove as it left his nose? Why?

    If the ball is given an initial KE, it will return to its starting position with that KE (moving in the other direction!) and hit the instructor. (The usual classroom procedure is to release the ball from the nose at rest. Then when it returns it will have no KE and will stop short of bumping the nose.)

27. Discuss the design of the roller coaster shown in the sketch in terms of the conservation of energy.

    The design is impractical. Note that the summit of each hill on the roller coaster is the same height, so the PE of the car at the top of each hill would be the same. If no energy were spent in overcoming friction, the car would get to the second summit with as much energy as it starts with. But in practice, there is considerable friction, and the car would not roll to its initial height and have the same energy. So the maximum height of succeeding summits should be lower to compensate for friction.

28. Consider the identical balls released from rest on Tracks A and B as shown. When each ball has reached the right end of its track, which will have the greater speed? Why is this question easier to answer than the similar question asked in Exercise 25 back in Chapter 2?

    Both will have the same speed, because both have the same PE at the ends of the track and, therefore, the same KEs. This is a relatively easy question to answer because *speed* is asked for, whereas the similar question in Chapter 2 asked for which ball got to the end sooner. The question asked for *time*—which meant first establishing which ball had the greater average speed.

29. Strictly speaking, does a car burn more gasoline when the lights are turned on? Does the overall consumption of gasoline depend on whether or not the engine is running? Defend your answer.

    Yes, a car burns more gasoline when its lights are on. The overall consumption of gasoline does not depend on whether or not the engine is running. Lights and other devices run off the battery, which "run down" the battery. The energy used to recharge the battery ultimately comes from the gasoline.

30. If an automobile had an engine that was 100% efficient, would it be warm to your touch? Would its exhaust heat the surrounding air? Would it make any noise? Would it vibrate? Would any of its fuel go unused?

An engine that is 100% efficient would not be warm to the touch, its exhaust would not heat the air, and it would not make any noise or vibrate. This is because all these are transfers of energy, which cannot happen if all the energy given to the engine is transformed to useful work.

Solutions to Chapter 4 Problems

1. A car with a mass of 1000 kg moves at 20 m/s. Show that the braking force needed to bring the car to a halt in 10 s is 2000 N.

From $Ft = \Delta mv$, $F = \Delta mv/t = (1000 \text{ kg})(20 \text{ m/s})/10 \text{ s} = 2000 \text{ N}$.

[Can you see this could also be solved by Newton's second law:

$F = ma = (1000 \text{ kg})(20 \text{ m/s}/10 \text{ s}) = 2000 \text{ N}$.]

2. A railroad diesel engine weighs four times as much as a freight car. If the diesel engine coasts at 5 km per hour into a freight car that is initially at rest, show that the two coast at 4 km/h after they couple together.

The answer is 4 km/h. Let m be the mass of the freight car, $4m$ the mass of the diesel engine, and v the speed after both have coupled together. Before collision, the total momentum is due only to the diesel engine, $4m(5 \text{ km/h})$, because the momentum of the freight car is 0. After collision, the combined mass is $(4m + m)$, and combined momentum is $(4m + m)v$. By the conservation of momentum equation:

$$\text{momentum}_{\text{before}} = \text{momentum}_{\text{after}}$$
$$4m(5 \text{ km/h}) + 0 = (4m + m)v$$
$$v = \frac{(20m \cdot \text{km/h})}{5m} = 4 \text{ km/h}$$

(Note that you don't have to know m to solve the problem.)

3. A 5-kg fish swimming at 1 m/s swallows an absent-minded 1-kg fish at rest. (a) Show that the speed of the larger fish after lunch is −5 m/s. (b)What would be its speed if the smaller fish were swimming toward it at 4 m/s?

(a) Momentum before lunch = momentum after lunch

$(5 \text{ kg})(1 \text{ m/s}) + 0 = (5 \text{ kg} + 1 \text{ kg})v$

$5 \text{ kg} \cdot \text{m/s} = (6 \text{ kg}) v$

$v = 5/6$ m/s.

(b) Momentum before lunch = momentum after lunch

$(5 \text{ kg})(1 \text{ m/s}) + 1 \text{ kg} (-4 \text{ m/s}) = (5 \text{ kg} + 1 \text{ kg})3v$

$5 \text{ kg} \cdot \text{m/s} - 4 \text{ kg} \cdot \text{m/s} = (6 \text{ kg})v$

$v = 1/6$ m/s

4. Comic-strip hero Superman meets an asteroid in outer space and hurls it at 800 m/s, as fast as a bullet. The asteroid is a thousand times more massive than Superman. In the strip, Superman is seen at rest after the throw. Taking physics into account, what would be his recoil velocity?

By momentum conservation,

asteroid mass × 800 m/s = Superman's mass × v.

Because the asteroid's mass is 1000 times Superman's,

$(1000m)(800 \text{ m/s}) = mv$

$v = 800,000$ m/s. This is nearly 2 million miles per hour!

5. Consider the inelastic collision between the two freight cars in Figure 4.11. The momentum before and after the collision is the same. The KE, however, is less after the collision than before the collision. How much less, and what has become of this energy?

The freight cars have only half the KE possessed by the single car before collision. Here's how to figure it:

$$KE_{before} = 1/2 \ mv^2.$$

$$KE_{after} = 1/2 \ (2m)(v/2)^2 = 1/2 \ (2m)v^2/4 = 1/4 \ mv^2.$$

What becomes of this energy? Most of it goes into nature's graveyard—thermal energy.

6. This question is typical on some driver's license exams: A car moving at 50 km/h skids 15 m with locked brakes. How far will the car skid with locked brakes at 150 km/h?

At three times the speed, it has nine times (3^2) the KE and will skid nine times as far—135 m. Because the frictional force is about the same in both cases, the distance has to be nine times as great for nine times as much work done by the pavement on the car.

7. In the hydraulic machine shown, it is observed that, when the piston is pushed down 10 cm, the large piston is raised 1 cm. If the small piston is pushed down with a force of 100 N, show that the large piston is capable of exerting 1000 N of force.

$$(Fd)_{input} = (Fd)_{output}$$
$$(100 \ N \times 10 \ cm)_{input} = (? \times 1 \ cm)_{output}$$

So we see that the output force is 1000 N (or less if the efficiency is less than 100%).

8. Consider a car with a 25% efficient engine that encounters an average retarding force of 1000 N. Assume that the energy content of the gasoline is 40 MJ/L. Show that the car will get 20 km per liter of fuel.

At 25% efficiency, only 1/4 of the 40 megajoules in one liter, or 10 MJ, will go into work. This work is

$$F \times d = 500 \ N \times d = 10 \ MJ.$$

Solve this for *d* and convert MJ to J to get

$$d = 10 \ MJ/500 \ N = 10,000,000 \ J/500 \ N = 20,000 \ m = 20 \ km.$$

Under these conditions, the car gets 20 kilometers per liter (which is 47 miles per gallon).

9. When a cyclist expends 1000 W of power to deliver mechanical energy to her bicycle at a rate of 100 W, show that the efficiency of her body is 10%.

Efficiency = (mechanical power output)/(power input) = 100 W/1000 W = 1/10, or 10%.

10. The decrease in PE for a freely falling object equals its gain in KE, in accord with the conservation of energy. (a) By simple algebra, find an equation for an object's speed *v* after falling a vertical distance *h*. Do this by equating KE to its change of PE. (b) Then figure out how much higher a freely falling object must fall to have twice the speed when it hits ground.

$v = \sqrt{2gh}$. As an object falls through a distance *h*, its loss of PE is *mgh*. This is converted to <u>KE</u> $(1/2 \ mv^2)$. From $mgh = 1/2 \ mv^2$, we see after canceling *m* and rearranging terms that $v = \sqrt{2gh}$.

Chapter 5: Gravity

Answers to Chapter 5 Review Questions

1. He realized they were both under the influence of Earth's gravity.

2. Tangential velocity is velocity that is parallel to (tangent) the curve at every point.

3. The moon falls beneath the straight line it would follow if no forces acted on it.

4. Every mass attracts every other mass with a force that for any two masses is directly proportional to the product of the masses involved and inversely proportional to the square of the distance separating them.

$$F \sim \frac{m_1 m_2}{d^2}$$

5. The force is $\frac{1}{4}$ as much in accord with the inverse square law: 6.67×10^{-11} N.

6. The paint is $\frac{1}{4}$ as thick (inv-sq law).

7. Brightness is $\frac{1}{4}$ as much (inv-sq law).

8. Nowhere! It approaches zero with great distances but never actually reaches zero. (At the Earth's center, however, gravitation *cancels* to zero!)

9. 6.67×10^{-11} N.

10. 9.8 N.

11. More compressed; less compressed.

12. Oops, almost a trick question: The scale readings would be unchanged. They change only with *changes* in velocity—acceleration.

13. When you are in a state of zero acceleration on the Earth's surface. Then any support force also has the value *mg*.

14. Your weight is more than *mg* when you're in an elevator that accelerates upward (or a rotating habitat with excess rotation).

15. You have zero weight when you're in free fall, or when you're in a part of the universe where gravitational forces on you are nil.

16. Inward, toward the center of the circle.

17. Weight is simulated by the centripetal force acting on a person moving in a circular path.

18. A projectile is any object projected by some means that continues in motion by its own inertia.

19. 10 m/s

20. The same.

21. The vertical component changes the same way a ball tossed straight upward changes, and changes on the way down just as a stone does in free fall.

22. It remains the same.

23. 15 degrees (the complimentary angle to 75 degrees).

24. 30 m/s, the same as the initial point.

25. Both are less due to air drag.

26. Because 8-km/s tangential speed is sufficient for the 5-m vertical drop at the end of the first second to match the corresponding 5-m drop of Earth's curvature.

27. The 8 km/s will persist only in the absence of air drag. Hence, the motion must be above the Earth's atmosphere.

28. Yes indeed!

29. Gravitational force varies, because the distance between gravitationally attracting masses varies.

30. Because half the time it is going away from gravity, and the other half going with gravity. When going against gravity, speed decreases; when going with gravity, speed increases.

Answers to Chapter 5 Multiple-Choice Questions

1c, 2b, 3a, 4d, 5c

Answers to Chapter 5 Integrated Science Concepts

Biology: Your Biological Gravity Detector

1. Yes, people have sense organs that allow them to sense gravity. They are called the vestibular organs, and they are located in the inner ear.

2. The feelings of nausea and disorientation suffered by astronauts happen because the vestibular organs cannot sense a gravitational gradient. The sense of body position in space—the vestibular sense—is set according to the direction of the gravitational field. Without this sense of direction, an astronaut becomes disoriented.

Biology: Center of Gravity of People

1. Its center of gravity lies within its base.

2. It expands the area of his base.

Astronomy: Escape Speed

1. Minimum speed is 8 km/s; maximum speed is 11.2 km/s. An object projected from the Earth at a speed greater than 11.2 km/s will escape the Earth's gravitational field and no longer orbit the earth.

2. Pioneer 10 was launched with a speed of 15 km/s—more than the escape velocity of the Earth but less than the escape speed of the solar system, 42 km/s. The spacecraft was directed toward Jupiter as it approached Earth. Pioneer was boosted by Jupiter's gravitational field, gaining speed in the process. The speed thus gained allowed Pioneer 10 to escape the solar system from the distance of Jupiter.

Answers to Chapter 5 Exercises

1. What would be the path of the Moon if somehow all gravitational force on the Moon vanished to zero?

   In accord with the law of inertia, the Moon would move in a straight-line path instead of circling both the Sun and Earth.

2. Is the force of gravity stronger on a piece of iron than it is on a piece of wood if both have the same mass? Defend your answer.

   The force of gravity is the same on each, because the masses are the same, as Newton's equation for gravitational force verifies.

3. Is the force of gravity on a piece of paper stronger when it is crumpled? Defend your answer.

   The force of gravity is the same on each, because the masses are the same, as Newton's equation for gravitational force verifies. When dropped, the crumpled paper falls faster only because it encounters less air drag than the sheet.

4. What is the magnitude and direction of the gravitational force that acts on a professor who weighs 1000 N at the surface of the Earth?

   1000 N, directed toward the center of the Earth (about 220 lb).

5. The Earth and the Moon are attracted to each other by gravitational force. Does the more massive Earth attract the less massive Moon with a force that is greater than, smaller than, or the same as the force with which the Moon attracts Earth?

   The Earth and Moon pull on each other equally in a single interaction. In accord with Newton's Third Law, the pull of Earth on the Moon is equal and opposite to the pull of the Moon on Earth.

6. What would you say to a friend who says that, if gravity follows the inverse-square law, the effect of gravity on you when you are on the 20th floor of a building should be one-fourth as much as it would be if you were on the tenth floor?

   You tell your friend that the force of gravity is measured from the center of the Earth, not from the ground up. Compared with the distance to the Earth's center, gravitational force is about the same on an object on the 10th and 20th floors. The difference is infinitesimal and can be neglected.

7. Why do the passengers of high-altitude jet planes feel the sensation of weight, while passengers in an orbiting space vehicle, such as a space shuttle, do not?

   The high-flying jet plane is not in free fall. It moves at approximately constant velocity so a passenger experiences no net force. The upward support force of the seat matches the downward pull of gravity, providing the sensation of weight. The orbiting space vehicle, on the other hand, is in a state of free fall. No support force is offered by a seat, for it falls at the same rate as the passenger. With no support force, the force of gravity on the passenger is not sensed as weight.

8. Is gravitational force acting on a person who falls off a cliff? Is it acting on an astronaut inside an orbiting space shuttle?

   Gravitational force is indeed acting on a person who falls off a cliff, and on a person in a space shuttle. Both are falling under the influence of gravity.

9. If you were in a freely falling elevator and you dropped a pencil, it would hover in front of you rather than falling to the floor. Is there a force of gravity that is acting on the pencil? Defend your answer.

The pencil has the same state of motion that you have. The force of gravity on the pencil causes it to accelerate downward alongside of you. Although the pencil hovers relative to you, it and you are falling relative to the Earth.

10. Are the planets of the solar system simply projectiles falling around the sun?

Yes!

11. What path would you follow if you fell off a rotating merry-go-round? What force prevents you from following this path while you're on the merry-go-round?

You'd follow a straight-line path; the force preventing this motion while you are riding is the centripetal force applied to you by the merry-go-round platform.

12. A heavy crate accidentally falls from a high-flying airplane just as it flies over a shiny red sports car parked in a car lot. Relative to the car, where will the crate crash?

The crate will not hit the car but will crash a distance beyond it determined by the height and speed of the plane.

13. How does the vertical component of motion for a ball kicked off a high cliff compare with the motion of vertical free fall?

When air drag is negligible, the vertical component of motion is identical to free fall.

14. In the absence of air drag, why does the horizontal component of a ball's motion not change, while the vertical component does?

There are no forces horizontally (neglecting air resistance), so there is no horizontal acceleration, and hence, the horizontal component of velocity doesn't change. Gravitation acts vertically, which is why the vertical component of velocity changes.

15. At what point in its trajectory does a batted baseball have its minimum speed? If air drag can be neglected, how does this compare with the horizontal component of its velocity at other points?

Minimum speed occurs at the top, which is the same as the horizontal component of velocity anywhere along the path.

16. Each of two golfers hits a ball at the same speed, one at 60°, and the other at 30°, above the horizontal. Which ball goes farther? Which hits the ground first? (Ignore air resistance.)

Both balls have the same range (see Figure 5.29). The ball with the initial speed of 30°, however, is in the air for a shorter time and hits the ground first.

17. A park ranger shoots a monkey hanging from a branch of a tree with a tranquilizing dart. The ranger aims directly at the monkey, not realizing that the dart will follow a parabolic path and, therefore, will fall below the monkey's position. The monkey, however, sees the dart leave the gun and lets go of the branch to avoid being hit. Will the monkey be hit anyway? Defend your answer.

The bullet falls beneath the projected line of the barrel. To compensate for the bullet's fall, the barrel is elevated. How much elevation depends on the velocity and distance to the target. Correspondingly, the gunsight is raised so the line of sight from the gunsight to the end of the barrel extends to the target. If a scope is used, it is tilted downward to accomplish the same line of sight.

18. Since the Moon is gravitationally attracted to the Earth, why doesn't it simply crash into the Earth?

The Moon's tangential velocity is what keeps the Moon coasting around the Earth rather than crashing into it. If its tangential velocity were reduced to zero, then it would fall straight into the Earth!

19. Does the speed of a falling object depend on its mass? Does the speed of a satellite in orbit depend on its mass? Defend your answers.

Neither the speed of a falling object (without air resistance) nor the speed of a satellite in orbit depends on its mass. In both cases, a greater mass (greater inertia) is balanced by a correspondingly greater gravitational force, so the acceleration remains the same ($a = F/m$, Newton's second law).

20. If you have ever watched the launching of an Earth satellite, you may have noticed that the rocket starts vertically upward, then departs from a vertical course and continues its climb at an angle. Why does it start vertically? Why does it not continue vertically?

The initial vertical climb gets the rocket through the denser, retarding part of the atmosphere most quickly. Eventually the rocket must acquire enough tangential speed to remain in orbit without thrust, so it must tilt until finally its path is horizontal.

21. A satellite can orbit at 5 km above the moon, but not at 5 km above the Earth. Why?

The moon has no atmosphere (because escape velocity at the moon's surface is less than the speeds of any atmospheric gases). A satellite 5 km above the Earth's surface is still in considerable atmosphere, as well as in range of some mountain peaks. Atmospheric drag is the factor that most determines orbiting altitude.

Solutions to Chapter 5 Problems

1. If you stood atop a ladder that was so tall that you were three times as far from the Earth's center than you would be if you were standing on the Earth's surface, how would your weight compare with its present value?

From $F = GmM/d^2$, three times d squared is $9d^2$, which means the force is one-ninth of surface weight.

2. Find the change in the force of gravity between two planets when the masses of both planets are doubled, and the distance between them stays the same.

From $F = GmM/d^2$, $(2m)(2M) = 4mM$, which means the force of gravity between them is four times greater.

3. Find the change in the force of gravity between two planets when the masses remain the same but the distance between them is **increased** by ten.

From $F = GmM/d^2$, $10d$ squared is $1/100 \, d^2$, with a force 100 times smaller.

4. Find the change in the force of gravity between two planets when distance between is *decreased* by ten.

From $F = GmM/d^2$, five times d squared is $1/100 \, d^2$, which means the force is 100 times greater.

5. Find the change in the force of gravity between two planets when the masses of the planets don't change, but the distance between them is decreased by five.

From $F = GmM/d^2$, five times d squared is $1/25 \, d^2$, with a force 25 times greater.

6. By what factor would your weight change if the Earth's diameter were doubled and its mass were also doubled?

From $F = G2m2M/(2 \, d^2) = 2/4 \, (GmM/d^2)$, with one-half the force of gravitation.

7. Find the change in the force of gravity between two objects when both masses are doubled, and the distance between them is also doubled.

From $F = G2m2M/(2 \, d^2) = 4/4 \, (GmM/d^2)$, with the same force of gravitation.

8. Consider a bright point light source located 1 m from a square opening with area of one-square meter. Light passing through the opening illuminates an area of 4m^2 on a wall 2 m from the opening. (a) Find the area illuminated if the wall is moved to distances of 3 m, 5 m, or 10 m. (b) How can the same amount of light illuminate more area as the wall is moved farther away?

(a) At 3 m it will cover 3^2 or 9 square meters; at 5 m it will cover 5^2 or 25 square meters; at 10 m it will cover 10^2 or 100 square meters. (b) The light is "spread out" over greater and greater area and gets dimmer and dimmer.

9. Calculate the force of gravity between the Earth (6.4×10^{24} kg) and the Sun (2×10^{30} kg, and 1.5×10^{11} m distant).

$F = GmM/d^2 = [(6.67 \times 10^{-11} \, \text{N} \cdot \text{m}^2/\text{kg}^2)(6 \times 10^{24} \, \text{kg})(2 \times 10^{30} \, \text{kg})]/(1.5 \times 10^{11} \, \text{m})^2 = 3.6 \times 10^{22} \, \text{N}$.

10. Students in a lab roll a steel ball off the edge of a table. They measure the speed of a horizontally launched ball to be 4.0m/s. They also know that if they simply dropped the ball from rest off the edge of the table, it would take 0.5 seconds to hit the floor. Question: How far from the bottom of the table should they place a small piece of paper so that the ball will hit it when it lands?

The distance wanted is horizontal velocity × time. The time to follow the parabolic path is the same 0.5 seconds it takes to drop vertically. So, distance from the edge of the table should be 4.0 m/s × 0.5 s = 2.0 m.

11. Calculate the speed in m/s at which the Earth revolves about the Sun. You may assume that the Earth's orbit is nearly circular.

One way is $v = distance/time$, where distance is the circumference of the Earth's orbit and time is 1 year. Then

$$v = \frac{d}{t} = \frac{2\pi r}{1 \text{ year}} = \frac{2\pi(1.5 \times 10^{11} \text{ m})}{365 \text{ day} \times 24 \text{ h/day} \times 3600 \text{ s/h}} = 3 \times 10^4 \text{ m/s} = 30 \text{ km/s}.$$

Chapter 6: Heat

Answers to Chapter 6 Review Questions

1. The thermal energy in a substance is the total energy of all its atoms and molecules, consisting of both the potential and kinetic energy of the particles in a substance.

2. Matter is made up of tiny particles, atoms or molecules, that are always moving.

3. Atoms in the metal jostle faster.

4. 0°C, 32°F, 100°C, 212°F.

5. Average.

6. Both the thermometer and whatever it measures reach a common temperature (thermal equilibrium). So, a thermometer measures its own temperature.

7. Zero.

8. Zero.

9. Energy travels, so when a cold surface is touched, energy goes from your hand to the surface.

10. Temperature is a measure of the average translational kinetic energy per molecule, while heat is the thermal energy transferred from one thing to another due to a temperature difference.

11. Temperature difference; heat flows from high to low temperatures.

12. Both are units of energy; 4.18 J = 1 cal.

13. The first law *is* the conservation of energy applied to thermal systems.

14. Increases. Increases.

15. It defines the direction—from hot to cold.

16. Silver (which has a lower specific heat).

17. Low.

18. Very high in comparison.

19. Liquids.

20. Ice crystals are open structured. So when water freezes, the crystals occupy more space. More volume means lower density.

21. As water goes through 4°C on the way to freezing, it sinks to the bottom—not cold enough to freeze. Any 0°C water floats at the top, where it freezes.

22. Loose electrons conduct energy by collisions throughout a substance.

23. Electrons are free to roam in conductors, which easily conduct heat. Electrons are firmly attached in insulators, which therefore don't conduct heat well.

24. Wood is a poor conductor, even when red hot. Very little heat conducts from the coal to your feet.

25. Because they are composed largely of air spaces, which are good insulators.

26. By movement of heated fluid—by currents.

27. The temperature decreases (as is evidenced by blowing on your hand with puckered lips).

28. In the daytime, the shore is warmed more than water, so winds blow from water toward shore. At night the reverse occurs; the shore cools more than water, and winds blow in the opposite direction.

29. (a) Energy of electromagnetic waves. (b) Electromagnetic radiation in the infrared part of the spectrum.

30. Frequency and absolute temperature are directly proportional.

31. All objects are also absorbing energy from the surroundings. Temperature will decrease only if the object is a *net* emitter—if it emits more than it absorbs.

Answers to Chapter 6 Multiple-Choice Questions

1a, 2a, 3b, 4b, 5c

Answers to Chapter 6 Integrated Science Concepts

Astronomy, Earth Science, Biology, Chemistry: Entropy—The Universal Tendency Toward Disorder

1. When energy is transformed, some of it is converted to heat. Heat is the least useful form of energy, because it is the least concentrated form.

2. Entropy is the physicist's term for the measure of energy dispersal.

3. No, it is not thermodynamically favored, because the products have less entropy than the reactants. So this reaction will not proceed without an energy input.

4. No, the deer converts grass to tissue, which represents a decrease in entropy. However, to perform this function, the deer uses energy. The second law says that entropy-increasing processes are spontaneous; processes reducing entropy require energy input.

Earth Science: The Specific Heat Capacity of Water Affects Global Temperature

1. North Atlantic water cools, and releases energy to the air, which blows over Europe.

2. The climate of Iceland is moderated by the surrounding water.

3. In winter months when the water is warmer than the air, the air is warmed by the water to produce a seacoast climate warmer than inland. In summer months when the air is warmer than the water, the air is cooled by the water to produce a seacoast climate cooler than inland. This is why seacoast communities and especially islands do not experience the high and low temperature extremes that characterize inland locations.

Answers to Chapter 6 Exercises

1. In your room there are things such as tables, chairs, other people, and so forth. Which of these things has a temperature (1) lower than, (2) greater than, and (3) equal to the temperature of the air?

   Inanimate things such as tables, chairs, furniture, and so on, have the same temperature as the surrounding air (assuming they are in thermal equilibrium with the air—i.e., no sudden gush of different-temperature air or such). People and other mammals, however, generate their own heat and have body temperatures that are normally higher than air temperature.

2. Why can't you establish whether you are running a high temperature by touching your own forehead?

   You cannot establish by your own touch whether or not you are running a fever because there would be no temperature difference between your hand and forehead. If your forehead is a couple of degrees higher in temperature than normal, your hand is also a couple of degrees higher.

3. Which is greater, an increase in temperature of 1°C or one of 1°F?

   Because Celsius degrees are larger than Fahrenheit degrees, an increase of 1°C is larger. It's 9/5 as large.

4. Which has the greater amount of internal energy, an iceberg or a cup of hot coffee? Explain.

   The hot coffee has a higher temperature, but not a greater internal energy. Although the iceberg has less internal energy per mass, its enormously greater mass gives it a greater total energy than that in the small cup of coffee. (For a smaller volume of ice, the fewer number of more energetic molecules in the hot cup of coffee may constitute a greater total amount of internal energy—but not compared to an iceberg.)

5. Use the laws of thermodynamics to defend the statement that 100% of the electrical energy that goes into lighting a lamp is converted to thermal energy.

Only a small percentage of the electric energy that goes into lighting a lamp becomes light. The rest is thermal energy. But even the light is absorbed by the surroundings, and also ends up as thermal energy. So by the first law, all the electrical energy is ultimately converted to thermal energy. By the second law, organized electrical energy degenerates to the more disorganized form, thermal energy.

6. When air is rapidly compressed, why does its temperature increase?

Work is done in compressing the air, which in accord with the first law of thermodynamics, increases its thermal energy. This is evident by its increased temperature.

7. What happens to the gas pressure within a sealed gallon can when it is heated? Cooled? Why?

Gas pressure increases in the can when heated and decreases when cooled. The pressure that a gas exerts depends on the average kinetic energy of its molecules and, therefore, on its temperature.

8. After driving a car for some distance, why does the air pressure in the tires increase?

The tires heat up, which heats the air within. The molecules in the heated air move faster, which increases air pressure in the tires.

9. If you drop a hot rock into a pail of water, the temperature of the rock and the water will change until both are equal. The rock will cool and the water will warm. Does this hold true if the hot rock is dropped into the Atlantic Ocean? Explain.

The hot rock will cool and the cool water will warm, regardless of the relative amounts of each. The amount of temperature change, however, does depend in great part on the relative masses of the materials. For a hot rock dropped into the Atlantic Ocean, the change in temperature would be too small to measure. Keep increasing the mass of the rock or keep decreasing the mass of the ocean and the change will be evident.

10. In the old days, on a cold winter night, it was common to bring a hot object to bed with you. Which would be better to keep you warm through the cold night—a 10-kilogram iron brick or a 10-kilogram jug of hot water at the same temperature? Explain.

The brick will cool off too fast, and you'll be cold in the middle of the night. Bring a jug of hot water with its higher specific heat to bed and you'll make it through the night.

11. Why does adding the same amount of heat to two different objects not necessarily produce the same increase in temperature?

Different substances have different thermal properties due to differences in the way energy is stored internally in the substances. When the same amount of heat produces different changes in temperatures in two substances of the same mass, we say they have different specific heat capacities. Each substance has its own characteristic specific heat capacity. Temperature measures the average kinetic energy of random motion, but not other kinds of energy.

12. Why will a watermelon stay cool for a longer time than sandwiches when both are removed from a cooler on a hot day?

Water has a high specific heat capacity, which is to say, it normally takes a long time to heat up, or cool down. The water in the watermelon resists changes in temperature, so once cooled, it will stay cool longer than sandwiches or other nonwatery substances under the same conditions. Be glad water has a high specific heat capacity the next time you're enjoying cool watermelon on a hot day!

13. Cite an exception to the claim that all substances expand when heated.

Water is an exception. Below 4 degrees Celsius, it expands when cooled.

14. An old method for breaking boulders was to put them in a hot fire then douse them with cold water. Why would this fracture the boulders?

When doused, the outer part of the boulders cooled while the insides were still hot. This caused a difference in contraction, which fractured the boulders.

15. Would you or the gas company gain by having gas warmed before it passed through your gas meter?

    Gas is sold by volume. The gas meter that tallies your gas bill operates by measuring the number of volume units (such as cubic feet) that pass through it. Warm gas is expanded gas and occupies more space, and if it passes through your meter, it will be registered as more gas than if it were cooled and more compact. The gas company gains if gas is warm when it goes through your meter, because the same amount of warmer gas has a greater volume.

16. A metal ball is just able to pass through a metal ring. When the ball is heated, however, it will not pass through the ring. What would happen if the ring, rather than the ball, were heated? Does the size of the hole increase, stay the same, or decrease?

    Every part of a metal ring expands when it is heated—not only the thickness, but the outer and inner circumference as well. Hence, the ball that normally passes through the hole when the temperatures are equal will more easily pass through the expanded hole when the ring is heated. (Interestingly enough, the hole will expand as much as a disk of the same metal undergoing the same increase in temperature. Blacksmiths mounted metal rims in wooden wagon wheels by first heating the rims. Upon cooling, the contraction resulted in a snug fit.)

17. After a machinist very quickly slips a hot, snugly fitting iron ring over a very cold brass cylinder, there is no way that the two can be separated intact. Can you explain why this is so?

    Brass expands and contracts more than iron for the same changes in temperature. Because they are both good conductors and are in contact with each other, one cannot be heated or cooled without also heating or cooling the other. If the iron ring is heated, it expands—but the brass expands even more. Cooling the two will not result in separation either, for even at the lowest temperatures, the shrinkage of brass over iron would not produce separation.

18. Suppose you cut a small gap in a metal ring. If you heat the ring, will the gap become wider or narrower?

    The gap in the ring will become wider when the ring is heated. Try this: draw a couple of lines on a ring where you pretend a gap to be. When you heat the ring, the lines will be farther apart—the same amount as if a real gap were there. Every part of the ring expands proportionally when heated uniformly—thickness, length, gap, and all.

19. Suppose that water is used in a thermometer instead of mercury. If the temperature is at 4°C and then changes, why can't the thermometer indicate whether the temperature is rising or falling?

    Water has the greatest density at 4°C; therefore, either cooling or heating at this temperature will result in an expansion of the water. A small rise in water level would be ambiguous and make a water thermometer impractical in this temperature region.

20. Why is it important to protect water pipes so they don't freeze?

    It is important to keep water in pipes from freezing, because when the temperature drops below freezing, the water expands as it freezes, whereas the pipes (if metal) will fracture if water in them freezes.

21. Wrap a fur coat around a thermometer. Will the temperature rise?

    No, the coat is not a source of heat but merely keeps the thermal energy of the wearer from leaving rapidly.

22. If you hold one end of a metal nail against a piece of ice, the end in your hand soon becomes cold. Does cold flow from the ice to your hand? Explain.

    Energy "flows" from higher to lower temperature, from your hand to the ice. It is the energy, heat, flowing from your hand that produces the sensation of coolness. There is no flow from cold to hot, only from hot to cold.

23. In terms of physics, why do some restaurants serve baked potatoes wrapped in aluminum foil?

    The main reason for serving potatoes wrapped in aluminum foil is to increase the time that the potatoes remain hot after being removed from the oven. Heat transfer by radiation is minimized, as radiation from the potatoes is internally reflected; heat transfer by convection is minimized, as circulating air cannot make contact with the shielded potatoes. The foil also serves to retain moisture.

24. Wood is a better insulator than glass. Yet fiberglass is commonly used as an insulator in wooden buildings. Explain.

Air is an excellent insulator. The reason that fiberglass is a good insulator is principally because of the vast amount of air spaces trapped in it.

25. Visit a snow-covered cemetery and note that the snow does not slope upward against the gravestones but, instead, forms depressions around them. Can you think of a reason for this?

Heat from the relatively warm ground is conducted by the gravestone to melt the snow in contact with the gravestone. Likewise for trees or any materials that are better conductors of heat than snow, and that extend into the ground.

26. Why is it that you can safely hold your bare hand in a hot pizza oven for a few seconds, but, if you were to touch the metal inside, you'd burn yourself?

Air is a poor conductor, whatever the temperature. So holding your hand in hot air for a short time is not harmful, because very little heat is conducted by the air to your hand. But if you touch the hot conducting surface of the oven, heat readily conducts to you—ouch!

27. In a still room, smoke from a candle will sometimes rise only so far, not reaching the ceiling. Explain why.

The smoke, like hot air, is less dense than the surroundings and is buoyed upward. It cools with contact with the surrounding air and becomes more dense. When its density matches that of the surrounding air, its buoyancy and weight balance and rising ceases.

28. From the rules that a good absorber of radiation is a good radiator and a good reflector is a poor absorber, state a rule relating the reflecting and radiating properties of a surface.

A good reflector is a poor radiator of heat, and a poor reflector is a good radiator of heat.

29. Suppose at a restaurant you are served coffee before you are ready to drink it. In order that it be as warm as possible when you are ready for it, would you be wiser to add cream to it right away or just before you are ready to drink it?

Put the cream in right away for at least three reasons. Because black coffee radiates more heat than white coffee, make it whiter right away so it won't radiate and cool so quickly while you are waiting. Also, by Newton's Law of Cooling, the higher the temperature of the coffee above the surroundings, the greater will be the rate of cooling—so again add cream right away and lower the temperature to that of a reduced cooling rate, rather than allow it to cool fast and then bring the temperature down still further by adding the cream later. Also, by adding the cream, you increase the total amount of liquid, which for the same surface area, cools more slowly.

Answers to Chapter 6 Problems

1. Pounding a nail into wood makes the nail warmer. Consider a 5-gram steel nail 6 cm long, and a hammer that exerts an average force of 500 N on it when it is being driven into a piece of wood. Show that the increase in the nail's temperature will be 13.3°C. (Assume the specific heat capacity of steel is 450 J/kg°C.)

Work the hammer does on the nail is given by $F \times d$, and the temperature change of the nail can be found from using $Q = cm \, \Delta T$. First, we get everything into more convenient units for calculating: 5 grams = 0.005 kg; 6 cm = 0.06 m. Then $F \times d = 500$ N $\times$ 0.06 m = 30 J, and 30 J = (0.005 kg) (450 J/kg°C)(ΔT) which we can solve to get $\Delta T = 30/(0.005 \times 450) = 13.3$°C. (You will notice a similar effect when you remove a nail from a piece of wood. The nail that you pull out is noticeably warm.)

2. If you wish to warm 100 kg of water by 20°C for your bath, how much heat is required? (Show that 8730 kJ of heat is required.)

Each kilogram requires 1 kilocalorie for each degree change, so 100 kg needs 100 kilocalories for each degree change. Twenty degrees means 20 times this, which is 2000 kcal. By formula, $Q = mc\Delta T =$ (100,000 g)(1 cal/g°C)(20°C) = 2000 kcal. We can convert this to joules knowing that 4.18 J = 1 cal. In joules, this quantity of heat is 8360 kJ.

3. The specific heat capacity of copper is 0.092 calories per gram per degree Celsius. Show that the heat required to raise the temperature of a 10-gram piece of copper from 0°C to 100°C is 92 calories.

Raising the temperature of 10 gm of copper by 1 degree takes $10 \times 0.092 = 0.92$ calories, and raising it through 100 degrees takes 100 times as much, or 92 calories. By formula, $Q = mc\Delta T = (10$ g$)(0.092$ cal/g°C$)(100$°C$) = 92$ cal.

Heating 10 grams of water through the same temperature difference takes 1000 calories, more than 10 times more than for the copper—another reminder that water has a large specific heat capacity.

4. When 100 g of 40°C iron nails are submerged in 100 g of 20°C water, show that the final temperature of the water will be 22.1°C. (The specific heat of iron is 0.12 cal/g C°. Here you should equate the heat gained by the water to the heat lost by the nails.)

   Heat gained by water = heat lost by nails

   $(cm\ \Delta T)$water = $(cm\ \Delta T)$nails

   $(1)(100)\ (T - 20) = (0.12)(100)(40 - T)$, giving $T = 22.1°C$.

5. A 10-kg iron ball is dropped onto a pavement from a height of 100 m. If half of the heat generated goes into warming the ball, show that the temperature increase of the ball will be 1.1°C. (In SI units, the specific heat capacity of iron is 450 J/kg·°C.) Why is the answer the same for an iron ball of any mass?

   $0.5mgh = cm\ \Delta T$

   $\Delta T = 0.5mgh/cm = 0.5gh/c = (0.5)(9.8\ \text{m/s}^2)(100\ \text{m})/450\ \text{J/kg} = 1.1°C.$

   Again, note that the mass cancels, so the same temperature would hold for any mass ball, assuming half the heat generated goes into warming the ball. As in the previous problem, the units check because 1 J/kg = 1 m²/s².

Chapter 7: Electricity and Magnetism

Answers to Chapter 7 Review Questions

1. Nucleus (with protons) is positive; electrons are negative.

2. That charge is rearranged and always there. It is not created or destroyed, similar to the way energy is conserved.

3. Both are similar in form, both an inverse-square law. Different in that there are both attractive and repelling forces in Coulomb's law, but only attractive in Newton's law of gravitation.

4. Very large. The charge of 6.25 billion electrons = 1 coulomb.

5. Gravitational, electrical (later, we'll see magnetic).

6. Field direction is defined to be the same as the force on a positive charge in the field.

7. Electric potential energy is measured in joules. Electric potential is potential energy *per* unit of charge—a ratio, measured in volts.

8. No, it means it has several thousand joules of energy *per coulomb of charge*. Only if the charge is 1 coulomb is the energy several thousand joules.

9. It's a matter of degree: conductors conduct electricity readily, semiconductors less so, and insulators even less.

10. Metals—they are good conductors, because their outer electrons are loosely attached to the nucleus and able to flow.

11. A temperature difference; a voltage difference.

12. A sustained voltage difference.

13. Protons are anchored in the nucleus. Electrons, at least the outermost ones in metals, are not strongly tied to the nuclei and can flow.

14. AC is alternating current, where charges surge to and fro. DC is direct current, where charges flow in only one direction.

15. Thin wire has more resistance, like a thin pipe is to water flow.

16. The unit of electrical resistance is the ohm (Ω).

17. Doubled also. If voltage and resistance are doubled, then there is no change.

18. 1.5 A.

19. Parallel. If it were wired in series and one lamp burns out, all go out!

20. Adds up to equal the current in the source.

21. Power = current × voltage.

22. The kilowatt is a unit of energy; the kilowatt-hour is a unit of power.

23. Just as like charges repel and unlikes attract, like poles repel and unlikes attract.

24. Whereas electric charges can be isolated, magnetic poles cannot. Electrons and protons are entities by themselves.

25. A magnetic field is produced by the motion of electric charge.

26. Wood has no concentrations of iron atoms and therefore no magnetic domains.

27. The direction of the magnetic force is always perpendicular to both the magnetic field lines and the beam of charged particles.

28. A galvanometer indicates current. When calibrated to measure current, it is an ammeter; when calibrated to measure voltage, it is a voltmeter.

29. By moving a loop of wire near a magnet; by moving a magnet near a loop of wire, or by changing the current in a nearby loop.

30. An electric field; a magnetic field.

Answers to Chapter 7 Multiple-Choice Questions

1c, 2c, 3b, 4d, 5d, 6a

Answers to Chapter 7 Integrated Science Concepts

Biology: Electric Shock

1. Electric current passing through the body produces electric shock.

2. Your own body.

3. In the first case, the current passes through your chest; in the second case, current passes though your arm only. You can cut off your arm and survive but cannot survive without your heart.

Biology, Earth Science: Earth's Magnetic Field and the Ability of Organisms to Sense It

1. Animals sense Earth's magnetic field and orient themselves with respect to it.

2. There is some uncertainty about the source of Earth's magnetic field; the predominant contributor appears to be the circulating charges in the outer core.

Answers to Chapter 7 Exercises

1. With respect to forces, how are electric charge and mass alike? How are they different?

   Charge and mass are alike in that both determine the strength of a force between objects. Both appear in an inverse-square law of force. They differ in that charge can be positive or negative, while mass is always positive. They differ also in the strength of force they determine.

2. When combing your hair, you scuff electrons from your hair onto the comb. Is your hair then positively or negatively charged? How about the comb?

   Excess electrons rubbed from your hair leave it with a positive charge; excess electrons on the comb give it a negative charge.

3. An electroscope is a simple device consisting of a metal ball that is attached by a conductor to two thin leaves of metal foil protected from air disturbances in a jar, as shown. When the ball is touched by a charged body, the leaves, which normally hang straight down, spread apart. Why?

   The leaves, like the rest of the electroscope, acquire charge from the charged object and repel each other because they both have the same sign of charge. The weight of the conducting gold foil is so small that even tiny forces are clearly evident.

4. The five thousand billion billion freely moving electrons in a penny repel one another. Why don't they fly out of the penny?

   The electrons don't fly out of the penny because they are attracted to the five thousand billion billion positively charged protons in the atomic nuclei of atoms in the penny.

5. Two equal charges exert equal forces on each other. What if one charge has twice the magnitude of the other? How do the forces they exert on each other compare?

   The forces they exert on each other are still the same! Newton's third law applies to electrical forces as well as all forces.

6. Suppose that the strength of the electric field about an isolated point charge has a certain value at a distance of 1 m. How will the electric field strength compare at a distance of 2 m from the point charge? What law guides your answer?

   At twice the distance, the field strength will be 1/4, in accord with the inverse-square law.

7. Why is a good conductor of electricity also a good conductor of heat?

   For both electricity and heat, the conduction is via electrons, which in a metal are loosely bound, easy flowing, and easy to get moving. (Many fewer electrons in metals take part in heat conduction than in electric conduction, however.)

8. When a car is moved into a painting chamber, a mist of paint is sprayed around it. When the body of the car is given a sudden electric charge and mist is attracted to it, presto—the car is quickly and uniformly painted. What does the phenomenon of polarization have to do with this?

   The paint particles in the mist are polarized and are therefore attracted to the charged chassis.

9. If you place a free electron and a free proton in the same electric field, how will the forces acting on them compare? How will their accelerations compare? How will their directions of travel compare?

   The forces on the electron and proton will be equal in magnitude but opposite in direction. Because of the greater mass of the proton, its acceleration will be less than that of the electron and will be in the direction of the electric field. How much less? Because the mass of the proton is nearly 2000 times that of the electron, its acceleration will be about 1/2000 that of the electron. The greater acceleration of the electron will be in the direction opposite to the electric field. The electron and proton accelerate in opposite directions.

10. You are not harmed by contact with a charged metal ball, even though its voltage may be very high. Is the reason similar to why you are not harmed by a Fourth-of-July sparkler, even though the temperatures of each of those sparks is greater than 1000°C? Defend your answer in terms of the energies that are involved.

    Yes, in both cases we have a ratio of energy per something. In the case of temperature, the ratio is energy/molecule. In the case of voltage, it is energy/charge. Even with a small numerator, the ratio can be large if the denominator is small enough. Such is the case with the small energies involved to produce high-temperature sparklers and high-voltage metal balls.

11. In which of the circuits below does a current exist to light the bulb?

    Only circuit number 5 is complete and will light the bulb. (Circuits 1 and 2 are "short circuits" and will quickly drain the cell of its energy. In circuit 3, both ends of the lamp filament are connected to the same terminal and are therefore at the same potential. Only one end of the lamp filament is connected to the cell in circuit 4.)

12. Sometimes you hear someone say that a particular appliance "uses up" electricity. What is it that the appliance actually uses up, and what becomes of it?

    An electric device does not "use up" electricity, but rather *energy*. And strictly speaking, it doesn't "use up" energy but transforms it from one form to another. It is common to say that energy is used up when it is transformed to less-concentrated forms—when it is degraded. Electrical energy ultimately becomes heat energy. In this sense, it is used up.

13. Will the current in a lightbulb connected to a 220-V source be greater or less than the current in the same bulb when it is connected to a 110-V source?

    Current will be greater in the bulb connected to the 220-volt source. Twice the voltage would produce twice the current if the resistance of the filament remained the same. (In practice, the greater current

produces a higher temperature and greater resistance in the lamp filament, so the current is greater than that produced by 110 volts but appreciably less than twice as much for 220 volts. A bulb rated for 110 volts has a very short life when operated at 220 volts.)

14. Are automobile headlights wired in parallel or in series? What is your evidence?

    Auto headlights are wired in parallel. Then when one burns out, the other remains lit. If you've ever seen an automobile with one burned out headlight, you have evidence they're wired in parallel.

15. A car's headlights dissipate 40 W on low beam and 50 W on high beam. Is there more resistance or less resistance in the high-beam filament?

    There is less resistance in the higher wattage lamp. Because power = current × voltage, more power for the same voltage means more current. And by Ohm's law, more current for the same voltage means less resistance. (Algebraic manipulation of the equations $P = IV$ and $I = V/R$ leads to $P = V^2/R$.)

16. To connect a pair of resistors so their equivalent resistance will be greater than the resistance of either one, should you connect them in series or in parallel?

    The equivalent resistance of resistors in series is their sum, so connect a pair of resistors in series for more resistance.

17. Why might the wingspan of birds be a consideration in determining the spacing between parallel wires on power poles?

    If the parallel wires are closer than the wingspan of birds, a bird could short circuit the wires by contacting them with its wings, be killed in the process, and possibly interrupt the delivery of power.

18. In the circuit shown, how do the brightnesses of the individual lightbulbs compare? Which lightbulb draws the most current? What will happen if bulb A is unscrewed? If bulb C is unscrewed?

    Bulb C is the brightest, because the voltage across it equals that of the battery. Bulbs A and B share the voltage of the parallel branch of the circuit and have half the current of bulb C (assuming resistances are independent of voltages). If bulb A is unscrewed, the top branch is no longer part of the circuit, and current ceases in both A and B. They no longer give light, while bulb C glows as before. If bulb C is instead unscrewed, then it goes out, and bulbs A and B glow as before.

19. As more and more bulbs are connected in series to a flashlight battery, what happens to the brightness of each bulb? Assuming heating inside the battery is negligible, what happens to the brightness of each bulb when more and more bulbs are connected in parallel?

    As more bulbs are connected in series, more resistance is added to the single circuit path, and the resulting current produced by the battery is diminished. This is evident in the dimmer light from the bulbs. On the other hand, when more bulbs are connected to the battery in parallel, the brightness of the bulbs is practically unchanged. This is because each bulb, in effect, is connected directly to the battery with no other bulbs in its electrical path to add to its resistance. Each bulb has its own current path.

20. Since every iron atom is a tiny magnet, why aren't all things made of iron themselves magnets?

    All iron materials are not magnetized because the tiny magnetic domains are most often oriented in random directions and cancel one another's effects.

21. What surrounds a stationary electric charge? A moving electric charge?

    An electric field surrounds a stationary electric charge. An electric field and a magnetic field surround a moving electric charge. (And a gravitational field also surrounds both.)

22. A strong magnet attracts a paper clip to itself with a certain force. Does the paper clip exert a force on the strong magnet? If not, why not? If so, does it exert as much force on the magnet as the magnet exerts on it? Defend your answers.

    Newton's third law again: Yes, the paper clip, as part of the interaction, certainly does exert a force on the magnet—just as much as the magnet pulls on it. The magnet and paper clip pull equally on each other to comprise the single interaction between them.

23. Wai Tsan Lee shows iron nails that have become induced magnets. Is there similar physics here with the sticking balloon of Figure 7.5? Defend your answer.

Yes, the physics is similar. The iron nails become magnetized as their domains are induced into alignment by the magnet's strong magnetic field. Similarly, the electric field of the balloon induces a charge on the surface of the wall.

24. Can an electron at rest in a magnetic field be set into motion by the magnetic field? What if it were at rest in an electric field?

An electron has to be moving across lines of magnetic field in order to feel a magnetic force. So an electron at rest in a stationary magnetic field will feel no force to set it in motion. In an electric field, however, an electron will be accelerated whether or not it is already moving. (A combination of magnetic and electric fields is used in particle accelerators such as cyclotrons. The electric field accelerates the charged particle in its direction, and the magnetic field accelerates it perpendicular to its direction, causing it to follow a nearly circular path.)

25. Residents of northern Canada are bombarded by more intense cosmic radiation than are residents of Mexico. Why is this so?

Charged particles moving through a magnetic field are deflected most when they move at right angles to the field lines, and least when they move parallel to the field lines. If we consider cosmic rays heading toward the Earth from all directions and from great distance, those descending toward northern Canada will be moving nearly parallel to the magnetic field lines of the Earth. They will not be deflected very much, and secondary particles they create high in the atmosphere will also stream downward with little deflection. Over regions closer to the equator, like Mexico, the incoming cosmic rays move more nearly at right angles to the Earth's magnetic field, and many of them are deflected back out into space before they reach the atmosphere. The secondary particles they create are less intense at the Earth's surface. (This "latitude effect" provided the first evidence that cosmic rays from outer space consist of charged particles—mostly protons, as we now know.)

26. A magician places an aluminum ring on a table, underneath which is hidden an electromagnet. When the magician says "abracadabra" (and pushes a switch that starts current flowing through the coil under the table), the ring jumps into the air. Explain his "trick."

The changing magnetic field produced when the current starts to flow induces a current in the aluminum ring. This current, in turn, generates a magnetic field that opposes the field produced by the magnet under the table. The aluminum ring becomes, momentarily, a magnet that is repelled by the hidden magnet. Why repelled? Lenz's law. The induced field opposes the change of the inducing field. (This question will stimulate a discussion of Lenz's law—worthy but beyond the scope of this book.)

27. A friend says that changing electric and magnetic fields generate one another, and this gives rise to visible light when the frequency of change matches the frequency of light. Do you agree? Explain.

Agree with your friend, for light is electromagnetic radiation having a frequency that matches the frequency to which our eyes are sensitive.

28. Write a letter to Grandma and convince her that whatever electric shocks she may have received over the years have been due to the movement of electrons already in her body—not electrons coming from somewhere else.

Answers will vary.

Solutions to Chapter 7 Problems

1. Two point charges are separated by 6 cm. The attractive force between them is 20 N. Show that the force between them when they are separated by 12 cm is 5 N.

By the inverse-square law, twice as far is 1/4 the force; 5 N. The solution involves relative distance only, so the magnitude of charges is irrelevant.

2. A droplet of ink in an industrial ink-jet printer carries a charge of 1.6×10^{-10} C and is deflected onto paper by a force of 3.2×10^{-4} N. Show that the strength of the electric field required to produce this force is 2×10^6 N/C.

Electric field is force divided by charge: $E = \dfrac{F}{q} = \dfrac{3.2 \times 10^{-4}\text{N}}{1.6 \times 10^{-10}\text{C}} = 2 \times 10^6$ N/C. (The unit N/C is the same as the unit V/m, so the field can be expressed as 2 million volts per meter.)

3. Find the voltage change when (a) an electric field does 12 J of work on a 0.0001 C charge, and (b) the same electric field does 24 J of work on a 0.0002 C.

(a) $\Delta V = \dfrac{\text{energy}}{\text{charge}} = \dfrac{12\ \text{J}}{0.0001\ \text{C}} = 120{,}000$ volts.

(b) ΔV for twice the charge is $\dfrac{24\ \text{J}}{0.0002} = $ same 120 kV.

4. Rearrange this equation

$$\text{Current} = \dfrac{\text{voltage}}{\text{resistance}}$$

to express resistance in terms of current and voltage. Then consider the following: A certain device in a 120-V circuit has a current rating of 20 A. Show that the resistance of the device is 6 Ω.

From $\text{current} = \dfrac{\text{voltage}}{\text{resistance}}$, $\text{resistance} = \dfrac{\text{voltage}}{\text{current}} = \dfrac{120\ \text{V}}{20\text{A}} = 6$ ohms.

5. Using the formula Power = current × voltage, find that the current drawn by a 1200-W hair dryer connected to 120 V is 10 A. Then using the method you used in the previous problem, show that the resistance of the hair dryer is 12 Ω.

From power = current × voltage, $\text{current} = \dfrac{\text{power}}{\text{voltage}} = \dfrac{1200\ \text{W}}{120\ \text{V}} = 10$ A.

From the formula derived above, $\text{resistance} = \dfrac{\text{voltage}}{\text{current}} = \dfrac{120\ \text{V}}{10\ \text{A}} = 12$ ohms.

6. Show that it costs $3.36 to operate a 100-W lamp continuously for a week if the power utility rate is 20¢/kWh.

$3.36. First, 100 watts = 0.1 kilowatt. Second, there are 168 hours in 1 week (7 days × 24 hours/day = 168 hours). So, 168 hours × 0.1 kilowatt = 16.8 kilowatt-hours, which at 20 cents per kWh comes to $3.36.

Chapter 8: Waves and Sound

Answers to Chapter 8 Review Questions

1. *Period* is the time for one complete vibration. *Amplitude* is the distance from the midpoint to the crest (or trough) of a wave. *Wavelength* is the distance along the wave between any successive identical parts of the wave. *Frequency* specifies the number of to-and-fro vibrations in a given time, usually 1 second.

2. A vibration.

3. Energy (also, a disturbance).

4. No. A *disturbance* in a medium moves, energy, not the medium itself. Water in a pond or grass in a field propagate waves, but go nowhere.

5. Wave speed = frequency × wavelength.

6. (a) Perpendicular (or transverse) to the direction of wave travel. (b) Along the direction of wave travel.

7. As the name implies, compression is a bunching of a medium, rarefaction is a spreading.

8. The wavelength of sound equals the distance between successive compressions (or refractions) in air (or other medium).

9. Sound cannot travel through a vacuum. It requires a medium, because sound waves are made up of zones of dense molecules (compressions) and zones of fewer molecules (rarefactions.)

10. It sets the surface of the table vibrating, which has greater area.

11. Forced vibration occurs at any frequency, whereas resonance occurs when vibration is at a frequency matching an object's natural frequency.

12. Different frequencies. Different frequencies.

13. The frequency of the electromagnetic wave as it vibrates through space is identical to the frequency of the oscillating electric charge that generates it.

14. The angle of incidence equals the angle of reflection.

15. Yes; for individual rays. Overall, the light is redirected in many directions.

16. Transmission (re-emission for molecule to molecule in glass).

17. (a) Resonance and absorption. Energy is passed on to neighboring atoms as heat, so UV is absorbed by glass. (b) Transmission (re-emitted from molecule to molecule in the glass).

18. Slower in glass, fastest in vacuum.

19. Color is determined by frequency (or equivalently, by wavelength).

20. Light is reflected by the blank part of a page and absorbed by ink.

21. It transmits light of all visible frequencies equally well.

22. Bending is caused by a change in light speed.

23. Both.

24. Converging lens converges parallel rays of light; diverging lens diverges the same.

25. Longer wavelength.

26. Asset in radio broadcast, where diffraction fills in shadow regions, particularly for longer wavelength AM radio. Asset for dolphins who use diffraction to sense detail in their environment. Liability in microscopy, where fuzziness of an image occurs.

27. Interference is characteristic of all waves.

28. Constructive interference results from crest-to-crest reinforcement; destructive interference results from crest-to-crest cancellation.

29. Successive waves have a shorter distance to travel, so distance between successive crests decreases.

30. Open: trains and whistles are common examples.

31. Interference. Photoelectric effect.

32. Violet, because each photon has more energy.

33. Light behaves as a stream of photons when it interacts with film or any detector and behaves as a wave in traveling from a source to the place where it is detected.

Answers to Chapter 8 Multiple-Choice Questions

1c, 2c, 3d, 4c, 5c, 6b

Answers to Chapter 8 Integrated Science Concepts

Biology: Sensing Pitch

1. The higher the pitch of a sound, the higher its frequency.

2. The shorter frequencies are heard by bats. (Higher frequencies have shorter wavelengths.)

Biology: Mixing Colored Lights

1. All colors of light can be obtained from red, green, and blue light, as described by the principles of additive color mixing. Because any color can be obtained by sensing red, green, and blue light, sensing these three primary colors of light is all that is needed.

2. The cones in your retina receptive to the color of the paper become fatigued; so you see an afterimage of the complementary color when you look at the white area. This is because the fatigued cones send a weaker signal to the brain. All the colors produce white, but all the colors minus one produce the complement of what's missing.

Astronomy: The Doppler Shift and the Expanding Universe

1. The pitch of the buzzer increases as it gets closer to your ears and decreases as it moves away. The reason is that, as the Doppler effect explains, the frequency of the waves increases as the source of sound approaches and decreases as the sound source gets farther away.

2. Radiation we receive from stars and other astronomical bodies is Doppler-shifted, which indicates they are receding.

Answers to Chapter 8 Exercises

1. What kind of motion should you impart to a stretched coiled spring (or to a Slinky) to produce a transverse wave? A longitudinal wave?

   Shake the Slinky up and down to produce a transverse wave; push the Slinky horizontally to produce a longitudinal wave.

2. What does it mean to say that a radio station is "at 101.1 on your FM dial"?

   The carrier frequency of electromagnetic waves emitted by the radio station is 101.1 MHz.

3. At the stands of a race track you notice smoke from the starter's gun before you hear it fire. Explain.

   Light travels about a million times faster than sound in air, so you see a distant event a million times sooner than you hear it.

4. What is the danger posed by people in the balcony of an auditorium stamping their feet in a steady rhythm?

   The rhythm may match the resonant frequency of the balcony, which could result in its collapse. (This mishap has happened before.)

5. The sitar, an Indian musical instrument, has a set of strings that vibrate and produce music, even though they are never plucked by the player. These "sympathetic strings" are identical to the plucked strings and are mounted below them. What is your explanation?

   The lower strings are resonating with the upper strings.

6. A railroad locomotive is at rest with its whistle shrieking, and then it starts moving toward you. (a) Does the frequency that you hear increase, decrease, or stay the same? (b) How about the wavelength reaching your ear? (c) How about the speed of sound in the air between you and the locomotive?

   (a) The frequency increases. (b) The wavelength decreases. (c) The speed is unchanged (because the air remains motionless relative to you).

7. What is the fundamental source of electromagnetic radiation?

   The fundamental source of electromagnetic radiation is oscillating electric charges, which emit oscillating electric and magnetic fields.

8. Which has the shorter wavelengths, ultraviolet or infrared? Which has the higher frequencies?

   Ultraviolet has shorter waves than infrared. Correspondingly, ultraviolet also has the higher frequencies.

9. Do radio waves travel at the speed of sound, at the speed of light, or at some speed in between?

   Radio waves most certainly travel at the speed of every other electromagnetic wave—the speed of light.

10. What determines whether a material is transparent or opaque?

    Transparency or opaqueness is determined by the match between incident light frequencies and the resonant frequency of the material. A substance that is transparent to a range of light frequencies will be opaque to those frequencies that match its own resonant frequency.

11. You can get a sunburn on a cloudy day, but you can't get a sunburn even on a sunny day if you are behind glass. Explain.

    Clouds are transparent to ultraviolet light, which is why clouds offer no protection from sunburn. Glass, however, is opaque to ultraviolet light, and will therefore shield you from sunburn.

12. Suppose that sunlight falls on both a pair of reading glasses and a pair of dark sunglasses. Which pair of glasses would you expect to become warmer? Defend your answer.

The sunglasses will be warmer in sunlight than regular reading glasses. This is because the reading glasses transmit most of the light energy that is incident upon them, whereas the sunglasses absorb more light energy, which increases their internal energy.

13. Fire engines used to be red. Now many of them are yellow-green. Why the change of color?

    They are most likely to be noticed if they are yellow-green. That is where the eye is most sensitive.

14. The radiation curve of the Sun (Figure 8.29) shows that the brightest light from the Sun is yellow-green. Why then do we see the Sun as whitish instead of yellow-green?

    We see not only yellow-green, but also red and blue. All together, they mix to produce the white light we see.

15. Her eye at point P looks into the mirror. Which of the numbered cards can she see reflected in the mirror?

    Only light from card number 2 reaches her eye.

16. Cowboy Joe wishes to shoot his assailant by ricocheting a bullet off a mirrored metal plate. To do so, should he simply aim at the mirrored image of his assailant? Explain.

    Cowboy Joe should simply aim at the mirrored image of his assailant, for the ricocheting bullet will follow the same changes in direction when its momentum changes (angle of incidence = angle of rebound) that light follows when reflecting from a plane surface.

17. If, while standing on the bank of a stream, you wished to spear a fish swimming in the water out in front of you, would you aim above, below, or directly at the observed fish to make a direct hit? If you decided instead to zap the fish with a laser, would you aim above, below, or directly at the observed fish? Defend your answers.

    You would throw the spear below the apparent position of the fish, because the effect of refraction is to make the fish appear closer to the surface than it really is. But in zapping a fish with a laser, make no corrections and aim directly at the fish. This is because the light from the fish you see has been refracted in getting to you, and the laser light will refract along the same path in getting to the fish. A slight correction may be necessary, depending on the colors of the laser beam and the fish.

18. What happens to light of a certain frequency when it is incident on a material that has a natural frequency that is the same as the frequency of the light?

    It is absorbed.

19. The ocean wave is cyan. What color(s) of light does it absorb? What colors does it reflect?

    A cyan wave absorbs red light and reflects blue-green light.

20. A rule of thumb for estimating the distance in kilometers between an observer and a lightning strike is to divide the number of seconds in the interval between the flash and the sound by 3. Is this rule correct?

    The rule of thumb is correct. This is because the speed of sound in air (340 m/s) can be rounded off to 1/3 km/s. Then, from distance = speed × time = (1/3) km/s × (number of seconds). Note that the time in seconds divided by 3 yields the same value.

21. If a single disturbance some unknown distance away sends out both transverse and longitudinal waves that travel at distinctly different speeds in the medium, such as the ground during earthquakes, how could the origin of the disturbance be located?

    If a single disturbance at some unknown distance away sends longitudinal waves at one known speed, and transverse waves at a lesser known speed, and you measure the difference in time of the waves as they arrive, you can calculate the distance. The wider the gap in time, the greater the distance—which could be in any direction. If you use this distance as the radius of the circle on a map, you know the disturbance occurred somewhere on that circle. If you telephone two friends who have made similar measurements of the same event from different locations, you can transfer their circles to your map, and the point where the three circles intersect is the location of the disturbance.

22. A bat flying in a cave emits a sound and receives its echo 0.1 s later. How far away is the cave wall?

    Assuming the speed of sound to be 340 m/s, the cave is 17 meters away. This is because the sound took 0.05 second to reach the wall (and 0.05 second to return). Distance = speed × time = 340 m/s × 0.05 s = 17 m.

23. Why do radio waves diffract around buildings, whereas light waves do not?

    Radio waves are much larger and therefore diffract more than the shorter waves of light.

24. Sun tanning produces cellular damage in the skin. Why is ultraviolet radiation capable of producing this damage whereas visible radiation is not?

    More energy is associated with each photon of ultraviolet light than with photons that make up visible light. This extra energy per photon alters the skin, producing the sunburn.

25. Explain briefly how the photoelectric effect is used in the operation of at least two of the following: an electric eye, a photographer's light meter, and the sound track of a motion picture.

    Electric eye: **A beam of light is directed to a photosensitive surface that completes the path of an electric circuit. When the beam is interrupted, the circuit is broken, compromising a switch for another circuit.** *Light meter:* **the variation of photoelectric current with variations in light intensity.** *Sound track:* **An optical sound track on motion picture film is a strip of emulsion of variable density that transmits light onto a photoelectric surface, which in turn produces a variable current. This current is amplified and activates a speaker.**

26. Does the photoelectric effect prove that light is made of particles? Do interference experiments prove that light is composed of waves? (Is there a distinction between what something is and how it behaves?)

    The photoelectric effect doesn't prove that light is corpuscular, but rather supports the corpuscular model of light, which is compatible with the particle-like behavior observed. The same is true with interference experiments that support the wave model of light and are compatible with the wave-like behavior of light. We have models to help us conceptualize what something is; knowledge of the details of how something behaves helps us to refine the model. It is important that we keep in mind our models for understanding nature as just that: models.

27. Write a letter to Grandpa explaining why we now say that light is not just a particle, and is not just a wave, but in fact is both—a "wavicle"!

    Letters to Grandpa should discuss the wave behavior of light as indicated by the wave properties it exhibits including interference. Letters should also discuss the particle behavior of light in its interaction with matter: the photoelectric effect. Taking into account all observations of light, scientists conclude it has properties of both waves and particles and therefore is both—a "wavicle."

Solutions to Chapter 8 Problems

1. What is the frequency, in hertz, that corresponds to each of the following periods: (a) 0.10 s, (b) 5 s, (c) 1/60 s?

   (a) $f = 1/T = 1/0.10$ s $= 10$ Hz; (b) $f = 1/5 = 0.2$ Hz; (c) $f = 1/(1/60)$ s $= 60$ Hz.

2. The nearest star beyond the Sun is Alpha Centauri, 4.2×10^{16} meters away. If we were to receive a radio message from this star today, show that it would have been sent 1.4×10^8 seconds ago (4.4 years ago).

   As in the previous problem, $t = \dfrac{d}{v} = \dfrac{4.2 \times 10^{16} \text{ m}}{3 \times 10^8 \text{ m/s}} = 1.4 \times 10^8$ s.

   Converting to years by dimensional analysis,

   $$1.4 \times 10^8 \text{ s} \times \frac{1 \text{ h}}{3600 \text{ s}} \times \frac{1 \text{ day}}{24 \text{ h}} \times \frac{1 \text{ yr}}{365 \text{ day}} = 4.4 \text{ yr.}$$

3. Blue-green light has a frequency of about 6×10^{14} Hz. Use the relationship $c = f\lambda$ to show that the wavelength of this light in air is 5×10^{-7} meters. How does this wavelength compare with the size of an atom, which is about 10^{-10} m?

From $c = c = f\lambda$, $\lambda = \dfrac{c}{f} = \dfrac{3 \times 10^8 \text{ m/s}}{6 \times 10^{14}\text{ Hz}} = 5 \times 10^{-7}$ m, or 500 nanometers. This is 5000 times larger than the size of an atom, which is 0.1 nanometer. (The nanometer is a common unit of length in atomic and optical physics.)

4. The wavelength of light changes as light goes from one medium to another, while the frequency remains the same. Is the wavelength longer or shorter in water than in air? Explain in terms of the equation: speed = frequency × wavelength.

   Light in water travels at 0.75c. $\lambda = \dfrac{c}{f}$ for light in a vacuum (or air), and $\lambda = \dfrac{0.75c}{f}$ for light in water. The ratio of λ_{water} to λ_{air} is, therefore, 0.75, the same for all frequencies.

5. A certain blue-green light has a wavelength of 600 nm (6×10^{-7} m) in air. Show that its wavelength in water, where light travels at 75% of its speed in air is 450 nm. Show that its speed in Plexiglas, where light travels at 67% of its speed in air, is 400 nm. (1 nm = 10^{-9}m).

   λ_{air} = 600 nm = (6×10^{-7} m). So λ_{water} = (0.75)(6×10^{-7} m) = 4.5×10^{-7} m = 450 nm. And $\lambda_{\text{Plexiglas}}$ = (0.67)(6×10^{-7} m) = 4.0×10^{-7} m = 400 nm

6. A certain radar installation used to track airplanes transmits electromagnetic radiation of wavelength 3 cm. (a) What is the frequency of this radiation, measured in billions of hertz (GHz)? (b) What is the time required for a pulse of radar waves to reach an airplane 5 km away and return?

   (a) Frequency = speed/wavelength = (3×10^8 m/s)/(0.03 m) = 1.0×10^{10} Hz = 10 GHz.

   (b) Distance = speed × time, so time = distance/speed = (10,000 m)/(3×10^8 m/s) = 3.3×10^{-5} s. (Note the importance of consistent SI units to get the right numerical answers.)

7. Suppose that you walk toward a mirror at 2 m/s. Show that you and your image both approach each other at a speed of 4 m/s (and not 2 m/s).

   You and your image are both walking at 2 m/s.

Chapter 9: The Atom

Answers to Chapter 9 Review Questions

1. An element.

2. Just as all words in the English language are made from 26 letters combined in different ways, so are all materials composed of atoms combined in different ways.

3. The nucleus—neutrons and protons.

4. Atoms are smaller than the wavelength of visible light. Therefore, they cannot be seen.

5. Atoms differ in the number of protons in their nuclei.

6. A proton is nearly 2000 times more massive than an electron.

7. A proton has a charge equal to, but opposite, that of an electron.

8. Atomic number is the number of protons in the nucleus of an atom.

9. Elements are listed in the periodic table by increasing atomic number.

10. Isotopes are atoms of the same element that contain different numbers of neutrons. Isotopes are identified by mass number.

11. Protons and neutrons are two nucleons.

12. Because isotopes of an element differ only in mass, not in electric charge, and therefore have similar chemical behavior.

13. No; different atoms emit different frequencies of light.

14. Atomic spectra are unique to each element.

15. The sum of the frequencies of two lines often equals the frequency of a third spectral line.

16. Energy is quantized.

17. It moves away from the nucleus and gains energy.

18. The energy of an emitted photon equals the difference in energy between the two orbits.

19. Due to their wave nature—the circumference of the smallest orbit can be no smaller than a single wavelength.

20. The wave nature of electrons in atoms is pronounced, because electrons move at speeds of about 2 million meters per second.

21. A probability cloud is therefore a close approximation to the actual shape of an electron's three-dimensional wave.

22. The *s* orbital is spherical. The *p* orbital consists of two lobes and resembles an hourglass.

Answers to Chapter 9 Multiple-Choice Questions

1c, 2d, 3b

Answers to Chapter 9 Integrated Science Concepts

Chemistry, Biology, Earth Science: Physical and Conceptual Models

1. When we use a scanning tunneling microscope, we see atoms indirectly, because we are seeing a computer-generated diagram of the contours of atoms.

2. Atoms are smaller than the wavelength of visible light. Therefore, they cannot be seen.

3. A physical model is tangible, while a conceptual model is a mental image.

4. An atomic model predicts the behavior of a system that we cannot see.

Chemistry: The Shell Model

1. The valence electrons are the electrons most responsible for the properties of an atom.

2. This model suffices to explain the organization of the periodic table. Remember that the value of a model lies in its utility as much as in its accuracy.

3. There are eight orbitals present in the third shell.

Solutions to Chapter 9 Exercises

1. A cat strolls across your backyard. An hour later, a dog with its nose to the ground follows the trail of the cat. Explain what is going on in terms of atoms.

   The cat leaves a trail of molecules on the grass. These, in turn, leave the grass and mix with the air, where they enter the dog's nose, activating its sense of smell.

2. Which are older, the hydrogen atoms in a young star or those in an old star?

   The age of the atoms in either a young star or in an old star are the same; appreciably older than the solar system.

3. In what sense can you truthfully say that you are a part of every person around you?

   You really are a part of every person around you in the sense that you are composed of atoms not only from every person around you, but from every person who ever lived on Earth!

4. Where are the atoms that make up a newborn baby manufactured?

   The atoms that make up a newborn baby are manufactured deep in the interior of stars.

5. Considering how small atoms are, what are the chances that at least one of the atoms exhaled in your first breath will be in your last breath?

With every breath of air you take, it is highly likely that you inhale one of the atoms exhaled during your very first breath. This is because the number of atoms of air in your lungs is about the same as the number of breaths of air in the atmosphere of the world.

6. Name ten elements that you have access to in macroscopic quantities as a consumer here on Earth.

Here is a list of eighteen. Aluminum (as in aluminum foil); tin (as in tin foil and tin cans); carbon (as in graphite and diamond); helium (as in a helium balloon); nitrogen (which comprises about 78% of the air we breathe); oxygen (which comprises about 21% of the air we breathe); argon (which comprises about 1% of the air we breathe); silicon (as in integrated circuits for computers and calculators); sulfur (a mineral used for many industrial processes); iron (as in most metal structures); chromium (as in chromium bumpers on cars); zinc (as in the coating of any galvanized nail or as the insides of any post-1982 copper penny); copper (as in copper pennies); nickel (as in nickel nickels); silver (as in jewelry and old silver coins); gold (as in jewelry); platinum (as in jewelry); and mercury (as in mercury thermometers).

7. Which of the following diagrams best represents the size of the atomic nucleus relative to the atom?

The one on the far right where the nucleus is not visible.

8. Which contributes more to an atom's mass: electrons or protons? Which contributes more to an atom's size?

The proton contributes much more to an atom's mass than does the electron. The electron, however, contributes much more to an atom's volume than does the proton.

9. If two protons and two neutrons are removed from the nucleus of an oxygen atom, a nucleus of which element remains?

The remaining nucleus is that of Carbon-12.

10. What element results if one of the neutrons in a nitrogen nucleus is converted by radioactive decay into a proton?

Oxygen, O.

11. The atoms that constitute your body are mostly empty space, and structures such as the chair you're sitting on are composed of atoms that are also mostly empty space. So why don't you fall through the chair?

The outsides of the atoms of the chair are made of negatively charged electrons, as are the outsides of the atoms that make up your body. Atoms don't pass through one another because of the repulsive forces that occur between these electrons. When you sit on the chair, these repulsive forces hold you up against the force of gravity, which is pulling you downward.

12. If an atom has 43 electrons, 56 neutrons, and 43 protons, what is its approximate atomic mass? What is the name of this element?

Atomic mass would be 99 amu, and the element would be technetium, Tc, atomic number 43.

13. The nucleus of an electrically neutral iron atom contains 26 protons. How many electrons does this iron atom have?

The iron atom is electrically neutral when it has 26 electrons to balance its 26 protons.

14. Why are the atomic masses listed in the periodic table not whole numbers?

The atomic masses listed in the periodic table are average numbers that reflect the variety of isotopes that exist for an element.

15. Where did the carbon atoms in Leslie's hair originate? (Shown below is a photo of Leslie Hewitt at age 16.)

The carbon atoms that make up Leslie's hair or anything else in this world originated in the explosions of ancient stars.

16. Would you use a physical model or a conceptual model to describe the following: brain, mind, solar system, birth of the universe, stranger, best friend, gold coin, dollar bill, car engine, virus, spread of a cold virus?

Many objects or systems may be described just as well by a physical model as by a conceptual model. In general, the physical model is used to replicate an object or system of objects on a different scale. The conceptual model, by contrast, is used to represent abstract ideas or to demonstrate the behavior of a system. Of the examples given in the exercise, the following might be adequately described using a physical model: the brain, the solar system, a stranger, a gold coin, a car engine, and a virus. The following might be adequately described using a conceptual model: the mind, the birth of the universe, your best friend (whose complex behavior you have some understanding of), a dollar bill (which represents wealth but is really only a piece of paper), and the spread of a contagious disease, such as a cold.

17. How might you distinguish a sodium vapor street lamp from a mercury vapor street lamp?

Observe the atomic spectra of each using a spectroscope.

18. How can a hydrogen atom, which has only one electron, have so many spectral lines?

The one electron can be boosted to many energy level and, therefore, make many combinations of transitions to lower levels. Each transition is of a specific energy and is accompanied by the emission of a photon of a specific frequency. Thus, the variety of spectral lines is seen.

19. Which color of light comes from the higher energy transition, red or blue? Explain.

The blue frequency is a higher frequency and, therefore, corresponds to a higher energy level transition.

20. Which has the greatest energy, a photon of infrared light, a photon of visible light, or a photon of ultraviolet light?

The photon of ultraviolet light has the greatest energy.

21. If we take a piece of metal at room temperature and begin to heat it continuously in a dark room, it will soon begin to glow visibly. What will be its first visible color, and why?

The first visible color will be red, because this is the visible frequency with the lowest amount of energy per photon.

22. Figure 9.20 shows three energy-level transitions that produce three spectral lines in a spectroscope. Note that the distance between the $n = 1$ and $n = 2$ levels is greater than the distance between the $n = 2$ and $n = 3$ levels. Would the number of spectral lines produced change if the distance between the $n = 1$ and $n = 2$ levels were exactly the same as the distance between the $n = 2$ and $n = 3$ level?

The drop from $n = 3$ to $n = 2$ would be the same energy difference as the drop from $n = 2$ to $n = 1$. The frequencies emitted from these transitions, therefore, would be the same and would overlap each other in the atomic spectrum. The effect would be that two otherwise separate lines would converge into a single more intense line.

23. What is the evidence for the claim that iron exists in the relatively cool outer layer of the Sun?

The spectral patterns emanating from the Sun indicate the spectral patterns of heated iron atoms.

24. What does it mean to say that something is *quantized*?

If something is "quantized," that means it consists of distinct units. Sand, for example, is quantized by each grain. Light is quantized by each photon.

25. The frequency of violet light is about twice that of red light. Compare the energy of the violet photon with the energy of a red photon.

Twice the frequency means twice the energy.

26. If a beam of red light and a beam of violet light have equal energies, which beam has the greater number of photons?

The red light will need more photons to match the energy of the violet light, because each red light photon carries less energy.

27. How does the wave model of electrons orbiting the nucleus account for the fact that the electrons can have only discrete energy values?

When a wave is confined, it is reinforced only at particular frequencies. The electron wave being confined to the atom, therefore, exhibits only particular frequencies, where each frequency represents a discrete energy value.

28. How might the spectrum of an atom appear if its electrons were not restricted to particular energy levels?

    An electron not restricted to particular energy levels would release light continuously as it spiraled closer into the nucleus. A broad spectrum of colors would be observed rather than the distinct lines.

29. How does an electron get from one lobe of a p orbital to the other?

    Because of its wave nature, it would be better to say that the electron actually exists in both lobes at the same time.

30. Light is emitted as an electron transitions from a higher-energy orbital to a lower-energy orbital. How long does it take for the actual transition to take place? At what point is the electron found in between these two orbitals?

    It takes no time at all for this transition to occur. It is instantaneous. At no point is the electron found in between these two orbitals.

31. Why is there only one spatial orientation for the s orbital?

    The s orbital is a sphere that cannot be rotated without being in the same orientation—the sphere is perfectly symmetrical!

32. Place the proper number of electrons in each shell for sodium, Na (atomic number 11); rubidium, Rb (atomic number 37); krypton, Kr (atomic number 36); and chlorine, Cl (atomic number 17).

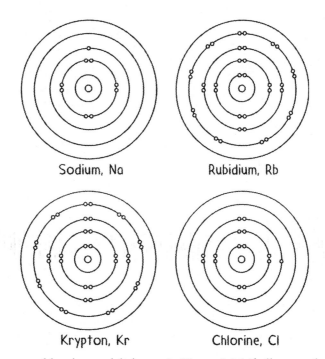

Sodium, Na   Rubidium, Rb

Krypton, Kr   Chlorine, Cl

33. Which element is represented by the model shown in Figure 9.26 if all seven shells are filled to capacity?

    This would make the element 118.

34. Does an orbital or shell have to contain electrons in order to exist?

    A shell is just a region of space in which an electron may reside. This region of space exists with or without the electron.

35. Use the shell model to explain why a potassium atom, K, is larger than a sodium atom, Na.

    Both the potassium and sodium atoms are in group 1 of the periodic table. The potassium atom, however, is larger than the sodium atom, because it contains an additional shell of electrons.

36. Light has been described as being a wave, and then as being a particle, and then again as a wave. Does this indicate that light's true nature probably lies somewhere in between these models?

No. Light truly does behave as a particle just as it truly behaves as a wave. What we need to understand is that it's okay to use different models to describe different behaviors. The utility of one model doesn't negate the utility of another.

37. Write a letter to Grandma telling her to what extent we can now "see" atoms.

Answers will vary.

Solutions to Chapter 9 Problems

1. Chlorine (atomic number 17) is composed of two principal isotopes, chlorine-35, which has a mass of 34.9689 atomic mass units, and chlorine-37, which has a mass of 36.9659 atomic mass units. Assume that 75.77 percent of all chlorine atoms are the chlorine-35 isotope and 24.23 percent are the chlorine-37 isotope. Show that the atomic mass of natural chlorine is 35.45.

    $[(0.7553) \times (34.97)] + [(0.2447) \times (36.95)] = 35.4545$.

2. Lithium (atomic number 3) is composed of two principle isotopes. The isotope lithium-7 has a mass of 7.0160 atomic mass units, and the isotope lithium-6 has a mass of 6.0151 atomic mass units. Assume that 92.58 percent of all lithium atoms found in nature are lithium-7 and 7.42 percent are lithium-6. Show that the atomic mass of lithium is 6.94.

Contributing . . .	(mass in amu)	(fraction of abundance)	
. . . mass of Li-6:	6.0151 ×	0.0742 =	0.446
. . . mass of Li-7:	7.0160 ×	0.9258 =	6.495
			6.941 (atomic mass)

3. The element bromine, Br (atomic number 35), has two major isotopes of similar abundance, both approximately 50%. The atomic mass of bromine is reported in the periodic table as 79.904 atomic mass units. Choose the most likely set of mass numbers for these two bromine isotopes: (a) ^{80}Br, ^{81}Br; (b) ^{79}Br, ^{80}Br; (c) ^{79}Br, ^{81}Br.

    A 50:50 mix of Br-80 and Br-81 would result in an atomic mass of about 80.5, while a 50:50 mix of Br-79 and Br-80 would result in an atomic mass of about 79.5. Neither of these is as close to the value reported in the periodic table as is a 50:50 mix of Br-79 and Br-81, which would result in an atomic mass of about 80.0. The answer is (c).

4. Gas A is composed of diatomic molecules (two atoms to a molecule) of a pure element. Gas B is composed of monatomic molecules (one atom to a "molecule") of another pure element. Gas A has three times the mass of an equal volume of Gas B at the same temperature and pressure. Show that the atomic mass of Element A is $^3/_2$ the mass of Element B.

    The atomic mass of element A is $^3/_2$ the mass of element B. Why? Gas A has three times the mass of Gas B. If the equal number of molecules in A and B had equal numbers of atoms, then the atoms in Gas A would simply be three times as massive. But there are twice as many atoms in A, so the mass of each atom must be half of three times as much—$^3/_2$.

5. The diameter of an atom is about 10^{-10} m. (a) How many atoms make a line a millionth of a meter (10^6 m) long? (b) Show that 10^8 atoms cover a square a millionth of a meter on a side. (c) Show that 10^{12} atoms fill a cube a millionth of a meter on a side. (d) If a dollar were attached to each atom, what could you buy with your line of atoms? With your square of atoms? With your cube of atoms?

    (a) 10^4 atoms (length 10^{-6} m divided by size 10^{-10} m).

    (b) 10^8 atoms ($10^4 \times 10^4$).

    (c) 10^{12} atoms ($10^4 \times 10^4 \times 10^4$).

    (d) $10,000 buys a good used car, for instance. $100 million buys a few jet aircraft and an airport at which to store them, for instance. $1 trillion buys a medium-sized country, for instance. (Answers limited only by the imagination of the student.)

6. Assume that the present world population of about 6×10^9 people is about $\frac{1}{20}$ of the people who ever lived on Earth. Show that the number of people who ever lived is incredibly small compared to the number of air molecules in a single breath.

The total number of people who ever lived ($6 \times 10^9 \times 20 = 120 \times 10^9$, which is roughly 10^{11} people altogether) is enormously smaller than 10^{22}. How does 10^{22} compare to 10^{11}? 10^{22} is $(10^{11})^2$! Multiply the number of people who ever lived by the same number, and you'll get 10^{22}, the number of air molecules in a breath of air. Suppose each person on Earth journeyed to a different planet in the galaxy, and every one of those planets contained as many people as the Earth now contains. The total number of people on all these planets would still be less than the number of molecules in a breath of air. Atoms are indeed small—and numerous!

Chapter 10: Nuclear Physics

Answers to Chapter 10 Review Questions

1. Most of the radiation we encounter is natural background radiation that originates in Earth and in space.

2. Atoms with unstable nuclei.

3. Alpha particles have a positive charge; beta particles have a negative charge; gamma rays are neutral.

4. It has been ejected from a nucleus.

5. About 20%.

6. REM.

7. The electrical force.

8. The strong nuclear force may be weaker than the repulsive electrical force.

9. To hold the nucleus together through the strong force.

10. More electrical repulsion.

11. The time it takes for half of an original quantity of an element to decay.

12. Radium-226 has a half-life of 1620 years; uranium-238 has a half-life of 4.5 billion years.

13. True.

14. There is a change in atomic number—a different element is formed.

15. No.

16. Artificial transmutation.

17. When an element ejects an alpha particle from its nucleus, the mass number of the resulting atom is decreased by four, and its atomic number is decreased by two.

18. Bombarding it with alpha particles.

19. About seven million times the energy released by the combustion of one TNT molecule.

20. A nuclear explosion occurs.

21. Reactors contain a moderator, a substance that slows neutrons.

22. Mass.

23. Less mass per nucleon.

24. Iron is the most stable nucleus, because it has the lowest mass per nucleon.

25. They liberate energy.

26. In both chemical and nuclear burning, a high temperature starts the reaction; the release of energy by the reaction maintains a high enough temperature to spread the fire. The net result of the chemical reaction is a combination of atoms into more tightly bound molecules. In nuclear fusion reactions, the net result is more tightly bound nuclei. In both cases, mass decreases as energy is released.

Answers to Chapter 10 Multiple-Choice Questions

1c, 2b, 3d, 4a, 5c

Answers to Chapter 10 Integrated Science Concepts

Biology: Doses of Radiation

1. Because the biological effects of radiation exposure are cumulative, the radiation received from artificial sources increases the potential hazards of radiation.

2. Radiation oncology; atomic bombs.

3. The most significant artificial source of radioactivity is smoking; which can be eliminated by giving up this habit which is hazardous in many ways.

4. Radioactivity can break molecules apart by disrupting chemical bonds.

5. A cell can survive a dose of radiation that would otherwise be lethal if the dose is spread over a long period of time to allow intervals for healing.

Biology, Earth Science: Isotopic Dating

1. The proportion of lead and uranium tells us that the oldest rocks are nearly 3.7 billion years old. Rock, for the moon, dates 4.2 billion years.

2. It loses a proton to become the carbon-14 isotope.

3. Radioactive isotopes are produced by cosmic-ray-induced transmutation.

4. The amount of carbon-14 in a fossil tells the amount of time that has elapsed since the organism died. The organism replenishes the carbon-14, in its body as it eats plants or plant-eating animals. When the organism dies, it no longer takes up carbon-14, so the proportion of decayed atoms indicates elapsed time.

Answers to Chapter 10 Exercises

1. Is radioactivity in the world something relatively new? Defend your answer.

   Radioactivity is a part of nature, going back to the beginning of time.

2. Why is a sample of radium always a little warmer than its surroundings?

   A radioactive sample is always a little warmer than its surroundings, because the radiating alpha or beta particles impart internal energy to the atoms of the sample. (Interestingly enough, the heat energy of the Earth largely originates with radioactive decay of the Earth's core and surrounding material.)

3. Some people say that all things are possible. Is it at all possible for a hydrogen nucleus to emit an alpha particle? Defend your answer.

   It is impossible for a hydrogen atom to eject an alpha particle, for an alpha particle is composed of a pair of hydrogen isotopes (deuterium). It is equally impossible for a 1-kilogram melon to spontaneously break into four 1-kilogram melons.

4. Why are alpha and beta rays deflected in opposite directions in a magnetic field? Why are gamma rays undeflected?

Alpha and beta rays are deflected in opposite directions in a magnetic field because they are oppositely charged—alpha are positive and beta negative. Gamma rays have no electric charge and are therefore undeflected.

5. In bombarding atomic nuclei with proton "bullets," why must the protons be accelerated to high energies to make contact with the target nuclei?

   The proton "bullets" need enough momentum to overcome the electric force of repulsion they experience once they get close to the atomic nucleus.

6. Just after an alpha particle leaves the nucleus, would you expect it to speed up? Defend your answer.

   Yes, the alpha particle will accelerate substantially just as it leaves the nucleus because of the repulsive electric force between it and the positively charged nucleus.

7. Within the atomic nucleus, which interaction tends to hold it together and which interaction tends to push it apart?

   The strong nuclear force holds the nucleons of the nucleus together, while the electric force pushes these nucleons apart.

8. What evidence supports the contention that the strong nuclear force is stronger than the electrical force at short internuclear distances?

   The fusing of hydrogen atoms into helium atoms suggests that the electric force of repulsions can be overcome by the strong nuclear force if two atomic nuclei are able to get close enough to each other.

9. A friend asks if a radioactive substance with a half-life of 1 day will be entirely gone at the end of 2 days. What is your answer?

   No, it will not be entirely gone. Rather, after 1 day, one-half of the sample will remain, while after 2 days, one-fourth of the original sample will remain.

10. Elements with atomic numbers greater than that of uranium do not exist in any appreciable amounts in nature because they have short half-lives. Yet there are several elements with atomic numbers smaller than that of uranium that have equally short half-lives and that do exist in appreciable amounts in nature. How can you account for this?

    The elements below uranium in atomic number with short half-lives exist as the product of the radioactive decay of uranium. As long as uranium is decaying, their existence is assured.

11. You and your friend journey to the mountain foothills to get closer to nature and escape such things as radioactivity. While bathing in the warmth of a natural hot spring, she wonders aloud how the spring gets its heat. What do you tell her?

    The Earth's natural energy that heats the water in the hot spring is the energy of radioactive decay, which keeps the Earth's interior molten. Radioactivity heats the water but doesn't make the water itself radioactive. The warmth of hot springs is one of the "nicer effects" of radioactive decay. You'll most likely encounter more radioactivity from the granite outcroppings of the foothills than from a nearby nuclear power plant. Furthermore, at high altitude, you'll be exposed to increased cosmic radiation. But these radiations are not appreciably different than the radiation one encounters in the "safest" of situations. The probability of dying from something or other is 100%, so in the meantime, we all should enjoy life anyway!

12. Coal contains minute quantities of radioactive materials, yet there is more environmental radiation surrounding a coal-fired power plant than a fission power plant. What does this indicate about the shielding that typically surrounds these power plants?

    Although there is significantly more radioactivity in a nuclear power plant than in a coal-fired power plant, the absence of shielding for coal plants results in more radioactivity in the environment of a typical coal plant than in the environment of a typical nuclear plant. All nukes are shielded; coal plants are not.

13. When we speak of dangerous radiation exposure, are we customarily speaking of alpha radiation, beta radiation, or gamma radiation? Defend your answer.

    Gamma radiation is generally the most harmful radiation, because it is so penetrating. Alpha and beta radiation is dangerous if you ingest radioactive material, which is comparatively uncommon.

14. People who work around radioactivity wear film badges to monitor the amount of radiation that reaches their bodies. These badges consist of small pieces of photographic film enclosed in a light-proof wrapper. What kind of radiation do these devices monitor?

Film badges monitor gamma radiation, which is very high-frequency X-rays. Like photographic film, the greater the exposure, the darker the film upon processing.

15. A friend produces a Geiger counter to check the local background radiation. It ticks. Another friend, who normally fears most that which is understood least, makes an effort to keep away from the region of the Geiger counter and looks to you for advice. What do you say?

You can tell your friend who is fearful of the radiation measured by the Geiger counter that his attempt to avoid the radiation by avoiding the instrument that measures it, is useless. He might as well avoid thermometers on a hot day in effort to escape the heat. If it will console your fearful friend, tell him that he and his ancestors from time zero have endured about the same level of radiation he receives whether or not he stands near the Geiger counter. There are no better options.

16. When food is irradiated with gamma rays from a cobalt-60 source, does the food become radioactive? Defend your answer.

There are no fast-flying subatomic particles in gamma rays that might collide with the nuclei of the atoms within the food. Transformations within the nuclei of the atoms of the food, therefore, are not possible. Rather, the gamma rays are lethal to any living tissues within the food, such as those of pathogens. The gamma rays kill these pathogens, which helps to protect us from dangerous diseases such as botulism.

17. Why will nuclear fission probably not be used directly for powering automobiles? How could it be used indirectly?

Nuclear fission is a poor prospect for powering automobiles primarily because of the massive shielding that would be required to protect the occupants and others from the radioactivity, and the problem of radioactive waste disposal.

18. Why does a neutron make a better nuclear bullet than a proton or an electron?

A neutron makes a better "bullet" for penetrating atomic nuclei because it has no electric charge and is, therefore, not deflected from its path by electrical interactions, nor is it electrically repelled by an atomic nucleus.

19. U-235 releases an average of 2.5 neutrons per fission, while Pu-239 releases an average of 2.7 neutrons per fission. Which of these elements might you therefore expect to have the smaller critical mass?

Because plutonium triggers more reactions per atom, a smaller mass will produce the same neutron flux as a somewhat larger mass of uranium. So, plutonium has a smaller critical mass than a similar shape of uranium.

20. Why is lead found in all deposits of uranium ores?

Because uranium transforms to lead.

21. Why does plutonium not occur in appreciable amounts in natural ore deposits?

Plutonium has a short half-life (24,360 years), so any plutonium initially in the Earth's crust has long since decayed. The same is true for any heavier elements with even shorter half-lives from which plutonium might originate. Trace amounts of plutonium can occur naturally in U-238 concentrations, however, as a result of neutron capture, where U-238 becomes U-239 and after beta emission becomes Np-239, and further beta emission to Pu-239. (There are elements in the Earth's crust with half-lives even shorter than plutonium's, but these are the products of uranium decay, between uranium and lead in the periodic table of elements.)

22. Why does a chain reaction not occur in uranium mines?

U-235 isn't in concentrated form in ordinary uranium ore.

23. A friend makes the claim that the explosive power of a nuclear bomb is due to static electricity. Do you agree or disagree? Defend your answer.

A nucleus undergoes fission because the electric force of repulsion overcomes the strong nuclear force of attraction. This electric force of repulsion is of the very same nature as static electricity. So, in a way, your friend's claim that the explosive power of a nuclear bomb is due to static electricity is valid.

24. If a nucleus of 232/90Th absorbs a neutron, and the resulting nucleus undergoes two successive beta decays (emitting electrons), what nucleus results?

This results in the uranium-233 isotope.

25. How does the mass per nucleon in uranium compare with the mass per nucleon in the fission fragments of uranium?

Less in the fission fragments.

26. How is chemical burning similar to nuclear fusion?

Both convert mass to energy.

27. To predict the approximate energy release of either a fission or a fusion reaction, explain how a physicist makes use of the curve of Figure 10.27 or a table of nuclear masses and the equation $E = mc^2$.

To predict the energy release of a nuclear reaction, simply find the difference in the mass of the beginning nucleus and the mass of its configuration after the reaction (either fission or fusion). This mass difference (called the "mass defect") can be found from the curve of Figure 10.27 or from a table of nuclear masses. Multiply this mass difference by the speed of light squared: $E = mc^2$. That's the energy released!

28. Which process would release energy from gold, fission or fusion? From carbon? From iron?

Energy would be released by the fissioning of gold and from the fusion of carbon, but by neither fission nor fusion for iron. Neither fission nor fusion will result in a decrease of mass for iron nucleons.

29. If uranium were to split into three segments of equal size instead of two, would more energy or less energy be released? Defend your answer in terms of Figure 10.27.

If uranium were split into three parts, the segments would be nuclei of smaller atomic numbers, more toward iron on the graph of Figure 10.27. The resulting mass per nucleon would be less, and there would be more mass converted to energy in such a fissioning.

30. Explain how radioactive decay has always warmed the Earth from the inside, and nuclear fusion has always warmed the Earth from the outside.

The radioactive decay of radioactive elements found under the Earth's surface warms the insides of the Earth and is responsible for the molten lava that spews from volcanoes. The thermonuclear fusion of our Sun is responsible for warming everything on our planet's surface exposed to the Sun.

31. Write a letter to Grandma to dispel any notion she might have about radioactivity being something new in the world. Tie this to the idea that people sometimes have the strongest views about that which they know the least.

Letters to Grandma should discuss natural sources of radiation, including the radioactive decay that occurs in Earth's interior, which is as old as Earth itself. Letters also should relate the public's fear of radioactivity to the general lack of knowledge of this subject.

Solutions to Chapter 10 Problems

1. Radiation from a point source obeys the inverse-square law. If a Geiger counter 1 m from a small sample reads 360 counts per minute, what will be its counting rate 2 m from the source? 3 m from the source?

In accord with the inverse-square law, at 2 m, double the distance, the count rate will be 1/4 of 360, or 90 counts/minute. At 3 m, the count rate will be 1/9 of 360, or 40 counts/min.

2. If a sample of a radioactive isotope has a half-life of 1 year, how much of the original sample will be left at the end of the second year? End of the third year? End of the fourth year?

   At the end of the second year, 1/4 will remain. At the end of the third year, 1/8 will remain. At the end of the fourth year, 1/16 will remain.

3. A certain radioactive substance has a half-life of 1 hour. If you start with 1 g of the material at noon, how much will be left at 3:00 PM? at 6:00 PM? at 10:00 PM?

   At 3:00 PM (after 3 half-lives) there will be 1/8 of the original remaining, 0.125 grams. At 6:00 PM, after 3 more half-lives, there are 1/8 of 1/8 left, 0.016 grams. At 10:00 PM the amount remaining has halved ten times, which leaves (1/2)10, or about 1/1000 of the original. So, the remaining amount will be 0.001 g, or 1 mg.

4. A sample of a particular radioisotope is placed near a Geiger counter, which is observed to register 160 counts per minute. Eight hours later, the detector counts at a rate of 10 counts per minute. Show that the half-life of the material is 2 hours.

   Two hours.

5. The isotope cesium-137, which has a half-life of 30 years, is a product of nuclear power plants. How long will it take for this isotope to decay to about one-sixteenth its original amount?

   It will take four half-lives to decrease to one-sixteenth the original amount. Four half-lives of cesium-137 corresponds to 120 years.

6. Suppose that you measure the intensity of radiation from carbon-14 in an ancient piece of wood to be 6% of what it would be in a freshly cut piece of wood. Show that this artifact is 22,920 years old.

   Six percent corresponds to about one-sixteenth, which means that the carbon-14 has undergone about four half-lives. Four half-lives of carbon-14 equals 5730 years times 4 equals 22,920 years.

7. Suppose that you want to find out how much gasoline is in an underground storage tank. You pour in 1 gallon of gasoline that contains some long half-life radioactive material that gives off 5000 counts per minute. The next day, you remove a gallon from the underground tank and measure its radioactivity to be 10 counts per minute. How much gasoline is in the tank?

   Your count is 10/5000 for the gallon you remove. That's a ratio of 1/500, which means the tank must hold 500 gallons of gasoline.

8. The kiloton, which is used to measure the energy released in an atomic explosion, is equal to 4.2×10^{12} J (approximately the energy released in the explosion of 1000 tons of TNT). Recall that 1 kilocalorie of energy raises the temperature of 1 kilogram of water by 1°C and that 4184 joules is equal to 1 kilocalorie, show that 4.0×10^8 kilograms of water can be heated 50°C by a 20-kiloton atomic bomb.

   The energy released by the explosion in kilocalories is

   (20 kilotons)(4.2×10^{12} J/kiloton)/(4,184 J/kilocalorie) = 2.0×10^{10} kilocalories.

   This is enough energy to heat 2.0×10^{10} kg of water by 1 °C. Dividing by 50, we conclude that this energy could heat 4.0×10^8 kilograms of water by 50 °C. This is nearly half a million tons.

9. An atom of uranium (m = 232.03174 amu) radioactively decays into an atom of thorium (m = 228.02873 amu) plus an atom of helium (m = 4.00260 amu). Show that about 6.1×10^{-14} J of energy is released in this decay.

   The atom of uranium has an initial mass m = 232.03174 amu. The products of radioactive decay have a combined mass of 228.02873 amu + 4.00260 amu = 232.03133 amu. Thus, a mass equal to 232.03174 amu − 232.03133 amu = 0.00041 amu has been "lost" or converted to energy in this reaction. Since 1 amu = 1.6605×10^{-27} kg, the converted mass = (0.00041 amu) × (1.6605×10^{-27} kg/1 amu) = 6.81×10^{-31} kg. By $E = mc^2$, the energy released in the decay of uranium to thorium and helium is: E = (6.81×10^{-31} kg)(3.0×10^8 m/s)^2 = 6.1×10^{-14} J.

Chapter 11: Investigating Matter

Answers to Chapter 11 Review Questions

1. Chemistry is often called a central science, because it touches all of the sciences.

2. The members of the Chemical Manufacturers Association pledge to manufacture without causing environmental damage through a program called Responsible Care.

3. Molecules are made of atoms. Atoms link together to form larger but still small basic units of matter called *molecules.*

4. The macroscopic, microscopi, and submicroscopic

5. Shape and volume of a gas are determined by its container.

6. Energy: In a solid, the particles are fixed in a three-dimensional arrangement. In a liquid, the particles have energy to overcome the bonds between them, and they tumble loosely around one another. The particles in a gas have so much energy that they overcome their attractions to each other and expand to fill all of the space available.

7. As heat is added to the solid, the particles vibrate more and more violently. If enough heat is added, the attractive forces between the particles are no longer able to hold them together. The solid melts.

8. Boiling.

9. The amount of energy needed to change any substance from solid to liquid (and vice versa) is the heat of fusion for the substance; the amount of energy required to change any substance from liquid to gas (and vice versa) is the heat of vaporization for the substance.

10. During a physical change, the chemical composition of a substance does not change.

11. New materials are formed by a change in the way atoms are bonded together.

12. Restoring the original conditions restores a substance to its original form.

13. Elements are made of atoms.

14. Eight.

15. Metals are shiny, opaque, good conductors of electricity and heat, *malleable,* and *ductile* in contrast to nonmetals.

16. 7 periods, 18 groups.

17. (a) Elements of group 2 also form alkaline solutions when mixed with water. Furthermore, medieval alchemists noted that certain minerals (which we now know are made up of group 2 elements) do not melt or change when placed in fire. These fire-resistant substances were known to the alchemists as "earth." As a holdover from these ancient times, group 2 elements are known as the *alkaline-earth metals.* (b) Elements of group 17 are known as the *halogens* ("salt-forming" in Greek) because of their tendency to form various salts.

18. Inserting the inner transition metals into the main body of the periodic table results in a long and cumbersome table.

19. Elements contain only one type of atom, in contrast to compounds, which contain more than one type of atom.

20. Indeed not!

21. This system is designed so that a compound's name reflects the elements it contains and how those elements are put together.

22. MgO.

23. Common names are more convenient or have been used traditionally for many years.

Answers to Chapter 11 Multiple-Choice Questions

1d, 2c, 3b, 4d, 5a, 6c, 7d, 8b, 9d, 10d

Answers to Chapter 11 Integrated Science Concepts

Astronomy: Origin of the Moon

1. Summaries should discuss the chemical analysis of moon rocks, specifically the similarity of the chemical composition of moon rocks to Earth's mantle and the lack of water and other volatile compounds from moon rocks.

2. No—no chemical elements beyond the periodic table are known to exist anywhere in the universe.

Physics and Biology: Evaporation Cools You Off, Condensation Warms You Up

1. Evaporation is a change of phase from liquid to gas at the surface of a liquid. Faster molecules evaporate, leaving slower ones.

2. Condensation is a change of phase from gas to liquid. Molecules gain speed when attracted to the liquid's surface and, therefore, warm the liquid.

3. Steam gives up considerable energy when it changes phase, condensing to a liquid and wetting the skin.

4. You are warmed by the condensation of water vapor in air upon your skin.

Answers to Chapter 11 Exercises

1. In what sense is a color computer monitor or television screen similar to our view of matter? Place a drop (and only a drop) of water on your computer monitor or television screen for a closer look.

   When looked at macroscopically, matter appears continuous. On the submicroscopic level, however, we find that matter is made of extremely small particles, such as atoms or molecules. Similarly, a TV screen looked at from a distance appears as a smooth continuous flow of images. Up close, however, we see this is an illusion. What really exists are a series of tiny dots (pixels) that change color in a coordinated way to produce the series of images.

2. Is chemistry the study of the submicroscopic, the microscopic, the macroscopic, or all three? Defend your answer.

   Chemistry is the careful study of matter and can take place at a number of different levels, including the submicroscopic, microscopic, or macroscopic levels.

3. Which has stronger attractions among its submicroscopic particles: a solid at 25°C or a gas at 25°C? Explain.

   At 25°C there is a certain amount of thermal energy available to all the submicroscopic particles of a material. If the attractions between the particles are not strong enough, the particles may separate from each other to form a gaseous phase. If the attractions are strong, however, the particles may be held together in the solid phase. We can assume, therefore, that the attractions among the submicroscopic particles of a material in its solid phase at 25°C are stronger than they are within a material that is a gas at this temperature.

4. Gas particles travel at speeds of up to 500 meters per second. Why, then, does it take so long for gas molecules to travel the length of a room?

   The gas particles take time to cross a room because they bump into each other as well as other particles in the air.

5. Humidity is a measure of the amount of water vapor in the atmosphere. Why is humidity always very low inside your kitchen freezer?

   At the cold temperatures of your kitchen freezer, water molecules in the vapor phase are moving relatively slowly, which makes it easier for them to stick to inner surfaces within the freezer or to other water molecules.

6. A cotton ball is dipped in alcohol and wiped across a tabletop. Explain what happens to the alcohol molecules deposited on the tabletop. Is this a physical or chemical change? Would the resulting smell of the alcohol be more or less noticeable if the tabletop were much warmer? Explain.

The molecules of the alcohol evaporate into the gaseous phase, which is a physical change; more noticeable.

7. Alcohol wiped across a tabletop rapidly disappears. What happens to the temperature of the tabletop? Why?

As the alcohol evaporates, it soaks up energy from the tabletop which is thus cooled. This transfer of energy that occurs during a change in phase was discussed in more detail in Chapter 8.

8. Try to explain how alcohol evaporates from the surface of a tabletop, assuming that matter is continuous and NOT made of tiny atoms and molecules.

If matter were continuous and not made of atoms and molecules, then this implies that there is no such thing as empty space! For example, just as you see no empty space when submerged in a swimming pool, you'd still see no empty space if you magically got to be infinitely small within that swimming pool. It must have been mind blowing when people first discovered that the atmosphere gets thinner and thinner at higher and higher altitudes, as was confirmed by high-altitude balloon flights in the 1800s. This might imply that beyond the atmosphere there was empty space. Interestingly, this idea was so inconceivable that most scientists at that time believed that beyond the atmosphere there was an essence they called aether. This hypothesis, of course, turned out to be wrong. Enough musing. Back to trying to explain the evaporation of alcohol without the idea of atoms and molecules. Sorry, I can't do it. Such a thought is too inconceivable for your author who has been too entrenched in this atom and molecule concept. The evidence for atoms and molecules and the empty space between them is too overwhelming.

9. A skillet is lined with a thin layer of cooking oil followed by a layer of unpopped popcorn kernels. Upon heating, the kernels all pop, thereby escaping the skillet. Identify any physical or chemical changes.

As each kernel is heated, the water within each kernel is also heated to the point that it would turn into water vapor. The shell of the kernel, however, is airtight, and this keeps the water as a superheated liquid. Eventually, the pressure exerted by the superheated water exceeds the holding power of the kernel, and the water bursts out as a vapor, which causes the kernel to pop. These are physical changes. The starches within the kernel, however, are also cooked by the high temperatures, and this is an example of a chemical change.

10. Red-colored Kool-Aid crystals are added to a still glass of water. The crystals sink to the bottom. Twenty-four hours later, the entire solution is red, even though no one stirred the water. Explain.

Even though the water appears to be still, the water molecules are bustling with kinetic energy. The red dye of the Kool-Aid gets knocked around by these molecules to the point that the dye is eventually dispersed throughout the water. This is another case where the existence of molecules helps to explain the observed phenomenon.

11. Gas molecules move 500 meters per second at room temperature, yet there is a noticeable delay in the time it takes for you to smell someone's perfume when she walks into the room. Explain.

The gas particles take time to cross a room because they bump into each other as well as other particles in the air.

12. Oxygen, O_2, has a boiling point of 90 Kelvin ($-183°C$), and nitrogen, N_2, has a boiling point of 77 Kelvin ($-196°C$). Which is a liquid and which is a gas at 80 Kelvin ($-193°C$)?

Expose the air to an object that is somewhere between 91K and 77K. The oxygen in the air will condense onto this object as a liquid, much like the water vapor in the air condenses onto the outer surface of a cold can of soda.

13. What happens to the properties of elements across any period of the periodic table?

Across any period (horizontal row), the properties of elements gradually change until the end of the period. The next element in the next period has properties that are abruptly different.

14. Each sphere in the diagrams below represents an atom. Joined spheres represent molecules. Which box contains a liquid phase? Why can you not assume that Box B represents a lower temperature?

Box B appears to contain a liquid as evidenced by the randomly oriented molecules condensed at the bottom of the box. These molecules in the liquid phase of Box B represent a compound, because they consist of different types of atoms joined together. The physical properties of the compound in Box B will be markedly different from the elements in Box A. For example, if the two boxes are of the same temperature, we would see that the compound of Box B has a higher boiling point. It could be, however, that the boiling point of the substance in Box B is lower than either of the elements in Box A. In such a case, the temperature of Box B must be lower than that of Box A. In short, there's no way to assume the relative temperatures of the boxes based upon the phases of the materials they contain, because these materials are uniquely different from each other.

15. Based on the information given in the following diagrams, which substance has the lower boiling point?

The change from A to B represents a physical change, because no new types of molecules are formed. The collection of blue/red molecules on the bottom of B represents these molecules in the liquid or solid phase after having been in the gaseous phase in A. This must occur with a decrease in temperature. At this lower temperature, the purely red molecules are still in the gaseous phase, which means that they have a lower boiling point, while the blue/red molecules have a higher boiling point.

16. What physical and chemical changes occur when a wax candle burns?

The melting of the wax near the flame is an example of a physical change. This liquid wax is drawn up the wick where it is burned, which is an example of a chemical change.

17. Germanium, Ge (number 32), computer chips operate faster than silicon, Si (number 14), computer chips. So how might a gallium, Ga (number 31), chip compare with a germanium chip?

Based upon its location in the periodic table we find that gallium, Ga, is more metallic in character than germanium, Ge. This means that gallium should be a better conductor of electricity. Computer chips manufactured from gallium, therefore, operate faster than chips manufactured from germanium. (Gallium has a low melting point of 30°C, which makes it impractical for use in the manufacture of computer chips. Mixtures of gallium and arsenic, however, have found great use in the manufacture of ultrafast, though relatively expensive, computer chips.)

18. Helium, He, is a nonmetallic gas and the second element in the periodic table. Rather than being placed adjacent to hydrogen, H, however, helium is placed on the far right of the table. Why?

Helium is placed over to the far right-hand side of the periodic table in group 18 because it has physical and chemical properties most similar to those of the other elements of group 18.

19. Strontium, Sr (number 38), is especially dangerous to humans, because it tends to accumulate in calcium-dependent bone marrow tissues (calcium, Ca, number 20). How does this fact relate to what you know about the organization of the periodic table?

Calcium is readily absorbed by the body for the building of bones. Because calcium and strontium are in the same atomic group, they have similar physical and chemical properties. The body, therefore, has a hard time distinguishing between the two, and strontium is absorbed just as though it were calcium.

20. Do all the molecules in a liquid have about the same speed, or do they have a wide variety of speeds? Likewise, do all the molecules in a gas have the same speeds?

Molecules have a wide variety of speeds in liquids and gases.

21. Why does increasing the temperature of a solid make it melt?

At higher temperatures the molecules of the material have sufficient kinetic energy to break loose of the attractions to neighboring molecules to form new attractions to other neighboring molecules and so on. In this way, the molecules are able to tumble around one another much like marbles in a bag, which describes the liquid phase.

22. (a) How many atoms are there in one molecule of H_3PO_4? (b) How many atoms of each element are there in one molecule of H_3PO_4?

(a) eight; (b) hydrogen-3; phosphorus-1; oxygen-4.

23. Why does decreasing the temperature of a liquid make it freeze?

At lower temperatures the molecules of the material have insufficient kinetic energy to prevent the electrical attractions between them from holding them within fixed positions.

24. Write a letter to Grandpa to explain to him, in molecular terms, why he will stay warmer if he pats himself dry in the stall after a shower.

   Letters to Grandpa should explain that the rate of evaporation of water molecules from Grandpa's skin will be slower in the humid shower stall than in dry air.

Solution to Chapter 11 Problem

Calculate the height from which a block of ice at 0°C must be dropped to completely melt upon impact. Assume no air resistance and that all the energy goes into melting the ice. [*Hint:* Equate the joules of gravitational potential energy to the product of the mass of ice and its heat of fusion (in SI units, 335,000 J/kg). Do you see why the answer doesn't depend on mass?]

mgh = *mL*, so *gh* = *L* and *h* = *L/g*.

h = (334000 J/kg)/(9.8 m/s^2) = 34000 m = 34 km.

Note that the mass cancels and that the unit J/kg is the same as the unit m^2/s^2. So in the ideal case of no energy losses along the way, any piece of ice that freely falls 34 km would completely melt upon impact. Taking air resistance into account, only partial melting would occur.

Chapter 12: The Nature of Chemical Bonds

Answers to Chapter 12 Review Questions

1. Seven

2. It can *share* electrons with another atom or *transfer* electrons to another atom through bonding.

3. Valence electrons

4. An ion has a net electric charge, while an atom is neutral.

5. Gain electrons.

6. Ionic compounds typically consist of elements found on opposite sides of the periodic table.

7. 2$^+$

8. Ionic

9. The mobility of electrons in a metal accounts for the metal's ability to conduct electricity and heat.

10. Atoms that tend to form covalent bonds are primarily atoms of the nonmetallic elements in the upper right corner of the periodic table (with the exception of the noble-gas elements).

11. Electric

12. Four

13. An atom or molecule that has an uneven distribution of charge so that one end is positive and the other negative.

14. Electronegativity is greatest for elements (such as fluorine) at the upper right of the periodic table and lowest for elements at the lower left (such as cesium).

15. Uneven charge distribution.

16. Carbon dioxide is an example—symmetry.

17. Strength of attractive force.

18. Ion-dipole attraction.

19. A hydrogen bond is an unusually strong dipole–dipole attraction between molecules that have a hydrogen atom covalently bonded to a highly electronegative atom, usually nitrogen, oxygen, or fluorine.

20. The component present in the largest amount is the solvent and the other component(s) the solute(s).

21. Solution A contains 2 grams of sucrose per liter of solution; Solution B contains 0.5 grams of sucrose per liter of solution. Which solution is more concentrated? Which is more dilute? A sucrose–water solution containing 2 grams of sucrose per liter of solution is more *concentrated,* and one containing only 0.5 gram of sucrose per liter of solution is less concentrated, or more *dilute.*

22. A saturated solution is one in which no more solute can dissolve. A solution that has not reached the limit of solute that will dissolve is called an unsaturated solution.

23. An interparticle attraction between solvent (water) molecules and solute (water) molecules.

24. A precipitate is solute that comes out of solution once it cools below its saturation point.

Answers to Chapter 12 Multiple-Choice Questions

1c, 2b, 3c, 4b, 5b, 6b, 7d, 8a, 9c, 10a

Answers to Chapter 12 Integrated Science Concepts

Physics, Biology: How Geckos Walk on Walls—The Adhesive Force

1. The adhesive force is an interparticle force that acts between two different substances, while the cohesive force is an interparticle force that acts between molecules of a single substance. The force between a wall and molecules in a gecko's setae is an adhesive force; cohesive forces between water molecules pull water into spherical drops.

2. A gecko's feet are covered with millions of microscopic hairs, spatulae. Each spatulae is only 100 millionth of a meter long. Adhesive forces between the spatulae and a climbing surface keep the gecko "glued" to the surface, because individual molecules on the spatulae and surface attract one another. Because there is so much surface area on all the tiny spatulae, the total adhesive force is enough to keep the gecko clinging to walls and ceilings.

Biology, Earth Science: Mixtures

1. A skin cell and Earth's layered atmosphere are examples of heterogeneous mixtures.

2. The particles making up a mixture held together by intermolecular forces.

Biology: Fish Depend on Dissolved Oxygen

1. The solubilities of gases in liquids *decrease* with increasing temperature.

2. The oxygen is dissolved in the water they live in.

3. In warmer water, there is less dissolved oxygen—causing fish to suffocate sometimes during hot summer months.

Answers to Chapter 12 Exercises

1. What happens when hydrogen's electron gets close to the valence shell of a fluorine atom?

   Hydrogen's electron joins the valence shell of the fluorine atom. Meanwhile, fluorine's unpaired valence electron joins the valence shell of hydrogen.

2. An atom loses an electron to another atom. Is this an example of a physical or a chemical change?

   This is an example of a chemical change involving the formation of ions, which are uniquely different from the neutral atoms from which they are made.

3. Why doesn't the neon atom tend to gain any electrons? Why doesn't it tend to lose any electrons?

   The neon atom tends not to gain electrons because there is no more room available in its outermost occupied shell; it doesn't lose electrons because its outermost electrons are held tightly to the atom by a relatively strong effective nuclear charge.

4. Which should be larger, the potassium atom, K, or the potassium ion, K^+?

   The potassium atom, K, with an additional shell of electrons is larger.

5. Which should have a higher melting point, sodium chloride, NaCl, or aluminum oxide, Al_2O_3?

The charges on the aluminum and oxide ions of aluminum oxide are greater than the charges on the sodium and chloride ions of sodium chloride. The network of aluminum and oxide ions within aluminum oxide, therefore, is more strongly held together, which gives the aluminum oxide a much higher melting point. (More thermal energy is required to allow these ions to roll past one another within a liquid phase.)

6. Two fluorine atoms join together to form a covalent bond. Why don't two potassium atoms do the same thing?

The valence electrons of a potassium atom are weakly held by the nucleus. The potassium atom has a hard enough time holding onto its one valence electron, let alone a second one, which is what would happen if the potassium joined in a covalent bond.

7. Why doesn't a hydrogen atom form more than one covalent bond?

The hydrogen atom has only one electron to share.

8. Is there an abrupt or gradual change between ionic and covalent bonds? Explain.

There is a gradual change. We get this change by noting the relative positions of the bonding elements across the periodic table. If they are close together toward the upper right-hand corner, then the bond is more covalent. When the elements are on opposite sides of the periodic table, the chemical bond between them is more ionic. For the bonding of atoms between these two extremes, the bonding tends to be a blend of both, which is also referred to as *polar covalent*.

9. Atoms of metallic elements can form ionic bonds, but they are not very good at forming covalent bonds. Why?

To form a covalent bond, an atom must have a fairly strong attraction for at least one additional electron. Metals atoms, however, tend not to have such an attraction. Instead, they tend to lose electrons to form positively charged metal ions.

10. What is the source of an atom's electronegativity?

The source of an atom's electronegativity is positive charge of the nucleus. More specifically, it is the effective nuclear charge experienced within the shell that the bonding electrons are occupying.

11. Which molecule is most polar?:

(a) S=C=S (b) O=C=O   (c) O=C=S

The most polar molecule is the least symmetrical molecule (c) O=C=S

12. Which is more polar, a sulfur–bromine (S—Br) bond or a selenium–chlorine (Se—Cl) bond?

A selenium–chlorine bond should be more polar. Observe their relative positions in the periodic table. Sulfur and bromine are more equidistant from the upper right-hand corner.

13. Water, H_2O, and methane, CH_4, have about the same mass and differ by only one type of atom. Why is the boiling point of water so much higher than that of methane?

Water is a polar molecule, because in its structure the dipoles do not cancel. Polar molecules tend to stick to one another, which gives rise to relatively high boiling points. Methane, on the other hand, is nonpolar because of its symmetrical structure, which results in no net dipole and a relatively low boiling point. The boiling points of water and methane are less a consequence of the masses of their molecules and more a consequence of the attractions that occur among their molecules.

14. Three kids sitting equally apart around a table are sharing jelly beans. One of the kids, however, tends only to take jelly beans and only rarely gives one away. If each jelly bean represents an electron, who ends up being slightly negative? Who ends up being slightly positive? Is the negative kid just as negative as one of the positive kids is positive? Would you describe this as a polar or nonpolar situation? How about if all three kids were equally greedy?

The single greedy kid ends up being slightly negative, while the two more generous kids are slightly positive (deficient of electrons). The greedy negative kids is actually twice as negative as one of the positive kids is positive. In other words, if the greedy kid had a charge of −1, each positive kid would have a charge of +0.5. This is a polar situation where the electrons are not distributed evenly. If all three kids were equally greedy, then the situation would be more balanced, that is, nonpolar.

15. Which is stronger: the covalent bond that holds atoms together within a molecule or the dipole—dipole attraction between two neighboring molecules?

The covalent bonds within a molecule are many times stronger than the attractions occurring between neighboring molecules. We know this because, while two molecules can move away from each other (as occurs in the liquid or gaseous phase), the atoms within a molecule remain stuck together as a single unit. To pull the atoms apart requires some form of chemical change.

16. Why is a water molecule more attracted to a calcium ion than a sodium ion?

The calcium ion, Ca^{2+}, has twice the positive charge. You might think, therefore, that water is attracted twice as much. Not so! The calcium ion is also larger, which means that the water cannot get so close to the source of this positive charge, which is the atomic nucleus.

17. The charges within sodium chloride are all balanced—for every positive sodium ion, there is a corresponding negative chloride ion. Because its charges are balanced, how can sodium chloride be attracted to water, and vice versa?

The charges in sodium chloride are balanced, but they are not neutralized. As a water molecule gets close to the sodium chloride, it can distinguish the various ions, and it is, thus, attracted to an individual ion by ion–dipole forces. This works because sodium and chloride ions and water molecules are of the same scale. We, on the other hand, are much too big to be able to distinguish individual ions within a crystal of sodium chloride. From our point of view, the individual charges are not apparent.

18. The volume of many liquid solvents expands with increasing temperature. What happens to the concentration of a solution made with such a solvent as the temperature of the solution is increased?

Assuming concentration is given in units of mass (or moles) of solute in a given volume of solution, then the concentration necessarily decreases with increasing temperature.

19. Suggest why sodium chloride, NaCl, is insoluble in gasoline. Consider the electrical attractions.

Salt is composed of ions that are too attracted to themselves. Gasoline is nonpolar, so salt and gasoline will not interact very well.

20. Would you expect to find more dissolved oxygen in ocean water around the North Pole or in ocean water close to the equator? Why?

No, because of the warmer temperatures. The solubility of oxygen in water *decreases* with increasing temperature.

21. Why are the melting points of most ionic compounds far higher than the melting points of most covalent compounds?

When an ionic compound melts, the ionic bonds between the ions are overcome. When a covalent compound melts, the molecular attractions between molecules are overcome. Because ionic bonds are so much stronger than molecular attractions, the melting points of ionic compounds are typically much higher.

Solutions to Chapter 12 Problems

1. Show that there are 2.5 grams of sucrose in 5 liters of an aqueous solution of sucrose having a concentration of 0.5 gram of sucrose per liter of solution.

Multiply concentration by volume: (0.5 g/L)(5 L) = 2.5 g.

2. Show that 45 grams of sodium chloride is needed to make 15 L of a solution having a concentration of 3.0 grams of sodium chloride per liter of solution.

Mass = (Concentration)(Volume) = 3.0 g/L)(15 L) = 45 g.

3. If water is added to 1 mole of sodium chloride in a flask until the volume of the solution is 1 liter, show that the molarity of this solution is 1 M. Show that a 4-M solution results when water is added to 2 moles of sodium chloride to make 0.5 liter of solution.

a) $\dfrac{1 \text{ mole}}{1 \text{ Liter}} = 1$ Molar (1 M)   b) $\dfrac{2 \text{ moles}}{0.5 \text{ Liters}} = 4$ Molar (4 M)

4. Show that one mole of sugar equals 342 grams.

   No calculations are necessary. As shown in the figure, one mole of sucrose equals 342 grams.

Chapter 13: Chemical Reactions

Answers to Chapter 13 Review Questions

1. Solid is represented by (s), (l) stands for liquid, (g) stands for gas, and (aq) for aqueous.

2. A chemical equation must be balanced, because the law of conservation of mass says that mass can neither be created nor destroyed. There must be the same number of each atom on both sides of the equation.

3. The subscript describes how the molecule is put together and cannot be changed or it will describe a different molecule.

4. An acid is any chemical that donates a hydrogen ion and a base is any chemical that accepts a hydrogen ion.

5. A hydronium ion, H_3O^+, is a water molecule after accepting a hydrogen ion. A hydroxide ion, OH^-, is a water molecule after losing a hydrogen ion.

6. When added to water, ammonia (NH_3) behaves as a base; water behaves as an acid

7. In everyday language, the word *salt* implies sodium chloride, NaCl, table salt. In the language of chemistry, however, *salt* is a general term meaning any ionic compound formed from the reaction between an acid and a base.

8. Salts are generally far less corrosive than the acids and bases from which they are formed.

9. Water has the ability to react with itself; in behaving as an acid, a water molecule donates a hydrogen ion to a neighboring water molecule, which in accepting the hydrogen ion is behaving as a base.

10. In an acidic solution, there is a higher concentration of hydronium ions than hydoxide ions, and just the reverse in a basic solution. A neutral solution has equal concentrations of hydronium and hydroxide ions.

11. Acidic solutions have pH values less than 7; basic solutions have pH values greater than 7.

12. Increase.

13. The electrons lost by one chemical are gained by the other.

14. The gain of hydrogen atoms indicates reduction; the gain of oxygen atoms indicates oxidation.

15. Zinc.

16. Corrosion is the deterioration of a metal by oxygen. Combustion is a redox reaction between a nonmetal and oxygen.

17. It increases the frequency of collisions between reacting particles.

18. To increase the rate of collisions is to increase the concentration of reactants; increase temperature; increase pressure.

19. 436 kilojoules.

20. Energy in the form of heat.

21. Energy in the form of heat.

22. Into the surroundings.

23. If the reaction results in an overall increase in entropy, then the answer is yes.

Answers to Chapter 13 Multiple-Choice Questions

1b, 2a, 3c, 4c, 5b, 6a, 7d, 8a, 9d, 10d

Answers to Chapter 13 Integrated Science Concepts

Earth Science: Acid Rain

1. It is the alkaline character of limestone (also known as calcium carbonate) that serves to neutralize waters that might be acidified in the Midwestern United States.

2. Acid rain is rain having a pH lower than 5.

3. The burning of fossil fuels produces sulfur dioxide, which reacts with water to produce sulfuric acid, acidifying rain.

Physics: Fuel Cells

1. As long as fuel is supplied, fuel cells don't run down, but batteries die when the electron-producing chemicals are consumed.

2. The answer is a. H_2.

Physics, Biology, Earth Science: The Effect of Temperature on Reaction Rate

1. Lightning results in the formation of nitrogen monoxide in the atmosphere, which reacts further to produce nitrates, which are chemicals plants need to survive.

2. The body temperature of an ectotherm rises and falls with its environment, slowing its biochemical reactions, which results in slowed movements.

Answers to Chapter 13 Exercises

1. Balance these equations:

   a. $Fe(s) + O_2(g) \rightarrow Fe_2O_3(s)$

   b. $H_2(g) + N_2(g) \rightarrow NH_3(g)$

   c. $Cl_2(g) + KBr(aq) \rightarrow Br_2(l) + KCl(aq)$

   d. $CH_4(g) + O_2(g) \rightarrow CO_2(g) + H_2O(l)$

   a) 4, 3, 2   b) 3, 1, 2   c) 1, 2, 1, 2   d) 1, 2, 1, 2 (Remember that, by convention, 1's are not shown in the balanced equation.)

2. Is the following chemical equation balanced?

   $$4\ C_6H_7N_5O_{16}(s) + 19\ O_2(g) \rightarrow 24\ CO_2(g) + 20\ NO_2(g) + 14\ H_2O(g)$$

   This equation is balanced.

3. Is this reaction balanced?

   There are the same numbers and types of atoms on both sides of the arrow, which means this reaction is balanced: atoms are neither created nor destroyed.

4. How many diatomic molecules are represented?

   Only two diatomic molecules are represented (not three!). These are the two shown in the left box, one of which is also shown in the right box. Remember, the atoms before and after the arrow in a balanced chemical equation are the same atoms only in different arrangements.

5. Which equation best describes this reaction?

   a. $2\ AB_2 + 2\ DCB_3 + B_2 \rightarrow 2\ DBA_4 + 2\ CA_2$

   b. $2\ AB_2 + 2\ CDA_3 + B_2 \rightarrow 2\ C_2A_4 + 2\ DBA$

   c. $2\ AB_2 + 2\ CDA_3 + A_2 \rightarrow 2\ DBA_4 + 2\ CA_2$

   d. $2\ BA_2 + 2\ DCA_3 + A_2 \rightarrow 2\ DBA_4 + 2\ CA_2$

   Equation "d" best describes the reacting chemicals.

6. What is the relationship between a hydroxide ion and a water molecule?

   A hydroxide ion is a water molecule minus a hydrogen nucleus.

7. What atom in the hydronium ion, H_3O^+, bears the positive charge?

   The oxygen atom.

8. Identify the acid or base behavior of each substance in these reactions:

a. $H_3O^+ + Cl^- \rightleftarrows H_2O + HCl$

b. $H_2PO_4 + H_2O \rightleftarrows H_3O^+ + HPO_4^-$

For (a) note that the H_3O^+ transforms into a water molecule. This means that the H_3O^+ loses a hydrogen ion, which is donated to the Cl^-. The H_3O^+, therefore, is behaving as an acid, while the Cl^- is behaving as a base. In the reverse direction, we see the H_2O gaining a hydrogen ion (behaving as a base) to become H_3O^+. It gets this hydrogen ion from the HCl, which in donating is behaving as an acid. You should be able to make similar arguments for (b) to arrive at the following answers:

a) acid, base, base, acid

b) acid, base, acid, base

9. What happens to the corrosive properties of an acid and a base after they neutralize each other? Why?

The corrosive properties are no longer present, because the acid and base no longer exist. Instead they have chemically reacted with each other to form completely new substances—salt and water—that are not so corrosive.

10. Why do we use the pH scale to indicate the acidity of a solution rather than simply stating the concentration of hydronium ions?

The concentration of hydronium ions is typically so small it needs to be stated using scientific notation. The pH scale, therefore, is one of convenience.

11. What is the concentration of hydronium ions in a solution that has a pH of -3? Why is such a solution impossible to prepare?

This solution would have a hydronium ion concentration of 10^3 M, or 1000 moles per liter. The solution would be impossible to prepare because only so much acid can dissolve in water before the solution is saturated and no more will dissolve. The greatest concentration possible for hydrochloric acid, for example, is 12 M. Beyond this concentration, any additional HCl, which is a gas, added to the water simply bubbles back out into the atmosphere.

12. What happens to the pH of an acidic solution as pure water is added?

As water is added to an acidic solution, the hydronium ions (and anything else that is dissolved in this acidic solution) become more dilute, that is, less concentrated. Thus, the pH increases.

13. A weak acid is added to a concentrated solution of hydrochloric acid. Does the solution become more or less acidic?

The hydrochloric acid solution becomes more dilute with hydronium ions as the weak acid is added to it. The pH of the hydrochloric acid solution, therefore, increases. Conversely, the pH of the weak acid solution has a relative decrease in its pH as the many hydronium ions from the hydrochloric acid solution are mixed in.

14. Many of the smelly molecules of cooked fish are alkaline compounds. How might these smelly molecules be conveniently transformed into less smelly salts just prior to eating the fish?

Squeeze lemon juice upon the fish. The citric acid found in lemon juice reacts with these smelly alkaline compounds to form less smelly salts. The smell and taste of the lemon also helps to mask any additional undesirable fishy odors.

15. What elements are oxidized in the following equations, and what elements are reduced?
a. $Sn_2^+ + 2\,Ag \rightarrow Sn + 2\,Ag^+$ b. $I_2 + 2\,Br^- \rightarrow 2\,I^- + Br_2$

(a) The tin ion, Sn^{2+}, gains electrons and is reduced, while the silver atom, Ag, loses electrons and is oxidized. (b). The iodine atoms, I, gain electrons and are reduced, while the bromine ions, Br^-, lose electrons and are oxidized.

16. What element behaves as the oxidizing agent in each of the following equations and what element behaves as the reducing agent? a. $Sn_2^+ + 2\,Ag \rightarrow Sn + 2\,Ag^+$ b. $I_2 + 2\,Br^- \rightarrow 2\,I^- + Br_2$

(a) The tin ion, Sn^{2+}, is the oxidizing agent, because it causes the silver, Ag, to lose electrons. Meanwhile, the silver atoms, Ag, are the reducing agents, because they cause the tin ion to gain electrons. (b) The iodine atoms, I, are the oxidizing agents, because they cause the bromine ions, Br^-, to lose electrons. Meanwhile, the bromine ions, Br^-, are the reducing agents, because they cause the iodine atoms to gain electrons.

17. The general chemical equation for photosynthesis is shown below. Through this reaction is the carbon oxidized or reduced? Are the oxygen atoms of the water molecules being oxidized or reduced?
$6\ CO_2 + 6\ H_2O \rightarrow C_6H_{12}O_6 + 6\ O_2$

Within carbon dioxide there are two oxygen atoms for every one carbon. With the product of photosynthesis (glucose), however, there is only one oxygen for every one carbon. Furthermore, the carbon now has more hydrogens around it. This all tells us that carbon is getting reduced. The oxygen of the water molecule winds up with fewer hydrogen atoms whether it ends up being an oxygen within the carbon-based product ($C_6H_{12}O_6$, glucose, where it needs to share these hydrogens with carbon) or within the oxygen molecule, O_2. This tells us that the oxygen of the water molecule is getting oxidized, which is not an easy thing for oxygen. It takes the energy of sunlight to make this happen.

18. During strenuous exercise there is little oxygen, O_2, available for muscle cells. Under these conditions, the muscle cells derive most of their energy from the anaerobic conversion of pyruvic acid, $C_3H_4O_3$, into lactic acid, $C_3H_6O_3$. The buildup of lactic acid makes the muscles ache and fatigue quickly. Is the pyruvic acid oxidized or reduced as it transforms into lactic acid?

There is a greater ratio of hydrogen atoms in the lactic acid product, which tells us that the pyruvic acid is being reduced.

19. As we digest and subsequently metabolize food, is the food gradually oxidized or reduced? What evidence do you have?

We exhale carbon dioxide and water vapor, which are the products of the oxidation of the food we eat.

20. Are the chemical reactions that take place in a disposable battery exothermic or endothermic? What evidence supports your answer? Is the reaction going on in a rechargeable battery while it is recharging exothermic or endothermic?

It is an exothermic reaction because of the energy that batteries provide.

21. Why do exothermic reactions typically favor the formation of products?

As an exothermic reaction proceeds from reactants to products, the result is a release (dispersion) of thermal energy, which is favorable. Typically, this amount of energy dispersion is significantly larger than the difference in chemical entropies of the products and reactants.

22. As the Sun shines on a snow-capped mountain, much of the snow sublimes instead of melts. How is this favored by entropy?

Water vapor has more entropy than liquid water.

Solutions to Chapter 13 Problems

1. When the hydronium ion concentration of a solution equals 1 mole per liter, what is the pH of the solution? Is the solution acidic or basic?

$H = -\log [H_3O^+] = -\log (1) = -(-0) = 0$

This is an acidic solution. Yes, pH can be equal to zero!

2. When the hydronium ion concentration of a solution equals 10 moles per liter, what is the pH of the solution? Is the solution acidic or basic?

Use a calculator to find the log of 2 (it's 0.301)

$pH = -\log [H_3O^+] = -\log (2) = -(0.301) = -0.301$

This is a very acidic solution. Yes, pHs can be negative!

3. Use the bond energies in Table 13.2 and the accounting format shown in Section 13.9 determine whether these reactions are exothermic or endothermic:

$H_2 + Cl_2 \rightarrow 2HCl$

$2\ HC\equiv CH + 5\ O_2 \rightarrow 4\ CO_2 + 2\ H_2O$

Energy to break bonds:

H—H = 436 kJ

Cl—Cl = 243 kJ
_____
Total = 679 kJ absorbed

Energy released from bond formation:

H—Cl = 431 kJ

H—Cl = 431 kJ
_____
Total = 862 kJ released

NET = 679 kJ absorbed − 862 kJ released = 83KJ released (exothermic)

Energy to break bonds:

C≡C = 837 kJ

H—C = 414 kJ

C—H = 414 kJ

O=O = 498 kJ

O=O = 498 kJ

O=O = 498 kJ

O=O = 498 kJ

O=O = 498 kJ
_____
Total = 4155 kJ absorbed

Energy released from bond formation:

4 × O=C = 3212 kJ

4 × C=O = 3212 kJ

H—O = 464 kJ

H—O = 464 kJ

O—H = 464 kJ

O—H = 464 kJ
_____
Total = 8280 kJ released

NET = 4155 kJ absorbed − 8280 kJ released = −4125 kJ released (very exothermic)

Chapter 14: Organic Chemistry

Answers to Chapter 14 Review Questions

1. These differ from one another by the number of carbon and hydrogen atoms they contain.

2. Structural isomers have different physical and chemical properties and different structures. They are similar in that they have the same molecular formula.

3. The hydrocarbons we use are obtained primarily from fossil fuels—coal and petroleum.

4. The term *saturated* means that each carbon has as many atoms bonded to it as possible—four.

5. An unsaturated hydrocarbon contains a multiple bond—either double or triple.

6. Aromatic compounds contain a benzene ring.

7. A heteroatom is any atom other than carbon or hydrogen in an organic molecule.

8. Organic molecules are classified according to the functional groups they contain.

9. Alcohols are often soluble in water because of the polarity of the oxygen–hydrogen bond. Water is also polar.

10. Alcohols are organic molecules in which a *hydroxyl group* is bonded to a saturated carbon; Phenols contain a phenolic group.

11. Ethers are organic compounds structurally related to alcohols. The oxygen atom in an ether group, however, is bonded not to a carbon and a hydrogen but rather to two carbons.

12. Amines are organic compounds that contain the amine group—a nitrogen atom bonded to one, two, or three saturated carbons.

13. Two appropriately named amines are putrescine and cadaverine, which have the odor of decaying flesh.

14. The carbonyl group consists of a carbon atom double bonded to an oxygen atom.

15. A ketone is a carbonyl-containing organic molecule in which the carbonyl carbon is bonded to two carbon atoms. In an aldehyde, the carbonyl carbon is bonded either to one carbon atom and one hydrogen atom, or, in the special case of formaldehyde, to two hydrogen atoms.

16. The aldehyde vanillin, introduced at the beginning of this chapter, is the key flavoring molecule derived from the vanilla orchid.

17. An amide is a carbonyl-containing organic molecule in which the carbonyl carbon is bonded to a nitrogen atom. A carboxylic acid is a carbonyl-containing organic molecule in which the carbonyl carbon is bonded to a hydroxyl group.

18. Salicylic acid is an important analgesic (painkiller), but it causes nausea and stomach upset because of its relatively high acidity.

19. Describe the general structure of a polymer.

    Polymers are exceedingly long molecules that consist of repeating molecular units called monomers. Monomers have relatively simple structures consisting of anywhere from 4 to 100 atoms per molecule.

20. What happens to the double bond of a monomer participating in the formation of an addition polymer?

    Polymerization occurs when two of the electrons from each double bond split away from each other to form new covalent bonds with neighboring monomer molecules.

21. What is released in the formation of a condensation polymer?

    A small molecule, such as water or hydrochloric acid.

Answers to Chapter 14 Multiple-Choice Questions

1c, 2e, 3a, 4d, 5d, 6a, 7c, 8c, 9b, 10d

Answers to Chapter 14 Integrated Science Concepts

Biology: Drug Action and Discovery

1. The drug is viewed as the key.

2. Molecular interactions, such as hydrogen bonding, hold a drug to its receptor site.

3. Whether a drug is isolated from nature or synthesized in the laboratory makes no difference as to "how good it may be for you." There are a multitude of natural products that are downright harmful, just as there are many synthetic drugs that are also harmful. The effectiveness of a drug depends on its chemical structure, not the source of this chemical structure.

Solutions to Chapter 14 Exercises

1. According to Figure 14.3, which has a higher boiling point: gasoline or kerosene?

    To make it to the top of the fractionating column, a substance must remain in the gaseous phase. Only substances with very low boiling points, such as methane (bp−160°C) are able to make it to the top. According to Figure 14.3, gasoline travels higher than kerosene and so it must have a lower boiling point. Kerosene, therefore, has the higher boiling point.

2. According to Figure 14.3, which consists of smaller molecules: kerosene or diesel?

    A hydrocarbon with smaller molecules tends to have a lower boiling point because of weaker attractions among the molecules. From Figure 14.3 you can tell that kerosene has a lower boiling point because it travels higher in the column. Kerosene, therefore, is made of smaller molecules.

3. There are five atoms in the methane molecule, CH_4. One out of these five is a carbon atom, which is $1/5 \times 100 = 20\%$ carbon. What is the percent carbon in ethane, C_2H_6? Propane, C_3H_8? Butane, C_4H_{10}?

The percent carbon increases as the hydrocarbon gets bigger. Methane's percent carbon is 20%; ethane, 25%; propane, 27%; butane, 29%.

4. What is the chemical formula of the following structure?

$C_4H_{10}O$

5. What is the chemical formula of the following structure?

C_4H_8O

6. Of the structures shown in Exercises 4 and 5, which is more oxidized?

According to Chapter 13, adding hydrogens to a compound is reduction, while subtracting hydrogens is oxidation. Transforming the compound of Exercise 4 into the compound of Exercise 5 requires the loss of hydrogens, which is an oxidation process. The ketone structure of Exercise 5 is more oxidized.

7. List the following compounds in order of least oxidized to most oxidized:

In order of least to most oxidized b < a < d < c, whereas c is the most oxidized. Note how this was the order of their presentation within the chapter. The most reduced hydrocarbons were introduced first, followed by the alcohols, followed by the aldehydes, followed by the carboxylic acids.

8. Circle the longest chain of carbon atoms in the following structure. How many carbon atoms are in this chain?

There are eight carbons in the longest chain:

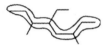

9. Carbon–carbon single bonds can rotate, while carbon–carbon double bonds cannot rotate. How many different structures are shown below?

The second and the fourth structures are the same. In all, there are three different structures shown.

10. Heteroatoms make a difference in the physical and chemical properties of an organic molecule, because

a. they add extra mass to the hydrocarbon structure.

b. each heteroatom has its own characteristic chemistry.

c. they can enhance the polarity of the organic molecule.

d. all of the above.

Answer: d.

11. One of the skin-irritating components of poison oak is tetrahydrourushiol. The long, nonpolar hydrocarbon tail embeds itself in a person's oily skin, where the molecule initiates an allergic response. Scratching the itch spreads tetrahydrourushiol molecules over a greater surface area, causing the zone of irritation to grow. Is this compound an alcohol or a phenol? Defend your answer.

The long, nonpolar hydrocarbon tail embeds itself in a person's oily skin, where the molecule initiates an allergic response. Scratching the itch spreads tetrahydrourushiol molecules over a greater surface area, causing the zone of irritation to grow.

12. Explain why caprylic acid, $CH_3(CH_2)_6COOH$, dissolves in a 5% aqueous solution of sodium hydroxide, but caprylaldehyde, $CH_3(CH_2)_6CHO$, does not.

The caprylic acid reacts with the sodium hydroxide to form a water-soluble salt, which dissolves in water. The aldehyde, on the other hand, is not acidic, so it will not form a water-soluble salt.

13. Suggest an explanation for why aspirin has a sour taste.

Aspirin's chemical name is acetyl salicylic acid. It is the acidic nature of aspirin that gives rise to its sour taste.

14. Identify the following functional groups in this organic molecule—amide, ester, ketone, ether, alcohol, aldehyde, amine:

    1. ether

    2. amide

    3. ester

    4. amide

    5. alcohol

    6. aldehyde

    7. amine

    8. ether

    9. ketone

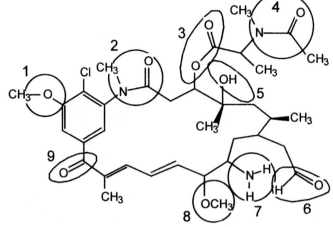

15. Benzaldehyde is a fragrant oil. If stored in an uncapped bottle, this compound will slowly transform into benzoic acid along the surface. Is this an oxidation or a reduction?

    The transformation of benzaldehyde to benzoic acid is an oxidation.

16. Which would you expect to be more viscous, a polymer made of long molecular strands or one made of short molecular strands? Why?

    A polymer made of long chains is likely to be more viscous because of the tendency of longer chains to get tangled among themselves.

17. Hydrocarbons release a lot of energy when ignited. Where does this energy come from?

    Ultimately, this is the energy that was capture from the sun by photosynthetic plants that turned into fossil fuels after decaying under anaerobic conditions.

18. What type of polymer would be best to use in the manufacture of stain-resistant carpets?

    A fluorine-containing polymer such as Teflon.

19. The copolymer styrene-butadiene rubber (SBR), shown here, is used for making tires as well as bubble gum. Is it an addition polymer or a condensation polymer?

    Note the similarities between the structure of SBR and polyethylene and polystyrene, all of which possess no heteroatoms. SBR is an addition polymer made from the monomers 1,3-butadiene and styrene mixed together in a 3:1 ratio. Notably, SBR is the key ingredient that allows the formation of bubbles within bubble gum.

20. Many of the natural product molecules synthesized by plants are formed by the joining together of isoprene monomers via an addition polymerization. A good example is the nutrient beta-carotene, which consists of eight isoprene units. Find and circle these units within the structure shown here.

    Initially, the beta-carotene structure looks rather complex. Upon careful examination, however, we find that this molecule is simply the result of the joining together of smaller units. Similarly, many of the molecules that you've been studying in this chapter may have initially looked rather intimidating. With a basic understanding of the concepts of chemistry, however, you'll find that you already have much insight into their properties.

21. Write a letter to Grandma summarizing how polymers were important in winning World War II. If Grandma lived through World War II, ask her if she was aware of the role polymers played!

    Dear Grandma, today we take polymers and their remarkable properties for granted. Not so back during the time of World War II when their remarkable properties had a significant impact on how the war was won—Nylon for parachutes, synthetic rubber for tires, polyethylene for RADAR, Plexiglas for airplane gunner turets, and Teflon to help in the development of the nuclear bomb.

Solutions to Chapter 14 Problems

1. Draw all the structural isomers for hydrocarbons having the molecular formula C_4H_{10}.

2. Draw all the structural isomers for hydrocarbons having the molecular formula C_6H_{14}.

3. Draw all the structural isomers for amines having the molecular formula C_3H_9N.

4. Cetyl alcohol, $C_{16}H_{33}OH$, is a common ingredient of soaps and shampoos. It was once commonly obtained from whale oil, which is where it gets its name (*cetyl* is derived from *cetacean*). Draw the chemical structure for this compound.

Cetyl alcohol

Chapter 15: The Basic Unit of Life—The Cell

Answers to Chapter 15 Review Questions

1. Living things share a set of characteristics. For one thing, living things all *use energy*. Living things *develop* and *grow*. Living things *maintain themselves*. Living things have the capacity to *reproduce*. Finally, living things are part of populations that *evolve*.

219

2. Populations do not remain constant from one generation to the next but change over time, across generations.

3. Eukaryotic cells have their DNA in a distinct nucleus, whereas prokaryotic cells lack a nucleus. In addition, the DNA of eukaryotic cells is found in linear, rather than circular, chromosomes. Eukaryotic cells also have numerous organelles, structures that perform specific functions for the cell, that are not present in prokaryotes. Finally, eukaryotic cells are larger than prokaryotic cells—where prokaryotic cells measure 0.1 to 10 micrometers, eukaryotic cells generally measure 10 to 100 micrometers.

4. The DNA of prokaryotes is found in circular chromosomes; the DNA of eukaryotes is found in linear chromosomes.

5. Some of the organelles in eukaryotic cells look suspiciously like whole prokaryotes. Mitochondria, organelles that obtain energy for the cell's use, are contained within their own membrane and have their own DNA, just like prokaryotes. Furthermore, mitochondrial DNA, like that of prokaryotes, exists in the form of a single circular chromosome. This has led to the hypothesis that certain prokaryotes started to live within early eukaryotes and eventually evolved into organelles.

6. The nucleus is a distinct structure within eukaryotic cells surrounded by a double membrane. The nucleus contains the cell's DNA, or genetic material, in the form of linear chromosomes.

7. *Mitochondria* are organelles that break down organic molecules to obtain energy for cells. *Ribosomes* are organelles that assemble proteins. *Lysosomes* are the garbage disposals of a cell—these organelles break down organic materials. Finally, in plants, organelles called *chloroplasts* capture energy from sunlight in order to build organic molecules.

8. The three primary components of the cell membrane are phospholipids, proteins, and short carbohydrates.

9. Phospholipids have hydrophilic "heads" and hydrophobic "tails." The hydrophilic heads are naturally drawn to the watery environment inside and outside the cell, whereas the hydrophobic tails naturally try to avoid it. The result is that the phospholipids form a double layer, or bilayer, with the hydrophobic tails pointing in and the hydrophilic heads pointing out.

10. Membrane proteins serve a variety of functions—they help cells communicate with other cells, control transport into and out of cells, control the chemical reactions that occur in cells, and join cells to one another.

11. Many hydrophobic molecules, including gases such as oxygen and carbon dioxide, can pass directly through the double layer of hydrophobic phospholipid tails. In addition, small, uncharged hydrophilic molecules—most importantly, water—are able to cross the cell membrane directly through tiny pores.

12. *Diffusion* is the tendency for molecules to move from an area of high concentration to an area of low concentration, that is, down a concentration gradient.

13. Carrier proteins are very specific for what they let through the cell membrane. This is because a molecule fits into its carrier protein the way a key fits in a lock—only the right combination will work.

14. In endocytosis, a portion of the cell membrane folds inward and pinches off, enclosing the material to be brought into the cell within a vesicle. In exocytosis, the opposite process occurs—a vesicle fuses its membrane with the cell membrane and dumps its contents outside the cell.

15. In animals and plants, special structures allow very local messages to pass directly from one cell to an adjacent cell. Plasmodesmata serve this function in plant cells. Plasmodesmata are slender threads of cytoplasm that link adjacent plant cells.

16. The binding of a message molecule to its receptor sets off a series of chemical reactions that results ultimately in the target cell's response to the message.

17. No—receptors are extremely specific about the molecules they bind. This is because a message molecule and its receptor fit together like a key in a lock—only the right combination will work.

18. The stages of the cell cycle are gap 1, synthesis, gap 2, and mitosis. During synthesis, or *S*, the cell creates an exact copy of its genetic material—its DNA.

19. The phases of mitosis are prophase, metaphase, anaphase, and telophase. During *prophase,* the normally loosely packed chromosomes condense, and the membranes surrounding the nucleus break down. When the chromosomes condense, it becomes clear that each consists of two identical sister chromatids attached at a point called the centromere. The mitotic spindle also forms during prophase. The mitotic spindle consists of a series of fibers that attach to the duplicated chromosomes and is responsible for splitting the genetic material between the two daughter cells. During *metaphase,* the chromosomes line up at the equatorial plane, the plane that passes through the imaginary "equator" of the cell. During *anaphase,* the two sister chromatids are pulled apart by the shortening of the mitotic spindle fibers and move to opposite poles of the cell. During *telophase,* new nuclear membranes form around each set of chromosomes, and the chromosomes decondense.

20. In mitosis, one parent cell divides into two daughter cells, each of which contains the same genetic information as the parent cell.

21. Cells rely on catalysts to lower the activation energy of reactions and allow them to happen more quickly. These catalysts are large, complex proteins called enzymes.

22. In competitive inhibition, an inhibitor binds to the active site of an enzyme, preventing it from binding its substrate. (If a substrate fits into an enzyme like a key in a lock, the inhibitor is like bubble gum stuck in the keyhole.) This type of inhibition is called competitive, because the inhibitor and substrate compete for the active site. In noncompetitive inhibition, an inhibitor binds to an enzyme somewhere other than the active site, changing the enzyme so that it can no longer bind its substrate.

23. The antibiotic penicillin kills bacteria by inhibiting an enzyme they need to build cell walls.

24. Almost all life on earth is either directly or indirectly dependent on photosynthesis for organic molecules and energy. This is because photosynthesizers (primarily plants) are food for herbivores, which are, in turn, food for carnivores. Organisms that photosynthesize are thus the ultimate source of all food.

25. During the light-dependent reactions, energy is captured from sunlight. During the light-independent reactions, carbon is fixed—that is, carbon atoms are moved from atmospheric carbon dioxide to carbon-containing organic molecules—specifically, glucose.

26. The end products of photosynthesis are glucose and oxygen.

27. During glycolysis, the six-carbon glucose molecule is split into two molecules of pyruvic acid, each of which contains three carbon atoms. Two molecules of ATP are produced in the process.

28. About 38 molecules of ATP are produced from a single molecule of glucose. The products of cellular respiration are carbon dioxide, water, and ATP.

29. In alcoholic fermentation, pyruvic acid is broken down into ethanol and carbon dioxide.

30. In animal muscle cells, lactic acid fermentation occurs during strenuous exercise, when oxygen supply—despite hard breathing—can't quite meet demand. By regenerating the molecules required for glycolysis, lactic acid fermentation allows muscle cells to continue to make ATP without oxygen. The lactic acid produced causes the familiar burning sensation. Red blood cells, which lack mitochondria, also rely on lactic acid fermentation to obtain ATP.

31. Telomeres are lengths of DNA at the ends of chromosomes that protect them from damage. Every time DNA is copied for cell division, the telomeres get a little shorter. This is because the machinery for copying DNA is unable to copy the linear chromosomes of eukaryotes all the way to their ends. It is sort of like peeling a carrot—because you have to hold the carrot at one end, that end doesn't get peeled all the way. When telomere shortening reaches a critical stage, the cell can no longer divide without losing critical genetic information from the ends of its chromosomes.

32. No, not all cells have a finite life span. The germ line cells that produce our eggs and sperm have a lot of telomerase and are immortal. Some abnormal cells, such as the tumor cells in cancers, also have a lot of telomerase, enabling them to divide indefinitely.

Answers to Chapter 15 Multiple-Choice Questions

1d, 2a, 3c, 4a, 5c, 6c, 7c, 8b, 9d, 10b

Answers to Chapter 15 Integrated Science Concepts

Chemistry: Macromolecules Needed for Life

1. Proteins perform a wide range of functions in living organisms. The protein keratin provides structure in the form of skin, hair, and feathers. Insulin is a protein that acts as a hormone, allowing cells to communicate with one another. Actin and myosin are proteins that allow muscles to contract. Hemoglobin, a protein found in red blood cells, transports oxygen to body tissues. Antibodies are proteins that protect the body from disease. And proteins known as digestive enzymes break down food during digestion.

2. (a) Glucose, fructose, starch, and glycogen are mentioned in the text. Other answers are possible.
   (b) Cellulose.

3. Four nitrogenous bases are used in DNA—adenine, cytosine, guanine, and thymine.

Physics: The Microscope

4. With a resolution of 10^{-6} meters, light microscopes allow us to view cells and to make out the larger features within them, such as the nucleus and mitochondria. However, they do not really allow us to see organelles and other cellular structures in detail.

5. Electron microscopes are able to resolve objects about a nanometer (10^{-9} meter) in size, which allows cellular structures to be viewed in fine detail.

Chemistry: Chemical Reactions in Cells

6. ATP consists of an adenosine molecule and three phosphate groups. Energy is obtained from ATP when one of its phosphate groups is removed, leaving adenosine diphosphate, or ADP. The ATP reaction releases seven kilocalories of energy per mole, an amount of energy that is suitable for most biological reactions.

7. No, it costs more energy to make ATP than cells eventually get out of it. This is consistent with the second law of thermodynamics.

8. ATP is required for the carrier protein to shift and open to the outside of the cell, where it then releases sodium ions and binds potassium ions.

Answers to Chapter 15 Exercises

1. What are the characteristics of life? Discuss how these are evident in human beings.

   Like other living things, humans use energy when we move, speak, or perform any activity. Like other animals, we obtain this energy from the food we eat. Humans certainly develop and grow—think how much a newborn differs from a two-year-old, and how much a two-year-old differs from you! Humans maintain themselves by repairing injuries to skin and bone and other organs, and we maintain a stable internal environment where body temperature, oxygen, water content, and numerous other variables are carefully controlled. (This will be discussed further in Chapter 19 and Chapter 20). Humans have the capacity to reproduce through sexual reproduction. And human populations evolve. In Chapter 16, for example, we will learn why the sickle cell anemia allele is comparatively common in people of African descent, but not in other human groups.

2. During their annual migrations, many birds fly hundreds or even thousands of miles over a relatively short period of time. Why do birds put on a layer of fat before their annual migration? Why don't they store this energy as carbohydrates?

   Birds need large energy supplies to complete long, strenuous migratory flights. If they store the energy as fat rather than as carbohydrate, they won't weight themselves down as much, because 1 gram of fat contains a lot more energy than 1 gram of carbohydrate.

3. Is it true that *all* the DNA contained in an eukaryotic cell is in the nucleus? If not, why not? How does this support the argument that there were once prokaryotes living inside eukaryotes?

Eukaryotic cells also have some DNA in their mitochondria (and in their chloroplasts, if they are plant cells). Both mitochondria and chloroplasts have their own cell membrane and their own circular chromosome of DNA—because of this resemblance to prokaryotes, it has been hypothesized that these organelles evolved from prokaryotes living inside early eukaryotes.

4. What organelle is found only in plants? What does it do? Does this explain why animals have to eat but plants don't?

Chloroplasts are found only in plant cells. Chloroplasts are responsible for photosynthesis. This does explain why plants don't need to eat but animals do—through photosynthesis, plants are able to make their own organic molecules that they can use to build structures or that can be broken down for energy.

5. Certain cells in the body, including nerve cells, muscle cells, and liver cells, have large numbers of mitochondria. Bone cells and fat cells generally have few mitochondria. What can you tell about a cell from the number of mitochondria it contains?

Cells with lots of mitochondria require lots of energy. The mitochondria are there to make lots of ATP for these busy cells.

6. In this chapter, we had three examples of molecules fitting together like "lock and key"? What were these? Why do you think it is important in each of these contexts to have such a specific fit?

Enzymes and their substrates fits together like lock and key—this assures that each enzyme catalyzes one specific reaction. Carrier proteins and the molecules they transport across cell membranes also fit together like lock and key—this assures that a carrier protein only transports a specific molecule. Finally, message molecules and their receptors fit together like lock and key—this assures that a receptor only responds to a specific message.

7. In all the instances of molecules fitting together like "lock and key," you'll notice that the molecules involved are proteins. How are proteins able to achieve the specificity required?

Proteins are made of carefully folded chains of amino acids—the varying amino acid sequences combined with the complex folding allows proteins to take on the complex shapes required to create many different types of "locks" and "keys."

8. We mentioned that controlling water flow in and out of cells is a problem all cells face. We also know that water is able to cross the cell membrane directly. Are organisms that occupy freshwater habitats likely to have the problem of too little water entering their cells or too much water entering their cells? Why?

Freshwater organisms have the problem of too much water entering their bodies. This is because organisms consist of water plus some solutes, whereas their environments consist of water with very few solutes. So, because of osmosis, water tends to move from the environment (few solutes, i.e., high concentration of water molecules) into the bodies of organisms (more solutes, i.e., lower concentration of water molecules). Because of this, many freshwater organisms have some means for getting rid of large amounts of water. Some single-celled organisms have special contractile vacuoles for disposing of water. Vertebrates such as fish get rid of water by excreting very dilute urine.

9. Glucose gets into cells through facilitated diffusion. Why isn't active transport of glucose necessary? That is, why is there usually a higher concentration of glucose molecules outside the cell than inside the cell?

Glucose is quickly broken down by cells to make ATP (through the process of cellular respiration). As a result, there usually isn't much glucose inside cells.

10. Why does oxygen diffuse into cells rather out of them? Why does carbon dioxide diffuse out of cells rather than into them?

Oxygen is used up by cells for cellular respiration. As a result, oxygen concentration in cells is low, and so oxygen diffuses in. Carbon dioxide, on the other hand, is a product of cellular respiration, and so its concentration in cells is higher than that outside cells. As a result, carbon dioxide diffuses out of cells.

11. In plants, roots absorb water (among other functions). Why are the roots of many plants highly branched?

   Highly branched roots increase the amount of available surface area for absorption of water and other soil nutrients.

12. What is the difference between endocytosis and using a carrier protein to cross the cell membrane?

   In endocytosis, a portion of the cell membrane folds inward and pinches off the transported material within a vesicle inside the cell. With a carrier protein, the molecule entering the cell binds to the carrier protein, the protein shifts, and the molecule is released inside the cell.

13. How are gap junctions and plasmodesmata similar? How do they differ?

   Both gap junctions and plasmodesmata allow messages to pass directly from one cell to an adjacent cell. So, they have similar functions. However, they are different structurally. Gap junctions are tiny channels in the cell membrane surrounded by specialized proteins. Plasmodesmata are slender threads of cytoplasm that link adjacent plant cells.

14. If a cell goes through all the phases in the cell cycle but for some reason fails to undergo cytokinesis, how will that cell differ from normal cells?

   It will have two nuclei, and twice the genetic material of a normal cell.

15. The figure below shows a cell in the process of cell division. Which stage of the cell cycle is it in?

   Mitosis.

16. The lethal nerve gas sarin binds to an enzyme called acetylcholinesterase, which breaks down acetylcholine in the body. If acetylcholine is not broken down, muscles are unable to relax after contracting. Without prompt treatment, sarin exposure leads to respiratory collapse and death. Sarin works by binding to acetylcholinesterase at the site where acetylcholine normally binds. What form of enzyme regulation does this represent?

   This is competitive inhibition, because it binds at the enzyme's active site, where the substrate normally binds.

17. Global warming has occurred because of the large amounts of carbon dioxide released by burning fossil fuels. Carbon dioxide traps heat. Why might deforestation, the loss of large forests, also contribute to global warming?

   Plants remove carbon dioxide from the atmosphere during photosynthesis.

18. What are some differences between fermentation and cellular respiration? Which process produces more ATP? Why do some cells in the human body use fermentation?

   Fermentation does not require oxygen, whereas cellular respiration does. Fermentation produces no ATP, in contrast to cellular respiration, which produces a lot of ATP. In humans, muscles use lactic acid fermentation when there isn't enough oxygen to meet demand. Red blood cells use fermentation because they have no mitochondria and, therefore, cannot conduct cellular respiration.

19. Where do the bubbles in champagne come from? *Hint*: unlike nonbubbly wines, champagne goes through an extra round of fermentation during which the bottles are capped tight.

   The bubbles come from carbon dioxide released during alcoholic fermentation.

20. Some animals that live in desert environments, like the kangaroo rat shown in the figure below, go their entire lives without drinking a drop of water. Kangaroo rats subsist entirely on the starches and fats found in the dry seeds they eat. Yet we know that all living organisms need water, and in fact, the bodies of kangaroo rats have about the same water content as those of other animals. How do kangaroo rats get their water?

   Kangaroo rats get water from cellular respiration—water is one of the products of this process.

21. Do prokaryotes have telomeres? Why don't they need them?

   Prokaryotes don't have or require telomeres, because they have circular, rather than linear, chromosomes.

Solutions to Chapter 15 Problems

1. As energy-storage substances, carbohydrates produce about 4 kilocalories of energy per gram, whereas fats produce about 9 kilocalories of energy per gram. The American black bear may hibernate for as long as seven months in the winter, during which it does not eat. Before hibernating, black bears put on a lot of weight, often spending 20 hours a day eating and storing as much as 50 kilograms of fat. Show that the bear would have to gain 112.5 kilograms if it stored energy as carbohydrate instead of as fat.

    The amount of energy the bear stores for the winter is:

    (50 kilograms of fat) (1000 grams/1 kilogram) (9 kilocalories/gram) = 450,000 kilocalories.

    In order to store the same amount of energy as carbohydrate:

    (x kilograms of carbohydrate) (1000 grams/1 kilogram) (4 kilocalories/gram)

    = 450,000 kilocalories

    x = 450,000/(4)(1000) = 112.5 kilograms

2. A typical cell in the body makes about 10 million molecules of ATP per second. About how many molecules of glucose does it break down per second?

    We know that about 38 molecules of ATP are obtained from the breakdown of one glucose molecule. So 10,000,000/38 = about 263,158 molecules of glucose.

3. Two bacteria have radii of 1 micrometer and 5 micrometers, respectively. What is the surface area of each cell? How does surface area compare to volume for each cell—that is, what is the surface area to volume ratio? Why is the larger cell able to obtain more molecules through diffusion? Why is it nonetheless more challenging for the larger cell to meet its needs through diffusion? (Recall that the surface area of a sphere is $4\pi r^2$, and the volume of a sphere is $4/3\pi r^3$.)

    For 1 micrometer cell, surface area = $4\pi(1)^2 = 4\pi$

    For 5 micrometer cell, surface area = $4\pi(5)^2 = 100\pi$

    Volume of a sphere is $^4/_3\pi r^3$

    For 1 micrometer cell, volume = $^4/_3\pi(1)^3 = {}^4/_3\pi$

    For 5 micrometer cell, volume = $^4/_3\pi(5)^3 = {}^{500}/_3\pi$

    So the surface area to volume ratio is

    For 1 micrometer cell, surface area/volume = $4\pi/{}^4/_3\pi = 3$

    For 5 micrometer cell, surface area/volume = $100\pi/{}^{500}/_3\pi = 3/5$

    The larger cell is able to obtain more molecules through diffusion because it has a larger surface area. It is nonetheless more challenging for the larger cell to meet its needs through diffusion because it has a smaller surface area to volume ratio—this ratio measures how easy it is for a cell to meet its needs through diffusion, because a cell's need for molecules depends on its volume, and its ability to obtain these molecules depends on its surface area.

4. We mentioned that diffusion works best over small distances. This is because the average time it takes a molecule to diffuse a certain distance is proportional to the square of that distance. If two cells have diameters of 1 micrometer and 5 micrometers, respectively, show that it takes a molecules 25 times longer to diffuse across the larger cell than the smaller cell.

    The average time it takes a molecule to diffuse a certain distance is proportional to the square of that distance, so the ratio of diffusion time across the larger cell to the diffusion time across the smaller cell is $(5)^2/(1)^2 = 25$; that is, it takes 25 times longer to diffuse across the 5 micrometer cell than the 1 micrometer cell.

5. Proteins are folded strings of amino acids. All the proteins in living organisms are made up of only 20 different amino acids. How many different ways can you make a string of two amino acids? A string of three amino acids? A string of 10 amino acids? Do you see why the number of proteins living organisms can make is practically countless?

A chain of two amino acids can include 20 amino acids for the first position and 20 amino acids for the second position, so the number of possibilities is (20)(20) = 400.

A chain of three amino acids can have any of 20 amino acids in the first position, any of 20 amino acids in the second position, and any of 20 amino acids in the third position—so the number of possibilities is (20)(20)(20) = 8000.

For 10 amino acids, the number of possibilities is

(20)(20)(20)(20)(20)(20)(20)(20)(20)(20) = 10,240,000,000,000.

Chapter 16: Genetics

Answers to Chapter 16 Review Questions

1. A gene is a section of DNA that contains the instructions for making a protein.

2. Each chromosome consists of a single long strand of DNA as well as small proteins called histones. DNA is wrapped around histone "spools" like string.

3. Most cells have two of each kind of chromosome, like a pair of matched shoes. These cells are diploid. Some cells, such as sperm and eggs, have only one of each kind of chromosome—these cells are haploid.

4. DNA is copied in a process called replication. During replication, DNA's two strands are separated as if the spiral ladder were unzipped down the middle. Because of the specific way the bases pair—because A always goes with T, and G always goes with C—each strand can serve as a template for building a new partner.

5. Because of the way replication occurs, with each old strand serving as the template for building a new partner, every new DNA molecule includes one old strand and one new strand.

6. RNA differs from DNA in three ways—RNA is single-stranded rather than double-stranded, it uses the sugar ribose rather than deoxyribose, and it uses the base uracil (U) instead of thymine (T).

7. Where DNA has bases A, C, G, and T, the mRNA transcript has U, G, C, and A, respectively.

8. First, a cap and tail are added to the beginning and end of the molecule—these allow the cell to recognize the mRNA molecule as mRNA. Second, stretches of nucleotides not relevant to building protein are removed from the mRNA molecule.

9. A codon is a triplet of nucleotides along the mRNA strand that stands for one of the 20 amino acids that make up proteins.

10. The binding of codon and anticodon follows the usual base-pairing rules—that is, A binds with U, and G binds with C.

11. *Crossing over* occurs when one chromosome exchanges corresponding parts with its homologue. It takes place during metaphase I of meiosis.

12. In meiosis, one diploid parent cell, with two of each kind of chromosome, divides into four haploid daughter cells, each with only one of each kind of chromosome.

13. Until 1900, the dominant theory of inheritance—how traits pass from one generation to the next—was blending inheritance. Under blending inheritance, the mixing of parental hereditary material was thought to produce offspring intermediate between the parents.

14. Mendel found that all the offspring resembled *one* of the two parents.

15. Mendel saw that the recessive trait, which had disappeared in the first generation, reappeared in this second generation.

16. In codominance, the combination of two alleles in a heterozygote results in both traits being expressed. For example, a person with blood type *AB* has both "A" and "B" molecules on his or her red blood cells—that is, both the *A* trait and the *B* trait are expressed. Consequently, the *A* and *B* alleles are codominant.

17. The genes for Mendel's pea traits happened to lie on different chromosomes, so they follow Mendel's law of independent assortment. However, if two genes are found on the *same* chromosome, they are often

inherited together (not quite all of the time, because sometimes crossing over shuffles them up) and do not obey Mendel's law of independent assortment.

18. Because males have only one X chromosome, they have only one allele for sex-linked traits. Consequently, males need only one recessive allele for the recessive trait to appear, whereas females need two. As a result, recessive sex-linked traits show up more frequently in males than in females.

19. No, most of the bases in the human genome are not part of genes. In fact, less than 2% of the genome carries instructions for making proteins!

20. SNPs, or single nucleotide polymorphisms, are locations in the genome where the base pair sequence differs among human beings.

21. A *point mutation* occurs when one nucleotide is substituted for another.

22. A *nonsense mutation* creates a stop codon in the middle of a protein-coding sequence. Nonsense mutations result in the production of shorter, often nonfunctional proteins.

23. A mutation in a single gene is never enough to produce cancer—mutations in many key genes are required.

24. *Oncogenes* stimulate abnormal cell division. *Tumor suppressor genes* prevent cancer by inhibiting cell division. Oncogenes behave as dominants—a mutation in only one of the two alleles promotes abnormal cell division. Tumor suppressor genes behave as recessives—both alleles have to be mutated before the protective effect is lost.

Answers to Chapter 16 Multiple-Choice Questions

1c, 2d, 3c, 4d, 5a, 6a, 7b, 8d, 9a, 10d

Answers to Chapter 16 Integrated Science Concepts

Chemistry: The Structure of DNA

1. DNA is often described as a double helix, because it consists of two strands twisted into a spiral or helix.

2. The "sides" of the ladder are made up of alternating molecules of deoxyribose sugar and phosphate. The "rungs" of the ladder are made up of paired nitrogenous bases (either A and T or G and C).

3. The four nitrogenous bases in DNA are adenine (A), guanine (G), cytosine (C), and thymine (T). A pairs with T, and G pairs with C.

Physics: How Radioactivity Causes Genetic Mutations

4. Radioactive materials release ionizing radiation—gamma rays, beta particles, and alpha particles. When these forms of radiation strike electrons in the body with enough energy, they free the electrons from the atoms they were orbiting. The free electrons can then strike and damage DNA directly. More frequently, however, the damage occurs indirectly when an electron freed by ionizing radiation hits a water molecule in a cell, producing a free radical. A free radical is a group of atoms that has an unpaired electron and is consequently unstable and highly reactive. Free radicals will react with a wide variety of molecules in the body, including DNA. Their interactions with DNA damage it, causing one or more genetic mutations.

5. Frequently dividing cells are particularly vulnerable to radiation damage. These include cells in the bone marrow (where blood cells are made), in the lining of the gastrointestinal tract, in the testes, and in the developing fetus.

6. Cancer cells divide frequently, so are particularly vulnerable to radiation damage.

Earth Science: Environmental Causes of Cancer

7. The most important cancer-related environmental risk factors include tobacco, diet, ionizing radiation, UV light, disease-causing viruses and bacteria, and mutagens present in air, water, and soil.

8. Exposure to UV light can impair a cell's ability to undergo programmed cell death when it is damaged. (It is this programmed death that causes skin to peel after a sunburn.) Without this ability, damaged cells survive, their DNA continues to accumulate mutations, and they ultimately give rise to cancer.

9. Radon is a radioactive gas produced by the decay of uranium. Because minute amounts of uranium are found in many rocks, radon is present in many areas. When radon decays, it releases small radioactive particles that can be inhaled. These radioactive particles damage DNA in lung cells, making lung cancer more likely to develop.

Answers to Chapter 16 Exercises

1. Look at your finger. Is it made of diploid cells or haploid cells?

   Your finger is made of diploid cells, like most of your body except for your sex cells (and, in women, eggs do not actually complete meiosis and become haploid until they are fertilized!).

2. What kind of sex chromosomes do you have? Where in your body are sex chromosomes found?

   Females are XX, males are XY. Sex chromosomes are found in every cell in your body (with the exception of cells that lack nuclei, such as red blood cells).

3. Explain why every new DNA molecule has one old strand and one new strand.

   Every new DNA molecule has one old strand and one new strand because during DNA replication, the old molecule is unzipped, and each strand is used as a template for putting together a new strand.

4. How is transcription similar to DNA replication? How is it different?

   Transcription is similar to DNA replication in that, in both processes, DNA is unzipped, and one strand is used as a template for building a new nucleic acid strand using base pairing. However, during transcription, a molecule of RNA is made, whereas during replication, a strand of DNA is made. Thus, differences would include the sugar used in the new strand (ribose for RNA and deoxyribose for DNA) as well as the nucleotides in the strand (RNA has uracil in place of thymine).

5. We compared mRNA processing to editing "*aggfr uidosa to be dfjklsdf or rewerwe not to be*" to obtain "*to be or not to be.*" In this analogy, is "*aggfr*" an exon or an intron? Is "*not*" an exon or an intron?

   "*aggfr*" is an intron "*not*" is an exon.

6. Do all codons code for amino acids? If not, what else can they code for?

   Some codons are stop codons that tell the ribosome there are no more amino acids in the protein being assembled.

7. Examine the genetic code table. Are point mutations in the first, second, and third positions of a codon equally likely to cause a change in the amino acid sequence of a protein? What type of point mutation is least likely to change the amino acid sequence?

   Point mutations in the different positions of a codon are not equally likely to change the amino acid sequence of a protein. Changes in the third position are least likely to change amino acid sequence.

8. If there were no such thing as recombination, would the offspring of two parents all be identical? Why or why not?

   No. Recall that each pair of homologous chromosomes separates independently during meiosis I. Even without crossing over and recombination, each egg would receive either the chromosome the woman inherited from her mother or the chromosome she inherited from her father. One egg could receive chromosomes 1, 3, 4, 5, 7, 10, 13, and so forth, from her mother and chromosomes 2, 6, 8, 9, 11, 12, and so forth, from her father. A second egg she produces is almost certain to receive a different set of chromosomes, perhaps chromosomes 2, 3, 5, 6, 7, and so forth, from her mother and chromosomes 1, 4, 8, 9, and so forth, from her father. It is clear that the independent separation of homologous chromosomes alone produces a huge number of possible egg cells. Crossing over and recombination only expand the possibilities.

9. The figure below shows a set of human chromosomes. What is unusual about this person's genetic makeup? What health issues might this person suffer from? How does meiosis relate to this condition?

   This person has Down syndrome, which is a result of trisomy 21 (having three copies of chromosome 21 rather than two). Down syndrome is characterized by mental retardation and defects of the heart and respiratory system. Chromosomal abnormalities such as trisomies usually result from mistakes that occur

during meiosis resulting in an egg or sperm having two copies of a chromosome rather than the usual single copy. (The third copy is added at fertilization.)

10. Explain how a trait can "skip" generations.

   Recessive traits can skip generations. For example, a straight hairline father can pass a straight hairline allele to his son. However, the son will have a widow's peak if he inherits a widow's peak hairline from his mother. Then, when the son has a child, he can pass the recessive straight hairline allele to his child. If this child also inherits a straight hairline allele from her mother, she'll have a straight hairline. The straight hairline allele thus appears to have skipped a generation to show up again in the granddaughter.

11. At first sight, incomplete dominance might be mistaken for blending inheritance. For example, the fact that breeding a red-flowered snapdragon with a white-flowered snapdragon produces pink-flowered offspring could be explained by either. How can you prove that blending inheritance is not what's going on here? *Hint*: Try breeding two of the pink-flowered offspring. What would you expect under blending inheritance? Is this what you get?

   If you breed two pink-flowered snapdragons, blending inheritance predicts you get all pink-flowered snapdragons. However, what you get are pink, red, and white snapdragons. Specifically, breeding two pink-flowered snapdragons RW × RW yields a quarter RR (red-flowered), half RW (pink-flowered), and a quarter WW (white-flowered) offspring.

12. Can you tell what alleles a pea plant with round seeds has? What about the alleles that a red snapdragon has? Why the difference?

   A pea plant with round seeds is either WW or Ww, because having round seeds is dominant. A red snapdragon must be RR, because flower color in snapdragons shows incomplete dominance.

13. Is it possible for two parents with widow's peaks to have a child that has a straight hairline? Is it possible for two parents with straight hairlines to have a child with a widow's peak?

   It is possible for two parents with widow's peaks to have a child that has a straight hairline if both parents are heterozygotes (Ss) and the child inherits a recessive (s) allele from each parent. Two parents with straight hairlines must be ss, so all their children will only inherit s alleles and will also have straight hairlines. Thus, two parents with straight hairlines cannot have a child with a widow's peak.

14. In birds, sex is determined by a pair of sex chromosomes, just like in mammals. However, birds differ from mammals in that females have two different sex chromosomes (WZ) and males have two of the same sex chromosome (ZZ). Do you think female birds or male birds suffer from more recessive sex-linked conditions? Why?

   Females do because they only have one Z chromosome. This means that they need only one recessive allele for the recessive trait to appear, whereas males need two.

15. People with type O blood are called universal donors because they can donate blood to anyone without having problems arise. Why is this? Which blood type do universal receivers—people who can receive blood from any other blood type—have? Why?

   People with type O blood are universal donors because their blood cells have neither A nor B molecules that could cause the cells to be rejected and attacked. People with type AB blood are universal receivers—their bodies accept both A and B molecules, so they can receive type O, type A, type B, or type AB blood.

16. Suppose you are studying traits in a mouse, and you notice that two traits seem to be found together more often than you would expect under Mendel's law of independent assortment. For example, you keep noticing that mice with blue eyes are often deaf too. Can you think of two possible explanations for this?

   This could be a situation of pleiotropy, in which a single gene causes both blue eyes and deafness. It could also be caused by linked genes, in which the blue-eye gene and the deafness gene are found close together and blue-eye alleles and deafness alleles are associated with each other more frequently than either is with non-blue-eye-color alleles and nondeafness alleles.

17. Duchenne muscular dystrophy is a condition that affects far more males than females. What might you guess about the way it is inherited? What chromosome do you think the relevant gene lies on?

Because it's a condition that affects more males than females, it is likely to be (and, in fact, is) a sex-linked trait found on the X chromosome.

18. At their genetic counseling session, a couple learns that one partner is a carrier of cystic fibrosis, while the other is not. Are their children at risk for inheriting the condition? Could their children be carriers of the disease?

Because cystic fibrosis is recessive, children are only at risk if both parents carry a recessive allele (that is, are carriers or are ill with the disease). So, the couple's children are not at risk for cystic fibrosis. However, they could be carriers if they inherit the carrier parent's disease allele.

19. Suppose you are studying two different mutations in a gene that codes for a protein. In the first, a nonsense mutation occurs near the beginning of the gene. In the second, a nonsense mutation occurs near the end of the gene. Which mutation is more likely to disrupt protein function?

A nonsense mutation produces a stop codon in the middle of a gene-coding sequence. The one that occurs near the beginning of the gene (and therefore ends amino acid assembly earlier) is more likely to affect protein function than the one that occurs near the end of the gene.

20. Suppose you are studying two different mutations in a gene that codes for a protein. In one mutation, a single nucleotide is inserted near the beginning of the gene. In the other mutation, three nucleotides are inserted near the beginning of the gene. Which mutation is more likely to disrupt protein function? Why?

The insertion of a single nucleotide is more likely to disrupt protein function because it will throw the codon reading frame off, i.e., cause a frameshift mutation drastically affecting the amino acid sequence. The insertion of three nucleotides causes the insertion of an extra amino acid, but the bulk of the amino acid sequence remains unaffected.

21. Although offspring typically resemble their parents in many ways, it is also possible for a child to differ from both of her parents in some trait. Think of at least three possible explanations for this observation.

First, with a trait that shows incomplete dominance, the child would resemble neither parent but have a phenotype in between. Second, the child could inherit a recessive allele from each heterozygous parent; thus, the parents would have the dominant phenotype and the child would have the recessive phenotype. Third, with codominance, the child could have a phenotype different from both parents—a blood type A mother and blood type B father could have a child with blood type AB.

22. If two genes are found on the same chromosome, are they always inherited together? Why or why not?

No—crossing over may shuffle them.

23. Give an example of a trait that is determined partly by an organism's genes and partly by the organism's environment. Give an example of a trait that is determined primarily by genes—that is, a trait the environment has little effect on.

Human height and weight are both determined partially by genetic factors and partially by environmental factors. The environment has little effect on traits such as eye color, dimples vs. no dimples, straight vs. widow's peak hairline, and so forth.

24. Write a letter to Grandpa telling him about the Human Genome Project. Tell him what it means that the human genome has been sequenced in its entirety and what implication that might have for medicine.

The Human Genome Project, completed in 2003, sequenced the entire human genome—that is, it determined the complete sequence of As, Ts, Gs, and Cs for all of the human chromosomes. As a follow-up to the Human Genome Project, scientists also identified more than 3 million locations in the genome where the base-pair sequence differs among human beings. These differences are called single nucleotide polymorphisms, or SNPs. SNPs make every person unique, of course, but may also help scientists identify genes related to human diseases.

Answers to Chapter 16 Problems

1. If an organism's diploid cells have 64 chromosomes, how many chromosomes will its haploid cells have?

   64/2 = 32 chromosomes in its haploid cells.

2. One strand of DNA has the base sequence CTGAGGTCAGGA. What are the bases on the opposite strand?

   Because G pairs with C and A pairs with T, the opposite strand has GACTCCAGTCCT.

3. Now suppose a molecule of mRNA is being constructed from the same sequence of DNA. What will the bases in the mRNA molecule be?

   For RNA, G, C, A, and T pair with C, G, U, and A, respectively. (That is, RNA uses U instead of T). So the RNA molecule will have nucleotides GACUCCAGUCCU.

4. If living organisms used 100 different amino acids to make proteins (rather than only 20), show that a triplet codon would not be sufficient. Also show that a quadruplet codon *would* be sufficient.

   A triplet codon allows for 4 × 4 × 4 = 64 different codons. This is enough to cover 20 different amino acids, but not 100. For 100, we'd need a quadruplet codon. 4 × 4 × 4 × 4 = 256 possible codons, more than enough.

5. Suppose a mRNA molecule with the nucleotide sequence AGUCGUUGGCAGGAAGUA is translated. What sequence of amino acids do you get?

   We can break the sequence into triplet codons and consult the genetic code table. (AGU)(CGU)(UGG)(CAG)(GAA)(GUA) = serine-arginine-tryptophan-glutamine-glutamic acid-valine.

6. What point mutation in the mRNA molecule in Problem 5 would produce a nonsense mutation?

   UGA is a stop codon, so a mutation from G to A in the ninth position of the sequence (i.e., to AGUCGUUGACAGGAAGUA) would produce a nonsense mutation.

7. Suppose a gene has the DNA sequence ACGTGTCCAGACTAATTGCAA. Give two examples of point mutations in this sequence that would not affect the protein the sequence codes for.

   Many answers are possible. ACATGTCCAGACTAATTGCAA and ACCTGTCCAGACTAATTGCAA are two possible answers—point mutations in the first codon still code for the amino acid threonine, so the amino acid sequence (and protein produced) are unaffected.

8. You have a pea plant with round seeds. Can you say for sure what pea shape alleles the plant carries? What are the two possibilities? You want to distinguish between these possibilities, so you decide to let the plant self-fertilize. What kind of offspring do you expect in each case?

   The two possibilities are WW and Ww, because round seeds are dominant. If you let a WW plant self-fertilize, you expect all the offspring to be WW and have round seeds. If you let a Ww plant self-fertilize, you expect offspring with round seeds as well as offspring with wrinkled seeds in a 3:1 ratio.

9. A woman carries an allele for red-green colorblindness on one of her X chromosomes. Her husband is not red-green colorblind. Show that her daughters are not at risk for red-green colorblindness, but that her sons are at risk.

   The red-green colorblindness allele is recessive, and the gene is found on the X chromosome. Because the woman's husband is not red-green colorblind, his allele must be normal. All the daughters will inherit this normal allele (because they all inherit an X chromosome from their father), so they will not be red-green colorblind no matter which allele they inherit from their mother. The sons, however, only receive an X chromosome from their mother, so they have a 50/50 chance of being red-green colorblind (because she has one red-green colorblindness allele and one normal allele).

Chapter 17: The Evolution of Life

Answers to Chapter 17 Review Questions

1. Pasteur designed a flask that kept out dust and other airborne particles, filled the flask with sterile meat broth, let the concoction sit, and watched for life to emerge. Pasteur observed that life did not arise from nonlife.

2. Miller and Urey modeled the early Earth by mixing together an "atmosphere" of water vapor, ammonia, methane, and hydrogen, and placing that atmosphere over a "sea" of water. They then shot electric sparks through the mixture to simulate lightning storms. The results were staggering—within a week, complex organic molecules had formed, including amino acids, the building blocks of proteins. Not only had these molecules formed quickly, there were lots of them. Further experiments showed that all the important organic molecules that make up life—amino acids, as well as sugars, lipids, even the nitrogenous bases found in RNA and DNA—can be generated in a similar way.

3. Liposomes have double membranes and behave in ways that are eerily cell-like, growing and shrinking, even budding and dividing. Liposomes also control the absorption of materials and run chemical reactions within their membranes.

4. Even without cells and enzymes, short strands of RNA can spontaneously assemble from individual nucleotides and even reproduce themselves.

5. Earth's early autotrophs included organisms that used sunlight energy to build molecules as well as chemoautotrophs that used energy from a variety of inorganic chemicals.

6. Cyanobacteria release oxygen as a by-product of photosynthesis, and it was their incredible success that first introduced oxygen into Earth's atmosphere.

7. Scientists believe mitochondria and chloroplasts evolved from prokaryotes living inside the earliest eukaryotic cells.

8. No, the nucleus and most eukaryotic organelles probably originated from inward foldings of the cell membrane.

9. According to Lamarck's theory, organisms acquired new characteristics over a lifetime of activity and then passed these characteristics onto their offspring.

10. Lyell, a geologist, argued that the geological features of the earth were created not by major catastrophic events—the favored theory of the time—but by gradual processes that produced their effects over long time periods. A deep canyon, for example, did not require a cataclysmic flood but could be the result of a river's slow erosion of rock over millenia. Darwin realized this could be true for biological organisms as well—the accumulation of gradual changes over long periods could produce all the diversity of living organisms, as well as all their remarkable features.

11. Malthus observed that human populations grow much faster than available food supplies and concluded, with despair, that famine was an inevitable feature of human existence. Darwin applied Malthus's idea to the natural world—because there are not enough resources for all organisms to survive and to reproduce as much as they can, living organisms are involved in an intense "struggle for existence." As a result, organisms with advantageous traits leave more offspring than organisms with other traits, causing populations to change over time. This process, which Darwin called natural selection, is the major driving force behind evolution.

12. The Galápagos finches showed remarkable variation in the size and shape of their beaks, with each beak being suited to, and used for, a different diet.

13. Variation describes the existence of traits that vary from individual to individual within a population.

14. Heritable traits are those that can be passed from parents to offspring.

15. Natural selection occurs when organisms with certain advantageous traits leave more offspring than organisms with other traits, causing populations to change over time.

16. Many of the adaptations organisms evolve through natural selection relate to survival. Other adaptations in organisms have evolved to help them acquire mates. Finally, many adaptations relate to bearing and raising young.

17. A species is a group of organisms whose members can interbreed among themselves but not with members of other species.

18. Prezygotic reproductive barriers prevent members of different species from mating in the first place or keep fertilization from occurring if they do mate. (A *zygote* is a fertilized egg, so *prezygotic* means before fertilization). There are many types of prezygotic barriers—organisms may differ in when they breed, where they breed, or in the details of their courtship rituals. Their sex organs may not fit together properly, preventing successful sperm transfer, or other factors may prevent fertilization even if sperm is transferred. Postzygotic reproductive barriers act after fertilization has taken place. Postzygotic barriers occur when mating produces hybrids that either don't survive or are sterile—unable to breed themselves. The mule, the offspring of a horse and a donkey, is sterile and cannot reproduce. Likewise, a liger, the product of the mating of a lion and a tiger, is sterile.

19. In plants, sympatric speciation is often the result of sudden chromosomal changes. One such chromosomal change is *polyploidy,* which occurs when organisms inherit more than the usual two sets of chromosomes, usually as a result of improper meiosis. Another instance of sympatric speciation through chromosomal change is *hybridization,* which occurs when two species interbreed and produce fertile offspring.

20. The rise of the Isthmus of Panama 3 million years ago divided the Caribbean Sea from the Pacific Ocean, splitting hundreds of types of marine organisms into separate Caribbean and Pacific populations. Most of these subsequently speciated by evolving reproductive barriers.

21. An adaptive radiation is the evolution of a large number of new species, each adapted to a distinct way of life, from a single ancestor. Adaptive radiations are most often seen after a few members of a species colonize a new habitat.

22. Artificial selection is the selective breeding of organisms with desirable traits in order to produce offspring with the same traits. Artificial selection provides evidence for evolution because organismal evolution (change over generations) is visible during the process.

23. If each of these mammals had originated independently, we would expect their limbs to look completely different. Yet, in fact, all mammalian limbs resemble each other and are made up of the same set of bones. This suggests that mammals inherited their limbs from a common ancestor and that these limbs were then modified by evolution for different purposes over time.

24. The fossil record frequently shows species appearing suddenly, not changing much for a long time, and then disappearing.

25. Spurts of rapid change occur during speciation.

26. *Australopithecus* fossils show that an upright posture dates to at least 4 million years ago.

27. *Homo erectus* was the first hominid species to migrate out of Africa and into much of what is now Europe and Asia.

Answers to Chapter 17 Multiple-Choice Questions

1a, 2b, 3b, 4d, 5c, 6c, 7a, 8a, 9d, 10d

Answers to Chapter 17 Integrated Science Concepts

Astronomy: Did Life on Earth Originate on Mars?

1. Because in 1996, NASA scientists found what could be fossils of tiny bacteria in a Martian meteorite. Moreover, the potential fossils were found very close to complex organic molecules and carbonate minerals that, on Earth, are associated with living organisms.

2. Scientists know that the meteorite is from Mars because of its similarity to another undoubtedly Martian meteorite that has gas bubbles that match the composition of the Martian atmosphere.

3. Perhaps, scientists proposed, life found its way to Earth in Martian dust set adrift in space when a comet collided with Mars.

4. Skeptics were quick to point out that the proposed fossils are much smaller than the tiniest bacteria on Earth and that they are likely to be too small to contain all the DNA, proteins, and other molecules a bacterium needs to function.

Physics: Animal Adaptations to Heat and Cold

5. The heat an animal generates is proportional to its volume. The heat an animal dissipates is proportional to its surface area, because heat is lost to the environment through its body surface. Consequently, animals are better able to lose heat if they have a high surface-area-to-volume ratio and better able to retain heat if they have a low surface-area-to-volume ratio.

6. Bergmann's Rule says that animals found in cold habitats are often larger than related forms in warm habitats. This is related to surface-area-to-volume ratio in that larger organisms tend to have smaller surface-area-to-volume ratios. This is because volume increases more quickly than surface area as organisms get bigger. An example of Bergmann's Rule is seen in bears. The smallest bear in the world is the sun bear, found in the tropical forests of Southeast Asia. Adult sun bears weigh between 27 and 65 kilograms (60 to 140 pounds). The largest bear in the world is the polar bear, which ranges throughout the Arctic. Adult polar bears weigh between 200 and 800 kilograms (440 to 1760 pounds).

7. Allen's Rule says that desert species typically have long legs and large ears that increase the surface area available for heat dissipation, whereas Arctic species typically have short appendages and small ears that help conserve heat. Desert and Arctic rabbit species provide an example of Allen's Rule.

8. Insulators conduct heat slowly and help retard heat loss. Insulators in animals include fur, feathers, and blubber.

Earth Science: Earth's Tangible Evidence of Evolution

9. Fossils of now-extinct relatives of the horse show that species grew larger in size over time, as well as more specialized for eating grass and running. Some fossil whales exhibit some of the characteristics of the hoofed animals they evolved from—hind limbs, nostrils on their noses rather than blowholes, and different types of teeth. *Archaeopteryx,* the famous 150-million-year-old fossil bird, has many birdlike features—feathers, wings, a wishbone—but also has dinosaur-like features absent in modern birds, including claws on its wings, bones in its tail, and teeth.

10. Biogeography, the study of how species are distributed on Earth, is consistent with evolution rather than with the idea that organisms were purposefully distributed around the planet. For example, the argument that each organism was specially designed to fit into its habitat is undermined by the observation that similar habitats are often home to completely different species. New World tropical forests and Old World tropical forests are occupied by entirely different life-forms, as are the similar environments of the Arctic and Antarctic. In addition, closely related species tend to be found close together. All of Darwin's finches are found in or near the Galápagos, and all the honeycreepers in Hawaii. Most of the world's marsupials (pouched mammals, such as koalas and kangaroos) are found in Australia. Island species are most closely related to species found on the closest mainland. This pattern holds for fossils as well—fossil armadillos are found only in the New World, where modern armadillos also occur, and fossil apes are found only in Asia and Africa, where modern apes reside. Islands tend to be occupied by many flying animals, but few or no terrestrial ones. All these biogeographical patterns suggest that organisms were not dispersed purposefully, but instead evolved in a certain place and then spread and left descendants where they could.

Answers to Chapter 17 Exercises

1. What types of experiments were necessary to show that living organisms were not spontaneously generated in nonliving matter? Why do you think the idea of spontaneous generation survived so long—why was it so difficult to disprove?

   The types of environments where living organisms were thought to spontaneously appear—rotting carcasses or meat broths—had to be isolated from living organisms so that they would not be contaminated by life that already existed. This isolation proved difficult to achieve, and contamination often did occur.

2. Why didn't Miller and Urey include oxygen in their model of the young Earth?

   There was no oxygen in the atmosphere of the young Earth. Oxygen did not enter the atmosphere until the rise of the cyanobacteria much later in Earth history.

3. How are liposomes similar to cells? How are they different from real cells?

Liposomes have double membranes and behave in ways that are eerily cell-like, growing and shrinking, even budding and dividing. Liposomes also control the absorption of materials and run chemical reactions within their membranes, like cells. However, they do not have genetic material like real cells.

4. How do scientists know that the first living organisms used anaerobic processes to obtain energy? Do any aerobic organisms predate cyanobacteria? Why or why not?

   The first living organisms used anaerobic processes to obtain energy because there was no oxygen in Earth's early atmosphere. Oxygen did not enter the atmosphere until the rise of the cyanobacteria much later in Earth history, so the first aerobic organisms would have appeared after that.

5. How might Lamarck have explained the streamlined shape of fish, which makes them effective swimmers? How would Darwin's theory of evolution by natural selection explain the same phenomenon?

   Lamarck would say that over a lifetime of swimming, the shapes of fish became more streamlined as they fought their way through the water. They then pass this more streamlined shape to their offspring. Darwin would say that fish vary in their body shape, and that more streamlined individuals were more effective swimmers, so survived and reproduced better, leaving more streamlined individuals in the population.

6. How is the story of myxoma virus and Australian rabbits similar to the story of antibiotic resistance in bacteria?

   In both cases, the administration of a lethal agent (antibiotics or myxoma virus) led to natural selection for resistant individuals in the population. These resistant individuals survived and reproduced. As a result, over time, populations evolved resistance to the lethal agent.

7. What are some human traits that do not show variation? What are some that do show variation?

   Answers will vary. Traits that don't show variation include having a four-chambered heart, five fingers on each hand, two arms, two legs, one nose, and so forth. Traits that show variation include height, weight, arm length, foot length, eye color, hair color, and so forth.

8. What are some heritable human traits? Some nonheritable human traits?

   Answers will vary. Heritable traits include having a four-chambered heart, five fingers on each hand, two arms, two legs, one nose, as well as height, weight, arm length, foot length, eye color, hair color, and so forth. Nonheritable traits include hairstyle, hair length, clothing, any scars, tattoos, pierced ears, language spoken, and so forth.

9. Nancy Burley of the University of California, Irvine, ran the following experiment—she placed red color bands on the feet of some male birds and green color bands on the feet of other male birds. Females preferred to mate with birds that had red color bands. Could this lead to natural selection? Why or why not?

   No, color band color is not a heritable trait.

10. How would you determine whether a trait you were interested in studying is heritable?

    One possibility would be to compare the traits of parents and offspring and see if offspring tend to resemble their parents more than they resemble nonparents. This experiment would have to be conducted in a controlled environment so that similarities between parents and offspring can be attributed to genetic rather than environmental factors.

11. You are studying a population of beetles that include some red individuals and some yellow individuals. You know that color is a heritable trait in the population. By counting the number of red and yellow beetles over a period of 5 years, you notice that the population is evolving toward more red individuals. How could you determine whether this is a result of natural selection? Are there other potential explanations?

    Alternative explanations are genetic drift, migration into or out of the population, and mutation pressure. To determine whether natural selection is responsible for the shift, you could compare the fitness (number of offspring left) of red individuals vs. yellow individuals. If this turned out to be difficult, you could also compare their survival or ability to acquire mates in an attempt to identify underlying causes of potential fitness differences.

12. On islands, many large animals, such as elephants, evolve to become miniaturized in size. On the other hand, many small animals, including some rodents, evolve to be exceptionally large in size. Why might natural selection produce these results? Do you think this phenomenon sheds light on *Homo floresiensis,* the miniature human relative?

The hypothesis is that large animals become miniaturized because of limited food resources on relatively small islands, and that small animals evolve to larger size because of the absence of predators. *Homo floresiensis,* the miniature human relative, was indeed found on a small island, so this could explain its small size.

13. In recent decades, average human height has increased in many parts of the world. Do you think this is an example of evolution?

It could be, but it could also be the result of better nutrition.

14. In a population of mice that you are studying, tail length appears to be increasing over time. However, you find no evidence that natural selection is acting on tail length. What are two alternate explanations for your observation?

Genetic drift could be affecting tail length, or perhaps migration from a population of longer-tailed individuals.

15. Two species of foxes are shown below. One is a kit fox in the Mojave Desert, California. The other is an Arctic fox in Manitoba, Canada. Which is which? How can you tell? Describe at least two traits that make each animal well-adapted to thermoregulating in its habitat.

The kit fox is the one with pale brownish fur, large ears, and long limbs. The fur color helps it reflect heat and stay camouflaged in its environment. The large ears and long limbs help it increase surface area available for heat dissipation. The Arctic fox has white fur, which helps it stay camouflaged, and small ears and short limbs that help it decrease the surface area from which heat is lost.

16. Individuals of two different fish species sometimes mate, but the offspring die soon after hatching. Is this a prezygotic or postzygotic reproductive barrier?

Postzygotic, because it occurs after fertilization.

17. Finches on two nearby islands look noticeably different from one another—individuals on one island have brown tail feathers, whereas individuals on the other island have black tail feathers. Can you conclude that they are two different species? What would you do to determine if they are, in fact, distinct species?

No, you cannot conclude they are distinct species merely because they are distinguishable. You can determine whether they are distinct species by figuring out whether they interbreed.

18. At your field site, there are butterflies with yellow wings and butterflies with orange wings. After observing them carefully, you conclude that the yellow butterflies always mate in shady areas under trees, whereas the orange butterflies always mate in sunny meadows. Can you conclude that they are different species?

Probably—your observations suggest that there is a prezygotic reproductive barrier.

19. Many of the living organisms on Hawaii are found nowhere else on earth. This includes species of plants, birds, insects, mammals, mushrooms, and so forth. Why do you think this is?

Hawaii is extremely isolated from all mainlands, so organisms that arrived there then had plenty of time to evolve in isolation and speciate from mainland species.

20. What are some examples of artificial selection? How are artificial selection and natural selection similar? How are they different?

We saw artificial selection in the breeding of dogs as well as in the breeding of corn from teosinte. Artificial selection and natural selection are similar in that both are driven by differences in reproductive success (this is imposed by human beings in the case of artificial selection, and by the environment in the case of natural selection). Artificial selection and natural selection are different in that humans can impose whatever conditions they like on artificial selection, and perhaps produce forms that wouldn't do very well in the wild. Humans can also make artificial selection much more stringent than natural

selection is, insofar as they can choose two specific racehorses and only breed those—as a result, evolution by artificial selection can occur surprisingly quickly compared to evolution by natural selection.

21. Islands tend to have fewer species than the mainlands they resemble. Furthermore, island species often include many flying organisms, and few terrestrial ones. Do these biogeographical patterns support evolution or the purposeful distribution of organisms? Why?

Both these biogeographical patterns suggest that organisms dispersed where they could, not that they were purposefully distributed across the globe.

22. Write a letter to Grandma telling her about drug resistance in living organisms. Explain to her why drug resistance is such a common phenomenon—including why insects become more resistant to pesticides over time, and why diseases such as tuberculosis and malaria have become harder to treat in recent years.

Dear Grandma—Drug resistance is an inevitable result of natural selection. During drug application, those organisms that are more resistant to the drug survive and reproduce better, passing on resistance genes to descendants. This has made insects resistant to commonly used pesticides over time and has also made pathogens resistant to medical drugs designed to eradicate them. Drug-resistant strains of tuberculosis and malaria in particular have appeared in recent years, worrying many public health officials.

Answers to Chapter 17 Problems

1. Let's look at how natural selection causes advantageous traits to become more common in populations. Suppose there is a population of bugs in which some individuals are green and some individuals are brown. Suppose that, because brown bugs are better camouflaged against predators, each brown bug leaves two brown offspring per generation, and each green bug leaves one green offspring per generation. (Is this natural selection? Why?) You start with two brown bugs and two green bugs in Generation 1. How many brown and green bugs are there in Generation 2? Calculate the number of brown and green bugs there are in Generations 1 to 10. Now what fraction of bugs is brown in Generation 1? Generation 2? Generation 5? Generation 10? What is happening here?

Yes, this is natural selection, because color is a variable, heritable trait, and brown and green individuals have different fitness. What is happening here is that, over time, the population is shifting toward a greater and greater proportion of brown individuals.

Generation	Brown	Green	Proportion Brown
1	2	2	0.50
2	4	2	0.67
3	8	2	0.80
4	16	2	0.89
5	32	2	0.94
6	64	2	0.97
7	128	2	0.98
8	256	2	0.992
9	512	2	0.996
10	1024	2	0.998

2. Suppose that, in the population above, migration is operating in addition to natural selection. Suppose that three green bugs migrate into the population each generation. Again, calculate the number of brown and green bugs in Generations 1 to 10, and the fraction of brown bugs in each generation. How does this compare to the results you obtained with natural selection alone? What effect does migration have on how quickly this population is adapting to its environment?

In the first 10 generations,

Generation	Brown	Green	Proportion Brown
1	2	2	0.50
2	4	5	0.44
3	8	8	0.50
4	16	11	0.59
5	32	14	0.70
6	64	17	0.79
7	128	20	0.86
8	256	23	0.92
9	512	26	0.95
10	1024	29	0.97

Because green individuals are continually migrating into the population, this population adapts more slowly to its environment.

3. Let's consider a very small population of snapdragons, one with only two individuals. One snapdragon has two red alleles for flower color—that is, it is RR. The other snapdragon has a red allele and a white allele for flower color—it is RW. (You may wish to read about the inheritance of flower color in snapdragons in Chapter 16.) Show that the frequency of the red allele R in the population is 0.75 and that the frequency of the white allele W is 0.25.

Because there is a RR organism and a RW organism, the frequency of the R allele in the population is 3/4 = 0.75. The frequency of the W allele is 1/4 = 0.25.

4. Now let's assume the two snapdragons in our tiny population mate and produce a single offspring. We now have a snapdragon population with only one individual. What are the two possibilities for the genotype of this individual? For each of the two possibilities, calculate the allele frequencies of the red and white alleles in the population. Show that, in either case, the allele frequencies are different from those found in the parental population (calculated in Problem 3). Is this an example of genetic drift?

The offspring of an RR and an RW snapdragon can have a genotype of either RR or RW. If the offspring is RR, then the frequency of the R allele is 1, and the frequency of the W allele is 0. If the offspring is RW, then the frequency of the R allele is 0.5, and the frequency of the W allele is 0.5. In either case, the frequencies are different from the parental generation, calculated in Problem 3 of the last page. Yes, this is an example of genetic drift.

Chapter 18: Biological Diversity

Answers to Chapter 18 Review Questions

1. In the Linnaean system, species are grouped together based on shared similarities.

2. A *clade* is a group that includes an ancestral species and all of its descendants.

3. Birds are descended from the last common ancestor of the reptiles, and so are reptiles.

4. Life is classified into three domains—Bacteria, Archaea, and Eukarya. Eukarya includes all eukaryotic organisms, organisms with nucleated cells.

5. Bacteria typically reproduce asexually by dividing. Most species exchange genetic material at least occasionally, when they take up small pieces of naked DNA from the environment, when bacterial viruses inadvertently transfer DNA between organisms, or when two bacteria join together and one passes DNA to the other.

6. In poor conditions, many bacteria form hardy spores that remain dormant until conditions improve.

7. Without bacterial decomposition, carbon (C) would remain trapped in dead organic matter and there eventually would be none available for photosynthesis.

8. Some archaea are adapted to extreme environments, such as very salty ponds or the scalding waters of hot springs and hydrothermal vents. These archaea are called "extremophiles"—lovers of the extreme.

9. Chemoautotrophs make food using chemical energy rather than energy from sunlight.

10. Protists are eukaryotes that are not plants, animals, or fungi.

11. *Amoebas* move by extending part of their body forward as a pseudopodium, a temporary protrusion of the cell, and then pulling the rest of the body behind. Amoebas surround and engulf prey. *Ciliates* move by beating numerous hair-like projections called cilia. *Flagellates* move by whipping long flagella.

12. The plant vascular system consists of the xylem and the phloem. The *xylem* is made up of dead tube-shaped cells through which water and nutrients move up from the roots. The *phloem* consists of living cells that pass the sugars produced during photosynthesis down from the leaves.

13. Mosses are unique among plants in that the gametophyte is much larger than the sporophyte.

14. In conifers, pollen released by male cones is carried by wind to female cones. In flowering plants, pollen is often transported from one flower to another by insects or other animals.

15. Fruits help spread seeds around—when fruits are eaten by birds or mammals, for example, the seeds pass unharmed through the digestive tract and eventually emerge far from the parent plants. Some fruits help plants spread their seeds using other strategies—the burrs that catch on your socks during a hike are also fruits.

16. They obtain food by secreting digestive enzymes over organic matter and then absorbing the nutrients.

17. Fungal spores are tiny reproductive bodies that can exist in a dormant state until conditions become favorable for growth.

18. In most plant species, roots and fungi form close associations known as mycorrhizae. The fungus receives nutrients from the plant while helping roots absorb water and minerals from soil.

19. Animals *ingest* food, taking it into their bodies for digestion. Fungi, those other multicellular heterotrophs, secrete digestive enzymes *out over* their food.

20. Cnidarians have a single opening that serves as both mouth and anus. Flatworms also have a single body opening that serves as both mouth and anus.

21. All arthropods have an external *exoskeleton* made of chitin that protects and supports the body. The exoskeleton is incapable of growth and must be shed periodically as animals grow. Arthropods also have segmented bodies and jointed legs.

22. Legs.

23. *Bivalves* have two hinged shells and include species such as clams, oysters, mussels, and scallops. Most bivalves are sedentary and feed by filtering small particles from the water. *Cephalopods* such as squids and octopuses are active predators that use arms (eight in octopuses and ten in squids) to capture prey. Cephalopods also have well-developed brains and eyes. *Gastropods* have a single, spiral shell and include species such as snails, abalone, and limpets. Most gastropods are herbivores.

24. *Annelids* are segmented worms. The muscles of annelids are arranged in both circular (around the body) and longitudinal (head-to-tail) orientations, allowing for great flexibility of motion.

25. Amphibians are restricted to moist environments because their skins are composed of living cells that are vulnerable to drying out. Amphibian eggs, which have no shells, also require moisture.

26. Ectotherms regulate their body temperature behaviorally, by seeking sun when they need to warm up and shade when they need to cool down. Endotherms maintain a constant and relatively high body temperature by metabolizing large amounts of food. During metabolism, when organic molecules are broken down to make ATP, energy is lost to the environment as heat—this energy helps warm the body. Birds and mammals are endotherms.

27. Monotremes such as the platypus and spiny echidna differ from other mammals in that they lay eggs.

28. Viruses are small pieces of genetic material wrapped in a protein coat.

29. Viruses reproduce by infecting a host cell and then using the cell's enzymes and ribosomes to copy their genetic material and build viral proteins. These are then assembled to form new viruses.

30. Most scientists believe viruses originated when little pieces of host DNA or RNA evolved the ability to move from one cell to another.

31. Prions are misfolded proteins believed to cause mad cow disease and the related Creutzfeldt-Jakob disease in humans. Both of these conditions are characterized by fatal brain degeneration. Prions infect cells, where they "reproduce" by converting normal proteins to the misfolded, prion variety.

Answers to Chapter 18 Multiple-Choice Questions

1a, 2c, 3c, 4b, 5a, 6d, 7c, 8a, 9a, 10c

Answers to Chapter 18 Integrated Science Concepts

Earth Science: Coral Bleaching

1. Increases in seawater temperature that last for an extended period of time.

2. When corals evict their dinoflagellates during a bleaching event, the corals quite literally turn white, because it is the dinoflagellates that give them their colors.

3. Because of continued global warming due to human greenhouse gas emissions.

Physics: How Birds Fly

4. The wings of birds are airfoils. The curved shape of the wing causes air to flow faster over the top of the wing than under the wing. This is because, as a bird cuts through the air, air molecules have a greater distance to travel over the wing and so must move faster. Bernoulli's Principle shows that when the speed of air over a surface increases, its pressure decreases. The result of greater air speed over the wing than under it is that air pressure above the wing is lower than air pressure below the wing. This produces lift, an upward force that counters gravity and keeps birds aloft.

5. Birds move forward through the air by flapping their wings. During the downstroke, the wings push against the air and the air pushes back. This propels them forward.

6. Some birds manage to fly for long periods without flapping their wings—this is called soaring. You often see eagles and vultures soar. Soaring is possible because the birds have located a thermal, a pocket of rising hot air, and are floating on it. It's sort of like sitting on top of a geyser but (luckily for the birds) considerably more controlled.

Answers to Chapter 18 Exercises

1. Of the three domains of life, Bacteria and Archaea both consist of prokaryotes, whereas Eukarya consists of eukaryotes. Why can't we lump Bacteria and Archaea together and call them all Bacteria?

   Because archaea are more closely related to eukaryotes than either is to bacteria, classifying archaea and bacteria together to the exclusion of eukaryotes obscures the evolutionary history of the three groups. It is like the example in the text of grouping humans and daisies together to the exclusion of elephants. In terms of a cladistic classification, the fact that archaea and bacteria are both prokaryotes is not relevant—only the evolutionary relationships among the three groups matters in constructing biological groups.

2. What is the difference between a heterotroph and an autotroph? Name two groups of living organisms that include both heterotrophs and autotrophs.

   Heterotrophs obtain energy and organic molecules from outside sources, whereas autotrophs make their own. Bacteria and protists both include heterotrophs and autotrophs.

3. What is the advantage of being able to produce spores, as many bacteria and fungi do?

   Spores are very hardy, able to survive for long periods under tough conditions. This allows bacteria, fungi, and other organisms capable of generating spores to produce descendants that can survive tough periods and then germinate when conditions improve.

4. Why is decomposition important? What are some important groups of decomposers?

   Decomposition frees up resources that would otherwise be locked in the corpses of dead organisms. Important decomposers include fungi and bacteria, among other groups.

5. We saw that life on Earth would be impossible without bacteria. Would life on Earth be impossible without eukaryotes?

   No, life would do just fine without eukaryotes, as it did for billions of years before the first eukaryotes evolved.

6. Do all autotrophs use photosynthesis to make food? If not, what do they do?

   Some autotrophs are chemoautotrophs that use chemical energy rather than energy from sunlight to make food.

7. Of the three major plant groups we discussed, which is most dependent on living in a moist habitat? Why? Which is least dependent?

   Mosses are most dependent on living in a moist environment. This is because they have no vascular systems, instead, every part of a moss plant receives water directly from the environment. In addition, mosses have swimming sperm that require moisture in the environment in order to travel to and fertilize moss eggs. Seed plants are least dependent on living in a moist environment, because they use pollen rather than swimming sperm during sexual reproduction, and they have vascular systems. (Ferns, the third group, have vascular systems but also use swimming sperm, so are more moisture dependent than seed plants.)

8. You may have heard that moss most often grows on the north sides of trees—a potentially useful fact if you are ever lost in a forest! Why do mosses do best on the north sides?

   The north sides of trees are least sunny and most shaded, so are most likely to provide the moist environments mosses need to thrive.

9. Which plants produce pollen? What are some strategies plants use for pollination? What strategy do most flowering plants employ?

   Seed plants produce pollen. Pollen is carried to the female flower/cone by wind or by animals. Most flowering plants use animal pollinators, particularly insects.

10. Some plants have green flowers. An artichoke, for example, is a green flower. How do you think green flowers are pollinated?

    Green flowers are not particularly visible, so likely are not attracting vision-oriented pollinators. In fact, many are wind pollinated.

11. Some people are allergic to pollen. Do you think bee-pollinated plants or wind-pollinated plants are more likely to cause allergies? Why?

    Wind-pollinated plants are most likely to cause allergies because they make larger quantities of pollen due to the haphazard nature of wind pollination.

12. What do fungi and animals have in common? How do they differ?

    Fungi and animals are both heterotrophs. However, fungi tend to release digestive enzymes out over their food and absorb the nutrients, whereas animals tend to ingest their food, taking it into their bodies for digestion.

13. What are two different strategies used by different species of cnidarians to obtain food?

   Many cnidarians, including jellyfish and sea anemones, catch prey using tentacles armed with barbed stinging cells. Corals, however, house dinoflagellates in their bodies and obtain the bulk of their nutrients from these photosynthesizers.

14. Although roundworms and arthropods are different in many ways, they are related groups. Name an important feature they have in common.

   They have a tough outer cuticle that is shed during growth. In arthropods, this is the exoskeleton.

15. How do the muscles of roundworms and earthworms differ? What does this mean about the way each type of worm moves?

   The muscles of roundworms all run longitudinally (from head to tail) down the body. As a result, roundworms move like flailing whips as muscles on alternate sides of the body contract. The muscles of annelids are arranged in both circular (around the body) and longitudinal (head-to-tail) orientations, allowing for great flexibility of motion. Unlike roundworms, for example, annelids are able to contract one part of the body while keeping the rest of the body still.

16. What features do insects and crustaceans share? How are they different?

   Crustaceans and insects are arthropods, and so share arthropod features. For example, all arthropods have an external exoskeleton that protects and supports the body. The exoskeleton is incapable of growth and must be shed periodically as animals grow. Arthropods also have segmented bodies and jointed legs, as well as a brain and a number of highly developed sense organs. Crustaceans and insects differ in that crustaceans are primarily marine, whereas insects are primarily terrestrial, and most insects have wings. (Other answers are possible.)

17. Why are amphibians more dependent on living in a moist habitat than amniotes?

   Amphibians have a skin made of living cells that is vulnerable to drying out. In addition, their eggs are unshelled and also vulnerable to drying out.

18. Many snakes can survive eating just once every few weeks. Why can't birds do this?

   Birds are endotherms and need a lot of food to help maintain their high, stable body temperatures. Snakes are also unusual in that they have adaptations for eating very large prey—this is part of the reason why they don't need to eat as frequently.

19. Birds and mammals are endotherms, and they both have four-chambered hearts. Why are birds classified as reptiles rather than as mammals?

   Because birds are descended from the last common ancestor of all reptiles. What they do or do not have in common with mammals is not a factor in how they are classified.

20. What are some organisms that reproduce asexually? What are some advantages of asexual reproduction?

   Most bacteria and archaea and many protists reproduce asexually. Fungi often reproduce asexually also. Asexual reproduction is less common in plants and animals but occurs sporadically in diverse groups. Asexual reproduction has the advantage that you needn't search for a mate—you can reproduce all on your own. From an evolutionary point of view, an organism that reproduces asexually passes all its genes to offspring, whereas one that reproduces sexually only contributes half the genetic material of the offspring.

21. Most living organisms reproduce sexually sometimes, or have some other mechanism for exchanging genetic material. What is the advantage of sexual reproduction or genetic exchange?

   The advantage of genetic exchange is genetic diversity among the offspring. This way, you don't put all your eggs in one (genetic) basket, and at least some of your offspring are likely to do well under a wide array of potential environmental conditions.

22. Scientists have never been sure whether to classify viruses as living things or nonliving things. In what ways do viruses resemble living things? In what ways do they resemble nonliving things?

   Viruses resemble living things in that they reproduce, possess genes, and evolve. However, they can reproduce only within a host cell. They also are not made up of cells.

23. Write a letter to Grandpa telling him about the current scare over bird flu. Be sure to explain to him what viruses are and why they sometimes mutate so quickly.

Viruses are small pieces of genetic material wrapped in a protein coat. Many viruses have normal, double-stranded DNA genomes, but others use single-stranded DNA, single-stranded RNA, or double-stranded RNA. Viruses reproduce by infecting a host cell and then using the cell's enzymes and ribosomes to copy their genetic material and build viral proteins. These are then assembled to form new viruses. One feature of viruses that makes them hard to deal with from the point of view of disease control is that they mutate very quickly. This is particularly true of viruses with RNA genomes, because there is no error-checking and repair system for copying RNA, as there is with DNA. Bird flu, which has devastated populations of domesticated birds, is caused by a virus that occurs naturally among wild birds. In 1997, the first case of a human infected by bird flu was reported in Hong Kong, and dozens of additional cases have been seen since then. So far, however, the virus cannot be transmitted easily from person to person. The evolution of this capability is the event scientists await with trepidation. This fear turns out to be more than justified. Scientists recently discovered that the infamous "Spanish flu" epidemic of 1918—which killed more people than any other disease over a similar length of time—was a bird flu that became easily transmissible among humans.

Answers to Chapter 18 Problems

1. Suppose a species of bacteria divides once every 20 minutes. You start with a single bacterium on your unrefrigerated egg-and-baloney sandwich at 8:00 a.m. Show that when you sit down to lunch at noon, there will be 4096 bacteria on your sandwich.

The population doubles every 20 minutes, or so.

8:00	1
8:20	2
8:40	4
9:00	8
9:20	16
9:40	32
10:00	64
10:20	128
10:40	256
11:00	512
11:20	1024
11:40	2048
12:00	4096

2. The lightest and heaviest flying birds are the bee hummingbird of Cuba, which weighs about 1.6 grams, and the great bustard of Europe and Asia, which can weigh as much as 21 kilograms. How much lift does each bird have to produce to stay aloft? Which species would you expect to have proportionally larger wings? Why?

Each bird has to produce enough lift to counter gravity.

For the bee hummingbird,

$$F = mg = (0.0016)(9.8) = 0.01568 \text{ Newtons}$$

For the great bustard,

$$F = mg = (21)(9.8) = 205.8 \text{ Newtons}$$

The great bustard has proportionally larger wings, because it is larger. Larger birds need disproportionately larger wings in order to produce enough lift. This is because all else being equal, volume increases more quickly than surface area, so larger birds have a harder time staying aloft. In order to help compensate for their greater size, larger birds have larger wings.

3. Draw a diagram showing how the following organisms are related; broad beech fern, cherry tree, shitake mushroom, hammerhead shark, red-eyed treefrog, sidewinder, albatross, duck-billed platypus, Albert Einstein.

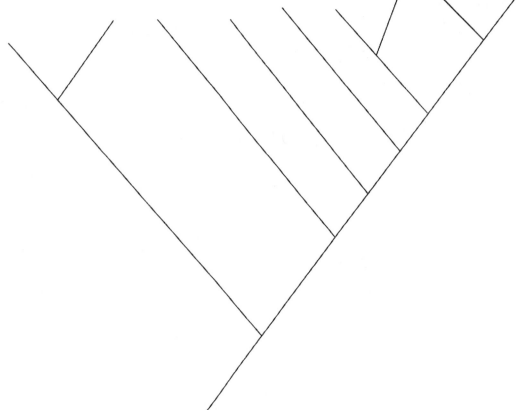

Chapter 19: Human Biology I—Control and Development

Answers to Chapter 19 Review Questions

1. Tissue.

2. Organs, organ system.

3. Homeostasis is the maintenance of a stable internal environment.

4. Oxygen supply and body temperature are only two of the many variables the body carefully maintains. The amount of water in the body, the concentration of nutrients such as glucose and waste products in the blood, the concentrations of important ions inside and outside cells, and blood pH—all these are carefully controlled as part of maintaining homeostasis.

5. The brain stem controls many of the body's involuntary activities, including heartbeat, respiration, and digestion. It is also the brain stem that wakes you up every morning, bringing your body from sleep to a state of conscious wakefulness.

6. The cerebellum, located in the posterior portion of the head, controls balance, posture, coordination, and fine motor movements.

7. The right hemisphere (right side) of the cerebrum receives information from and controls the left side of the body and vice versa, which is why damage to one side of the brain (such as from a tumor or stroke) affects functioning on the opposite side of the body.

8. The *frontal lobes* deal with reasoning, control of voluntary movements, and speech. The *parietal lobes* hold sensory areas for temperature, touch, taste, and pain. The *occipital lobes* process visual information. The *temporal lobes* interpret sound and play an essential role in comprehending language.

9. The nervous system has two parts—the central nervous system, which includes the brain and spinal cord, and the peripheral nervous system, which includes all the other nerves in the body.

10. A typical neuron consists of extensions called dendrites, which function to receive information from other neurons or cells; a cell body, which contains the nucleus and organelles; and an axon, a cell extension that transmits information to other neurons or cells.

11. The neurons of the nervous system are divided into three categories depending on the origin and destination of their messages—sensory neurons, interneurons, and motor neurons.

12. Motor neurons are divided into two groups, the *somatic nervous system*, which controls voluntary actions and stimulates our voluntary muscles, and the *autonomic nervous system*, which controls involuntary actions and stimulates involuntary muscles and other internal organs.

13. First, like other cells, neurons have more potassium ions inside the cell than outside and more sodium ions outside the cell than inside. Second, neurons contain many other negatively charged ions, including proteins and other organic molecules. As a result of these two factors, the inside of a neuron is normally negatively charged, and the outside of a neuron is normally positively charged, creating a resting potential of about -70 millivolts (mV) across the cell membrane.

14. If a neuron's membrane potential reaches a certain *threshold value*—typically around -55 mV—sodium channels in the neuron's cell membrane suddenly open, allowing positively charged sodium ions to flow into the neuron. This influx of positively charged ions causes the membrane potential to spike and become positive.

15. If a neuron's membrane potential reaches *threshold*, sodium channels in the neuron's cell membrane suddenly open, allowing the action potential to begin.

16. A neuron either fires or it doesn't. So, a neuron can't fire "harder" when a stimulus is more intense.

17. When an action potential begins at the cell body end of the axon, sodium ions enter the axon there. These ions then diffuse into adjacent areas where, because of their positive charge, they cause the local membrane potential to increase. When this local membrane potential hits threshold, a new action potential, further along the axon, begins. In this way, the action potential travels down the entire axon.

18. In electrical synapses, ions flow directly from a neuron to a target cell through gap junctions, tiny channels in the cell membrane, and cause an action potential to happen in the target cell. In a chemical synapse, there is a narrow space between the neuron and its target cell. When the action potential arrives at the end of the axon, the neuron releases chemical messengers called neurotransmitters into this space. The neurotransmitters are released through exocytosis; that is, small vesicles containing the neurotransmitters fuse to the neuron's cell membrane and release their contents outside the cell. The neurotransmitters then diffuse across the space between the neuron and its target cell and bind to receptor proteins on the cell membrane of the target cell. The binding of neurotransmitters causes the receptor proteins to change, opening ion channels and allowing ions to flow into the target cell.

19. Light enters the eyes through a tough, transparent layer called the *cornea*, which is continuous with the whites of the eyes. It then passes through a small hole, the *pupil*. The *iris*, the part of the eye that gives us our eye color, controls the size of the pupil. In bright light, the pupil is small. In dim light, the pupil expands to let in more light. From the pupil, light passes through the *lens*, which focuses it on the *retina* at the back of the eyeball.

20. The two types of light-sensitive cells in the eyes are rods and cones. *Rods* are very sensitive to light and are responsible for vision in dim light. Rods cannot discriminate colors, and so allow us to see only black, white, and shades of gray. *Cones* detect color. Our eyes have three types of cones that respond most strongly to red, green, and blue light, respectively.

21. Sound waves move through the air to the outer ear, or *pinna*, which funnels them in. Inside the ear, the waves hit a thin membrane of skin—the *eardrum*—and cause it to vibrate, just the way blowing on a piece of paper causes it to shake. The eardrum's vibrations move three middle ear bones—the hammer, the anvil, and the stirrup—in sequence. These bones amplify the vibrations, making them more pronounced. The final bone, the stirrup, then transfers the vibrations on to the fluid-filled inner ear, where they enter the cochlea. The cochlea is a coiled tube that contains the *organ of Corti*, which holds the sensory cells responsible for hearing. Fluid vibrations in the inner ear move the organ of Corti's basilar membrane, causing sensory "hairs" embedded in it to bend against an overlying membrane. This bending opens ion channels, starting action potentials that are transmitted to the brain.

22. Chemicals bind to receptors on the surface of special chemosensory cells. The binding causes ion channels to open and action potentials to happen.

23. Pain receptors respond to stimuli that cause damage to the body. These sensory cells generally require strong stimulation before they will respond. However, damaged tissues release chemicals called *prostaglandins* that increase the sensitivity of pain receptors.

24. The two types of hormones are protein hormones and steroid hormones. Protein hormones bind to receptors on the cell membrane of their target cells. This binding initiates a series of chemical reactions that ends with the cell's response to the hormone. Steroid hormones cross the cell membrane and bind to receptors in either the cytoplasm or nucleus of target cells. The hormone and receptor then bind to DNA in the nucleus and directly impact gene transcription.

25. The anterior pituitary is sometimes called the "master gland" because many of its hormones control the function of other endocrine organs.

26. The adrenal glands, located above the kidneys, secrete *epinephrine* (adrenaline) and *norepinephrine*. These hormones are involved in the "fight or flight" response.

27. *Antidiuretic hormone* helps regulate the amount of water in the body—it helps the body conserve water by producing a more concentrated urine.

28. Eggs are the result of *unequal meiosis*—during cell division, the future egg gets almost all the cytoplasm, while the other cells (which quickly degenerate) receive almost nothing. This maximizes the resources contained in the egg.

29. Enzymes released from the head of the sperm eat away at the *zona pellucida*.

30. The placenta provides oxygen and nutrients to the developing embryo, and carries away wastes.

31. All the fetus's major organs and body parts develop during the first trimester.

32. One function of the skeleton is to protect the body. The skull surrounds and protects the brain, the vertebrae protect the spinal cord, and the ribs protect the heart and lungs. The skeleton also supports the body and, in cooperation with the muscles, moves it.

33. Motor neurons connect to muscles through a chemical synapse that uses the neurotransmitter *acetylcholine*. When acetylcholine binds to receptors on muscle cells, it starts an action potential in the cells, which respond by contracting.

34. When an action potential arrives at a muscle cell, calcium ions are released from the cell's endoplasmic reticulum. Calcium ions allow a series of pivoting heads on the myosin fibers to attach to actin. The myosin heads attach and pivot, pulling on the actin. Each pull shortens the length of the sarcomere a tiny bit and, consequently, the length of the muscle as a whole. After pulling, the myosin heads release, re-cock, re-attach, and pull again. This cycle repeats until the signal to contract ends or until the muscle has fully contracted.

35. ATP is required for the myosin heads to release actin, an essential step in the contraction cycle.

Answers to Chapter 19 Multiple-Choice Questions

1b, 2c, 3a, 4c, 5d, 6a, 7d, 8d, 9c, 10b

Answers to Chapter 19 Integrated Science Concepts

Physics: How Fast Can Action Potentials Travel?

1. An action potential's speed depends in part on how quickly successive parts of the axon's cell membrane (that is, parts further down the axon) can be induced to increase to threshold. How quickly the membrane reaches threshold is, in turn, dependent on how fast sodium ions flow downstream to increase the membrane potential there. And how fast sodium ions flow down an axon depends on Ohm's Law. Ohm's Law tells us that current = voltage/resistance, so the lower the resistance, the more current (that is, ions) flows and the faster the action potential travels. Like any other material, an axon has lower resistance if it is thicker around—a thick axon resists current less than a thin axon the same way a wide pipe resists water flow less than a thin pipe.

2. They take up too much space.

3. The myelin sheath that surrounds an axon insulates it so that ions cannot escape out the cell membrane but must flow down the axon. The end result is the same as for a giant axon—sodium ions are able to travel more efficiently down the axon. Moreover, in myelinated axons, the action potential is not regenerated at every point along the axon; instead, it "jumps" from one gap in the sheath to the next. An action potential at one gap causes sodium ions to move into the axon, flow down to the next gap, generate a new action potential there, and so on. This jumping propagation makes for extremely rapid signal transmission.

Chemistry: Endorphins

4. Endorphins are proteins made by the brain in times of stress or pain. Endorphins are neurotransmitters that bind to opiate receptors on neurons—the same receptors targeted by drugs such as morphine, codeine, opium, and heroin.

5. Because they bind to the same receptors (opiate receptors).

6. Besides sports, endorphin release has also been associated with activities such as laughter, orgasm, acupuncture, massage, and deep meditation. Certain foods—notably chocolate and chili peppers—also increase the release of endorphins.

Answers to Chapter 19 Exercises

1. You have a conversation with a friend on the telephone. What parts of the brain are you using?

   The temporal lobes interpret sound, including language comprehension. The frontal lobes control the voluntary movements required to produce speech.

2. The following figure shows a map of the primary motor control area of the brain, found in the frontal lobes of the cerebrum. Why do think controlling the actions of body parts such as the hands and the lips requires such large portions of the brain? Why does controlling the back require only a small portion?

   The hands and lips are engaged in extremely fine movements when we manipulate objects and produce the sounds of speech, respectively. The back isn't required to perform fine movements.

3. Of the three types of neurons, sensory neurons, motor neurons, and interneurons, which type goes to your biceps muscle and tells you to bend your elbow? Which type transmits information from your feet as to whether they feel cold?

   A motor neuron goes to your biceps muscle and tells you to bend your elbow. A sensory neuron transmits information from your feet as to whether they feel cold.

4. Is a neuron that slows your heartbeat part of the somatic or autonomic nervous system? Is this neuron part of the sympathetic or parasympathetic division?

   A neuron that slows your heartbeat is part of the autonomic nervous system. It is part of the parasympathetic division.

5. What would happen if you artificially excited a neuron, producing an action potential in the middle of the axon? How and why is this different from how action potentials actually move along axons?

   The action potential would travel both forwards and backwards along the axon away from the spot where you artificially excited it. It travels backwards in addition to forwards, unlike a "real" action potential, because the area behind where the axon is stimulated has not just experienced an action potential, and so is able to be stimulated.

6. If the myelin sheath were removed from the axon of a neuron, what effect would that have on the neuron's action potential?

   The action potential would travel much more slowly along the axon, and not "jump" from one gap in the myelin sheath to the next.

7. Do neurotransmitters enter the target cell? If not, how do they have an effect on the target cell?

   Neurotransmitters do not enter the target cell. Instead, they have their effect by binding to receptors on the target cell, starting a sequence of events that results in the target cell's response to the neurotransmitter.

8. Do all neurotransmitters cause the target cell to fire?

   No, some stimulate the target cell, but not enough to cause it to fire, and others actually inhibit the target cell from firing.

9. Why do a lot of nocturnal species have only rods in their retinas?

   Rods are more light sensitive than cones and are responsible for vision in dim light.

10. Are your rods or cones more important for reading a book?

    Your cones—cones are responsible for making out fine details, such as the letters in the words of the book we're reading.

11. In some people, the middle ear bones stiffen with age. This can result in deafness. Why?

    If the middle ear bones stiffen, they are less effective at transferring and amplifying sound vibrations from the outer ear to the inner ear, where "hearing" actually occurs.

12. How are the senses of smell and taste similar? How are they different?

    Both smell and taste rely on chemoreception, a process in which chemicals bind to receptors on the surface of special chemosensory cells. The binding causes ion channels to open and action potentials to happen. They differ in that smell detects odor molecules in the air, whereas taste detects chemical molecules inside the mouth. In addition, we have over 1000 different types of smell receptors but only five basic tastes.

13. Provide three examples of hormones that help maintain homeostasis in the body.

    Antidiuretic hormone helps regulate the amount of water in the body. Specifically, it helps the body conserve water by producing a more concentrated urine. Parathyroid hormone, which raises calcium levels in the blood, and calcitonin, which lowers calcium levels in the blood, help regulate calcium levels. Insulin and glucagons regulate the amount of glucose in the blood. Insulin lowers blood glucose levels by directing muscle and other cells to take in glucose and by stimulating the liver to convert glucose to the storage substance glycogen. Glucagon increases blood glucose levels by causing the liver to break down glycogen. (Other answers are possible.)

14. Suppose you know that the receptor for a hormone you are studying lies in the cytoplasm of cells. Can you tell whether the hormone is a protein or steroid hormone?

    It is a steroid hormone. Steroid hormones have receptors in the cytoplasm or nucleus, whereas protein hormones have receptors on the cell membrane.

15. Osteoporosis is a disease that primarily affects postmenopausal women, causing decreased bone density and brittle bones vulnerable to fracture. The hormone calcitonin is sometimes used to treat osteoporosis. Why? (*Hint*: It might be helpful to start by considering what parathyroid hormone does and how it has its effect.)

    Parathyroid hormone raises calcium levels in the blood, partly by causing calcium to be released from bones. Calcitonin has the opposite effect—it lowers blood calcium levels by causing bones to take up

calcium. This is why it is useful for treating osteoporosis. Calcitonin helps increase bone strength by increasing bone calcium.

16. On a brilliant, sunny day, you take a long hike through open country. You sweat a lot, losing a lot of water. What hormone does this cause you to produce? Why?

    Antidiuretic hormone—this hormone helps you conserve water by producing a more concentrated urine.

17. How does meiosis in women differ from meiosis in men?

    Meiosis in women is unequal meiosis, with one of the four daughter cells—the future egg—getting the bulk of cytoplasm and nutrients. So, meiosis in women produces only a single egg. Meiosis in men is not unequal, and produces four functional sperm.

18. Vasectomy is a form of male sterilization in which a section of each vas deferens is removed. How does this cause sterility?

    Sperm are unable to reach the ejaculate.

19. Tubal ligation is a form of female sterilization in which the oviduct is cut and the tubes tied. How does this cause sterility?

    Sperm are unable to reach the unfertilized egg, which also cannot reach the uterus.

20. Does a fertilized human egg make anything other than the embryo?

    The fertilized egg also makes the membranes that surround and protect the embryo, including the amnion and the embryonic contribution to the placenta.

21. Each time myosin heads pull on actin, the sarcomere contracts only 10 nanometers or so. Given that, how are we able to produce large motions?

    In each of our muscles, there are many sarcomeres lined up end to end. If each of these contracts and shortens a tiny amount, the entire muscle shortens by a significant distance.

22. Can muscle contraction occur without the presence of calcium ions? Why or why not? Where are the calcium ions in a muscle cell stored, and what causes their release?

    No, muscle contraction requires calcium. Calcium allows myosin to bind to actin. Calcium is stored in the endoplasmic reticulum of muscle cells. An action potential moving through the muscle cell causes the release of the ions.

23. Both the arrow poison curare and the nerve gas sarin affect the nerve-to-muscle connection. Do they work the same way? If not, how do they differ?

    Both curare and sarin affect the nerve-to-muscle connection, and both cause death through asphyxiation. However, their precise mechanisms differ. Curare, an arrow poison used in the South American tropics for hunting, binds to acetylcholine receptors on muscle cells, preventing acetylcholine itself from binding. Curare causes paralysis and then death as the respiratory muscles become paralyzed. The powerful nerve gas sarin prevents acetylcholine from being broken down after muscles contract. Muscles are stimulated continuously and soon become exhausted. Again, death occurs through asphyxiation as the respiratory muscles stop working.

24. Write a letter to Grandma explaining how the new generation of antidepressants, selective serotonin reuptake inhibitors (SSRIs) such as Prozac and Zoloft, work. Explain to her how neurons signal each other and what SSRIs do to influence this process.

    Some cases of depression are believed to be associated with the inability of signaling neurons to stimulate target neurons. Prozac, Paxil, and Zoloft are among a group of drugs known as selective serotonin reuptake inhibitors (SSRIs). SSRIs work by preventing signaling neurons from taking up ("reuptaking") the neurotransmitter serotonin once it has been released at synapses. That way, more serotonin remains to bind to and stimulate target neurons.

Solutions to Chapter 19 Problems

1. Action potentials travel at speeds anywhere between 0.5 and 120 meters/second, depending on factors such as temperature, the size of the axon, and whether the axon is myelinated. We have two different types of neurons that conduct pain signals from, say, our hand to our central nervous system. The slower

type conducts signals at 0.5 meters/second. The faster type conducts signals at 25 meters/second. Let's say that the distance from your hand to your central nervous system is about 1 meter. Now, you touch a hot stove. Show that you become aware of the first type of pain in 0.04 seconds, but only become aware of the second type of pain after 2 seconds. (You may have noticed that when you do something like touch a hot stove, you feel a flash of sharp pain first, followed by a slow throbbing pain.)

For the fast type, time = distance/speed = 1/25 = 0.04 seconds. For the slow type, time = distance/speed = 1/0.5 = 2 seconds.

2. The human retina has an area of about 1000 mm^2. If we have a total of 125 million rods and 6.5 million cones in each eye, show that we have about 131,500 sensory cells per square millimeter in the retina.

We have a total of 125 + 6.5 = 131.5 million rods and cones.

131,500,000/1000 mm^2 = 131,500 sensory cells per mm^2.

3. We have about 1000 different kinds of smell receptors. Each of these is a distinct protein coded for a specific gene. In Chapter 16, we learned that the Human Genome Project revealed that humans have a total of about 30,000 genes. Show that about 3.3 percent of our genes are dedicated to helping us smell.

1000/30,000 = 0.033 or 3.3%

4. The egg is a large cell and contributes almost all the nutrients to the zygote (fertilized egg) created at fertilization. The sperm contributes little more than its set of chromosomes. Just how much bigger is a human egg than a human sperm? The human egg is about 100 micrometers in diameter. The head of a human sperm is about 4 micrometers in diameter. (And, in case you're curious, human sperm are about 50 micrometers long.) Show that the volume of a human egg is 15,625 times larger than the volume of a human sperm. Recall that the volume of a sphere is $4/3 \pi r^3$.

Volume of a human egg = $4/3 \pi r^3 = 4/3 \pi (50)^3 = 4/3 \pi (125,000)$

Volume of a human sperm = $4/3 \pi r^3 = 4/3 \pi (2)^3 = 4/3 \pi (8)$

So, a human egg is 125,000/8 = 15,625 times bigger in volume than a human sperm.

Chapter 20: Human Biology II—Care and Maintenance

Answers to Chapter 20 Review Questions

1. Supplying the body with oxygen is a job that's split by two systems—the respiratory system brings oxygen into the body, and the circulatory system distributes it to the tissues.

2. Getting rid of cellular wastes requires the coordinated efforts of the circulatory, respiratory, and excretory systems—the circulatory system collects wastes from the tissues, and the respiratory and excretory systems remove them from the body via exhalation and urine production, respectively.

3. Each heartbeat begins in a part of the right atrium called the *sinoatrial node*, or pacemaker. The pacemaker initiates an action potential that sweeps quickly through the right and left atria, which contract simultaneously. The signal also passes to the *atrioventricular node*, and from there to the two ventricles, which also contract simultaneously.

4. The atrioventricular node conducts action potentials slowly, producing a delay between the contraction of the atria and the contraction of the ventricles.

5. The sounds come from heart *valves* snapping shut after each contraction.

6. Capillaries allow materials to be exchanged between blood and tissues.

7. Valves in the veins help make sure the blood doesn't flow backwards.

8. Deoxygenated blood returning from the tissues flows from veins into the right atrium of the heart. The right atrium pumps it to the right ventricle. The right ventricle pumps it out arteries that go to the lungs. There, the blood picks up oxygen and drops off carbon dioxide—the blood is now oxygenated. This oxygenated blood flows back to the heart, along veins that lead to the left atrium. The left atrium pumps it to the left ventricle, which then pumps it out to arteries that go to tissues all over the body. After carrying oxygen to the tissues, the blood becomes deoxygenated again and returns to the heart via veins.

9. Red blood cells carry oxygen. White blood cells are part of the immune system and help our bodies defend against disease. Platelets are involved in blood clotting.

10. As we inhale, air comes in through the nose or mouth. Air continues up the nasal passages. From the nasal passages, air passes through the *pharynx,* the part of the throat above the esophagus and respiratory tract. Then it proceeds through the *larynx,* or voice box, and down the *trachea,* or windpipe. The trachea branches into two tubes called *bronchi* that lead to the right and left lungs, and then into smaller and smaller tubules that finally dead-end at small sacs called *alveoli.*

11. Gas exchange occurs through diffusion—that is, gas molecules move from an area of greater concentration to an area of lower concentration. Both the alveolus and the surrounding capillaries have extremely thin walls, consisting of only a single flattened cell, to allow diffusion to proceed efficiently.

12. When we inhale, the diaphragm contracts. This causes it to flatten, increasing the volume of the thoracic cavity. Muscles between our ribs also contract, pulling the ribcage up and out from the chest and further increasing the volume of the thoracic cavity. So, the volume of the thoracic cavity increases, while the amount of air inside it remains constant. What happens? The air pressure in the thoracic cavity drops. Air is sucked into the lungs and fills the alveoli.

13. When we exhale, the diaphragm and rib muscles relax, decreasing the volume of the thoracic cavity. This increases the air pressure in the thoracic cavity and pushes air out of the lungs.

14. During digestion, food is broken down into organic molecules that can be absorbed and used by the body.

15. Our taste buds can only detect chemicals dissolved in liquid.

16. The *epiglottis,* a small flap of cartilage at the back of the tongue, covers the trachea during swallowing so that food can't get into it.

17. Swallowing begins as a voluntary activity—the muscles at the top of the esophagus are voluntary muscles. However, at a certain point, it becomes involuntary. The lower part of the esophagus is made of involuntary smooth muscle like that found in the rest of the digestive tract.

18. In the stomach, digestive enzymes and a muscular churning action combine to reduce food to a thick liquid called *chyme.*

19. In the *duodenum,* the first foot of the small intestine, digestion continues with the breakdown of proteins, fats, carbohydrates, and nucleic acids. Beyond the duodenum, the rest of the small intestine functions primarily in absorbing nutrients into the body.

20. Bile is an emulsifier—it breaks fats into tiny droplets that are more easily attacked by enzymes.

21. The small intestine has a huge surface area. It is covered with fingerlike projections called *villi,* each of which is covered with tiny little projections called *microvilli.*

22. In the large intestine, water and minerals such as sodium are absorbed into the body.

23. Humans are unable to make 8 of the 20 amino acids needed to build proteins. This is why it's important for us to eat a "complete protein"—one containing all the amino acids—regularly.

24. Regular exercise reduces the risk of many health problems, including heart disease, high blood pressure, colon and breast cancer, osteoporosis, diabetes, and obesity.

25. Exercise improves the functioning of the heart and lungs, increasing oxygen consumption, the amount of blood the heart pumps, and lung capacity, while decreasing heart rate and blood pressure.

26. Each nephron in our kidneys is associated with a cluster of capillaries called the *glomerulus.* The glomerulus is surrounded by a cup-shaped structure called *Bowman's capsule,* part of the nephron. Blood pressure in the glomerulus pushes fluid out of the capillaries and into Bowman's capsule.

27. The loop of Henle functions in reabsorbing water from the filtrate.

28. Antidiuretic hormone causes the walls of the collecting duct to be permeable to water, allowing additional water to be reabsorbed.

29. The skin is a crucial barrier to pathogens, forming a tough outer layer that is nearly impenetrable when intact. The frequent shedding of skin cells also makes it harder for potential pathogens to establish a

foothold. In addition, hair follicles in the skin produce acidic secretions that help to kill bacteria and fungi.

30. Receptors of the innate immune system recognize carbohydrates, proteins, or nucleic acids that characterize many different pathogens.

31. When tissues are damaged, they release chemicals called *histamines*. Histamines increase blood flow to the site of the injury and cause local capillaries to leak fluid. This fluid causes swelling, which helps to isolate the injury from other body tissues. Histamines also attract innate immune system cells. Innate immune cells squeeze out of the capillaries, migrate to the site of the wound, and attack any microorganisms that have entered the body.

32. Each cell of the acquired immune system has receptors that respond to a single antigen—a molecule or part of a molecule belonging to a foreign pathogen. Most often, antigens are parts of foreign proteins.

33. When the receptor of a B cell binds to an antigen, the cell begins to divide, making many *clones*, or copies, of itself.

34. *Memory cells* remain in the body for a long time, years or even a lifetime. If the same antigen is encountered again, the memory cells initiate an immune response that is much faster and much more aggressive.

Answers to Chapter 20 Multiple-Choice Questions

1b, 2a, 3c, 4b, 5d, 6d, 7c, 8b, 9d, 10c

Answers to Chapter 20 Integrated Science Concepts

Chemistry: Hemoglobin

1. A molecule of hemoglobin consists of four subunits, each of which contains a component known as a heme group that includes an iron atom at its center. It is this iron atom that binds oxygen.

2. Lower blood pH (a more acidic environment) decreases hemoglobin's oxygen affinity.

3. An active, working tissue makes and uses more ATP and so releases more carbon dioxide during cellular respiration. Because carbon dioxide reacts with water in the blood to form carbonic acid, the presence of high carbon dioxide levels decreases blood pH. This acidity decreases the oxygen affinity of local hemoglobin molecules, making it easier for them to unload oxygen to the working tissue.

Physics and Chemistry: Low-Carb Versus Low-Cal Diets

4. How do you lose weight? The answer is simple—use up more calories than you take in. This forces your body to use stored energy, such as fat, to support its activities.

5. Studies have confirmed that, for many people, low-carb diets do produce weight loss more quickly and more consistently than low-calorie diets. This appears to be because many people find low-carb diets easier to stick to because of their permissive attitude towards fats. People on low-carb diets lose weight for the same reason that people on low-calorie diets lose weight—they consume fewer total calories. In addition, low-carb diets cause you to retain less water in the body, and this water is used during excretion to flush out the extra proteins consumed.

6. They tend to be high in saturated fats and cholesterol, which are associated with heart disease, and they tend to be short on whole grains and fruit, which are known to protect against many diseases. Finally, not a whole lot is known about potential long-term effects of low-carb diets. For example, water loss and the processing of large amounts of proteins may be hard on organs such as the liver and kidneys.

Answers to Chapter 20 Exercises

1. Several of our senses provide examples of how multiple body systems work together to accomplish important tasks. What body systems are involved in hearing? In smelling? In tasting?

   Hearing requires the functioning of our skin (makes up part of the eardrum) and skeleton (the cartilaginous outer ear as well as the middle ear bones). Smelling requires the functioning of the respirator system, which brings air in to be "sampled" by our sensory cells for smell. Tasting requires saliva, part of the digestive system, because molecules must be dissolved in liquid in order to be sensed.

2. How does reproduction require the integrated action of multiple organ systems?

   Aside from the organs of the reproductive system, mate-finding, wooing, and copulation require the work of our senses, our brains and nervous systems, and our muscles. Pregnancy requires the functioning of our endocrine, respiratory, and circulatory systems. (Other answers are possible.)

3. The pumping of the heart does the bulk of the work that is required to move blood around the body. What else contributes?

   The contractions of our voluntary muscles help move blood back toward the heart.

4. Why do you think the atria of the heart are less muscular than the ventricles? Why is the left ventricle more muscular than the right ventricle?

   The atria merely have to pump blood to the ventricles, whereas the ventricles have to pump blood to the lungs and body. The left ventricle has to pump blood to the body, so must generate more pressure than the right ventricle, which only has to pump blood to the lungs.

5. Where in the body is blood most oxygenated?

   Near the source of oxygen, by the alveoli.

6. How does the body control the amount of blood that different tissues receive?

   By controlling the diameters of arterioles that go to different parts of the body.

7. What bodily activities is the respiratory system involved in besides acquiring oxygen for the body?

   It contributes to our sense of smell by bringing chemical molecules in the air to the cells responsible for smelling. It also is involved in speech, which depends on air vibrating our vocal cords as we exhale.

8. Why shouldn't you talk with your mouth full (not just because it's impolite)?

   Talking with your mouth full can disrupt the functioning of the epiglottis, which covers the trachea to be sure food doesn't enter the respiratory tract. This disruption sometimes leads to choking.

9. What waste materials are produced in the process of making ATP, and what body systems are responsible for removing them from the body?

   Carbon dioxide and nitrogen-containing wastes (in the form of ammonia, which is then quickly converted to urea) are the waste products produced during cellular respiration. Carbon dioxide is removed from the body by the respiratory system. Nitrogenous wastes are removed by the excretory system.

10. The liver is an organ that plays important roles in multiple organ systems. What role does the liver have in digestion? In excretion?

    The liver makes bile, which is important as an emulsifier for digestion. The liver also converts ammonia to the less toxic urea, an important function related to excretion.

11. How does the endocrine system interact with the excretory system? Give examples.

    Antidiuretic hormone causes more water to be reabsorbed from the filtrate during excretion. Parathyroid hormone decreases calcium excretion. Mineralocorticoids help regulate water and salt balance in the body by affecting excretion of these substances. (Other answers are possible.)

12. Kangaroo rats, which live in dry desert habitats, have very long loops of Henle. Why might this be?

    A long loop of Henle allows kangaroo rats to create a strong concentration gradient of solutes, which aids in water reabsorption. This is essential to surviving in a desert environment, where limited water is available.

13. What is the difference between elimination (feces) and excretion (urine)? What is the body getting rid of in each case?

    Elimination is associated with the digestive system and excretion with the excretory system. Elimination eliminates substances in food that cannot be absorbed or used by the body. (Feces are composed primarily of living and dead bacteria and indigestible materials such as plant cellulose.) Excretion helps control the amount of many substances in the body, but it helps us get rid of urea in particular, which is a product of breaking down proteins during cellular respiration.

14. Why might eating a high-protein diet be particularly hard on the liver and kidneys?

    Breaking down proteins to make ATP results in the production of ammonia. The liver is responsible for converting ammonia to urea, and the kidney is responsible for excreting urea. So both organs are particularly taxed when the body breaks down large amounts of protein.

15. Why is the innate immune system described as "nonspecific"? Why is the acquired immune system described as "specific"?

    The innate immune system is described as nonspecific because its defenses work against a wide variety of potential pathogens. The acquired immune system is described as specific because the cells of this system recognize specific features of specific pathogens and take action only when these features are encountered.

16. What are some differences between the innate immune system and the acquired immune system?

    The acquired immune system is specific in its response to pathogens and other foreign substances, whereas the innate immune system has defenses that work against a wide variety of potential pathogens. Each cell of the acquired immune system has receptors that respond to a single antigen, whereas innate immune receptors respond to features that characterize multiple pathogens. The acquired immune response is much slower than that of the innate immune system, usually taking between 3 and 5 days to reach full force; the innate immune response is immediate. The acquired immune system retains a "memory" of pathogens it has encountered in the past, so that subsequent responses to the same pathogen can be faster and more aggressive. The innate immune system has no such "memory."

17. Allergies occur when the immune system is abnormally sensitive to particular substances. Why do people sometimes take antihistamines for their allergies?

    Many of the symptoms of allergies result from an excessive inflammatory response to irritants. In order to trigger the inflammatory response of the innate immune system, injured tissues produce histamines. Antihistamines help to counter these histamines and reduce the redness and swelling that make up the inflammatory response.

18. How are the antigens B cells respond to different from the ones T cells respond to?

    B cells respond to antigens in bodily fluids. T cells respond to antigens that infected body cells display (like SOS flags) on their surface.

19. A mother kisses her child's "owie." Do you think this might result in the child feeling less pain? Why or why not?

    Perhaps it does, via the placebo effect.

20. Write a letter to Grandpa telling him about the trend toward low carb diets. Tell him why many people have been able to lose weight on low-carb diets, and explain some potential dangers of the diets as well.

    Low-carb diets have become extremely popular, and it's easy to see why. Studies have confirmed that, for many people, low-carb diets do produce weight loss more quickly and more consistently than low-calorie diets. This appears to be because many people find low-carb diets easier to stick to because of their permissive attitude toward fats. People on low-carb diets lose weight for the same reason that people on low-calorie diets lose weight—they consume fewer total calories. In addition, low-carb diets cause you to retain less water in the body—this water is used during excretion to flush out the extra proteins consumed. Are there any problems with low-carb diets? Yes—they tend to be high in saturated fats and cholesterol, which are associated with heart disease, and they tend to be short on whole grains and fruit, which are known to protect against many diseases. Finally, not a whole lot is known about potential long-term effects of low-carb diets. For example, water loss and the processing of large amounts of proteins may be hard on organs such as the liver and kidneys.

Answers to Chapter 20 Problems

1. Show that the blood can carry as many as 3×10^{22} molecules of oxygen. Here's some information you may find useful: You have 25 trillion red blood cells. Each red blood cell contains 300 million molecules of hemoglobin. Each molecule of hemoglobin can carry four molecules of oxygen.

   (25,000,000,000,000) (300,000,000) (4) = 30,000,000,000,000,000,000,000 molecules of oxygen.

2. Because red blood cells have no nuclei and are therefore unable to make the proteins necessary to maintain themselves, they have a relatively short life span of about 120 days. Given that we have about 25 trillion red blood cells in all, show that more than 208 billion red blood cells die and are replaced each day. Also show that, in the 20 seconds it took you to read this problem, about 48 million red blood cells died and were replaced.

(25,000,000,000,000)/(120) = 208,333,333,333 red blood cells per day. This is the same as 208,333,333,333/((24)(60)(60)) = 2.4 million red blood cells per second. In other words, in the 20 seconds it took you to read the problem, about 48 million red blood cells died and were replaced.

3. A typical person has a heart rate of 70 beats per minute and takes 12 breaths in a minute. Show that her heart beats about 4200 times an hour, 100,800 times a day, and 36.8 million times a year. Show also that she takes about 720 breaths per hour, 17,280 breaths per day, and 6.3 million breaths per year.

For heartbeat:

70 beats per minute (60 minutes per hour) = 4200 beats per hour

4200 beats per hour (24 hours per day) = 100,800 beats per day

100,800 beats per day (365 days per year) = 36.8 million beats per year

For breathing:

12 breaths per minute (60 minutes per hour) = 720 breaths per hour

720 breaths per hour (24 hours per day) = 17,280 breaths per day

17,280 breaths per day (365 days per year) = 6.3 million breaths per year

Chapter 21: Ecosystems and Environment

Answers to Chapter 21 Review Questions

1. Ecology is the study of how organisms interact with their environments.

2. An organism's environment includes nonliving, or abiotic, features, such as temperature, sunlight, precipitation, rocks, ponds, and so forth. It also includes biotic features—that is, other living organisms.

3. A community consists of all the organisms that live within a given area. An ecosystem consists of all the organisms that live within a given area *and* all the abiotic features of their environment.

4. Food chain or food web.

5. A food chain begins with producers, species that live by making organic molecules out of inorganic materials and energy.

6. Decomposers such as bacteria and fungi consume dead organic matter.

7. No two species in a community have exactly the same niche. Otherwise, the species that is better at exploiting the resources eventually outcompetes the other and drives it to extinction—this is called the *competitive exclusion principle*.

8. *Parasitism* benefits one member of the interaction and harms the other. Familiar examples include fleas, tapeworms, and other organisms that live on or in their hosts and obtain nutrients from them. Pathogens such as bacteria or viruses are parasites as well. A strikingly different form of parasitism is brood parasitism, in which the female of one species lays eggs in the nest of another species, causing individuals of the other species to raise her young.

9. *Commensalism* is a form of symbiosis that benefits one species of the interaction while having no effect on the other. *Mutualism* is a form of symbiosis that benefits both species.

10. For most ecosystems, energy comes ultimately from the sun.

11. Sunlight enters the biotic world when plants and other photosynthesizers use it to build organic molecules in the process of photosynthesis.

12. On average, only about 10% of the energy at one trophic level becomes available to the next level. What happens to the other 90%? First, not every organism at one trophic level is exploited by the next level—

for example, not every plant gets eaten by a herbivore. Second, when a consumer eats, the energy it receives from food goes into things other than building biomass—feces and maintenance, to be specific.

13. The flow of energy through trophic levels is sometimes diagrammed in an *energy pyramid*. The shape of the pyramid emphasizes the loss of energy as you go up trophic levels.

14. The type of biome found in a habitat is determined primarily by climatic variables, such as temperature, precipitation, and the presence or absence of distinct seasons.

15. Each biome is characterized by specific types of communities and, particularly, by specific types of plant life.

16. Because of the tremendous density and diversity of life, most of the nutrients present in tropical forests are being used by one or another living organism. As a result, the soil there tends to be poor. The soil of temperate forests is fertile, and these forests make good farmland. (Other answers are possible.)

17. Dry season fires help maintain savannas by preventing tree growth.

18. Desert plants typically have special adaptations for living in dry conditions, including extensive root systems and the ability to store water when it is available.

19. Habitats close to the water surface and to shore are part of the *littoral zone*. The *limnetic zone* includes habitats that are close to the water surface but far from shore. The *profundal zone* describes deep water habitats in ponds and lakes.

20. Plankton, including diatoms and the larvae of animals such as clams, lobsters, and sea urchins, float wherever water currents take them. Unlike plankton, *nekton* such as fish and sea turtles actively swim through the water.

21. The intertidal zone, which is closest to shore, is periodically underwater and exposed to air as the tide moves in and out. Many species, including certain barnacles, sea anemones, starfish, and other species, are specialized for life in the intertidal zone.

22. *Primary succession* describes the colonization of bare land devoid of soil. *Secondary succession* occurs when a disturbance destroys existing life in a habitat, but leaves soil intact.

23. The activities of earlier waves of colonizers cause nutrients and organic matter to accumulate in the habitat, allowing later colonizers to thrive.

24. During the process of succession, the total biomass of the ecosystem typically increases, as does the number of species.

25. According to the *intermediate disturbance hypothesis,* regular disturbances, if not too extreme, actually contribute to biodiversity because different species make use of different habitats, and periodic disturbances guarantee that there will always be habitat at varying stages of recovery.

26. Exponential growth characterizes populations with unlimited resources.

27. Populations that occupy highly unstable environments, where resources are periodically plentiful and scarce, experience repeated cycles of exponential growth and crash. Good conditions trigger exponential growth. When resources run out, the population crashes. When another opportunity arises, the population explodes again, and so on.

28. At low population densities, logistic growth looks a lot like exponential growth. This is because resources are effectively unlimited when there are few or sparsely distributed individuals. At high population densities, however, growth slows as the population approaches the habitat's carrying capacity.

29. Organisms that make a lot of inexpensive offspring are described as *r-selected*. Organisms that make few expensive offspring are described as *K-selected*.

30. Type I organisms have low death rates early in life, with most individuals surviving until fairly late in life. Elephants are a good example of Type I survivorship, as are humans—most humans survive infancy and childhood and die late in life. Type III organisms have high death rates early in life, with few individuals surviving until late in life. Many invertebrates, including razor clams, have Type III survivorship. Type II organisms have a steady death rate that does not depend on age. Individuals are as likely to die early in life as late in life. Certain songbirds are good examples of Type II survivorship.

31. In the unstable environments of exponential growth, life and death are often chance events. By producing huge numbers of offspring (that is, by being *r*-selected), organisms are more likely to have one or two of these survive. In the stable environments of logistic growth, where many populations are at or near carrying capacity, an offspring that receives a lot of parental investment (such as in a *K*-selected species) is more likely to be able to compete and do well.

32. Exponentially.

33. No—in fact, carrying capacity has already increased twice in human history, once as agriculture spread through the world and again with the onset of the industrial revolution.

34. A population's age structure describes the distribution of people's ages within the population. We can learn something about how a population is growing from its *age structure*.

Answers to Chapter 21 Multiple-Choice Questions

1b, 2a, 3c, 4d, 5c, 6b, 7c, 8a, 9c, 10d

Answers to Chapter 21 Integrated Science Concepts

Physics: Energy Leaks Where Trophic Levels Meet

1. The Second Law of Thermodynamics states that natural systems tend to move from organized energy states to disorganized energy states; that is, useful energy dissipates to unusable energy. Specifically, any time energy is converted from one form to another—including in any chemical reaction—and some energy is lost to the environment as heat. Moving energy from one trophic level to another—such as by breaking down plant matter in the digestive tract of a rabbit, and then using the molecules to build more rabbit muscle—involves a long series of chemical reactions, one after another. So, the Second Law of Thermodynamics explains the reason for energy loss between trophic levels.

2. Yes. The chemical reaction for burning glucose is:

$$C_6H_{12}O_6 + 6O_2 \rightarrow 6CO_2 + 6H_2O + 673 \text{ kcal/mole}$$

   That is, glucose and oxygen react to form carbon dioxide and water, releasing 673 kilocalories of energy per mole in the process. If this reaction were perfectly efficient in organisms, the entire 673 kilocalories per mole released would be captured as ATP. Is it? We know that about 38 molecules of ADP are converted to ATP as the result of burning a single glucose molecule. ATP then provides 7 kilocalories per mole when it is broken down into ADP and phosphate during cellular processes. But, $38 \times 7 = 266$, much less than 673. Clearly, a lot of energy is missing! What happened to it? It was lost as heat.

Earth Science: Materials Cycling in Ecosystems

3. The word "biogeochemical" emphasizes that substances cycle between living organisms ("bio") and the Earth ("geo")—in particular, Earth's atmosphere, crust, and waters.

4. Carbon moves into the biotic world when plants and other producers convert carbon dioxide to glucose during photosynthesis. Carbon is returned to the environment by living organisms as carbon dioxide, a product of cellular respiration.

5. Legumes such as peas, beans, clover, and alfalfa have evolved a mutualistic symbiotic relationship with nitrogen-fixing bacteria. These bacteria live in nodules on legume roots and provide them with nitrogen.

Answers to Chapter 21 Exercises

1. A scientist studies how the number of coyotes in San Diego County has changed over the last decade. Is this a population-level study, a community-level study, or an ecosystem-level study?

   This is a population-level study, because it considers a group of individuals of a single species that occupies a given area.

2. Another scientist examines how the presence of a nonnative species, the starling, affects other species of birds in Alameda County. Is this a population-level study, a community-level study, or an ecosystem-level study?

   This is a community-level study, because it considers interactions between different species occupying the same area.

3. Are all producers autotrophs? Do all producers photosynthesize?

Yes, all producers are autotrophs—they make their own food from inorganic substances. Not all producers photosynthesize; some are chemoautotrophs.

4. Cattle egrets live in close association with cows (hence, their name). They eat insects flushed out by the activity of the cows. Is their relationship with cows parasitism, commensalism, or mutualism?

Commensalism—they benefit from the activity of the cows, but they do not affect the cows either positively or negatively.

5. Some flowering plants rely on insects to carry pollen from male flowers to female flowers. The insects receive nectar. Is this an example of parasitism, commensalism, or mutualism?

Mutualism—both species benefit. The insects receive food, and the plants are pollinated, a key step in their reproduction.

6. Give an example of an organism that is parasitic on humans. Give an example of an organism with which humans have a commensal relationship. Finally, give an example of an organism with which we have a mutualistic relationship. Explain.

Many answers are possible. Human parasites include lice, disease-causing bacteria and viruses, fleas, bed bugs, and so forth. Human commensals include dust mites, pigeons, squirrels, and other species that live in human communities and receive food from humans without either benefiting or harming us. Species with which we have a mutualistic, mutually beneficial, relationship include dogs, cats, and so forth.

7. Why can't an ecosystem's energy pyramid be inverted (that is, upside-down)?

Because, in all ecosystems, a huge amount of energy is lost as you go up the food chain. On average, only about 10% of the energy at one trophic level becomes available to the next level. First, not every organism at one trophic level is exploited by the next level—for example, not every plant gets eaten by a herbivore. Second, when a consumer eats, the energy it receives from food goes into things other than building biomass—feces and maintenance, to be specific. Feces contains organic materials that the consumer is unable to digest. Maintenance is the energy the consumer requires to live—the energy it takes to find and eat food, run, mate, breathe, and so on. During these activities, a lot of energy is also lost to the environment as heat. So, by the time feces and maintenance have taken their share, only about 10% is left for growth and reproduction—for building new biomass.

8. If you eat a pound of pasta, will you gain a pound of weight? Why not?

No, much of the energy in that pound of pasta will go to feces and maintenance.

9. Was every carbon atom in your body once part of a plant? Why or why not?

We heterotrophs get all our carbon from the food we eat. Ultimately, this all comes from producers such as photosynthesizing plants. As to whether every carbon atom in our body came ultimately from a plant, the answer is that *most* of the carbon in our bodies came to us via a plant. However, *some* may have come to us through diatoms or other oceanic plankton, seaweeds, and so forth.

10. Why do legumes grow better in nutrient-poor soil than many other plants?

Legumes have a mutualistic relationship with nitrogen-fixing bacteria, which occupy the plants' root nodules. They obtain nitrogen from these bacteria.

11. Why do tropical forests typically have poor soil?

Because of the tremendous density and diversity of life, most of the nutrients present in tropical forests are being used by one or another living organism—as a result, the soil tends to be poor.

12. What are the major factors that determine what kind of plant life, and therefore what kind of biome, is found in a habitat? Do living organisms ever affect the type of biome found in an area?

The type of biome found in a habitat is determined primarily by climatic variables such as temperature, precipitation, and the presence or absence of distinct seasons. As a result, latitude and altitude are major influences on the distribution of biomes on Earth. Living organisms sometimes do affect the biome found in a particular area. For example, organisms help maintain savanna habitats, preventing them from growing into tropical forest—elephants eat and kill trees, and humans burn forests for cropland.

13. Give an example of marine plankton and marine nekton. Give an example of a benthic species.

   Many answers are possible. Marine plankton include diatoms, dinoflagellates, and the larvae of many animals. Marine nekton include most fishes, whales, seals, penguins, and so forth. Benthic species include mussels, clams, marine worms, lobsters, and so forth.

14. Why do you think most of the early animal colonizers of Krakatoa were flying insects and birds?

   Flying insects and birds had the easiest time getting to the island.

15. Does primary succession or secondary succession occur more frequently?

   Secondary succession occurs more frequently—it is much more common for soil to remain intact than for bare rock to be revealed. Examples of the latter occur when volcanism creates new land or when glaciers retreat.

16. Once a habitat is occupied by its climax community, does its species composition continue to change? Why or why not?

   Yes, species composition changes when there are disturbances that remove climax community species from a patch of habitat. This patch of habitat then goes through succession.

17. Could a habitat that received regular, but not extreme, disturbances be more diverse than one that received no disturbances? How would it compare to a habitat that received regular, extreme disturbances?

   Yes. According to the intermediate disturbance hypothesis, regular disturbances, if not too extreme, actually contribute to biodiversity because different species make use of different habitats, and periodic disturbances guarantee that there will always be habitat at varying stages of recovery. However, a habitat that received regular, extreme disturbances would probably always be found in the early stages of succession and would probably be less diverse.

18. The graph below shows the growth of a *Paramecium* population in the lab. Does the population grow exponentially or logistically? Can you estimate the carrying capacity of the habitat?

   This is an *S*-shaped logistic curve. Carrying capacity appears to be around 900 individuals per milliliter.

19. Are humans *r*-selected or *K*-selected? What type of survivorship curve do we have? Which other correlates of *r*- or *K*-selection characterize humans?

   Humans are *K*-selected. We are described by Type I survivorship. Like other *K*-selected species, we have large body size, relatively few offspring, high investment in offspring (lots of parental care, for example), we reach sexual maturity slowly, and we have long life expectancy.

20. What is demographic transition? Provide an example of a country where demographic transition has occurred, and one where it has not.

   Demographic transition involves a shift from high birth and death rates to low birth and death rates. Most often, death rate decreases first, due to medical and public health advances such as better care, improved nutrition, and immunization. After some time, birth rate also declines. During the period between the fall in death rate and the fall in birth rate, the combination of low death rate and high birth rate causes the population to grow very rapidly. The United States has undergone demographic transition; Kenya has not completed it.

21. The following figure shows the age structure in Afghanistan in 2000. Are most people young or old? Do you think Afghanistan has a growing, stable, or declining population?

   Most people are young. The population is growing rapidly.

22. The graph below shows survivorship curves for males and females in England and India in 1999, as well as for 17th century England. What differences do you see between England and India in 1999? What might explain these differences? How did survivorship in England change from the 17th century to 1999?

   There is more infant and early mortality in India than in England in 1999. This is likely because poverty affects more people in India, and more people are unable to get proper medical care. There is a huge difference between 17th century survivorship curves in England and survivorship curves there in 1999. In fact, 17th century survivorship curves resemble Type III curves. This means that there were very high levels of infant and childhood mortality in 17th century England.

23. Write a letter to Grandma telling her about recent changes in the rate of human population growth. Be sure to tell her what it means that world human population is no longer growing exponentially. Also tell her about exponential and logistic growth, and explain which model describes human population growth over the last many thousand years.

Human population has grown exponentially for thousands of years. Exponential growth occurs when a population grows at a rate that is proportional to its size. Logistic growth occurs when population growth slows as it reaches the habitat's carrying capacity, that is, the maximum number of individuals or maximum population density the habitat can support. Interestingly, it has become evident in the last several decades that, although world population continues to grow rapidly, the *rate* of growth has slowed, so that growth is no longer exponential. In fact, scientists now believe that if present trends continue, the global human population will peak at around 10 billion soon after 2050.

Solutions to Chapter 21 Problems

1. A grassland supports 25 two-kilogram carnivores—they are secondary consumers in the community. Assuming that 10% of the energy available at each trophic level is captured by the next trophic level, how many kilograms of herbivores (primary consumers) does the grassland support? How many kilograms of grass and other producers?

   25 two-kilogram carnivores = 50 kilograms of carnivores

   This means there were 500 kilograms of herbivores (since 10% of 500 = 50).

   And 5000 kilograms of grass and other producers (since 10% of 5000 = 500).

2. In a population of songbirds, 100 young are born in the year 2000. Each year, 10 individuals die. Make a table showing how many individuals are alive in each year from 2000 to 2010. Now draw a survivorship curve for the population. Does this songbird population have Type I, Type II, or Type III survivorship?

   This is the table:

Year	Individuals Alive
2000	100
2001	90
2002	80
2003	70
2004	60
2005	50
2006	40
2007	30
2008	20
2009	10
2010	0

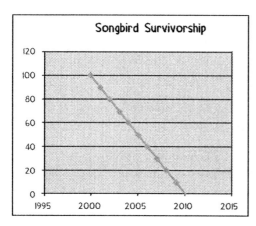

This is Type II survivorship.

3. In a population of insects, 1 million young are born in the year 2000. Each year, 95% of the living individuals die. Make a table showing how many individuals are alive in each year from 2000 to 2005 (round your answers as necessary). Now draw a survivorship curve for the population. Does this insect population have Type I, Type II, or Type III survivorship?

This is the table:

Year	Individuals Alive
2000	1,000,000
2001	50,000
2002	2,500
2003	125
2004	6
2005	0

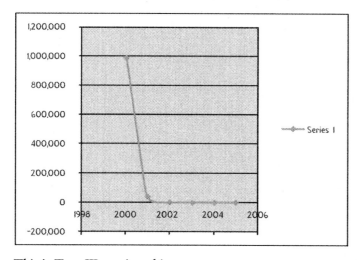

This is Type III survivorship.

Chapter 22: Plate Tectonics

Answers to Chapter 22 Review Questions

1. False. Very little was known until seismology could be employed to investigate Earth's interior.

2. Newton—portions of Earth's interior must be very dense; da Vinci—mountains are formed by compacted sediments that become rock and are uplifted; Hutton—the Principle of Uniformitarianism.

3. Crust, mantle, core.

4. S-waves cannot penetrate the earth at a certain depth; P-waves slow and refract at this same depth; P-waves and S-waves refract in such a way that their shadow regions indicate that there is a core that is part solid and part liquid.

5. The Mohorovičić discontinuity—the boundary between crust and mantle.

6. Layers of differing composition.

7. They showed the depth and the sharpness of the mantle–core boundary, that the outer core is liquid, and that the inner core is solid.

8. It is thin, rigid, and can crack.

9. Oceanic crust and continental crust. They are distinguished on the basis of the type (in particular, the density) of rock found there.

10. Earth's crust is mainly made of granitic rocks.

11. Oceanic crust is mostly basalt.

12. The mantle.

13. The lithosphere is the relatively rigid layer of rock made up of crust and upper mantle.

14. The asthenosphere is the relatively plastic portion of the mantle.

15. Metals—mostly iron.

16. Estimates range from 7000°F to 13,000°F—about as hot as the surface of the sun.

17. P waves reflect and gain speed at the boundary, and S waves are able to travel there.

18.

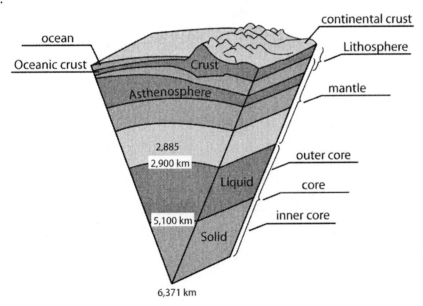

19. Continental drift is the hypothesis that the continents travel about the surface of the earth and are not fixed in one location.

20. The eastern shoreline of Africa and the western shoreline of South America fit together like pieces of a jigsaw puzzle. It looks as if the continents had been one landmass at one time and then tore apart along the matching edges and drifted apart to their present locations.

21. There was no known mechanism.

22. It happens too slowly relative to human lifetimes.

23. Hess confirmed that the seafloor was not flat as traditionally thought but had widely varying topography.

24. Along a divergent plate boundary, plates diverge as they are carried by convection in the asthenosphere. Lava oozes out of the spreading center, cools to form oceanic crust, and then moves outward from the spreading center to expand the seafloor.

25. Ocean trenches. Lithosphere is returned to the interior of the earth in the subduction zone that occurs at the trenches.

26. Seafloor spreading provided the missing mechanism—it explained that the continents move apart due to thermal convection in the plastically yielding asthenosphere.

27. The youngest rocks are located nearest the mid-ocean ridges. The rocks get progressively older away from the ridges, which is consistent with the idea that new lithosphere is generated at the ridges and then spreads outward on both sides of them.

28. Magnetic striping correlates bands of rock with eras of alternating magnetic polarity. The pattern of the bands shows that rock ages as it moves farther from the rifts.

29. Before Harry Hess measured depth variations in the seafloor, it was presumed to be flat because there was little geologic activity there. The uneven sea bottom suggests that the sea bottom undergoes geologic movement.

30. A mobile piece of lithosphere.

31. Estimates are that there are eight major plates with additional minor plates.

32. No; continents and oceanic crust as well ride atop the tectonic plates.

33. The site of lithospheric expansion at a divergent plate boundary.

34. Convergent; divergent; transform.

35. Different plates move with different speeds ranging from approximately 2 to 10 cm per year.

36. Seafloor spreading.

37. Continents tear apart.

38. New lithosphere.

39. Oceanic–oceanic; continental–continental; oceanic–continental.

40. The more-dense tectonic plate descends (subducts) below the less-dense plate. Material of the subducting plate that warms and softens in the high temperatures and pressures of earth's interior can recycle into the mantle.

41. High mountain chains.

42. Plates move along beside one another scraping one another as they go.

43. Linear valleys can sometimes be found along transform boundaries. The valleys form from the grinding together of plates.

44. The San Andreas Fault is a transform boundary. The slice of California to the west of the fault is moving north relative to the rest of California. The sticking and slipping of the plates along the boundary create earthquakes.

45. Along plate boundaries.

46. Intraplate quakes.

47. A tsunami is a very large, fast-moving ocean wave generated by an earthquake, explosion, or other disturbance.

48. It is logarithmic to accommodate the wide variation in earthquake magnitudes.

49. 10 times more; 10 times less.

50. A one-point increase in Richter magnitude corresponds approximately to a 30-fold increase in the earthquake's energy.

Answers to Chapter 22 Multiple-Choice Questions

1a, 2b, 3a, 4a, 5c, 6a, 7b, 8c, 9b

Answers to Chapter 22 Integrated Science Concepts

Physics: Isostasy

1. Continental crust is less dense than oceanic crust, so it must sink further to achieve sufficient bouyant force to counter gravity.

2. Mountains have large portions of their mass sunk deep within the mantle—"roots"—to achieve isostatic balance.

Physics: What Forces Drive the Plates?

1. Heat transfer away from Earth's extremely hot interior toward its surface, as required by the Second Law of Thermodynamics, is currently considered to be a main reason there is convection in the mantle and, thus, the reason there are moving plates.

2. Plates ride on convection cells as asthenosphere moves laterally at the top of a cell.

3. The core is like a spherical set of burners. There is convection in Earth's interior just as there would be convection in the water heating on the stove.

4. According to the Slab-pull model, cooler, denser edges of plates sink by gravity into the asthenosphere and then pull the rest of the plate gradually along. In the Ridge-push model, the inclined lithosphere at a mid-ocean ridge gravitationally pushes the previously formed, older lithosphere away from the spreading center.

Biology: Life in the Trenches

1. Zero light, extreme cold, and crushing pressure.

2. Bacteria consume minerals released at hydrothermal vents and produce oxygen as a by-product.

3. Hydrothermal vents are fissures created by the grinding action of the plates.

Physics: Anatomy of a Tsunami

1. Both are waves, but a ripple's energy moves across a surface as it travels, whereas a tsunami's energy moves inside the body of water as it goes.

2. A massive underwater disturbance such as an earthquake.

3. A tsunami can be generated by subduction at a convergent boundary as the subducting plate "sticks" beneath the overriding plate. When the compressive force on the plates exceeds the force of friction between them, the plates jerk, which causes an earthquake. As rock snaps upward, it acts like a piston by pushing the water above it, generating a wave.

Answers to Chapter 22 Exercises

1. Is Earth's inner core solid and the outer core liquid because the inner core is cooler than the outer core? Explain your answer.

   No—the inner core is solid and the outer core is liquid because the greater weight of overlying earth makes pressure greater at the core. The pressure packs the atoms of the inner core too tightly to allow them to be in the liquid state.

2. What is the principal difference between the theory of plate tectonics and the continental drift hypothesis?

   Plate tectonics incorporates the essential ideas of continental drift but goes on to explain that tectonic plates—pieces of lithosphere—are what actually move about on Earth's surface, rather than just the continents.

3. How is magma generated at divergent plate boundaries?

   As plates pull apart, the weight of overlying crust on the asthenosphere is reduced. Under reduced pressure, rock in the asthenosphere partially melts to form magma.

4. What would happen if new lithosphere were created faster than it is destroyed?

   The surface area of the Earth would increase.

5. What kinds of plate boundaries feature subduction zones?

   Oceanic–oceanic convergent boundaries and oceanic–continental convergent boundaries.

6. Why are earthquakes common in subduction zones?

   The subducting and overlying plate stick together, build up strain, then slip in a jarring motion that generates seismic waves.

7. Briefly describe how an island arc forms.

   An island arc, or arc-shaped region of volcanic islands, forms where there is oceanic–oceanic convergence of plates. The subducting plate partially melts as it descends, creating magma. This magma in addition to magma from partial melting of the overlying plate rises toward the surface and erupts. The erupted magma cools and accumulates to form a volcanic mountain. This process is repeated in various locations along the subduction zone so that a string of volcanic mountains forms.

8. Why are there so many expressions like "solid earth," "old as the hills," and "terra firma" that suggest the Earth is unchanging?

   The human perception of a stable Earth is based on our limited lifetimes.

9. How did seismic waves contribute to the discovery of Earth's deep internal layers?

   The speed and direction of seismic waves depends on the density and physical state of the medium. The increases and decreases in speed of P waves and the inability of S waves to penetrate the outer core led scientists to deduce the presence of Earth's layers.

10. Why does crust "float" on the mantle?

    Crust is less dense than mantle.

11. Briefly describe the fossil evidence that Wegener cited to support continental drift.

    Fossils of single species were found on facing edges of continents. It would be highly improbable for an organism to evolve in exactly the same way in two separate locations. And such organisms would have no way of swimming or otherwise transporting themselves across the intervening ocean.

12. Why are volcanic mountain ranges often found along oceanic–continental convergent boundaries?

    The denser subducting plate partially melts to create magma beneath the overlying continental crust. When the magma rises and erupts through the overlying continental crust, volcanoes form.

13. What is the evidence that tectonic plates move?

    The evidence comes largely from seafloor spreading, which is suggested by the ages of rocks, magnetic striping, and the existence of mid-ocean ridges, trenches, and other signs of underwater geological activity. Correlation of intense geologic activity along plate boundaries also supports the movement of plates. Finally, evidence for continental drift (the migration of ancient ice sheets, and the matching of fossils and rock formations on opposite sides of oceans, etc.) all support plate tectonics as well.

14. Why are most earthquakes generated near plate boundaries?

    Earthquakes are caused by the sticking and slipping of huge masses of Earth—this happens at plate boundaries.

15. Magnetic stripes that were laid down on the Pacific Ocean seafloor are wider than the magnetic stripes laid down over the same time period on the Atlantic Ocean seafoor. What does this tell you about the rate of seafloor spreading of the Pacific Ocean compared to the Atlantic Ocean?

    Sea floor spreading is faster in the Pacific.

16. Are continents a permanent feature of our planet? Discuss why or why not. Estimates are that up to 80% of Earth's surface is covered with volcanic rocks. Use what you know about plate tectonics to explain why this would be true.

    No, continents can tear apart at divergent plate boundaries and water can fill the gap between them.

17. Could Los Angeles fall into the ocean, as is popularly thought? Why or why not?

    It cannot. It is traveling northward with respect to the rest of California, not westward, into the ocean. Besides, isostasy would prevent this.

18. Is plate tectonics a theory based on integrated science? Why or why not?

    Yes it is. Plate tectonics incorporates information from many scientific disciplines. For example, plate tectonics relies on geological information such as the types of rock found in the earth and on physics concepts such as heat transfer, gravity, and density. Fossil evidence (biology) provides evidence for the theory, and astronomical instruments (radio telescopes) are used to measure the actual motions of the plates.

19. Evidence of ancient ice sheets has been found in areas near the equator. Give two possible explanations for this.

    Either the climate changed or the regions themselves have migrated away from the poles. As it turns out, explanation #2 is correct.

20. What is meant by magnetic pole reversals? What useful information do they provide about earth's history?

    A magnetic pole reversal is the exchange of north and south magnetic poles. The switching of poles is recorded in the seafloor by magnetic striping. So the age and rate of spreading of the seafloor can be determined.

21. What is a very likely cause for the Earth's magnetic field?

    The circulation of charges within the liquid outer core.

22. Relate the generation of magma to pressure changes at divergent plate boundaries.

    At divergent plate boundaries, overlying weight of the earth and, thus, pressure are reduced. This allows asthenosphere rock to melt to the point of magma.

23. Cite one piece of evidence that suggests subduction once occurred off the West coast of the United States.

    The Cascade mountain range is a coastal volcanic mountain range. This type of mountain range is formed when an oceanic plate subducts beneath a continental plate.

24. Where is the oldest oceanic crust? The youngest?

    The oldest crust is the furthest from the seafloor spreading center and the youngest is at the rift valley.

25. Your friend who lives in Los Angeles says he is relieved when there are tiny earthquakes because that releases strain and prevents "the big one." Do you share his sense of relief? Why or why not?

    Tiny quakes do not release enough strain to prevent major quakes. The Richter scale is logarithmic—quakes with low magnitude can have millions time less energy than large magnitude quakes, so they do not necessarily help significantly in releasing built-up strain in the rocks.

Solutions to Chapter 22 Problems

1. $t = d/r = (600 \text{ km})/(3.5 \text{ cm/yr}) = (6 \times 10^7 \text{ cm})/(3.5 \text{ cm/yr}) = 1.7 \times 10^7$ years = about 17 million years.

2. $d = rt = (3.5 \text{ cm/yr})(20 \text{ yr}) = 70$ cm.

3. $t = d/r = (1 \times 10^2 \text{ km})/(14.2 \text{ cm/yr}) = 7.04 \times 10^5$ years = about 700,000 years.

4. As the diagram shows, lithosphere at this divergent boundary moves 50 km away from where it originates in 3 million years. So, using $r = d/t$, we see this new lithosphere moves at a rate of (50 km)/(3 × 10^6 years) = 1.7 cm/year. However, the rate of seafloor spreading is double the rate at which new lithosphere moves from a central fissure. So the rate of seafloor spreading = 2 × 1.7 cm/year = 3.4 cm/yr.

Chapter 23: Rocks and Minerals

Answers to Chapter 23 Review Questions

1. Iron, oxygen, silicon, magnesium, nickel, calcium, aluminum, and sodium.

2. Both contain layers that are separated by differentiation.

3. Silicon and oxygen.

4. A naturally occurring solid material that has both a definite chemical composition and crystalline structure.

5. Every mineral has a crystalline structure—a repeating, orderly arrangement of its atoms or molecules.

6. They are polymorphs.

7. It cleaves along the planes of weakness—planes along which atoms that are held together by weak bonds.

8. The stronger the bonds within a mineral, the harder the mineral.

9. Because each mineral has a unique combination of crystal structure and composition.

10. (b) does not exhibit the crystal form of quartz, which is likely attributable to it having grown in a cramped environment.

11. When magma starts to cool, atoms in the hot liquid lose kinetic energy. Then, the attractive forces among them pull them into orderly crystal structures.

12. No, they revert to graphite when removed from high pressure conditions, though the process takes a billion years.

13. About 4000.

14. Silicates—they make up 92% of Earth's minerals.

15. Many ores are oxides.

16. An aggregate of minerals.

17. Formed by fire. Changed form.

18. Igneous rocks; Earth was covered by molten rock during the time of its formation. This molten rock slowly cooled to produce igneous rock.

19. Intrusive rocks are crystallized from magma below Earth's surface; extrusive rocks cool and solidify at the surface.

20. Due to increased temperature, decreased pressure, and added water.

21. 30°C for each kilometer of depth; geothermal gradient.

22. There are only three principal kinds of magma. Each of them produces many kinds of igneous rocks because rocks are composed of minerals, and minerals cystallize from magma according to their melting points.

23. Sediments making up detrital sedimentary rocks are particles weathered from other rocks. A chemical sedimentary rock is made up of sediments that originate as dissolved material.

24. Weathering; erosion; deposition; sedimentation.

25. Mechanical and chemical.

26. To become stable at new temperatures and pressures.

27. Foliated and nonfoliated.

28. When it melts.

29. The graphical representation of the processes of change that affect rock.

30. The conversion of sedimentary rock to sediment.

31. Hydrologic and atmospheric cycles, for example.

Answers to Chapter 23 Multiple-Choice Questions

1b, 2d, 3e, 4b, 5b, 6b, 7c, 8b

Answers to Chapter 23 Integrated Science Concepts

Chemistry: The Silicate Tetrahedron

1. Silicon and oxygen.

2. Silicon and oxygen form strong bonds to give each atom a full valence shell.

3. It has four unpaired electrons available for bonding.

Physics: The Texture of Igneous Rocks

1. The magma that produced the rock crystallized over a broad range of temperatures—the large crystals cooled slowly, but the small ones cooled quickly; porphyritic.

2. Crystals grow by adding on atoms to their exteriors. A slowly cooling crystal has plenty of time to grow large before it has to compete with its neighbors for space and available atoms. In other words, the rate of nucleation is slow compared to the rate of crystal growth. Possible examples: granite and gabbro.

3. Large numbers of small crystals form quickly in a fast-cooling magma as the atoms lose energy. They cannot grow large without bumping into neighboring crystals. Possible example: rhyolite.

4. The atoms lose energy so quickly that they freeze in place. Possible example: pumice or obsidian.

5. Large.

Biology: Coal

1. Photosynthesis.

2. The remains fall to the bottoms of oxygen-deficient swamps.

3. It is combusted.

4. Coal is the product of successive stages of development. At each stage, heat and pressure remove impurities (particulary volatiles) leaving energy-rich organic molecules behind.

5. It is made of plant remains rather than minerals.

6. Coal could not begin to form until land plants evolved. This occurred some 400 million years ago.

Answers to Chapter 23 Exercises

1. What does roundness tell us about sediment particles?

   They have been weathered.

2. What can we say about a rock that is composed of various sizes of sediments in a disorganized fashion?

   It is not well sorted; it hasn't been transported far from its source.

3. Describe the process of crystallization.

   In crystallization, ions, molecules, or atoms solidify into orderly arrangements characterized by a repeating basic structural unit. It is characterized by two steps: nucleation and crystal growth.

4. How does the atomic structure of glass differ from the atomic structure of the mineral calcite?

   Calcite has a regular, repeating crystal structure, while the atoms of glass are randomly distributed.

5. Calcite is a nonsilicate mineral. Is it therefore rare?

   No, it is actually very common, making up limestone, and so forth. It is the most abundant nonsilicate mineral.

6. The chemical formula for quartz is SiO_2. What is the chemical formula of coesite, a polymorph of quartz?

   SiO_2.

7. An impression—a type of fossil—is made by an organism that is buried quickly, before it can decompose. Is this impression of a fish contained in an igneous, sedimentary, or metamorphic rock? Why do you think so?

   All fossils are contained in sedimentary rocks.

8. Your friend makes the following remark. Is he right or wrong? Defend your answer: "Minerals in Earth's crust generally do not contain oxygen because oxygen exists in the gaseous state at surface temperatures."

   He is suffering from a few misconceptions. Pure oxygen is gaseous at surface temperatures but compounds of oxygen are not, necessarily. Countless millions of compounds containing oxygen are solid at surface temperatures—take iron oxide, or rust, just as one example. Oxygen is the second most abundant element in the crust and the silicates, which comprise 92% of minerals, all contain oxygen. Other classes of mineral such as the carbonates and oxides contain oxygen as well. Oxygen isn't just for breathing!

9. Retrograde metamorphosis is the process of a metamorphic rock returning to its original unmetamorphosed state. (a) What surface conditions encourage retrograde metamorphism to occur? (b) Why don't rocks undergo retrograde metamorphism as easily as they undergo metamorphism?

   (a) Decreasing temperature and pressure. (b) Retrograde metamorphism occurs when temperature and/or pressure are reduced. Chemical processes occur more slowly as temperature is decreased.

10. What is more plentiful on Earth—the group of minerals known as feldspars or the group of minerals known as silicates?

    The feldspars are a subset of the nonferromagnesian silicates, so the silicates are more plentiful.

11. Does a mineral's stability depend on temperature and pressure? Explain.

    Yes; added thermal energy can break apart bonds in a mineral, while added pressure can alter a crystal's geometry by squeezing positive and negative ions.

12. How does recrystallization produce a metamorphic rock?

    New mineral crystals form at the expense of existing ones—a rock changes the minerals it contains without changing the atoms that are present.

13. Name a common intrusive igneous rock often found on the surface of mountains. Explain how this intrusive igneous rock, formed underground, is exposed at the surface.

    Granite is exposed as layers of surface rock are eroded.

14. Describe the different conditions that produce the four different kinds of igneous rocks.

    Fine-grained rocks form rapidly at the Earth's surface or within the upper crust; coarse-grained rocks cool slowly; porphyritic rocks form from minerals that cooled at different rates; glassy rocks are those that cooled almost instantly.

15. Why are metamorphic rocks created underground?

    They are formed at high temperatures and/or pressures or from solutions associated with magma.

16. Cycles in nature, such as the rock cycle, can be viewed as consisting of materials and processes. What are the processes of change that take place in the rock cycle?

    Crystallization; weathering, erosion, transportation, deposition, lithification, metamorphism, and melting.

17. Is rock conserved in the same sense that energy is conserved? Why or why not?

Rock is not conserved in the sense that energy is conserved. Rock can be created (by crystallization of magma) and destroyed (by melting), although the atoms rock is composed of cannot be created or destroyed (except by nuclear means).

18. Why does rock melt to form magma?

It melts because overlying pressure is reduced, because water is added and thereby lowers magma's melting point, and when it is heated by other magma flowing nearby.

19. How can one parent magma produce a variety of igneous rocks?

Minerals with high melting points crystallize out of a magma first; the remaining magma, therefore, has a different composition. Rocks form successively as different mixtures of minerals are produced from different magmas at different temperatures.

20. Why are coarse-grained igneous rocks generally intrusive igneous rocks? Why are extrusive igneous rocks usually fine-grained?

Coarse-grained rocks are formed by slow cooling; fine-grained rocks have small crystals and are, therefore, cooled quickly.

21. Would you expect to find any fossils in limestone? Why or why not?

Yes; limestone is a sedimentary rock formed from calcium carbonate which can be obtained from the hard body parts of animals.

22. What makes gold so soft while quartz and diamond are so much harder?

Hardness relates to the strengths of bonds in a crystal. Quartz and diamond have stronger internal bonds than gold.

23. The Earth's mineral resources are used in many ways. Many of these resources are plentiful, yet they are also nonrenewable. Once extracted and used, they do not grow back over the span of human lifetimes. What are some possible problems associated with the extraction of minerals?

High consumption of fossil fuels to supply the energy needed for processing minerals; disruption of ecosystems; erosion and landslides; toxic waste.

24. Many minerals can be identified by their physical properties, such as hardness, crystal form, cleavage, color, luster, and density (specific gravity). Why is identifying a mineral by its crystal form usually difficult?

Well-shaped crystals occur only rarely in nature, because minerals typically grow in cramped spaces.

25. Can dikes and plutons be observed above ground? Can they form above ground? Explain.

Dikes and plutons are igneous rock intrusions, forming only below Earth's surface. They are visible only when overlying rock erodes.

26. Why is the ocean salty?

The ocean is salty due to sodium and potassium and sodium compounds which have been carried far from their source of weathering in solution.

27. Why is asbestos in drinking water much less harmful than asbestos in air?

Asbestos is primarily harmful to lung tissue when inhaled.

28. Is cleavage the same thing as crystal form? Why or why not?

No, the planar surfaces we see in cleavage are where a mineral breaks due to a weakness in crystal structure or bond strength. The planar surfaces in a crystal form are the external shape from the crystal's internal arrangement of atoms.

Solution to Chapter 23 Problem

Refer to the geothermal gradient. Does temperature change faster with increasing depth between 0 km and 10 km or between 40 km and 50 km? Can you offer an explanation?

Approximating the curve as a linear graph, the slope is about 30°C per kilometer. Temperature changes faster near the surface because, deeper in the Earth, rock is surrounded by more insulating rock that slows heat loss.

Chapter 24: Earth's Surface—Land and Water

Answers to Chapter 24 Review Questions

1. 71%.

2. Highest point is Mt. Everest at 8,848 meters; the Mariana Trench is the deepest point at 10,668 meters deep.

3. (a) *Compressional stress* is the pushing together of masses of rock; *tensional stress* is the pulling apart of rock; *shear stress* is produced by rock blocks sliding past one another. (b) Rock can deform plastically or elastically or fracture under stress.

4. Folding occurs when rock can flow and bend, which requires elevated temperature or pressure.

5. Reverse fault: the hanging wall and footwall are pushed together resulting in the rocks in the hanging wall being pushed above the footwall. Normal fault: rocks in the hanging wall and footwall are pulled apart, and rocks in the hanging wall drop down relative to the rocks in the footwall. Strike-slip fault: rock masses have side-to-side motion with respect to one another with no vertical displacement.

6. Most earthquakes are located along faults. Also, they provide clues about Earth's geologic history, affect the movement of groundwater, and indicate subsurface deposits of resources, including fossil fuels.

7. Possible answers: (1) folded mountains—The Appalachians, Rockies, and Himalayas; (2) upwarped mountains—Black Hills of South Dakota and Adirondack Mountains; (3) fault-block mountains: Tetons in Wyoming and the Sierra Nevada in California; (4) Volcano—Mauna Loa, Mt Fuji, Sunset Crater.

8. They increase the plasticity of overlying rock so that it convects upward, melts under reduced pressure near the surface, and erupts as lava which accumulates to form a volcano.

9. In the Ring of Fire in the Pacific Ocean.

10. Mid-ocean ridges.

11. Most water is located in the oceans (97.6%); most freshwater is located in ice caps and glaciers.

12. (a) Water evaporates at the Earth's surface, enters the atmosphere as water vapor, condenses into clouds, precipitates (usually as rain or snow), and falls back to the surface, only to evaporate again and go through the cycle once again. (b) The portion of the water cycle that shapes landmasses most (not surprisingly) occurs when the water resides on Earth's surface, after precipitation and before evaporation.

13. Continental shelf—underwater extension of the continent; continental slope—sloping boundary between continental and oceanic crust; continental rise—a wedge of sediment built up at the base of the continental slope.

14. It is varied, featuring expansive flat areas (abyssal plains) but also towering seamounts and trenches that are even deeper than Mt. Everest, the world's tallest surface mountain.

15. About 80% of freshwater is frozen in ice caps and glaciers; about 20% is in groundwater; less 1 percent is in streams and lakes.

16. About 75% of it evaporates immediately; most of the rest soaks into the ground; whatever is left becomes runoff.

17. Yes; a watershed is the land that drains into a stream. Water where you live drains somewhere, so everyone lives in a watershed.

18. In the saturation zone.

19. It is not flat but roughly approximates surface contours.

20. Groundwater.

21. A large percentage of precipitation does not become runoff—it infiltrates into the ground and slowly moves until it empties into stream channels, which convey it to the surface.

22. (a) Water, wind, gravity, and glacial ice; (b) gravity; (c) running water—streams, in particular.

23. They no longer have enough energy to carry the sediments.

24. A delta.

25. Groundwater is removed which compacts sediments so that the land surface is lowered.

26. Agree; recharging can take hundreds or thousands of years.

27. Sinkholes and caves and caverns.

28. Wind has a weaker effect on the land surface. It lacks the eroding and carrying power of water and ice. Additionally, it's more intermittent and cannot cause chemical weathering.

29. Alpine glaciers are found in high mountainous valleys. Continental glaciers cover broad areas.

30. Plow: it scrapes and plucks up rock and sediment. Sled: it transports and deposits rocks and sediments.

Answers to Chapter 24 Multiple-Choice Questions

1d, 2b, 3a, 4c, 5c, 6a, 7d

Answers to Chapter 24 Integrated Science Concepts

Physics: Ocean Waves

1. They become too tall from the bunching of many waves.

2. Wind is the disturbance that creates waves.

3. Energy.

4. The bottom part of the orbital motion that characterizes an ocean wave is affected by the depth of the water. When the water's depth gets shallower and approaches half of the wave's wavelength, the bottom part of the wave slows due to friction between the wave and ocean bottom. Therefore, longer waves are slowed at depths that would not affect shorter waves.

Chemistry: Ocean Water

1. Only a few elements and compounds are present in abundance.

2. Just five: they are sodium chloride ($NaCl$); magnesium chloride ($MgCl_2$); sodium sulfate (Na_2SO_4); calcium chloride ($CaCl_2$); sodium fluoride (NaF).

3. The composition of seawater remains relatively constant.

Chemistry: Groundwater Contamination

1. Sewage, agricultural chemicals such as nitrate fertilizers, and pesticides.

2. Groundwater recharges very slowly, plus it is difficult to clean up because it is difficult to access.

3. Gas stations typically store MTBE in underground tanks. If a tank leaks, MTBE can infiltrate underground and pollute wells.

Answers to Chapter 24 Exercises

1. Relate plate tectonics to mountain building.

   Colliding tectonic plates produce compressive forces that deform rock plastically into folds. Folds on a large scale produce folded mountains and upwarped mountains. Volcanoes form where magma erupts and then accumulates—often where tectonic plates diverge. Fault-block mountains result where huge blocks of rock are subject to tension that occurs as tectonic plates move apart.

2. List five major landforms in the United States and describe them in as much geologic detail as you can.

   Answers will vary. Some possible answers include the Mississippi Delta, the Black Hills, the San Andreas Fault; the Great Plains; the Appalachian Mountains; and the Grand Canyon. Geologic details about all of these can be found in the chapter.

3. Where is the continental crust lower than it is under the ocean?

   Where it is below sea level—for example, on the shores of the Dead Sea, 400 meters below sea level.

4. Why must aquifers consist of material that has both high permeability and high porosity?

   Aquifers are regions in the saturation zone through which water can flow.

5. How did the development of groundwater resources lower the land elevation in certain regions of the Southwest?

   Extraction of groundwater caused subsidence.

6. How are a deep-sea fan and a continental rise similar? What is the relationship between them?

   They are both depositional bodies. Sea fans are bodies of deposited sediments that over time merge to create a continental rise.

7. Rain falls on land. What will happen to it?

   Some will evaporate, some will become surface run-off; the rest will percolate underground.

8. Why does the area of the continental shelf change over geologic time?

   When sea level rises, seas spill onto the shore, expanding the continental shelf.

9. What is the relationship between the level of the water table and the depth to which a well must be drilled?

   A well must be drilled past the level of the water table.

10. What do sinkholes and caverns have in common?

11. Which of the three kinds of tectonic plate boundaries is most strongly associated with mountain building?

    Convergent plate boundaries

12. In the formation of a river delta, why are large particles deposited first, followed by smaller particles further out? Defend your answer.

    Large particles are deposited first, because it takes more energy to move them. As the stream slows as it moves toward the sea, it deposits smaller and smaller particles.

13. Which of the following three agents of transportation—wind, water, or ice—transports the largest boulders? Why?

    Ice. Glaciers moving across a landscape loosen and lift up blocks of rock and incorporate them into the ice. They literally pick up everything in their paths. As the ice melts, the rock debris is deposited.

14. How do deposits from glacial ice differ from rocks deposited by rivers?

    They are not as well sorted.

15. Can a stream erode land that lies below sea level? Explain.

    No. Water flows downhill from higher elevations to the sea. So, it can't carry sediment up to sea level from where the land is below sea level.

16. Removal of groundwater can cause subsidence. If removal of groundwater is stopped, will the land likely rise again to its original level? Defend your answer.

    If groundwater removal is stopped, land subsidence will stop. The ground, however, does not return to its original level. The weight of overlying sediments prevents the clays from expanding. Once the aquifer has been compacted, it cannot expand to its original level.

17. Is groundwater stored in underground rivers? What's your reasoning?

    Underground rivers occur, but they are rare. Water typically moves through pore spaces, faults, and fractures and does not have large channels to move through.

18. How is surface water both a creator and a destroyer of sediments and sedimentary rocks?

    Surface water creates sediments by weathering sedimentary rock; surface water destroys sedimentary rock for the same reason.

19. If you look at a map of any part of the world, you'll see that older cities are located beside rivers or where rivers existed when cities were built. What is your explanation?

    Freshwater provides the sustenance for life. This includes water for drinking, agricultural uses, sanitation, and transportation.

20. The oceans consist of saltwater, yet evaporation over the ocean surface produces clouds that produce freshwater. Why no salt?

    As evaporation occurs over the ocean surface, only the H_2O evaporates, the NaCl is left behind, thus making the seawater saltier. Although most of the NaCl is left behind, minute salt particles in the ocean spray can act as condensation nuclei, which aid in the formation of water vapor droplets. The amount of salt particles, however, is so small that precipitation is essentially freshwater.

21. Is the infiltration of water greatest on steep rocky slopes or on gentle sandy slopes? Defend your answer.

    Infiltration is greater on gentle sandy slopes, because sandy materials have a high porosity, and because runoff is greater on steeper slopes.

22. If the water table at location X is lower than the water table at location Y, does groundwater flow from X to Y or Y to X?

    Groundwater flows from areas where the water table is high to where the water table is low. So groundwater would flow from Y to X.

Solutions to Chapter 24 Problems

1. The volume of solids in a sediment sample is 975 cm^3, and the volume of open space is 325 cm^3. What is the porosity of the sediment? Describe what the result of your calculation means in physical terms.

    Porosity = (volume of open space)/(volume of open space + volume of solids) = 325 cm^3/325 cm^3 + 975 cm^3 = .25; the volume of open space is one-fourth the total volume of rock.

2. Show that freshwater is 2% of the water on Earth; Frozen water is 1.9%; and groundwater is 0.49% based on the data in Figure 24.9.

    From Figure 24.16: freshwater is 2.4% of water on Earth. Frozen water is found in ice caps and glaciers and equals 1.9%. Groundwater is 0.49%.

3. Show that a mountain that can be approximated by a box 4 km × 3 km × 4 km would exist for about 329 million years.

    Volume of the mountain = 4 km × 3 km × 4 km = (4000 m) × (3000 m) × (4000 m) = 4.8 × 10^{10} m^3. Assume the rate of erosion is about 146 m^3 per year as stated in the *Math Connection* example. Then the duration of the mountain = (volume of mountain)/(rate of erosion) = 3.29 × 10^8 years or 329 million years.

Chapter 25: Weather

Answers to Chapter 25 Review Questions

1. Weather is the state of the atmosphere at a particular time and place; climate is the general pattern of weather over a long period of years.

2. Atmospheric pressure; temperature; wind; precipitation; cloudiness; and humidity.

3. Rays of the Sun strike the poles at a steep angle with the result that solar radiation is less intense than nearer the equator, resulting in lowered temperature.

4. The tilt of Earth's axis produces the differences in solar intensity; this gives rise to seasons and affects the length of daylight.

5. Radiation emitted from Earth has a lower frequency than radiation emitted by the Sun.

6. Molecules of atmosphere absorb solar or terrestrial radiation which energizes them and sends them aloft.

7. Atmospheric pressure decreases with altitude.

8. The troposphere.

9. Temperature decreases steadily as density decreases. Fewer atmospheric molecules to trap terrestrial radiation.

10. Uneven heating of Earth's surface.

11. Warm air is characterized by low density and low air pressure, while cool air is characterized by high density and high pressure.

12. Local differences in surface heating give rise to small-scale convection cells and pressure gradients, and these create small-scale local winds which are changeable. Planet-scale temperature differences produce much larger convection cells and pressure gradients that give rise to prevailing winds, which are on a global scale and are relatively permanent.

13. An ocean current is a stream of water that moves relative to the larger ocean.

14. The Gulf Stream flows northward along the North American Coast warming Norway and Great Britain.

15. Increases.

16. It condenses.

17. Air rises, expands, and cools. As the air cools, water molecules move slower and condensation occurs. If there are larger and slower-moving particles or ions present in the air, water vapor condenses on these particles to create a cloud.

18. (a) They do sink. (b) However, as they fall, they are carried upward by rising air currents (updrafts).

19. A cold front develops as a colder, denser air mass advances into and displaces a stationary warm air mass; a warm front is air that moves into territory that had been occupied by a cold air mass.

20. They are associated with day-to-day weather variation.

21. (a) A hurricane is a cyclone—an area of low pressure that winds flow around and they occur in the warm moist conditions of the tropics; (b) latent heat released by large amounts of condensing water in warm, moist air.

22. A tornado is a rotating column of air extending from a thunderstorm to the ground.

23. (a) There is a strong observed correlation between the rise of carbon dioxide emissions from human activities and average global temperature increases. (b) When trees are cut down, the carbon dioxide they would have absorbed is released into the atmosphere.

24. Disagree—climatologists cannot predict the future climate in this much detail.

Answers to Chapter 25 Multiple-Choice Questions

1b, 2d, 3b, 4a, 5a, 6c, 7b, 8d, 9a

Answers to Chapter 25 Integrated Science Concepts

Chemistry: The Atmospheric "Ozone Hole"

1. Good ozone is the O_3 molecule when it is present in the stratosphere; bad ozone is O_3 found in the air we breathe.

2. CFCs release chlorine atoms high up in the stratosphere, where they react with and destroy ozone molecules. Further, the chlorine atom catalyzes the ozone-destroying reaction so that one of them can destroy 100,000 or more ozone molecules.

Physics: The Coriolis Effect

1. The Coriolis influence winds as well as surface currents by causing them to rotate with respect to the Earth from left to right (as viewed from above the Earth at the North Pole).

2. (a) A cyclone moves counterclockwise in the Northern hemisphere. (b) An anticyclone moves counterclockwise in the Southern hemisphere. Cyclones and anticyclones both rotate in the directions they do because of the Coriolis effect.

Physics: The Greenhouse Effect

1. Whitewash is sometimes applied to greenhouses to better reflect light, thus reducing the amount of incoming solar radiation and subsequent indoor temperature.

2. Without the greenhouse effect, the Earth's average temperature would be a frigid −18°C otherwise. An intensified greenhouse effect would be a bad thing, because it could lead to global warming.

Answers to Chapter 25 Exercises

1. In what direction does a sea breeze blow? Does it blow in the day or at night? What causes a sea breeze?

   A sea breeze blows from the sea toward the shore and occurs mostly during the day. The reason is that land cools off faster than the ocean, so during the day, cooler, high-pressure air blows toward the land. At night, the cooler, high-pressure air forms over land, so it flows toward the area of lower pressure out to sea.

2. What are Hadley cells? Why are they important?

   Hadley cells are the pairs of convection cells that comprise the prevailing winds. Winds as well as precipitation and air pressure vary according to the flow described by these convection cells.

3. What slows low-altitude winds relative to winds high in the troposphere?

   Friction.

4. What kind of weather is associated with an approaching cold front? With an approaching warm front?

   As a cold front approaches, cirrus clouds typically form, wind shifts direction, and temperature and air pressure drop. As a warm front approaches, cirrus clouds may form then thicken so that the sky becomes overcast. Winds usually pick up and snow or rain may fall.

5. After a day of skiing in the Rocky Mountains, you decide to go indoors and get a cup of hot cocoa. As you enter the ski lodge, your eyeglasses fog up. Why?

   The change in environment from cold to warm. As we leave the cold outdoors the warm air inside comes into contact with the cold surface of the eyeglasses. As the air touching the glasses cools to its dew point, water vapor condenses onto the eyeglasses. Notice the similarity to Exercise 13—same physics, different situation.

6. Use what you learned about air pressure and barometers to analyze and explain how a straw works.

   An old-fashioned mercury barometer works in a way similar to a straw: as the weight of the atmosphere pushes the mercury in a dish down, the mercury rises in a low-pressure glass column. Similarly, when one sucks on a straw, one reduces the pressure in the straw and this allows the weight of the atmosphere to press the liquid up into the straw.

7. In some places, temperature inversions (areas where the air above is warmer than the air below) are common. Local air pollution can then become a serious problem. Why is that?

   The layer of cold air only allows minimal convection currents to occur.

8. Identify the clouds shown in the photo. How are they formed? What cloud group do they belong to?

   These clouds are cumulus clouds, which are clouds of vertical development. Like other clouds, these formed from water vapor in rising air that expanded, cooled, and condensed.

9. The Earth is closest to the Sun in January, but January is cold in the Northern Hemisphere. Explain.

   Seasonal temperatures are caused by solar intensity, solar radiation per area. In the winter in the Northern Hemisphere, the tilt of Earth's axis leads to solar radiation at the widest angle, reducing solar intensity to a minimum.

10. During a summer visit to Cancun, Mexico, you stay in an air-conditioned room. Getting ready to leave your room for the beach, you put on your sunglasses. The minute you step outside, your sunglasses fog up. Why?

The change in environment from cold to warm. As you leave the air-conditioned room, the warm air outside comes into contact with the cold surface of the sunglasses. During contact, the cold surface cools the air by conduction, and the warm air's ability to hold water vapor decreases. As the air cools to its dew point, water vapor condenses onto the sunglasses.

11. Air is warmed and rises at the equator and then cools and sinks at the poles, as shown in the figure below. Is this an accurate picture of the global circulation of air? Explain why or why not.

It is not accurate. Atmospheric circulation is broken up into six convection cells due to the influence of the Coriolis effect.

The low cloud cover acts as an insulation blanket inhibiting the outflow of terrestrial radiation.

12. As an air mass moves first upslope and then downslope over a mountain, what happens to the air's moisture and heat content?

As an air mass is pushed upward over a mountain, the rising air cools, and if the air is humid, clouds form and precipitation occurs. As the air mass moves down the other side of the mountain (the leeward slope), it warms. This descending air is dry, because most of its moisture was removed in the form of clouds and precipitation on the windward (upslope) side of the mountain.

13. Why are condensation and saturation more likely to occur on a cold day than on a warm day?

Because cool air has slower moving molecules, and warm air can hold more water vapor than cold air.

14. How do fronts cause clouds and precipitation?

When two air masses make contact, differences in temperature, moisture, and pressure can cause one air mass to ride over the other, forming clouds and causing precipitation.

15. Why does the surface temperature of the ground increase on a calm, clear night as low cloud cover moves overhead?

The low cloud cover acts as an insulation blanket inhibiting the outflow of terrestrial radiation.

16. Why does dew form on the ground during clear, calm summer nights?

On a clear summer night, the ground cools as it radiates away heat absorbed during daytime and this has a cooling effect on surrounding air. As air temperature lowers, relative humidity increases. If leaves of grass or other surfaces cool below the cooled air's dew point, dew will form as the humid air comes into contact with them.

17. Why does warm, moist air blowing over cold water result in fog?

Warm air is able to hold more water vapor before becoming saturated than can cold air. As warm moist air blows over cold water, it cools, which causes the water vapor to condense into tiny droplets of fog.

18. Explain why your ears pop when you ascend to higher altitudes.

The air pressure at higher altitudes is less than at the surface. Time is required for your body to adjust to this new pressure, so the air inside your body pushes outward more than the atmosphere pushes inward, producing that popping feeling.

19. What role does the Sun play in ocean currents?

The Sun heats the ocean unevenly; equatorial waters are warmed more than parts of the ocean nearer the poles. Currents redistribute heat so that it is dispersed more evenly.

20. How does the ocean influence weather on land?

The ocean acts to (1) moderate the temperature of coastal lands; and (2) provide a reservoir for atmospheric moisture.

21. Why is it important that mountain climbers wear sunglasses and sunblock even when temperatures are below freezing?

At high altitudes, there is a higher concentration of UV radiation due to a decrease in the concentration of UV-absorbing atmospheric gases.

22. Why does the East Coast of the United States experience wider seasonal variation than the West Coast, even though both areas have oceans along their margins?

23. The aneroid barometer, which measures atmospheric pressure, is at the heart of the altimeters (devices that measure altitude) used in modern aviation. What's the connection between a barometer and an altimeter?

Because pressure decreases in a regular way with altitude, a device for measuring pressure can be used to measure altitude by recalibrating the scale.

24. What does convection in Earth's atmosphere produce? What does convection in the Earth's mantle produce?

Wind; plate tectonics.

25. What would be a good state for you to live in if you like extreme temperatures? If you like a moderate climate? Explain why your preferred area has the weather patterns it has.

People who prefer definite seasons prefer inland areas, while those who like more moderate climates would prefer to live in coastal areas, due to the moderating effect of large bodies of water on climate (due to water's high specific heat capacity).

26. While hiking, you survey the sky from a mountaintop. The sky is blue everywhere except for a puffy cloud directly over a mountain. Explain how orographic lifting caused this cloud to form.

This cloud apparently formed though orographic lifting. This means that a parcel of warm, moist air moved up the mountain's upward-sloping side. As the air lifted, it cooled and water vapor in it condensed to form a cloud.

27. How might you expect vegetation on the leeward side of a mountain to differ from the vegetation on the windward side?

The leeward side of a mountain has a much drier climate than the windward side, so leeward vegetation would consist of plants adapted for dry climates—cacti and succulents, rather than ferns and conifers, for example.

Answers to Chapter 25 Problems

1. Consider a house at sea level that has 2000 square feet of floor area. What is the total force that the air inside this house exerts upward on the ceiling?

   Standard atmospheric pressure = 14.7 lb/in^2. Convert this to units of feet: (14.7 lb/in^2) × (144 in^{2}ft^2), and we have atmospheric pressure = 2100 lb/ft^2. Knowing that pressure is defined as force per area, we have $F = P \times A$. So the total force that the air inside the house exerts upward on the ceiling is (2100 lb/ft^2) × (2000 ft^2) = 4.2 × 10^6 lb of force.

2. If a tornado passed next to the front of the house, the pressure there could easily drop by 15% in less than a second. Calculate the net force on the front door of a closed house if the outside pressure suddenly dropped by 15%.

   The air inside the house is at standard atmospheric pressure; from Table 25.1 this is 14.7 lbs. per square inch. The outside air is at 85% of this pressure or (0.85)(14.7 lbs./in^2) = 12.5 lbs./in^2. Thus, the net pressure pushing the door outward = (14.7 lbs./in^2) − (12.5 lbs./in^2) = 2.2 lbs./in^2. The area of the door is 6.5 feet by 3 feet or (78 in)(36 in) = 2,808 in^2. To find the outward force on the door, we use the relation Force = Pressure × Area. We have: Force = (2.2 lbs./in^2)(2,808 in^2) = 6178 lbs. Employing significant figures, the outward force on the door due to the tornado is 6200 lbs. It's easy to see why the door will be flung far in the storm.

3. At 50°C, the maximum amount of water vapor in the air is 9 g/m^3. If the relative humidity is 40%, what is the mass of water vapor in 1 m^3 of air?

   Relative humidity = [(water vapor content)/(water vapor capacity)] × 100%. Rearrange to solve for the mass of water in 1 m^3 of air: water vapor content = [(relative humidity)(water vapor capacity)]/100%. Then: water vapor content at 50°C = [(40%)(9 g/m^3)]/100% = 3.6 g/m^3.

Chapter 26: Earth's History

Answers to Chapter 26 Review Questions

1. Bacterial life: end of March; *Homo sapiens*: 11:50 December 31; recorded history 11:59 December 31.

2. The present is the key to the past; the natural laws of physics, chemistry, and biology that we know of today have been constant over the geologic past.

3. 1) Original horizontality. Layers of sediment are deposited evenly, with each new layer laid down nearly horizontally over older sediment.

   2) Superposition. In an undeformed sequence of sedimentary rocks, each layer is older than the one above and younger than the one below.

   3) Crosscutting. An igneous intrusion or fault that cuts through preexisting rock is younger than the rock through which it cuts.

   4) Inclusion. Any inclusion is older than the rock containing it.

   5) Faunal succession. Fossil organisms succeed one another in a definite, irreversible time sequence.

4. The collection of clues to Earth's past buried in its rocks.

5. An unconformity.

6. Eon.

7. About 4.5 billion years.

8. Almost 90%.

9. Hadean eon: A crust formed; Archaean eon: formation of oceans.

10. Cambrian, Ordovician, Silurian, Devonian, Carboniferous (Mississippian and Pennsylvanian), and Permian.

11. The Silurian brought the emergence of terrestrial life, the earliest known being terrestrial plants that had a well-developed circulatory system (vascular plants).

12. The Carboniferous.

13. The age of reptiles.

14. A worldwide rise in sea level occurred during the Cretaceous period, probably due to the breakup of Pangaea.

15. Only that of Europe and Asia has survived to the present time.

16. Tertiary: Paleocene, Eocene, Oligocene, Miocene, Pliocene.

    Quaternary: Pleistocene, Holocene.

17. Humans evolved during the Cenozoic era in the Quaternary period and Pleistocene epoch.

18. Warm, woolly coats.

19. A relatively warm, interglacial period.

Answers to Chapter 26 Multiple-Choice Questions

1c; 2d; 3b; 4a; 5c; 6b; 7c

Answers to Chapter 26 Integrated Science Concepts

Physics: Radiometric Dating of Rock

1. The half-life of uranium-238 is 4.5 billion years; potassium-40 has a half-life of 1.3 billion years; carbon-14 has a half-life of 5730 years.

2. Uranium-238.

3. Carbon-14.

Biology, Chemistry: The Great Transformation of Earth's Atmosphere

1. (a) The early Earth atmosphere had a much higher concentration of carbon dioxide (perhaps 80%) compared to what it has today (only 1/10 of 1%).

   (b) Free oxygen was not present in appreciable amounts in the Earth's early atmosphere but is plentiful enough now to support air-breathing organisms.

2. The availability of free oxygen in the air allowed land animals to evolve.

3. Earth's atmosphere was drastically transformed by cyanobacteria that absorbed carbon dioxide and produced free oxygen through photosynthesis.

Biology: The Permian Extinction

1. The Permian extinction caused the demise of about 90% of species living at the time.

2. A million-year-long volcanic eruption in Siberia; climate changes associated with the formation of Panagaea.

Biology, Astronomy: The Cretaceous Extinction

1. The iridium layer in the rock record corresponding to the Cretaceous.

2. The Nemesis theory argues that Earth experiences a mass extinction approximately once every 26 million years and that this periodicity is due to a hypothetical star named Nemesis, binary to the Sun. Every 26 million years, proponents argue, Nemesis comes close enough to the solar system to disturb comets, which proceed to bombard the inner solar system. The alternative view that a meteorite triggered the Cretaceous extinction neither posits a Nemesis star nor holds that mass extinctions are periodic.

Answers to Chapter 26 Exercises

1. Suppose a certain type of sediment is deposited in all modern streams. On a geologic expedition into unknown territory, we find the same type of deposit in ancient rocks. What can we say about the ancient rocks? What assumption are we making?

   We can assume that the ancient rocks represent the location of an ancient stream. This is an application of the Principle of Uniformitarianism.

2. Why don't all rock formations show a continuous sequence from the beginning of time to the present?

   Weathering and erosion, crustal uplifts, and other geologic processes can interrupt the normal sequence of deposition (which gives rise to unconformities).

3. How are fossils used in determining geologic time?

   Fossils are used to establish the relative ages of rocks, because geologists have been able to arrange different groups of fossils—and the time periods they were associated with—in a chronological sequence.

4. In a sequence of sedimentary rock layers, the oldest layer is on the bottom, and the youngest layer is at the top. What relative dating principle applies here?

   Superposition.

5. What role did tectonic activity play in the formation of the San Andreas fault?

   The collision between the westward moving North American Plate and the Pacific Ridge system occurred about 30 million years ago, creating the San Andreas fault.

6. What kinds of mammals evolved to occupy niches left vacant by the extinction of many Mesozoic reptiles?

   Bats, some large land mammals, and marine animals such as whales and dolphins.

7. Did life exist on Earth in the Precambrian? If so, cite two or three examples.

   Abundant microscopic life appeared at the end of the Precambrian.

8. If a sedimentary rock contains inclusions of metamorphic rock, which rock is older? Defend your answer.

   Sedimentary rock is older by the principle of inclusion.

9. Which isotopes are most appropriate for dating rocks from the following ages? (a) Early Precambrian time. (b) The Mesozoic era. (c) The late Pleistocene epoch.

   (a) Uranium-238 (or possibly Potassium-40, depending on how early). (b) Uranium-235 or Potassium-40 are best, but Uranium-238 will work too (but is not as precise). (c) Carbon-14.

10. Geologists often refer to the early Paleozoic era as the "Cambrian Explosion." What is meant by this phrase? What conditions prevailed at the time, allowing the "explosion"?

    The Cambrian explosion was a time when Paleozoic invertebrates radiated to produce a great diversity of marine organisms; many low-elevation areas of the world were flooded at the time of the Cambrian explosion.

11. Suppose that, in an undeformed sequence of rocks, you find a trilobite embedded in shale layers at the bottom of the formation and fossil leaves embedded in shale at the top of the formation. From your observation, what can you say about the ages of the formation?

    The fossil leaves must be older than the shale, but the shale is on top of the formation. Most of the rocks in the sequence are older than the fossil leaves. So we can say that the average age of the formation is younger than the trilobite and older than the fossil leaves. By average, we mean that the formation was deposited over some finite time period, and the age we get from the fossil brackets the beginning and end of that formation.

12. What key developments in life occurred during Precambrian time?

    Appearance of cyanobacteria and transformation of Earth's atmosphere.

13. Coal beds are formed from the accumulation of plant material that has become trapped in swamp floors. Yet coal deposits are found on the continent of Antarctica, where no swamps or vegetation exist. What is your explanation?

    At the time of deposition, the climate of Antarctica was mild enough to support swamps.

14. In what ways can sea level be lowered? What effect might the lowering of sea level have on existing life forms?

    Rising temperatures can melt ice sheets and glaciers, which makes sea levels rise—potentially increasing habitat for marine organisms promoting radiation of new species as in the Cambrian. Conversely, lower temperatures promote glaciation, which causes sea levels to drop and can produce a surge in the rate of extinctions of shallow-water marine organisms.

15. What can cause a rise in sea level? Is this likely to happen in the future? Why or why not?

    Melting of the polar ice caps, caused by global warming, for example. An increase in the rate of seafloor spreading could also make sea levels rise.

16. What general principle is used to make sense of what must be the processes that occurred throughout Earth's history?

    The Principle of Unitarianism.

Solutions to Chapter 26 Problems

1. If fine muds were laid down at the rate of 1 cm per 1000 years, show that it would take 100 million years to accumulate a sequence 1 km thick.

   By ratio and proportion, a 1-km thick sequence would accumulate in 100 million years.

2. How long has *Homo sapiens* existed? State your answer in terms of a percentage of Earth's history.

   ***Homo sapiens* evolved 195,000 years ago; the Earth is approximately 4.5 billion years old. Humans have existed for 0.0043% of the Earth's history—a few thousandths of 1%.**

3. Chart the data given in "Science and Society: Extinction in the Modern Times" in pie graphs; one for each group of organisms: mammals, birds, reptiles, amphibians, fishes, insects, mollusks, mosses, ferns, and flowering plants.

   Pie graphs should depict this data: 23% mammals, 12% birds, 61% reptiles, 31% amphibians, 46% fishes, 73% insects, 45% mollusks, 86% mosses, 67% ferns, and 73% flowering plants.

Chapter 27: The Solar System

Answers to Chapter 27 Review Questions

1. If Earth were the size of a grape, the Moon would be the size of a pea, and it would be about a foot (30 cm) away from Earth. The Sun would be the size of a Sumo wrestler and it would be 150 meters from Earth.

2. The planets revolve in the same direction (counterclockwise), orbit in the plane of the ecliptic (except Pluto), and mostly rotate in the same direction (counterclockwise).

3. Planets, moons, asteroids, comets, interplanetary medium of gas and dust particles.

4. (1) The orderly motions among large bodies of the solar system (2) the neat division of planets into two main types.

5. About 5 billion years.

6. Gravity; gas pressure.

7. The Sun loses mass. By $E = mc^2$ the "lost" mass is converted to radiant energy. Some of this energy is intercepted by photosynthesizing organisms and used for life.

8. The core: comprises 10% of the Sun's total volume; hot—over 15,000,000°C; dense; composed of hydrogen, helium, and minute quantities of other elements in the plasma state. Radiation zone: thick internal layer where atoms absorb and reradiate electromagnetic energy, slowly transferring it toward the Sun's surface. Convection zone: a turbulent layer consisting of low-density gases that are stirred by convection. Photosphere: The Sun's surface, a glowing, 6000-K plasma, about 100 kilometers thick. Chromosphere: transparent layer above photosphere, about 10,000 kilometers thick, composed of plasma. Corona: The Sun's outermost layer, composed of streamers and filaments of outward-moving, high-temperature plasmas curved by the Sun's magnetic field.

9. Solar wind: a whirl of high-speed protons and electrons. Sunspots: cooler and darker regions of photosphere caused by magnetic fields that impede hot gases from rising to the surface. Solar prominences: dense clouds of plasma pulled into looped and twisted shapes by the Sun's magnetic field.

10. Mercury, Venus, Earth, Mars.

11. They are much like Earth—small and rocky.

12. Two reasons: slow rotation of Mercury and its lack of atmosphere.

13. Mercury, Venus.

14. They are different from the inner planets in size, composition, and the way they were formed.

15. Jupiter, Saturn, Uranus, Neptune, Pluto.

16. They are much like Jupiter—large and gaseous (except Pluto).

17. Most likely it is a minor planet. Pluto is not a full planet, because it is quite small and has a highly eccentric, tipped orbit. Objects similar to Pluto have been discovered in the outer regions of the solar system so either they should be considered planets or Pluto should not be classified as a planet.

18. Too little mass to exert strong gravitational pull.

19. During a full moon, the Sun, Earth, and Moon are lined up, with Earth in between.

20. The Moon is between the Earth and the Sun at a new moon.

21. Solar eclipse: The Moon is in front of the Sun, so the Moon's shadow falls upon Earth. Lunar eclipse: the Moon and Sun are on opposite sides of Earth, and the shadow of Earth falls on the full Moon.

22. The Kuiper belt is a region of the sky beyond Neptune that is populated by many icy bodies and is a source of short-period comets. The Oort Cloud is a region beyond the Kuiper Belt that is populated by trillions of icy bodies—noted as a source of long-period comets.

23. A meteoroid is a piece of debris chipped off an asteroid or comet. Asteroids and rocky bodies usually orbit the Sun in the inner solar system; comets are icy bodies that generally inhabit the outer solar system.

24. The coma of a comet is produced when a comet gets close enough to the Sun to produce glowing vapors which surround its icy nucleus. The tail is produced when the solar wind pushes particles of the coma.

25. A meteor shower is produced, usually, when Earth passes through a stream of particles left behind by an orbiting comet.

Answers to Chapter 27 Multiple-Choice Questions

1a, 2a, 3c, 4a, 5d, 6a, 7b, 8d

Answers to Chapter 27 Integrated Science Concepts

Physics: The Solar Nebula Heats Up, Spins Faster, and Flattens

1. It spun faster and became flatter and hotter.

2. By conservation of angular momentum, it spun faster as it contracted.

Chemistry: The Chemical Composition of the Solar System

3. Astronomers call the elements heavier than hydrogen the "heavy elements." Elements form lithium through iron are formed through thermonuclear fusion in stars. Elements heavier than iron are formed by large-mass stars that supernovae.

4. The inner planets formed from materials that remained solid at high temperatures; the outer planets consist mainly of hydrogen and helium gas that coalesced in the cold regions of the solar system far away from the Sun.

Biology: What Makes a Planet Suitable for Life?

5. Scientists believe that most, perhaps all, life in the universe is based on carbon, because carbon can form four covalent bonds and therefore serve as the backbone for large biomolecules.

6. Liquids allow molecules to move around and react with one another.

Physics: Why One Side of the Moon Always Faces Us

7. The rates are the same.

8. They both tend to line up with their respective fields, gravitation for the moon, magnetic for the compass needle.

9. The fact we see one side is evidence that it rotates. If it didn't rotate, we'd only need to wait until it completed a half orbit to see its opposite side.

Answers to Chapter 27 Exercises

1. Copy the diagram and label the planets.

   From left to right: Mercury, Venus, Earth, Mars, Jupiter, Saturn, Uranus, Neptune, Pluto.

2. Why aren't eclipses more common events?

   They occur only when the plane of the moon's orbit intersects the plane of the Earth's orbit about the Sun, which seldom occurs.

3. What causes comet tails to point away from the Sun?

Comet tails point away from the Sun because they are blown away from the Sun by the solar wind.

4. Cite as many of the features of the solar system as you can that are explained by the nebular theory.

Features explained by the nebular theory include orderly motions among large bodies of the solar system; the neat division of planets into two main types—terrestrial and Jovian; existence of asteroids, comets, and moons; chemical compositions of the Sun and planets.

5. Is there evidence that Mars was at one time wetter than it presently is?

Yes; the Martian poles are covered with ice, and the surface exhibits dry river beds or flood plains— surface features produced by flowing water.

6. We know that the Sun is much larger than the Moon, but both appear the same size in the sky. What is your explanation?

Quite simply, the Sun is much farther away than the moon (as measured by Aristarchus in about 240 B.C.).

7. The giant impact theory is believed to explain the origin of the Moon. Does this mean that the nebular theory does not explain the Moon's formation? Explain.

The giant impact theory is a subset of the nebular theory, so there is no contradiction between the nebular theory and Giant Impact Theory.

8. Why are there many more craters on the surface of the Moon than on the surface of Earth?

Erosion hasn't occurred on the moon, so craters have not been covered up. Another way of saying the same thing is that the Moon wears no makeup.

9. Do star astronomers make stellar observations during the full Moon part of the month or during the new Moon part of the month? Does it make a difference?

Observations are made during the new moon part of the month, when the sky is moonless. It makes a difference, because moonlight is not there to be scattered and obscure a good view.

10. Nearly everyone has witnessed a lunar eclipse, but relatively few people have seen a solar eclipse. Why?

A lunar eclipse is in view of the whole hemisphere of the Earth facing the moon. But a solar eclipse is in view only on a small part of the hemisphere that faces the sun at that time, so few see it.

11. Because of Earth's shadow, a partially eclipsed Moon looks like a cookie with a bite taken out of it. Explain, with a sketch, how the curvature of the bite indicates the size of Earth relative to the size of the Moon. How does the tapering of the Sun's rays affect the curvature of the bite?

Extend the bite to complete a circle, and the patch of the Earth's shadow appears to be a circle with a diameter of 2.5 moon diameters. Does this mean the Earth's diameter is 2.5 moon diameters? No, because the Earth's shadow at the distance of the moon has tapered. How much? According to the tapering that is evident during a solar eclipse, by 1 moon diameter. So add that to the 2.5, and we find the Earth is 3.5 times wider than the moon.

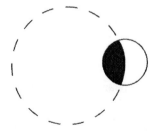

12. Why is it not totally dark in the location where a total solar eclipse occurs?

Brightness of the solar corona somewhat lights up the Earth.

13. What energy processes make the Sun shine? In what sense can it be said that gravity is the prime source of solar energy?

    The Sun's output of energy is that of thermonuclear fusion. Because fusion in the Sun is the result of gravitational pressure, we can say the prime source of solar energy is gravity. Without the strong gravity, fusion wouldn't occur.

14. A TV screen is normally light gray when it is not illuminated. How is the blackness of sunspots similar to the blackness in images on a TV screen?

    Both look black due to the large contrast between the bright and dark parts.

15. When a contracting ball of hot gas spins into a disk shape, it cools. Why?

    It has more surface area in the disk shape, which allows it to radiate more energy not re-radiated.

16. The greenhouse effect is very pronounced on Venus, but it doesn't exist on Mercury. Why?

    Mercury is too small and too hot to hold any appreciable atmosphere.

17. Where are the elements heavier than hydrogen and helium formed?

    In star interiors.

18. What is the cause of winds on Mars (and on almost every other planet, too)?

    Unequal heating of the surface.

19. What is the major difference between the terrestrial and Jovian planets?

    The Jovian planets are large gaseous low-density worlds and have rings. The terrestrial planets are rocky and have no rings.

20. What does Jupiter have in common with the Sun that the terrestrial planets don't? What differentiates Jupiter from a star?

    Its composition resembles that of the Sun. It differs from a star in that nuclear fusion doesn't occur at its core.

21. Using the following mnemonic to state the order of the planets: *My very excellent mother just served us nine pizzas,* state the order of the planets.

    Mercury, Venus, Earth, Mars, Jupiter, Saturn, Uranus, Neptune, Pluto.

22. Why are the seasons on Uranus different from the seasons on any other planet?

    A planet like Earth rotates through an axis that is slightly nonperpendicular to the orbital plane. This means that the angle that the Sun's rays make with a given part of its surface depends on the time of the planet's year. A slight tilt results in slight changes of season. Uranus, however, is enormously tilted, with its polar axis nearly in the plane of its orbit. Its seasons are very exaggerated, so that when the polar axis is aligned with the Sun, a full summer is at one pole and a full winter at the opposite pole.

23. Why are meteorites so much more easily found on Antarctica than on the other continents?

    Because so many are imbedded in ice. On regular ground, they are not so obvious. Being found on the surface of ice indicates they came from above.

24. Draw a comic strip illustrating the formation of the Sun.

    Open ended.

25. A meteor is visible only once, but a comet may be visible at regular intervals throughout its lifetime. Why?

    A comet continually orbits the sun.

26. Explain the connection between meteor showers and comets.

    Meteor showers often occur when Earth passes through a stream of particles left behind by an orbiting comet.

27. Why are the inner planets rocky while the outer planets are gaseous?

The essential reason is the relative proximity of the inner planets to the Sun. Distance from the Sun determines the temperature differences of the planets, which in turn accounts for differences in the planets chemical composition. The inner planets consist of materials that stay solid at the higher temperatures found nearest the Sun. The outer planets consist largely of hydrogen and helium gases that cohere under the influence of gravity in regions distant from the Sun, where gas pressure is lowered because the thermal energy of the gases is lower.

28. Chances are about 50/50 that, in any night sky, there is at least one visible comet that has not been discovered. This keeps amateur astronomers busy looking, night after night, because the discoverer of a comet receives the honor of having it named for him or her. With this high probability of comets being visible in the sky, why aren't more of them found?

Quite simply, the sky is big. A far-away comet occupies a pinpoint in the sky, and there are oodles of pinpoints!

Solutions to Chapter 27 Problems

1. How many Earth diameters fit between the Earth and the Moon?

The mean distance from the Earth to the Sun is defined as 1 AU = 1.5×10^8 km. From Table 27.1, the diameter of the Earth is 12,760 km. So the number of Earth diameters between the Earth and the Sun is 1.5×10^8 km/1.276×10^4 km = 11,800. So, about 12,000 Earths would fit in the distance between Earth and Sun.

2. What is the diameter of the Earth–Moon system?

The diameter of the Earth–Moon system is twice the mean distance from Earth to the Moon, or (2)(384,401 km) = 768,802 km. Note that the distance from the Earth to the Moon is stated in the Math Connection feature: *The Scale of the Solar System*.

3. To send a radio signal from Earth to Saturn, show that it would take about 71 minutes to arrive there. Then show that it would take about 321 minutes for a radio signal from Earth to reach Pluto.

Radio signals travel at the speed of light, 3×10^8 m/s = 3×10^5 km/s. From Table 27.1, the distance from the Sun to Saturn is 9.54 AU so the distance from Saturn to the Earth is 9.54 AU − 1 AU = 8.54 AU. Convert this to kilometers: 8.54 AU $\times$ (1.5×10^8 km/AU) = 1.28×10^9 km. Using the distance formula, we have $t = d/r = (1.28 \times 10^9$ km$)/(3 \times 10^5$ km/s$) = 0.4267 \times 10^4$ s = 1.19 h or about 71 minutes. A similar calculation shows that the time required for the radio signal to reach Pluto is 5.4 h or about 321 minutes.

4. Show that it takes 8.3 minutes for visible light from the Sun to reach Earth. Infra-red radiation? Ultraviolet radiation?

The distance from the Sun to the Earth = 1 AU = 1.5×10^8 km. The distance formula shows that the time of travel for the radiation (whether in the IR, visible, or UV range) is $t = d/r = (1.5 \times 10^8$ km$)/3 \times (10^5$ km/s$) = 500$ s = 8.33 minutes.

Chapter 28: The Universe

Answers to Chapter 28 Review Questions

1. Groups of stars.

2. Seasonal variation of constellations is due to the fact that the night-side of the Earth faces different parts of the universe as it orbits the Sun; diurnal motion is a consequence of the daily rotation of the earth on its axis.

3. A light-year is a measurement distance.

4. Its temperature.

5. To avoid confusing brightness with energy output.

6. A plot of the luminosity vs. surface temperature of stars.

7. The main sequence.

8. Main sequence; red giants, supergiants, white dwarfs.

9. Thermonuclear fusion.

10. (a) Thermal pressure, (b) gravity, (c) outward thermal pressure balances inward gravitational pressure so that the star's size and mass stabilize.

11. Massive stars consume their fuel so fast that they die billions of years younger than smaller stars.

12. What will happen to the Sun in its old age? The supply of hydrogen fuel will diminish, the burned-out hydrogen core will contract due to gravity, its temperature will rise and launch *helium burning*—the fusion of helium to carbon—helium will fuse to carbon at the center, while hydrogen fuses to helium in a surrounding shell, energy output will soar, moving the Sun off the main sequence to become a red giant, carbon ash collects in its core, the Sun turns blue and moves to the left in the H-R diagram, the Sun will cease producing energy, become a planetary nebula, and finally a white dwarf.

13. No possibility of energy coming from fusion in an iron core.

14. A black hole is the remains of a supergiant star that has collapsed into itself.

15. Because a black hole is so dense and has such an intense gravitational field.

16. Spiral galaxy.

17. Galaxy clusters appear to be part of even larger clusters, the galaxy super clusters.

18. The beginning of both space and time for our universe.

19. The observed Doppler shift (red shift) of light emitted by stars shows that they are receding from Earth. The fact that all stars appear to be receding indicates the universe is expanding.

20. Hubble's Law: $v = H \times d$ states that the universe is expanding at an accelerating rate and that it began at a certain point in time 8–16 billion years ago.

21. Particle accelerators are used to generate ultra high-speed collisions simulating conditions right after the Big Bang.

22. Perhaps, quasars are the cores of very distant spiral galaxies.

23. Current speculation is that quasars may be gigantic black holes that pull enormous amounts of material toward them. The resulting collisions may liberate the energy that characterizes quasars.

Answers to Chapter 28 Multiple-Choice Questions

1b, 2a, 3d, 4a, 5c, 6b, 7d, 8c

Answers to Chapter 28 Integrated Science Concepts

Physics: Radiation Curves of Stars

1. The hotter a star is, the shorter the wavelength of its peak frequency.

2. They are different temperatures.

Biology: The Search for Extraterrestrial Life

3. The SETI (Search for Extraterrestrial Intelligence) program is an effort to locate evidence of past or present communicative civilizations in the universe, particularly within our own galaxy.

4. It would increase the value of F_l, the fraction of Earth-like planets where life develops by 1. This would, in turn, increase the all-important value of N, the number of civilizations with which we could possibly communicate.

5. Answers will vary.

1. Thomas Carlyle wrote, "Why did not somebody teach me the constellations and make me at home in the starry heavens, which are always overhead and which I don't half know to this day?" What besides the names of the constellations did Thomas Carlyle not know?

   He didn't know that the constellations are not always overhead in the sky, but vary with the Earth's motion around the Sun.

2. Why do we not see stars in the daytime?

   Stars aren't seen in daytime because their relatively dim light is overwhelmed by skylight.

3. Which figure in the chapter best shows that a constellation seen in the background of a solar eclipse is one that will be seen 6 months later in the night sky?

   Figure 28.2, which shows that the background of a solar eclipse is the nighttime sky normally viewed 6 months earlier or later.

4. We see the constellations as distinct groups of stars. Discuss why they would look entirely different from some other location in the universe, far distant from Earth.

   Both near and faraway stars appear as if on the inner surface of one great sphere, with us at the center. Two stars that appear very close together are on the same line of sight, but may actually be an enormous distance apart, and would not appear close together at all when viewed from the side. Astronomers distinguish between double stars and binary stars. Double stars are on the same line of sight, yet are actually far apart. Binaries are stars that are both on the same line of sight and are in close interaction.

5. In what sense are we all made of stardust?

   The nuclei of atoms that compose our bodies were once parts of stars. All nuclei beyond iron in atomic number were in fact manufactured in supernovae.

6. How is the gold in your mother's ring evidence of the existence of ancient stars that ran through their life cycles long before the solar system came into being?

   The gold in any ring was made in the death throes of stars during supernovae explosions.

7. Would you expect metals to be more abundant in old stars or in new stars? Defend your answer.

   Because all the heavy elements are manufactured in supernovae, the newer the star, the greater percentage of heavy elements available for its construction. Very old stars were made when heavy elements were less abundant.

8. Why is there a lower limit on the mass of a star? Why is there an upper limit to the mass of a star?

   Too low a mass, and gravitational pressure in the inner core is insufficient to provoke thermonuclear fusion. No fusion, no star. There is an upper limit because stars with masses above 100 times the Sun's mass would undergo such furious nuclear fusion that gravity could not keep them collected—they would explode.

9. What keeps a main-sequence star from collapsing?

   Thermonuclear fusion reactions produce an outward pressure that counteracts the inward pressure that would lead to collapse due to gravity.

10. How does the energy of a protostar differ from the energy that powers a star?

    A protostar is not yet a star, and is made up of an aggregation of matter many times more massive than the Sun and much larger in size than the solar system. While a protostar derives its energy from the gravitational force acting on its particles, stars derive their energy principally through nuclear fission and fusion.

11. Why do nuclear fusion reactions not occur on the outer layers of stars?

    Thermonuclear fusion is caused by gravitational pressure, wherein hydrogen nuclei are squashed together. Gravitational pressures in the outer layers are insufficient to produce fusion.

12. Why are massive stars generally shorter lived than low-mass stars?

Massive stars burn at a greater rate and are the first to burn out.

13. With respect to stellar evolution, what is meant by the statement, "The bigger they are, the harder they fall"?

Bigger stars live faster, and collapse more energetically when they burn out.

14. Why will the Sun not be able to fuse carbon nuclei in its core?

There is insufficient gravitational pressure within the Sun to initiate carbon fusion, which requires greater squashing than hydrogen to fuse.

15. Some stars contain fewer heavy elements than our Sun contains. What does this indicate about the age of such stars relative to the age of our Sun?

Stars with fewer heavier elements formed at an earlier time than the Sun.

16. Which has the highest surface temperature: a red star, a white star, or a blue star?

Blue stars are hottest, red stars are coolest. White hot stars have surface temperatures in between.

17. A black hole is no more massive than the star from which it collapsed. Why, then, is gravitation so intense near a black hole?

You are simply closer to the center of gravity of the star, in accord with Newton's law of gravitation.

18. If the nucleus of our galaxy undergoes a gigantic explosion at this very moment, should we be concerned about its possible effects on us during our lifetime? Defend your answer.

The center of our galaxy is some 25,000 light years distant. An explosion there would take at least 25,000 years to reach the solar system. So no, we'd not notice any effect in our finite lifetimes.

19. Are there galaxies other than the Milky Way that can be seen with the unaided eye? Discuss.

Yes, the central bulge of the Andromeda Galaxy, which covers an area about five times that of the full moon, can be seen with the naked eye on a clear night. The Magellanic clouds are two galaxies visible to the naked eye in the Southern Hemisphere.

20. Quasars are the most distinct objects we know of in the universe. Why do we therefore say their existence goes back to the earliest times in the universe?

Because they are the most distant stellar objects detected—since the universe is expanding, the most distant objects are the oldest.

21. What is meant by saying that the universe does not exist in space? Change two words around to make the statement agree with the standard model of the universe.

Space exists in the universe, not the other way around.

22. Why are the long-wavelength microwaves that permeate the universe considered to be evidence of the Big Bang?

Radiation at the time of the Big Bang has been bouncing to and fro in the expanding universe, stretching out just as sound waves bouncing from a receding wall stretch out. The amount of stretch conforms to the Big Bang event some 15 billion years ago.

23. In your own opinion, do you have to be at the center of your class to be special? Does Earth have to be at the center of the universe to be special?

Both you and the Earth don't have to occupy a central location to be special. The Earth is certainly special among planets in the solar system in that it is the only one with abundant water and an atmosphere—and us.

24. How is the universe like a lump of rising raisin-bread dough?

   The raisin-bread dough analogy is a popular conceptual model of the universe, because both expand outward, with the distance between points (stars or raisins) continually increasing. This is much like the ants-on-a-balloon model used in the text.

25. Why does the Big Dipper change its position in the night sky over the course of the evening but Polaris remains relatively fixed in its position?

   Polaris lies on the axis of Earth's rotation, other stars do not. As Earth revolves on its axis, the celestial sphere seems to rotate.

26. Explain why, in terms of the life cycle of the Sun, Earth cannot last forever.

   It will eventually consume its nuclear fuel and no longer be able to undergo thermonuclear fusion.

27. Elements heavier than iron are created in stars—are they formed in the same way as elements lighter than iron? Explain.

   Elements heavier than iron are created by high-mass stars that supernova while elements lighter than iron are created by fusion in low- and medium-mass stars.

28. Will the Sun become a supernova? A black hole? Defend your answer.

   The Sun has too little mass to become a supernova and therefore too little mass to become a black hole. Instead it will become a white dwarf.

29. What property of a star relates to the amount of energy it is producing?

   Brightness relates to how much energy a star is producing.

30. How are neutrons and pulsars related to one another?

   A pulsar *is* a neutron star—one that sends detectable pulses of radiation to Earth.

31. Why did ancient cultures study the constellations?

   For some cultures, study of the constellations involved storytelling; to other cultures, they served as navigational aids for travelers and sailors; to other cultures, the constellations provided a guide for the planting and harvesting of crops, because constellations were seen to move in the sky in concert with the seasons.

32. Write a letter to Grandma telling her why we think the universe is 13.7 billion years old.

   Letters to Grandma should discuss how Hubble's law can be used to determine the time of the Big Bang.

Solutions to Chapter 28 Problems

1. Suppose Star A is four times as luminous as Star B. If these stars are both 500 light years away from Earth, how will their apparent brightness compare? How will the apparent brightness of these stars compare if Star A is twice as far away as Star B?

   If these stars were the same distance from Earth, apparent brightness would depend just on luminosity, and Star A appears four times as bright as Star B. However, if Star A were twice as far away as Star B, the stars would have equal apparent brightness, because apparent brightness is related to distance through the inverse-square law.

2. The brightest star in the sky, Sirius, is about 8 light-years from Earth. Show that if you could somehow travel there at jet-plane speed, 2000 kilometers per hour, the trip would take about 4.3 million years.

   Use the distance formula: distance = speed × time and rearrange to solve for time: $t = d/s =$

   $$(8 \text{ LY})/(2000 \text{ km/hr}) = \frac{(8)(9.46 \times 10^{12} \text{ km})}{2 \times 10^3 \text{ km/hr}} = 3.8 \times 10^{10} \text{ hr and}$$

   $$(3.8 \times 10^{10} \text{ hr})\left(\frac{1 \text{ day}}{24 \text{ hrs}}\right)\left(\frac{1 \text{ yr}}{365 \text{ days}}\right) = 4.3 \times 10^6 \text{ years}$$

Lab Notes and Questions
Answers for Activities and Experiments

Part 1: Physics
Chapter 2: Describing Motion
Go! Go! Go!
Sonic Ranger
Walking the Plank
Chapter 3: Newton's Laws of Motion
Putting the Force Before the Cart
Chapter 4: Momentum and Energy
Egg Toss
Bouncy Board
An Uphill Climb
Rolling Stop
Dropping the Ball
Chapter 5: Gravity
The Weight
Reaction Time
The Big BB Race
Bull's Eye
Chapter 6: Heat
Dance of the Molecules
Temperature Mix
Spiked Water
Specific Heat Capacities
Canned Heat I
Canned Heat II
I'm Melting! I'm Melting!
Chapter 7: Electricity and Magnetism
A Force to be Reckoned
Charging Ahead
Ohm, Ohm on the Range
Batteries and Bulbs
An Open and Short Case
Be the Battery
Magnetic Personality
Electric Magnetism
Motor Madness
Chapter 8: Waves — Sound and Light
Slow-Motion Wobbler
Sound Off
Pinhole Image
Pinhole Camera
Mirror, Mirror, on the Wall . . .
Chapter 9: The Atom
Thickness of a BB Pancake
Oleic Acid Pancake
Bright Lights
Chapter 10: Nuclear Physics
Get a Half-Life!
Chain Reaction

Go! Go! Go! [Experiment]

This experiment affords students an opportunity to collect data from an observable event, make measurements, and plot a graph of the results. They can then interpret the graph. The car speed and size of table should allow at least four data points.

Answers to Summing Up Questions

1. a. The marks would be farther apart.

    b. The car would reach the edge in fewer seconds.

    c. The slope would have been steeper (more vertical).

2. A steeper straight line should be added to the graph.

3. a. The marks would be closer together.

    b. The car would take more seconds to reach the edge.

    c. The slope would have been shallower (more horizontal).

4. A shallower straight line should be added to the graph.

5. a. The marks would get closer and closer together.

    b. A curved line having a decreasing slope (concave down) should be added to the graph.

6. Line A shows an object moving in the opposite ("negative") direction compared to the direction of the moving car with constant speed.
   Line B shows a car moving in the "positive" direction and speeding up.

Sonic Ranger [Activity]

To some extent, this is a high-tech version of "Go! Go! Go!" in which the computer plots the graph. Sonic ranging has revolutionized the pedagogy for graph interpretation. Students making real-time measurements and seeing the graphical representation of their own motions on a monitor are truly remarkable (where were these when we were students?).

Answers to Procedure Questions

1. Remain at rest.

2. Move away from the sensor (slowly).

3. Move away from the sensor (more quickly).

4. Move toward the sensor, slowing down as you approach it.

5.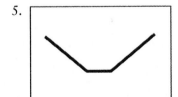

Time t (seconds)

6.

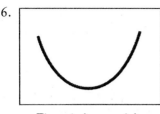

Time t (seconds)

7.

Time t (seconds)

Answers to Summing Up Questions

1. Forward motion results in an upward (positive) sloping graph. Backward motion results in a downward (negative) sloping graph.

2. Slow motion results in a line with a shallow slope; fast motion results in a line with a steep slope.

3. First segment: speeding up, second segment: moving forward with constant speed, third segment: slowing down, fourth segment: at rest, fifth segment: moving backward with constant speed.

Walking the Plank [Activity]

This activity centers on the questions that led textbook author Paul Hewitt to study physics. The key finding here is that the net force for a body in equilibrium is zero. The forces that support the plank need not be equal to each other, but they will add to an amount equal to the weight being supported.

Answers to Procedure Questions

1. Answers vary with the wide variety of metersticks in circulation. Older metersticks tend to be heavier and easier to get readings from.

2. Forces L and R should be about equal to each other, and $W = L + R$.

3. Zero (or nearly zero).

4. Answers will vary, but should be about 4 N greater than the value reported in question 1.

6. Zero (or nearly zero).

7. The value should be the same as the value reported in question 4.

9. Zero (or nearly zero).

10. The net force must be zero.

11. Answers will vary but should be 7 N greater than the value reported in question 1, and equal to the sum of the scale readings found in Step 8.

12. Answers will vary but should be equal to the difference between the value reported in question 11 and the measurement recorded in Step 10.

13. Answers will vary; most students find their measurement matches their prediction.

14. About 25 cm.

Answers to Summing Up Questions

1. Yes—as observed in Steps 4–5, for example.

2. Yes—as observed in Steps 6–7, for example.

3. Yes. The support forces would balance the weight so the net force would be zero.

4. The 200-g mass needs to be 2.5 times farther from the center of the meterstick than the 500-g mass. If the 500-g mass is 20 cm from the center, the 200-g mass would need to be placed at the 100-cm mark (2.5×20 cm = 50 cm from the center).

5. The 200-g mass would have to be 75 cm away from the center of the meterstick, so this is not possible.

Putting the Force Before the Cart [Experiment]

This experiment allows students to develop Newton's second law ($a = F/m$) from direct, laboratory experience. First they find that the acceleration of an object is directly proportional to the net force acting on it. Next they find that the acceleration of an object is inversely proportional to the mass of the object. Newton's second law is the synthesis of these findings.

Answers to Procedure Questions

1. The graph has increasing slope (concave up). Uniform motion yields a straight-line (constant slope) graph.

2. Predictions typically call for greater acceleration.

3. Most observations confirm predictions.

4. Most predictions call for less acceleration.

5. Most observations confirm predictions.

Answers to Summing Up Questions

1. Greater force results in greater acceleration. Acceleration is directly proportional to force.

2. Greater cart mass results in less acceleration. Acceleration is inversely proportional to mass.

3. Directly; inversely

4. b. $a = F/m$

Egg Toss [Activity]

This is an outdoor activity that works well as an in-class competition between lab groups. Combined with the chance to make a bit of a mess, this activity is generally a student favorite!

Answers to Summing Up Questions

1. Many groups can make it to 10 yards or meters. Some to 20; few to 30.

2. Allowing the egg to continue moving while catching it; this extends the stopping time.

3. a. The mass is the same either way.

   b. The change in velocity is the same either way.

   c. The change in momentum is the same either way.

   d. The stopping time is greater for the gradual-stop catch.

   e. The stopping force is greater in the sudden-stop catch.

4. Airbags extend the stopping time for a person moving forward in the car during a collision. It therefore reduced the stopping force compared to what it would be if they were to hit the steering wheel or dashboard.

5. Elastic cords used in bungee jumping, nearly any kind of "shock-absorption" padding, crumple zones designed into automobile frames, bending one's knees upon landing from a jump.

Bouncy Board [Activity]

This activity comes from Earl Feltyberger, who in turn got it from rock climber Bill Berner in 1985, who used this idea to explain the value of stretch in safety ropes used to stop a climber in the event of a fall. It makes a nice lecture demo—nice enough to be shared with students as an activity.

Answers to the Questions

1. A sudden halt will probably either break the cord, or break the body!

2. $Ft = \triangle mv$ is central. The impulse that brings the dropped mass to a halt equals the change in momentum the mass undergoes. The breaking force of the string is greatly affected by the "give" of the stick, which lengthens time and reduces the force needed to stop the mass.

3. Less give means less time to stop; less time to stop means more stopping force—more than the string could provide.

4. Ordinarily the strength of a string has to do with its thickness, not its length. The length of the string plays an important role in that it allows the falling object to fall farther and gain more momentum. So a greater stopping force is needed when the string is long. In short, increasing string length increases $\triangle v$, which increases F.

5. The mass of the falling object is directly proportional to the momentum of the falling object; twice the mass at a given speed means twice the momentum, which in turn means twice the needed stopping force. So the greater the mass, the stronger the string needs to be. Just as sheet music guides the musician's tune, $Ft = \triangle mv$ guides our thinking in answering this and the previous questions.

6. Bending increases the time, so it decreases the force that might break the fishing string.

An Uphill Climb [Experiment]

Students often think that using a ramp will result in doing less work to lift a heavy object. They are surprised to find that this is not the case. A common procedural pitfall is that students lose sight of the task: to raise an object 20 cm *above the tabletop*. They errantly think the task is to raise an object 20 cm *along the incline*. The procedure was written to keep students aligned to the task, but you'll want to reinforce this during the experiment.

Because dynamics cart masses vary widely, force values measured during the procedure and consequent work values will vary as well. Distance values (along the incline) should range from 59 cm for a 20° incline through 28 cm at 45° to 20 cm at 90° (straight up).

To determine whether or not the difference between two values is significant, have students use this formula: Percent Difference $= \frac{|a - b|}{(a + b)} \times 200$. Notice that this is not a percent error calculation—neither value is more reliable than the other. Rather, this formula compares the difference between the two values to the average of the two values.

Answers to Summing Up Questions

1. The force increases significantly.

2. The distance decreases significantly.

3. The work remains about the same.

4. The force required to lift an object is reduced.

5. The distance required to lift the object is increased.

6. There is no significant difference between taking the shallow path and taking the steep path in terms of fuel consumption. The work along the shallow path was about the same as the work done along the straight-up path.

Rolling Stop [Experiment]

Students will enjoy this activity. For one thing, they may notice that all balls gain the same speed in rolling down equal-angle inclines. They may not have an explanation for this, and because the textbook does not treat rotational motion, they won't get help there. The explanation for this is not unlike that of the equal accelerations of free fall for objects of different masses—which is that the ratio of weight to mass is the same for all objects—g. Similarly, the ratio of torque to rotational inertia is the same for all balls on the same incline. It is not necessary to get into this with your class, however, for it may obscure the central idea here. And that idea is the value of looking only at the beginning and end points in a problem that involves energy (almost like considering only the limits when doing integral calculus). Question 4 addresses this.

Here they should see that the potential energy (PE) of the raised ball is directly proportional to the work that the rug does in stopping it. In your discussion, your students may be bothered about the idea of the rug doing work on the rolling ball. Ask if the rug exerts a force on the ball. And to answer this, ask if the ball exerts a force on the rug. Then think of Newton's third law, where it was learned that when one object exerts a force on a second object, the second object exerts an equal and opposite force on the first. We see the rug does exert a force on the ball—which is why the ball slows to a stop!

In discussing this activity, you can emphasize that speed can be measured either as $\triangle L/\triangle t$, or as $\triangle t/\triangle L$. A marathon is usually reported as minutes per mile, as "Joe started with a five minute mile, slowed to 10 on the hill, and settled down to a smooth six." You may or may not be surprised to see how many of your students cannot translate these speeds into miles per hour in less than 10 seconds.

After Step 3, you may wish to ask this follow-up question: "Would it be incorrect to reverse the axes and plot height vertically on Y, and distance horizontally on X? Why, or why not? Isn't height on Y, and distance on X, more natural?"

Point out that in Summary Question 4, we have the freedom to choose any level for zero potential energy, tabletop, or floor, or ceiling, and treat it as a relative signed quantity. Ask, "Where is the absolute level where PE cannot be negative?" [Answer: Earth's center.] Follow-up question: "What about relative and absolute KE?" and "Does a decrease of 10 J PE equal an increase of 10 J KE? Why or why not?" [*Answer*: "Yes, because 10 = 10; No, because 10 is 20 more than −10."] We'll have more on "relative" or "absolute" when we get to temperature.

Answers to the Questions

1. The data (or graphs) should indicate direct proportions (straight-line graphs).

2. Yes, because height and ramp length are directly proportional to each other.

3. The speed of the ball was the same for different ramps at the same starting height ($v = \sqrt{2gh}$). At the same height, the same potential energy changes to kinetic energy.

4. One of the beauties of conserved quantities like energy is that the beginning amount and the end amount will be the same, regardless of the details involved in the middle. Now the details may be interesting, and have a lot of good physics. But if it's the final state we're interested in, we can bypass the details and go straight to it. In this activity, the ball begins with PE, gains KE of translation and KE of rotation (not covered in the text), then spends this gain across the friction enhanced rug. Mechanical energy is completely converted to thermal energy of the rug (and ball). That is to say, the initial PE is all dissipated along the rug (if we neglect the friction of the ramp—which is reasonable, for ramp friction simply enabled rolling—there was no "dragging" across the ramp and the generation of thermal energy on the ramp). In equation form, we can describe the energy changes of the ball as

   PE top of ramp = KE bottom of ramp = Work across rug.

   Note if we are not asked for KE details, then we can simply say PE top of ramp = Work across rug.

Dropping the Ball [Experiment]

This experiment can provide a hands-on, quantitative support for the principle of conservation of energy. More than most activities and experiments in this manual, this experiment demands that careful attention be paid to the setup and to distance measurements. Of particular concern is measured distance between the photogate beams. If this measurement bears significant error, so will the results. It will appear as if energy is *not* conserved! But when carried out with deliberate concern for accuracy and precision, the results are impressive.

Equipment notes: Acrylic tubes can be found at plastics supply companies. Neodymium "supermagnets" (disc-shaped: ~13 mm dia. × ~5 mm thick) and steel balls (16 mm ball bearings) can be found at scientific supply companies.

Some specific values will vary depending on available equipment; the values provided below assume a 16-g ball and a 5.0-cm photogate beam separation. Student values will vary.

To determine whether or not the difference between two values is significant, have students use this formula: Percent Difference $= |a - b|/(a + b) \times 200$. Notice that this is not a percent error calculation—neither value is more reliable than the other. Rather, this formula compares the difference between the two values to the average of the two values.

Answers to Procedure Questions

1. $PE = mgh = 0.016 \text{ kg} \cdot 9.8 \text{ m/s}^2 \cdot 0.40 \text{ m} = 0.063 \text{ J}$

2. $v = d/t = 0.050 \text{ m}/0.0178 \text{ s} = 2.8 \text{ m/s}$

5. $KE = (1/2)mv^2 = (1/2) \cdot 0.016 \text{ kg} \cdot (2.8 \text{ m/s})^2 = 0.063 \text{ J}$

Answers to Summing Up Questions

1. The potential energy at the drop height and the kinetic energy after falling.

2. The potential energy and the kinetic energy are about the same.

3. a. $PE = 0.25 \text{ J}$

   b. $KE = 0.25 \text{ J}$

   c. $v = 5.6 \text{ m/s}$ [This determination is the trickiest; expect a range of answers.]

Answers to Going Further Questions

1. Double the height.

2. Quadruple the height (doubling the height won't double the speed!).

3. Energy from the roller coaster is transferred to the environment through friction and air resistance.

The Weight [Activity]

This is a simple, straightforward lab activity. Students typically get excellent results. The activity is also intended to help drive a division between the concepts of mass and weight. While weight and mass are usually related to each other, they are distinct quantities.

Answers to the Procedure Question

1. Slopes of 10 N/kg are typical with the apparatus described. Slopes of 9.8 N/kg are typical if a computer-connected force sensor is used in place of the spring scale.

Answers to Summing Up Questions

1. About 10 N.

2. The slope of the moon line is shallower.

3. Jupiter has a stronger gravitational field than Earth.

Reaction Time [Activity]

This activity can easily be converted into an experiment by dividing the class into three groups and recording measurements. A hypothesis could be that there is no significant difference in reaction time for the sense of sight, hearing, or touching. Group "A" would measure reaction times for several students using a sight signal—they see the holder drop the bill. In Group "B," they close their eyes and hear the holder say "Drop!" at the instant of release. In Group "C," they close their eyes and receive a simultaneous tap on the shoulder from the dropper's other hand.

A fourth group could explore the hypothesis that reaction times would differ between using a wooden 12 inch ruler and a wooden meterstick—the meterstick is heavier and would fall (a) faster? Or (b) slower? Or the (c) same? What if the ruler were made of steel?

If you happen to have a subgroup of psychology or political science majors, suggest a hypothesis that persons who believe (a), (b), or (c) will report data that support their expectations. You may have a future doctor who is ready to understand "double-blind experiment"!

Answers to Summing Up Questions

1. Evidence ought to be the comparison between sound, sight, and touch on reaction time.

2. For one thing, the individual differences among people.

3. Reaction time can affect measurements that change with time. When the changes are small compared to reaction time, then the effects may be negligible. When they're not, for example, in timing a falling object, then choosing the longest time interval lessens the error due to reaction time. Just like measuring the thickness of a page is more accurate when more pages are measured at one time.

4. Reaction time plays an important role in driving. For a reaction time of 0.7 second, a car going 100 km/h (28 m/s) travels nearly 20 m (about 60 feet) in 0.7 s, which is considerable—and has too many times been fatal.

5. In many sports, a single second is a long time. Baseball is an obvious one, where top players must have extraordinary reaction times. The same is true for soccer, football, and even boxing. The winners of races of all kinds usually are discerned in fractions of a second.

The Big BB Race [Activity]

The purpose of this activity is to demonstrate the independence of the horizontal and vertical motion of a projectile. This activity should inspire some lively in-class discussion prior to the demonstration. Students should be allowed to argue for an incorrect outcome. The teacher must keep a strict poker face throughout the discussion phase so as to let all lines of reasoning be explored. All this makes for a dramatic and memorable conclusion!

Answers to Procedure Questions

1. Sketches will vary; all projectile paths should start at the launch point and end at the impact point.

2. Arguments will vary.

   Student X: The dropped ball falls straight down; the launched ball travels forward, delaying its arrival on the ground.

   Student Y: The launched ball was given a high speed upon launch, so it will travel faster and reach the ground first.

   Student Z: Both will fall downward at the same rate regardless of their horizontal motion. "Gravity affects both the same way."

3. Responses will vary. Some things students might suggest:

   "No-fall distance" is increased by greater launch speed or launch force.

   "No-fall distance" is decreased by air resistance or weight of the projectile.

6. It's a tie!

Answers to Summing Up Questions

1. The horizontal motion of the launched ball has no effect on its vertical motion.

2. There is no no-fall distance! Both balls begin to fall simultaneously—right when they're launched.

3. Both would hit the ground at the same time—horizontal motion and vertical motion are independent!

Bull's Eye [Experiment]

This experiment requires careful measurement of speed and subsequent calculations to determine the horizontal range of a ball rolled off a table. The one-shot authentic assessment nature of this experiment makes it a student favorite. The instructor is given latitude in terms of the size of can to be used. Pick a large one if your students need some encouragement. Pick a small one if your students need a challenge!

Answers to Summing Up Questions

1. Answers will vary; most groups are able to get a bull's eye on the first attempt.

2. The ball was traveling at a speed greater than had been determined in the experiment. The height of the can was overestimated.

3. The height of the can was not taken into account. The ball was traveling at a speed less than had been determined in the experiment.

4. A higher speed would be needed for the ball to land in a taller can. If the ball were moving faster in the horizontal direction, it would not fall as far by the time it got to the can.

Dance of the Molecules [Activity]

This activity is intended to show the difference between hot and cold on a molecular level. Food coloring mixes more quickly in hot water than in cold water due to the greater motion of molecules in the hot water.

Answers to Procedure Questions

2. Predictions will vary.

3. The food coloring is more thoroughly mixed in the hot water than in the cold water. Sketches should reflect this.

Answers to Summing Up Questions

1. The fast-moving molecules in the hot water move the food coloring around and mix it more rapidly than the slow-moving molecules in the cold water. If the molecules had equal speeds in hot and cold water, the mixing would have occurred at an equal rate.

2. Both jars would look the same; the food coloring would be thoroughly mixed in both jars.

3. Air molecules moving around in the room would mix the fragrance molecules throughout the room just like the water molecules mixed the food coloring.

4. It would take longer for the fragrance to mix throughout the room if the air were colder, just like the food coloring in the cold water takes longer to mix.

Temperature Mix [Experiment]

The distinction between temperature and thermal energy (or quantity of heat Q) is reinforced in this experiment. This experiment is fairly foolproof. Of course a pail of water may get tipped over, so filling no more than two-thirds full may be a good precaution. Also, hot water in the hot pail should not be hot enough to scald anyone who tries to "test the water" by putting their hand in it!

Your students will see that they can average the temperature of two equal volumes of water at different temperatures when mixed—common sense. What they'll discover is that this is not so when unequal volumes of water are mixed. In this case, the final temperature will have an average nearer the temperature of the greater amount of water—refined common sense.

Answers to the Questions

1. Perhaps inaccurate temperature readings.

2. Answers will vary.

3. The cold water changed more because there was less of it, and it absorbs heat from both cups of hot water. By energy conservation, heat lost by one part of the system is heat gained at another. The temperature of the mixture is closer to that of the hot water.

4. Answers will vary.

5. The hot water changes more because there is less of it, and it gives off heat to both cups of cold water. The temperature of the mixture is closer to that of the cold water.

6. The amount of water determines final temperature, as seen in Questions 3 and 5.

7. Observations are consistent with $Q = mc\Delta T$; quantity of heat that transfers equal mass of water times its specific heat times the temperature change. We see the direct relation between the mass involved and the quantity of heat it can transfer (or absorb). The transfer is always from high temperature to low temperature; not from the body with the most thermal energy to the body with less thermal energy.

Spiked Water [Activity]
This activity compares the capacity of nails and water to store thermal energy. A mass of nails and an equal mass of water will be used to heat equal volumes of cold water. The hot water will cause the temperature of the cold water to rise more than the hot nails will.

Answers to Summing Up Questions

1. The nails and hot water had the same temperature; they were in contact long enough to come to thermal equilibrium.

2. The hot water made the temperature of the cold water rise more than the nails did.

3. Hot water: it holds more thermal energy!

4. The first student was correct. The specific heat capacity of water is greater than that of iron (or steel), so any hot water clinging to the nails will help raise the temperature of the cold water the nails went into to a greater extent than the nails would have by themselves. (And any water clinging to the nails also holds thermal energy "robbed" from the hot water to be used to warm the cold water.)

Specific Heat Capacities [Experiment]
Because this experiment requires no special equipment, it is suitable to having several groups, each working with different substances using slightly different procedures so that much can be gained by having groups discuss and compare their results.

Students may not notice much of an increase in temperature for some of the specimens because of their low specific heats. Exercising care, however, their values for specific heat capacities should come within 10% or so of accepted values.

Canned Heat I [Experiment]
This experiment allows a comparison of the thermal absorption of different surfaces. The surfaces are black, white, and silver. The data-taking is slow; the more restless students will find it somewhat tedious. But time is a critical element in this experiment, so the tedium must be endured!

Answers to Summing Up Questions

1. Fastest: black, slowest: silver.

2. White T-shirt is better; it doesn't absorb radiant energy as quickly as black does.

3. Silver: mostly reflected, black: mostly absorbed, white: mostly reflected.

Canned Heat II [Experiment]
This experiment allows a comparison of the thermal radiation of different surfaces. The surfaces are black and silver. The data-taking is slow; the more restless students will find it somewhat tedious. But time is a critical element in this experiment, so the tedium must be endured!

Answers to Summing Up Questions

1. Faster: black, slower: silver.

2. Silvery surfaces hold thermal energy better.

3. It should be colored black (and often is!).

I'm Melting! I'm Melting! [Activity]

This activity explores the heat transfer between various surfaces and an ice cube. The surfaces vary in color and material. And the transfer rates vary dramatically!

Answers to Procedure Questions

1. Both metal surfaces feel colder than both Styrofoam surfaces.

2. and 3. Predictions will vary.

4. The ice cube on the black defrosting tray melts most quickly.

5. The ice cube on the white Styrofoam melts most slowly. (It may be a close call between it and the ice cube on the black Styrofoam.)

Answers to Summing Up Questions

1. Answers will vary.

2. Heat flowed from the various objects (defrosting tray and Styrofoam plates) to the ice cubes.

3. Defrosting trays are metal and therefore conductors; Styrofoam plates are insulators.

4. The black defrosting tray can radiate better than the silvery (foil-covered) defrosting tray.

5. The blackened plate can radiate better than the white plate.

6. a. This is supported: both defrosting tray ice cubes melt faster than either Styrofoam plate ice cubes.

   b. This conclusion is only supported when comparing surfaces made of the same material: The black defrosting tray ice cube melts faster than the silvery (foil-covered) defrosting tray.

A Force to be Reckoned [Activity]

This is an introduction to electrostatic force. It shows students evidence of a force but demands they eliminate gravitational force and magnetic force before giving it a new name. Pith ball electroscopes may be used; or just hang a pith ball on a thread from a convenient support.

Answers to Procedure Questions

2. The brick has no effect on the pith ball; the force between the plastic and the pith ball is not gravitational.

3. Gravitational force is always attractive (as far as we know). Objects don't repel each other gravitationally.

4. The magnet has no effect on the pith ball; the force between the plastic and the pith ball is not magnetic.

Answers to Summing Up Questions

1. Negative (like charges repel).

2. The force is stronger when the objects are closer together.

Charging Ahead [Activity]

This activity can be done as a demonstration. The Van de Graaff generator is a classic electrostatics demonstration tool. Students really get a charge out of this one. Despite the fact that the dome may develop tens or hundreds of thousands of volts of electric potential, the total charge on the dome is fairly small. Common electric outlets provide only about a hundred volts but are much more dangerous because they can supply large quantities of charge. Thus, shocks from the Van de Graaff dome cannot do much damage while shocks from electrical outlets can kill!

Answers to Procedure Questions

2. Repel.

3. The tins fly off into the air. First the top one, then the next one down, and so on until all the tins have flown.

4. The Styrofoam bowls do not fly off as the pie tins did. They just sit there.

5. The bubbles are unaffected by the uncharged dome. But when the generator is running, bubbles are first attracted to and then repelled from the charged dome.

6. The student's hair will stand out as shown in the illustration in the activity. They will also experience a tingling sensation as the charge covers their bodies and leaks off into the air.

Answers to Summing Up Questions

1. The balloons repelling, the pie tins flying, and the bubbles repelling from the dome are explained by attraction and repulsion of charge. The Styrofoam bowls not moving is a demonstration of the difference between conductors and insulators.

2. When a flame is brought near the charged dome, note that it interacts with the field. Ions in the flame are drawn toward or blown away from the dome, depending on sign of charge.

Ohm, Ohm on the Range [Experiment]

Students typically have no experience connecting electric meters to circuits. So before collecting data to determine Ohm's Law, they will be instructed to make correct and incorrect meter connections. Direct experience will be their guide to which connections are correct and which are incorrect. The current and voltage data typically yield excellent graphs and resistance values.

Equipment note: Power resistors are relatively large, rectangular or cylindrical objects. They are not the common, small, color-coded resistors. Power resistors can typically handle 10 W. They allow students to collect "normal" values of current and voltage. The small resistors typically blow out past 0.25 W. Power resistors can be found at electronics supply companies and scientific supply companies.

Answers to Procedure Questions

Part A

1. As the power supply is turned up, the ammeter reading increases, and the bulb gets brighter.

2. As the power supply is turned up, the ammeter reading increases, but the bulb does not light.

3. As the power supply is turned up, the voltmeter reading increases, but the bulb does not light.

4. As the power supply is turned up, the voltmeter reading increases, and the bulb gets brighter.

5. Series.

6. Parallel.

Part B

1. The best-fit slope should match the value of each power resistor. So a 5-Ω resistor would have a best-fit slope of 5 V/A.

Answers to Summing Up Questions

1. $R = V/I$.

2. A yielded a line with a greater slope, so it is the device with the greater resistance.

3. The resistance increases as the current (or voltage) increases.

4. The resistance decreases as the current (or voltage) increases.

Batteries and Bulbs [Activity]

This activity includes essential experiences for students to have when learning about electric circuits.

Answers to Procedure Questions

1. Anatomy of a lightbulb:

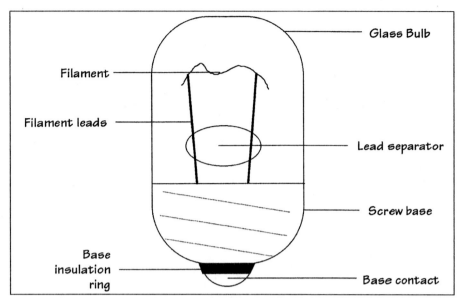

2. Conducting parts: screw base and bottom contact.

   Insulating: glass bulb and insulation ring.

   Two-wire circuits: connect terminals of the battery to the screw base and base contact.

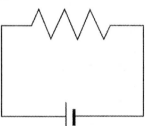

3. One-wire circuits: place the base contact on one terminal and connect the wire from the other terminal to the screw base. While the artistic efforts of the students may differ, the diagrams should be essentially the same (as shown here).

   No-wire circuits are not possible: cannot get connections from both terminals to both conducting parts of the bulb.

4. Each bulb is dimmer in the series circuit than it was in the simple circuit.

5. Both bulbs go out.

6. Each bulb is about as bright in the parallel circuit as the original bulb was in the simple circuit.

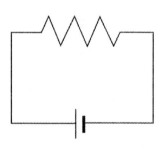

7. The unscrewed bulb goes out, but the other bulb stays on.

Answers to Summing Up Questions

1. The screw base and the bottom contact.

2. They all involve connecting the two terminals of the battery to the two conducting parts of the bulb.

3. In parallel; when one item is turned off or removed, the others continue to work.

4. In parallel; when one bulb goes out, the other remains lit.

An Open and Short Case [Activity]

To understand how electric circuits work, it is important to understand how electric circuits *don't* work. In this activity, open circuits and short circuits are investigated. Both are considered faulty circuits, but they are very different in nature.

Answers to Procedure Questions

1. Student predictions will vary but should address the bulb and the ammeter.

2. The bulb goes out; the ammeter drops to zero.

3. Student predictions will vary but should address the bulb and the ammeter.

4. The bulb goes out (or dims significantly), and the ammeter shoots up to a very high (if not its maximum) reading.

5. The open circuit.

6. The short circuit.

7. a. When point c is connected to point d, bulb 1 remains lit, and bulb 2 remains lit.

   b. When point d is connected to point e, bulb 1 remains lit, and bulb 2 goes out.

   c. When point e is connected to point f, bulb 1 remains lit, and bulb 2 remains lit.

   d. When point f is connected to point a, bulb 1 goes out, and bulb 2 goes out.

   e. When point a is connected to point c, bulb 1 goes out, and bulb 2 remains lit.

   f. When point a is connected to point d, bulb 1 goes out, and bulb 2 remains lit.

   g. When point a is connected to point e, bulb 1 goes out, and bulb 2 goes out.

   h. When point b is connected to point d, bulb 1 goes out, and bulb 2 remains lit.

   i. When point b is connected to point e, bulb 1 goes out, and bulb 2 goes out.

8. a. When point c is connected to point d, bulb 1 goes out, and bulb 2 goes out.

   b. When point d is connected to point e, bulb 1 remains lit, and bulb 2 goes out.

   c. When point e is connected to point f, bulb 1 remains lit, and bulb 2 remains lit.

   d. When point f is connected to point a, bulb 1 goes out, and bulb 2 goes out.

   e. When point a is connected to point c, bulb 1 goes out, and bulb 2 goes out.

   f. When point a is connected to point d, bulb 1 remains lit, and bulb 2 remains lit.

   g. When point a is connected to point e, bulb 1 goes out, and bulb 2 goes out.

   h. When point b is connected to point d, bulb 1 remains lit, and bulb 2 remains lit.

   i. When point b is connected to point e, bulb 1 goes out, and bulb 2 goes out.

Answers to Summing Up Questions

1. The bulb doesn't light in either circuit.

2. In open circuits, no current flows; in short circuits, a large amount of current flows.

3. There is a path from one terminal of the battery to the other terminal of the battery that doesn't require current passing through a bulb.

Be the Battery [Activity]

This activity should be done only after students have completed "An Open and Short Case." Material covered in this activity assumes an understanding of open and short circuits. This activity affords students an opportunity to "feel" what it is like to be a battery. Well, they feel how much effort is required to power a simple electric circuit.

Answers to Procedure Questions

1. Crank the generator more rapidly; this requires more effort.

2. It gets easy to crank; effort goes down.

3. Open circuit.

4. Low electrical resistance.

5. It gets difficult to crank; effort increases.

6. Short circuit.

7. High electrical resistance.

8. Parallel is harder to power.

Answers to Summing Up Questions

1. Low electrical circuits are harder to power.

2. Series; it's easier to power, so it has more electrical resistance.

3. Low resistance circuits.

4. Series.

Magnetic Personality [Activity]

Everybody loves to play with magnets. Their actions are mysterious, because the explanation of their attractions and repulsions are far removed from simpler phenomena that we do understand. Explanations involve quantum phenomena, so like the similar attractions and repulsions of electrostatics, we simply say they are fundamental.

Don't underestimate the amount of dry iron filings you may need. Students tend to use too much, and to consider used filings as trash to be thrown away. Field patterns should approximate those shown in the textbook figures of Chapter 10.

Answers to Procedure Questions

1.
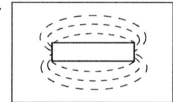

2.
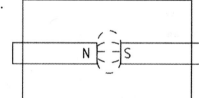

3.
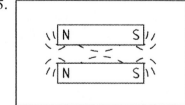

4.
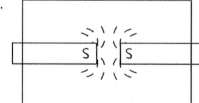

5.
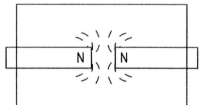

6.
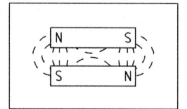

7. Possible: place three north poles or south poles together.

8. Not possible to have three mutually attracting poles.

Answers to Summing Up Questions

1. Not possible to identify the poles.

2. Not possible to identify the poles.

3. B is a south pole.

4. D is a north pole.

5. E: north, F: south, G: north, H: south, J: north, I: south, L: north, K: south.

6. Figure 14a is possible; Figure 14b is impossible.

Electric Magnetism [Activity]

This activity allows students to reenact Øersted's discovery of the link between electricity and magnetism. It also allows them to see the geometry of magnetic fields as it relates to electric currents.

Answers to Procedure Questions

A. 3. The current affects the compass; the compass needle can be redirected by the current-carrying wire.

4. North–south.

5. Yes, the current affects the needle even if it's running beneath the compass.

6. Reversing the current reverses the deflection of the compass needle.

Answers to Summing Up Questions

1. a. Current is moving away from observer.

b. Current is moving toward observer.

2. Right hand.

3. Moving electric charge (current) is the source of all magnetic fields.

Motor Madness [Activity]

This activity shows the link between magnetism and electric motors.

Answer to Discussion Question

A magnet can exert a force on an electric current.

Answers to Procedure Questions

A. 1. The magnets can push the current in the swing.

2. If the magnets aren't there, the swing doesn't move.

3. The observations support the idea that a magnet can exert a force on an electric current.

B. 1. The handle of the generator starts to move.

2. The motion of the handle is faster.

Answers to Summing Up Questions

1. Stronger magnets, magnetic poles closer to the wire, or more current in the wire, for example.

2. Answers will vary, and some devices could be argued either way. Generally speaking, the blow dryer, shaver, cassette player, CD/DVD player, vending machine, VCR, washing machine, and car are easy to make arguments for.

3. Answers will vary. Count on anything that uses electric energy to make something move.

Generator Activator [Activity]

This activity shows how magnets can be used to generate electricity.

Answers to Procedure Questions

1. Moving a pole of the magnet in and out of the coil generates a current.

2. Motion of the pole relative to the magnet is what's key to generating current. So, a and b are possible, but c is not.

3. The hand-crank generator generates current when the handle is turned.

4. If the handle is turned in the opposite direction, current is produced in the opposite direction.

5. The other handle turns and acts as a motor (uses electrical energy to produce motion).

6. The other handle doesn't turn as fast as the handle that's being cranked. If the cranking handle is turned too slowly, the other handle doesn't turn at all.

Answers to Summing Up Questions

1. a. Motor.

   b. Battery.

   c. Generator.

2. Some energy is turned into sound, and some is turned into thermal energy which heats up the gears of the generator.

3. Not a good idea; energy is lost when going from the generator to the motor (and more will be lost going from the motor to the generator).

Slow-Motion Wobbler [Activity]

All students know the tines of a tuning fork move when they vibrate. They can't see the motion because of the high frequency. But dip a vibrating fork in water, and the motion is evidenced in the splashing water. Larger forks work best.

The best evidence is obtained with a strobe light. *Caution:* Some people have unfavorable reactions to strobe lights (particularly epileptics). Casually ask if strobe lights bother anybody *before* using them.

Air near the vibrating tines is set in vibration—sound. Placing the tuning fork against a tabletop, or any sounding board, causes the tines to spend their energy faster. Ask your students to explain this in terms of the conservation of energy. Sound energy eventually degrades to thermal energy.

A vibrating tuning fork in outer space would vibrate longer, but its energy would eventually degrade to thermal energy.

Sound Off [Activity]

This is a great one! It is actually a demo, but it is so impressive that students will appreciate doing it themselves. They'll one day remember it nostalgically when antinoise technology is commonplace.

You'll want to have your department invest in a common "boom box" and insert a DPDT switch in one of the speaker wires. This will likely become a routine demo in all courses where interference is taught.

Where does the energy go when sound is canceled? It turns out that each loudspeaker is also a microphone. When the speakers face each other, they "drive" each other, inducing back voltages in each other that cut the currents down in each. Thus, energy is diminished but not canceled. As the speakers are brought closer, and as sound is diminished, the electric bill for powering the sound source diminishes accordingly!

Answers to the Questions

1. Volume is "normal" when speakers are in phase.

2. When out of phase, cancellation of sound occurs as regions of compression from one speaker fill in regions of rarefaction from the other. If the overlap of out-of-phase waves is exact, then complete cancellation occurs (barring stray waves). Exact overlap cannot occur, however, because of the displacement between the speaker cones. So, much of the interference is partial. For long waves, the displacement of the speaker cones is small compared to their wavelength, overlap is relatively exact, and these waves cancel well. But overlap is less exact for shorter wavelengths, producing cancellation that is more partial. For very short waves, reinforcement rather than cancellation occurs. This occurs if the displacement of the cones is a half wavelength of such higher-frequency sound. Then overlap is *in* phase. For these reasons, high-frequency sound survives, giving the music that "tinny" sound.

3. Answers will vary. But interestingly enough, students were asked 25 years ago for the practical applications for a laser. Today we ask the same question at the outset period of a growing antinoise technology.

Pinhole Image [Activity]

Both a prism and a lens deviate light, because their faces are not parallel (only at the center of a lens are both faces parallel to each other). As a result, light passing through the center of a lens undergoes the least deviation. If a pinhole is placed at the center of the pupil of your eye, the undeviated light forms an image in focus, no matter where the object is located. Pinhole vision is remarkably clear—not magnified, but clear.

Answers to the Questions

1, 2. Yes. Just as the image in a pinhole camera is clear near and far, likewise for this activity.

3. The page is dimmer simply because less light energy gets through the pinhole.

Pinhole Camera [Experiment]

The word camera is derived from the Greek word *kamara*, meaning "vaulted room." Royalty in the 16th century were entertained by the "camera obscura"—a large "pinhole camera" without the film.

Answers to the Questions

1–4. Image is inverted in all directions, up and down as well as left and right.

5. All distances are in focus. Actually, the consideration is the size of the pinhole compared to the distance to the screen. Openings of a few centimeters act as pinholes if the screen distance is in meters. Openings in the leaves of trees act as pinholes, for example, and cast images of the sun on the ground!

6. A lens gathers more light and is brighter.

7. There is much in common with the eye and a pinhole camera. Image formation is much the same for each.

Mirror, Mirror, on the Wall . . . [Activity]

Beware of treating this activity too lightly. Nearly all your students will fail to distinguish between mirror size and image size. They all know image size is less with increased distance—which it is. But mirror size is also, in the same proportion. A half-size mirror lets you see your full-size image at any distance. This is evident in a pocket mirror that you can hold near or far. You'll see a part of your face that's twice the height of the mirror.

The question often arises why a mirror inverts left and right but not up and down. Well quite simply, it doesn't reverse left and right; the hand on the east is still on the east—the reason for this misunderstanding has mainly to do with left–right convention of the human body. What *is* inverted, is back and front. That person facing you in the mirror points to the east when you do, and looks upward when you do. The only difference is his or her nose is pointing in a direction opposite yours. So front and back are inverted, not left and right.

Thickness of a BB Pancake [Experiment]

Consider a quick pre-lab activity that shows that the diameter of a marble is the same as the thickness of a monolayer of a dozen or more marbles. The volume of the monolayer divided by its top or bottom area equals the diameter of the marble.

Note: Because of the three-dimensional close packing of BBs in a graduated cylinder, the volume of the same BBs spread into a monolayer is slightly greater. This produces a 5 to 10% higher value than the actual diameter. A typical BB measures about 4.5 mm using a micrometer.

Consider having your students find the density of a rectangular block of aluminum (or look it up in the textbook). Then hand them a sheet of aluminum foil and ask them to find its thickness. From the mass, they can calculate the volume, and because volume is simply surface area multiplied by thickness, they can calculate thickness. This sets the stage for this activity and the following experiment.

This experiment presents an opportunity for students to learn to use a micrometer (for those who haven't already).

Answers to the Questions

1. It was assumed that the volume occupied by the BBs in the graduated cylinder and the volume when spread in a monolayer was the same. This is not quite true. Because the BBs are spheres, they pack together more compactly than cubes of the same width. Spreading them into a thin layer slightly increases the volume they occupy compared to when packed in the graduated cylinder.

2. Answers will vary; typically, BBs are about 4.3 to 4.7 mm in diameter.

3. Drop a known volume of oleic acid on water, and measure the area it covers. Divide the volume of the drop by the area of the monolayer to estimate its thickness.

Oleic Acid Pancake [Experiment]

Inform your students that the oleic acid solution will be mostly alcohol with a small amount of oleic acid in it, mainly to allow portioning out less than a drop of oleic acid. When they add a drop of solution to a tray of water, the alcohol dissolves in the water, but the oleic acid floats on top, just as a drop of oil floats on water.

Caution your students not to put too much powder on the water surface, which may interrupt spreading.

The computations that follow treat the oleic acid molecules as a sphere. The conclusion of the lab is an appropriate time to relate that the molecule is actually hot-dog shaped, and they are measuring the *length* of the molecule. Still, the method and the outcome are good.

Sample Calculations

In Step 3, a typical value for the average diameter is 30 cm. The radius, r, is then

$$r = d/2 = 30 \text{ cm}/2 = 15 \text{ cm}.$$

The area of the circle is

$$A = \pi r^2 = (3.14)(15 \text{ cm})^2 = 706 \text{ cm}^2 = 7.06 \times 10^2 \text{ cm}^2.$$

The number of drops in 1 cm^2 of 5% solution is about 38.

The volume of one drop is

$$1 \text{ cm}^3/38 = 0.026 \text{ cm}^3 = 2.6 \times 10^{-2} \text{ cm}^3.$$

In Step 4, the volume of acid in a single drop equals 0.005 multiplied by the volume of one drop:

$$(0.005)(2.6 \times 10^{-2}) \text{ cm}^3 = 1.3 \times 10^{-4} \text{ cm}^3.$$

In Step 5, the diameter of an oleic acid molecule equals the volume of oleic acid in one drop divided by the area of the circle:

$$\text{Diameter} = (\text{volume})/(\text{area}) = (1.3 \times 10^{-4} \text{ cm}^3)/(7.06 \times 10^2 \text{ cm}^2) = 0.18 \times 10^{-6} \text{ cm} = 1.8 \times 10^{-7} \text{ cm}.$$

Good measurements yield values between 1.0×10^{-7} and 2.0×10^{-7} cm. If time permits a second trial, be sure students clean the trays thoroughly before making a second measurement of the diameter.

Answers to the Questions

1. A monolayer is a layer one molecule thick.

2. At full strength, a single drop would cover a huge area.

3. Assume a rectangular shape for simplicity: The volume of one rectangular molecule would be its length multiplied by one-tenth the length multiplied by one-tenth the length—which means the volume of the long molecule is actually about one-hundredth the volume of a cube of the same thickness.

Bright Lights [Experiment]

Most students are able to finish this lab within 75 minutes. Be sure not to darken the room so much that students can't see what they're writing or where they are going. During your pre-lab presentation, talk about how helium was discovered in the sun by an examination of the spectral patterns of sunlight. Note how helium's name is derived from the Greek word for sun, *helios*.

It is good to start students off with the gas discharge tubes, as they are easiest to observe using the spectroscopes. For the flame tests, it is difficult for the students to observe the spectra, because the colors do not last for very long. To help out in the observations, consider having the students use clamps and ring stands to point their spectroscopes at the flames directly. Bringing the spectroscope close to the flame also helps.

Sodium is an impurity found in most alkalis and alkali Earth salts, as well as tap water. Students should not confuse the bright yellow lines from sodium impurity with the lines of other salts. Sodium's yellow line, however, provides a good reference when sketching line spectra.

Static electricity sparks (St. Elmo's Fire) are blue because of the emission spectrum of nitrogen.

Colored pencils are good for drawing the spectra of elements. Whether using colored or regular pencils, the students should be careful in accurately drawing what they see. Students who understand what's going on will draw their lines with appropriate spacing between the lines, regardless of the hue.

Answers to the Questions

1. Residual sodium chloride.

2. Metal salts, such as the salts of strontium and barium.

3. Neon is a bright orange-red color when it glows. Any light that glows blue must contain another element, such as argon.

4. The hydrogen and oxygen atoms in water are bound together by chemical bonds. These bonded atoms give a different spectrum, because the electrons are in a completely different environment.

Get a Half-Life! [Activity]

The simplest version of this lab is tossing coins, and using heads and tails to simulate radioactive decay. Then the half-life is each toss. The cubes add variety. If you have multifaceted cubes available, so much the better. You can amend the lab by equating each color with one of the facets. For example, the square facet may equal the red color, the triangular facet may equal the blue color, and a square facet with a blue dot in the center may equal the white face.

If not covered in lecture, the pre-lab meeting is a good place to introduce the concept of radioactive dating—carbon-14 dating gets the most attention.

Answers to the Questions

1. Answers will vary with the data table. Red should take the longest to reduce by half.

2. The unit of half-life in this experiment is the number of throws. One half-life is the number of throws required for half the cubes to leave.

3. Answers will vary with the data table. Red should take the most rolls.

4. The most radioactive is the one that decays fastest: white.

5. Roll the cubes that were removed again. They will have new half-lives.

6. Yes, but not very accurate. Accuracy is increased with the number of cubes tossed.

7. The lines should curve, corresponding to a constant rate of decay.

8. a. 10 years: 500 g; 20 years: 250 grams; 50 years: 31.25 grams; 100 years: 0.977 grams.

    b. Yes, substance X will disappear after the last atoms disintegrate. An estimate can be made from your graph in Step 8—between 500 and 1000 years.

Chain Reaction [Activity]

Answers to the Questions

1. The close-spaced dominoes took a shorter time to fall.

2. For the straight-column reaction, the number of dominoes being knocked over per second did not change. For the chain reaction, however, the number of dominoes being knocked over per second increased rapidly.

3. There were no more dominoes to fall over. Similarly, a nuclear fission chain reaction stops only when there are no more fissionable nuclei to fission.

4. Both are exponential functions. In other words, they each lead to rapidly increasing rates of reaction.

5. The domino chain reaction occurs in two dimensions, while the nuclear fission process is three-dimensional. Also, each domino reaction causes two additional reactions, while each uranium-235 nuclear reaction causes, on average, about three additional reactions.

Part 2: Chemistry
Chapter 11: Investigating Matter
Chemical Personalities
Mystery Powders
Chapter 12: The Nature of Chemical Bonds
Dot to Dot: Electron-Dot Diagrams
Repulsive Dots: VSEPR Theory
Molecules by Acme
Salt and Sand
Sugar Soft
Bubble Round-Up
Circular Rainbows
Pure Sweetness
Chapter 13: Chemical Reactions
Sensing pH
Upset Stomach
Tubular Rust
Chapter 14: Organic Chemistry
Smells Great!
Name That Recylable

Chemical Personalities [Experiment]
This experiment takes most students an entire lab period. Some variations on equipment needed or procedure may include the following:
• Place aqueous reagents into squirt bottles to avoid the need for pipettes or droppers.
• If the change in the steel wool is not very evident, students could weigh the sample before and after heating to show an increase in mass.
• A Bunsen burner could be used in Part B with caution due to the presence of methanol and acetone.

A fun chemical change to demonstrate at the beginning of this experiment is the addition of concentrated sulfuric acid to sugar. It is very visual but not safe for students to perform. One way to perform this demonstration is to add about a tablespoon of sugar to a large test tube. Wearing gloves and safety goggles and by working under a fume hood, add enough fresh concentrated sulfuric acid so that the acid just covers the sugar (avoid excess). Within a minute, the dehydration of the sugar (and hydration of the sulfuric acid) results in boiling hot temperatures and a carbonous material that pushes upwards within the test tube. Note the water that also condenses at the top of the test tube and how it is that sugar is also known as a "carbohydrate," which means it is made from carbon and water. Cleaning the test tube after this demonstration is not easy. In the least, be sure to rinse the carbonous material before discarding. The test tube itself might also be worthy of discarding in the broken glassware bin.

For Part A of this experiment, it is helpful to provide the student with a large assortment of elements and compounds, including metals, nonmetals, solids, liquids, and gases of a variety of colors and texture. Students may be asked to determine the odor of selected substances if the proper technique for smelling chemicals is first demonstrated. Note that students are typically amazed to find that the smell of elemental sulfur, S_8, is minimal. Be sure to follow this observation with the concept of how elemental sulfur, S_8, and hydrogen sulfide, H_2S, are not the same thing.

The boiling point of methanol is 64.7°C. Given variations in thermometers, we generally accept answers that range from 63°C to 67°C.

For Part B, Step 1, you might choose to squirt a little acetic acid or hydrochloric acid onto a small region of your students' piece of steel wool prior to heating.

For Part B, Step 2, the fact that the white color persists after the anhydrous copper sulfate cools down suggests to students that a chemical change has occurred—that the previous material has not reformed after the original conditions were reestablished. The deformation and formation of the copper sulfate hydrate, therefore, is perceived as a chemical change.

For Part B, Step 5, it is a good idea to accompany students while they make their observations and draw conclusions. Because of the purple fumes, many students initially believe that a chemical change has occurred. But if the crystals formed beneath the evaporating dish can be shown to be iodine, then the students can conclude that the vapors formed in between were also iodine, but in a gaseous phase. Have students compare the color and luster of the sublimed crystals with those of the original sample of iodine. Ask the students about the solubility of iodine in acetone, which they should have learned from Part A, Step 3b. Squirt a little acetone on the inverted evaporating dish to show how the crystals collected there are also soluble in acetone. Last, use a microspatula and scrape off some of the sublimed crystals and smear them onto a hot hot-plate. The purple fumes that form confirm that the material collected at the bottom of the evaporating dish is iodine. At this point, most students aptly see that the changes that occurred are merely physical.

Answers to the Questions

1. A quantitative observation involves a number (and unit), whereas a qualitative observation does not. The only quantitative observation made was the boiling point of methanol. There were many qualitative observations, including color, state of matter, luster, and so forth.

2. a) physical.   b) chemical.   c) physical.   d) chemical.

3. a) physical.   b) chemical.   c) physical.   d) chemical.

Mystery Powders [Experiment]
The unknowns for this experiment are generally regarded as safe. Students should be advised, however, to take serious precautions against accidentally spilling these unknowns, mixing them together, or letting them come in direct contact with skin. Consider drawing an analogy of what students are doing in this lab with what "real lab technicians" do in trying to identify an unknown—from the start, *anything* is possible, and so all precautions should be followed, especially the wearing of safety glasses.

Alert students to the hazard of working with the 0.3 *M* solution of sodium hydroxide (test #5). Skin will become slippery upon contact with this reagent. In such a case, the student should thoroughly rinse the affected area with water for many minutes even after the slippery sensation has gone. Consider also pouring some white distilled vinegar onto the affected skin.

Use parafilm to cover the test tubes to avoid contact with skin. The use of well-plates is recommended over the use of test tubes, because they make cleanup of this lab so much easier; it also forces the students to minimize the quantities they use. You may wish, however, for your students to work with both. The Hot-Water test (#6), for example, works best with a test tube, while the phenolphthalein test (#3) works well with the well-plate. Because students may have a tendency to overflow their wells with reagents, you should advise them on the minimal amounts of reagents needed for each test. In general, "if you can see it, it's probably more than enough."

Perhaps, the most difficult test to discern is the Hot-Water test (#6). This test requires lots of patience and careful observation. No taste testing allowed! You might consider not crushing the salt in a mortar and pestle beforehand. This way, the cubic shapes of the sodium chloride crystals will be of some assistance.

All unknowns are common household chemicals that can be safely washed down the drain or, preferably, disposed of in the trash can.

Answers to the Questions

2. Tests 1, 6, and 7 measure physical properties. Tests 2, 3, 4, and 5 involve chemical properties.

3. There is no contradiction in that sugar is both a food and a chemical—all foods are made of chemicals.

4. The students' answer should be the same as the number of test tubes or individual wells that they used.

Dot to Dot: Electron-Dot Diagrams [Activity]

Most students can complete this experiment in less than one lab period. Some variations on equipment needed or procedure may include the following:

- Have students work collaboratively, small groups work very well.
- Assign a challenge molecule to each group, or add bonus questions such as why the arrangement is HOCl and not HClO for hypochorous acid.
- Have students complete this experiment at home, after some discussion of the octet rule.

This experiment flows into the Molecular Shapes experiment very nicely, and it is possible to combine the two into a single lab meeting, although it may not be possible to completely finish both within a single meeting.

Repulsive Dots: VSEPR Theory [Experiment]

Most students can complete this experiment in one lab period. Some variations on equipment needed or procedure may include the following:

- If a limited number of model kits are available, students could work collaboratively in small groups.
- If model kits are not available, colored Styrofoam balls representing different atoms and toothpicks can be used. The difficulty is to get the proper geometry for the bonding, so marks (black spots) on the Styrofoam balls showing where the bonds would occur (where to insert the toothpicks) are extremely helpful.

It is very important that students be given a chart for the identification of the atoms for the model sets being used. It is also helpful to remove any atoms that may form expanded octets from the model sets.

A possible bonus assignment could include the molecules from the Electron-Dot Structures lab. Students could be asked to predict the shape of the molecules based on the Lewis structures they have previously drawn without the use of models.

1. BCl_3 is a nonpolar substance due to its triangular planar shape. Even though it contains three polar bonds, their effects cancel due to their positions. NCl_3 is a polar molecule due to its triangular pyramidal shape. It also contains three polar bonds, but their effects do not cancel.

2. SCl_2 is a bent molecule. It has four substituents with two nonbonding pairs. O_3 is also a bend molecule. It has three substituents with one nonbonding pair. It could be pointed out that even though they both have bent shapes, the bond angles would be different. SCl_2 would have a bond angle of approximately 109°, while O_3 would have a bond angle of approximately 120°.

Salt and Sand [Experiment]

This experiment takes most students an entire lab period. Some variations on equipment needed or procedure may include the following:

*   A list of available equipment could be provided to the students. It is helpful for running the experiment and provides hints for the astute student.
*   Sugar could be used in place of the salt. If this is done, it is best to ask students to determine the mass percent for the sand only. Also, if the sand is not thoroughly rinsed off the sugar, then it will remain somewhat sticky, even after drying, which is a consequence worthy for the students to discover on their own.

After approving the students' procedures, it may be helpful to demonstrate some techniques to the class. In particular, consider demonstrating filtration. (Gravity filtration takes a long time if the paper is not fluted.)

You may find it preferable for each student to work alone. Three goals include (1) learning the limitations of laboratory equipment; (2) gaining first-hand experience on how to control variables so as to achieve reliable data; and (3) achieving a certain amount of independence.

It is most helpful to alert students of the advantages and disadvantages of using their entire sample on the first run. For example, some students completely forget that the mass of the sample is needed. They go through their procedure only to find that they cannot calculate the mass percents without it. If they use only part of their original sample, they could repeat their experiment to correct any problems encountered in the first run. If they use the entire sample, however, then they need not worry about the homogeneity of their sample.

Having drying lamps or a drying oven available will greatly decrease the time required to complete this experiment. Consider allowing students to store their samples in a safe cupboard so that they may dry thoroughly overnight before being weighed.

Consider a grading scheme where half of the credit is based solely upon the accuracy of the student's results, while the other half is credit for completing the lab and answering the questions. Most students are able to get within plus or minus 2.00 percentage points of the actual value. If the student wants to repeat the procedure, you might consider deducting only 2 points where 25 points is the maximum number of points possible. This is good for students whose answers are way off because of poor procedures or some mishap. Rather than saying that you are "deducting points" for repeating the procedure, tell students that they are permitted to "buy" another sample for testing, but that the sample will cost them 2 points each. This is in line with what occurs in a research laboratory, where researchers need to be most careful with the samples they have, often because of financial concerns.

The following grading scheme is based upon the difference between the actual percentage of sand and the student's experimental percentage of sand, where 25 points is the maximum number of points possible.

Points awarded	Difference in % actual and experimental
25	+/− 0.10
24	+/− 0.20
23	+/− 0.30
22	+/− 0.40
21	+/− 0.50
20	+/− 0.60
19	+/− 0.70
18	+/− 0.80
17	+/− 0.90
16	+/− 1.00
15	+/− 1.20
14	+/− 1.40
13	+/− 1.60
12	+/− 1.80
11	+/− 2.00
10	+/− 2.20
9	+/− 2.40
8	+/− 2.60
7	+/− 2.80
6	+/− 3.00
5	+/− 3.20
4	+/− 3.40
3	+/− 3.60
2	+/− 3.80
1	+/− 4.00
0	> 4.00

Answers to the Questions

Student answers and responses are very dependent on the procedure used. The two most common errors encountered are
• Not rinsing the salt with sufficient quantities of water
• Not waiting for the samples to dry completely

Sugar Soft [Experiment]

You will need to talk about calibration curves and their function during your pre-lab discussion. A typical calibration curve may look as shown below once completed. Regarding the calibration curve for this experiment, ask your students why it doesn't pass through the origin, even if the origin were shown on the graph. Also ask the students what kind of slope they might expect at sugar concentrations beyond 20%. Stress the importance of being able to relate a graph to the physical reality it represents. Last, you might share with students how beer and wine manufacturers measure alcohol content by way of the hydrometer. The more alcohol, the less dense the solution and the lower the hydrometer floats. Calibrated properly, the reading of the hydrometer can be translated into percent alcohol.

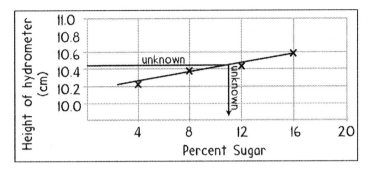

The students' data tables may show that most all soft drinks have about the same percentage of sugar. Exceptions include diet soft drinks. Also, root beer tends to be on the denser side. Consider showing students what happens when a can of diet soda and a can of root beer are thrown into a tub of water (one floats and the other sinks!).

Bubble Round-Up [Activity]

This is the same technique used by early chemical investigators in studying the nature of gases.

In preparing the setup, the second flask should be filled with water from the beaker, which has been filled close to the brim. This guarantees that water will not overflow as it is being displaced. You may either inform students of this technique or provide sponges and let them discover it on their own.

Many students will want to repeat the CO_2 collection to permit further experimentation.

Challenge students as to how many candles they can extinguish using their collected CO_2. You might direct students to use the stopper with the tubing attached to better concentrate the CO_2 over individual flames.

Students may "pour" some of the carbon dioxide into their mouths. The taste will be familiar to them.

"Going Further" with Step 5 easily changes this activity into an experiment, for it requires critical thinking and careful technique. The density of carbon dioxide at 1 atm and 25°C is about 1.80 g/L. Ideally, students should measure the precise volume of the stoppered 2-liter bottle by filling it with water and then pouring that water into a graduated cylinder. This should be done after everything else, as it will make for a bottle full of "heavy" water drops. This is the volume that the student should use in calculating the density of the carbon dioxide.

Answers to the Questions

1. A 2-liter plastic soda bottle does not contain exactly 2 liters of air. The best way to find out the actual volume is to fill the bottle with water and then measure this volume of water in a graduated cylinder.

2. The flask was not initially stoppered so that the newly formed carbon dioxide would push the less dense air out. This step helps to increase the purity of the collected CO_2.

3. The displaced water filled up the beaker, which would overflow if it had been filled to capacity.

Molecules by Acme [Experiment]

The formulas presented in Table 3 are listed in order of increasing complexity. The structures students tend to have the most difficulty with include chloroethanol, acetylene, acetic acid, benzene, and iron (III) oxide. Note that there are a couple versions of the model for iron oxide that students might build. Have them keep trying until they get to the one that has no double bonds and looks like a football, where the two iron atoms are linked together by three bridging oxygen atoms.

Here are two-dimensional renditions of some of the more difficult-to-build models:

2-chloroethanol   acetylene   acetic acid

benzene   iron (III) oxide

Answers to the Questions

1. a. Yes.   b. No, you would have hydrogen peroxide.

2. a. Both have the same shape.   b. Dichloromethane is less symmetrical and more lopsided.

3. Five.

4. Hydrogen, oxygen, nitrogen, carbon dioxide, and acetylene.

5. Oxygen, nitrogen, carbon dioxide, acetylene, acetic acid, benzene.

6. Benzene.

Circular Rainbows [Activity]

Chromatography is a technique often used by chemists to separate components of a mixture. In 1906, the Russian botanist Mikhail Tsvett separated color pigments in leaves by allowing a solution of these pigments to flow down a column packed with an insoluble material such as starch, alumina, or silica. Because different colored bands appeared along the column, he called the procedure chromatography. (*Note:* Color is not a required property to achieve separation of compounds by this procedure.) Because of its simplicity and efficiency, this technique is widely used for separating and identifying compounds such as drugs and natural products.

The basis of chromatography is the partitioning (separation due to differences in solubility) of compounds between a stationary phase and moving phase. Stationary phases such as alumina, silica, or paper (cellulose) have highly polar surface areas that attract the components (molecules) of a mixture to different extents. The components of the mixture to be separated are thought to be continuously adsorbed and then released from the stationary phase into the solvent that moves over the surface of the stationary phase. Because of differences in the attraction of each component for the stationary phase, each component travels at different speeds, thus causing the separation.

In paper chromatography, where paper is the stationary phase, a small spot of a mixture is carried by solvent through the paper via capillary action. The solvent and various components of the mixture each travel at different speeds along the paper, resulting in the separation of the mixture.

Technique really counts in this activity. Many students will have the tendency to add the solvent too quickly, which will cause the colors to bleed into one another. Point out to students that with a good separation, they should be able to cut out individual colors using a pair of scissors. The best separations will show colors with distinct boundaries and white spaces in between colors. Have each student turn in his or her best and most spectacular separation. The name or PIN of each student should be marked on the perimeter in pencil. Base your grading or judging on the degree of separation.

Food coloring is an alternative to pen ink. Felt-tip and overhead transparency pens tend to work best.

Answers to the Questions

1. The ionic component would stick to the paper by ion–dipole interactions and not travel with the solvent.

2. A different hue of blue may be obtained by changing the proportions of a secondary or tertiary color.

Pure Sweetness [Activity]

This activity may take over a month for students to accomplish. Thus, it shouldn't be started close to the end of the academic term. Students should know that in producing these crystals, patience is the greatest virtue. You will need to emphasize the importance of not overcooking the brown sugar. It doesn't take too much cooking time before the brown sugar simply hardens upon cooling. Students should maintain a crystal journal and tape a few of the best crystals they ultimately obtain. How well they keep their journal may be used to assess their grade for this activity. You might also grade them, in part, based upon the colorlessness of their crystals. To make your assessments less arbitrary, exhibit a set of samples along with the number of points you would have assigned to each.

Answers to the Questions

1. Make a concentrated solution of sugar in water. If any molasses is present, it should give the concentrated sugar solution a yellow color, which indeed it does.

2. White sugar is more pure than brown sugar.

3. Brown sugar is more natural than white sugar.

4. The greater the quality (colorlessness) of the sugar crystals, the less of them you have!

Sensing pH [Activity]

Have each student prepare his or her small batch of red cabbage pH indicator. A single head of red cabbage should be sufficient for a class of 30 students. Bring dry ice to the laboratory, and allow students to drop pieces into test tubes of their indicator solution. After the students have become familiar with the colors that the cabbage indicator turns at various pHs have them gather around a 2-liter glass beaker containing about 300 mL of a fairly concentrated broth that is a slight shade of red from small amounts of acetic acid. Have students note the color of the broth, and ask them what the color change of the broth might be if you were to quickly fill the beaker with water. Some students may argue that it should remain the same color because no acid or base has been added—only water. Others may say that the color will remain the same but will become fainter, because the solution is becoming more dilute. Remind the students that pH is a measure of the concentration of hydronium ions. Thus, as you dilute the solution, shouldn't the concentration of hydronium ions become less and the pH rise? The color should thus turn from its slight reddish color to purple. Sure enough, if it's not too concentrated with acetic acid, this will be the case. Follow up by asking students whether adding more water will ever bring the indicator to a slightly alkaline green color. Why or why not? Try it and see.

Answers to the Questions

1. A green color forms around one of the electrodes. This occurs because of the formation of hydroxide ions at this electrode.

2. The hydroxide ions form at the positive terminal.

3. Bubble formation occurs at the negative terminal. These are bubbles of hydrogen gas.

Tubular Rust [Activity]

References:
"Percent Oxygen in Air" Martins, G.F. *J. Chem. Ed.* 1987, 64 (9), 809. George F. Martins, Newton North High School, Newtonville, MA 02160.

Answers to the Questions

1. The actual percent oxygen in air is about 21%.

2. The volume of a gas is affected by the pressure exerted upon it. For this reason, it is important that the pressures inside and outside the test tube remain the same. Accomplish this by keeping the water levels even.

3. It would take longer because of less surface area.

Upset Stomach [Experiment]

Spilled acid can be neutralized with baking soda, and spilled sodium hydroxide can be neutralized with boric acid or vinegar. Inform students to wash and thoroughly rinse any acid or base away from their skin. The sodium hydroxide will be most apparent due to its slippery feel—slippery because it reacts with skin oils to form a layer of soap. So that students exercise proper precautions, you might tell them that the sodium hydroxide *dissolves* flesh and then reacts with skin oils to form a soap-like layer.

Neutralized solutions may be poured down the drain flushed with plenty of water.

Answers to the Questions

1. The antacid that required the fewest number of drops of sodium hydroxide can be considered the "strongest."

2. The neutralizing power of an antacid, of course, also depends on the size of the tablet. The more massive the tablet, the more acid it will be able to neutralize.

3. Dividing the number of drops of stomach acid relieved by the mass of the antacid tablets allows a comparison of the antacids based upon their formulation, rather than the mass of the tablet.

4. The order of strengths here may or may not be the same as that cited in Question 1.

5. a. Two tablets have twice the neutralizing strength as one tablet.

   b. With less of the tablet entering the "stomach," there will be a perceived decrease in the strength of the antacid.

   c. The fewer number of drops of sodium hydroxide added to complete the neutralization, the stronger the antacid. Thus, if extra drops of sodium hydroxide were added, this would make the antacid appear as though it were not as effective.

Smells Great! [Activity]

In a pre-lab discussion, consider addressing the receptor site model for smelling. Beforehand, however, make sure that students understand that only gaseous chemicals are detected by the nose. An odorous chemical is odorous because it has the right shape to fit within the olfactory receptors in the nose. The chemical fits into the receptor much like a key fits into a lock. Once there, it triggers a neurological signal to the brain. Receptor sites in our nose work in tandem with receptor sites on our taste buds to give distinctive flavor. This receptor site model is the same as the one addressed in Chapter 13 of the textbook.

Essential oils are often formulations of many odorous chemicals. The smell of pineapple, for example, consists of at least ten chemicals, most of them esters. Artificial extracts reproduce these formulations only close enough to fool most people.

A special note about butyric acid: It has the smell of rancid butter and it stays with you for quite some time. Because of this, you may not wish to work with this chemical. Interestingly enough, butyric acid is a component of body odor. Animals can readily detect a human when downwind because of its strong scent. Also, bloodhounds are trained to follow remnant trails of this chemical when tracking humans.

Notes on Disposal

Have students deposit their reaction mixtures into a single waste container such as a 1-liter Erlenmeyer flask. Students may need to rinse their tubes with methanol to make cleaning easier. These rinsings may also be combined in the waste container.

Add a solution of sodium bicarbonate to neutralize the sulfuric acid. (It is neutralized when added sodium bicarbonate ceases to cause bubbling.) Decant the aqueous layer, which may be poured down the drain. The remaining oils are biodegradable and may be sealed in a jar and thrown into the trash.

Table 1.

Alcohol	Carboxylic Acid	Observed Smell
Methanol	Salicylic acid	Wintergreen
Octanol	Acetic acid	Oranges
Benzyl alcohol	Acetic acid	Peach
Isoamyl alcohol	Acetic acid	Banana
n-Propanol	Acetic acid	Pear
Isopentenol	Acetic acid	"Juicy Fruit"
Methanol	Butyric acid	Apple
Isobutanol	Propionic acid	Rum

Answers to the Questions

1. Nothing. An ester produced in the laboratory is no different from the same ester produced in nature. The plant producing this ester, however, might also produce many other esters. It is the unique combination of these many esters that will give the plant a unique odor.

2. Molecules have a greater tendency to vaporize at higher temperatures. The assumption here, of course, is the understanding that a substance has odor because of the gaseous molecules it emits.

Name That Recyclable [Activity]

A main purpose of this short activity is to let students know what those recycling imprints on plastics mean. Cut out small pieces of plastic for the students to work with. One separation scheme is as follows:

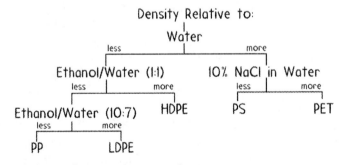

Students may also choose a scheme that separates one plastic at a time.

Students may be expecting all the unknowns to be different. To challenge their trust in their experimental observations, you might consider making two unknowns from the same plastic.

Code 3 (polyvinyl chloride) and code 7 (mixed resins) are not included in this activity because of their variable densities. For your information, because PVC contains a halogen (chlorine), it can be identified using the Beilstein test (touching the plastic with a hot copper wire and then placing the wire in a flame: a blue green flame is positive for a halogen).

References: "Method for Separating or Identifying Plastics" Kolb, K.E., Kolb, D.K. *J. Chem. Ed.* 1991, 68(4), 348.

Answers to the Questions

1. Melting points.

2. Throw all the pieces into a large container of water. The less dense polypropylene pieces will float to the top, while the more dense polystyrene pieces will float to the bottom.

Part 3: Biology

Magnifying Microscopes [Experiment]

In the interest of time, bring in premixed saltwater and prepared isotonic solution (for example, a normal saline .9% NaCl solution), hypotonic solution (such as distilled water), and hypertonic solutions (like a 10% NaCl solution) for students to use. It is best to leave the *Elodea* leaves out of water for at least an hour before the lab session begins.

Answers to Summing Up Questions

1. Upside down and backwards.

2. The leaf stayed the same size, but the cells (inside the cell walls) shrunk, because water moved out of them. Water left the cells because of osmosis.

3. The plant cells swelled until they were restrained from enlarging further by the cell walls. This occurred as water flowed into the cell due to osmosis.

4. When we eat potato chips, we get thirsty because we take in salt. Like the potato slice in saltwater, the body needs to absorb extra water to balance out the salt in the chips.

5. We could have viewed cells from the body and watched them shrink, swell, or stay the same. (Other answers are possible.)

In and Out [Experiment]

The Jell-O should be prepared, poured into small containers, and allowed to set prior to the lab period. Make sure to use only fresh pineapple slices, not canned—otherwise the lab will not work! If you do not have access to stopwatches, a clock with a second hand will work fine.

Answers to Summing Up Questions

Activity 1

1. It stood up straight, stiffened, and turned the same color as the dye in the parts with veins.

2. The water level dropped over the course of the period. (Students should provide an exact measurement in centimeters.)

3. Answers will vary.

4. Osmosis.

5. Osmosis is necessary for water balance in our cells.

Activity 2

1. The Jell-O turned watery over the course of the lab period.

2. The fresh pineapple affects the Jell-O, because its cells contain digestive enzymes that are released via exocytosis. The enzymes break down the sugars in the Jell-O, and the cells then use endocytosis to take in the sugar. This will not work with canned pineapple, because the pasteurization process denatures the proteins within the cell.

Activity 3

1. The highest temperature. (Students should provide exact temperature in degrees Celsius.)

2. Diffusion occurred faster in the air, because molecules move more quickly in air.

3. They moved from areas of high concentration to areas of low concentration.

Ufroom Pollywoggles [Activity]

Before beginning the activity, ensure that students remove the aces and jokers from each deck of cards.

Answers to Summing Up Questions

1. We obtain only half of our genes from each parent. If gametes all had *all* of the alleles from both parents, then the offspring would have twice the amount of genetic material they should.

2. *Homozygous* indicates that an organism possesses two identical alleles; *heterozygous* indicates that an organism possesses two different alleles.

3. It is possible if both parents have the heterozygous genotype.

4. This is impossible, because if both parents have a recessive phenotype, neither would have a dominant allele to pass on to their offspring.

Real-Life Inheritance [Activity]

You may find that assigning a genetic disease to each group in Activity 3 will help things go more smoothly than having students choose their own disorders to research. Some possibilities include Down syndrome, cystic fibrosis, sickle cell disease, hemophilia, Tay-Sachs disease, Huntington disease, and more.

Answers to Activity 2: Procedure Questions

Step 1: Possible gametes for mom: $X_H X_H$
        Possible gametes for dad: $X_h Y$

	X_H	X_H
X_h	$X_H X_h$	$X_H X_h$
Y	$X_H Y$	$X_H Y$

Step 2:

	X_h	X_h
X_H	$X_h X_H$	$X_h X_H$
Y	$X_h Y$	$X_h Y$

Step 3:

	X_h	X_h
X_h	$X_h X_h$	$X_h X_h$
Y	$X_h Y$	$X_h Y$

Answers to Summing Up Questions

Activity 1

1. Answers will vary. If you have a widow's peak, at least one parent must also have a widow's peak, because it is a dominant trait. This means that at least one parent must have a dominant allele. If you have a straight hairline, however, you do not know for sure what phenotype your parents have.

2. No, this is not possible. No hairy knuckles is a recessive trait, so both parents have only the no-hairy-knuckle allele, and neither has a hairy-knuckle allele to pass to you.

Activity 2

1. 100%, because she only has an affected X chromosome to pass on.

2. His daughters will have an affected X chromosome, because this is all he has to pass on, but his sons will have a normal X chromosome, because he only passes on the Y chromosome to his sons.

3. The daughters have a 0% chance of having hemophilia since all will inherit a normal allele X_H from their dad. The sons have a 50% chance of having hemophilia, depending on whether they inherit X_H or X_h from their mother.

Activity 3

1. Answers will vary.

2. Answers will vary.

3. Answers will vary.

Understanding Darwin [Activity]

If you find that some students are shy about participating in classroom activities, offer a reward to the last four people "surviving" at the end of Activities 1 and 2.

Answers to Summing Up Questions

Activity 1

1. The answer *might* be that different students were left at the end of both activities. Reasons provided for this will vary.

2. An entirely different group of students would survive, because they would need to be able to perform both skills well, not just one or the other.

3. Answers will vary, but they should be something along the lines of the following: Natural selection means that organisms with traits best-suited for success in their environment will be able to survive and reproduce best, with the result that those traits become more common in the population.

Activity 2

1. Yes.

2. The population will be able to evolve to adapt to a wider variety of circumstances.

3. Answers will vary, but students should be able to illustrate a clear shift in one or more characteristics due to a change in the environment. For example, peppered moths changed color during the Industrial Revolution to adapt to the changing color of the environment.

Activity 3

1. The separation of the two halves of the island *could* lead to the formation of two different species. Whether it did or not would depend on how the populations evolved on the two sides of the island—specifically, does some evolutionary change make it impossible for organisms from opposite sides of the island to produce fertile offspring?

2. Answers will vary.

Investigating Evolution [Activity]

This lab should be presented after students read Section 17.7 of their text. To guide students in their research, feel free to provide a list of relevant Web sites at the start of the lab.

Answers to Procedure Questions

Step 1: Answers will vary, but could include natural selection in action, artificial selection imposed by humans, similarities in the anatomy, molecules, development, and DNA sequences of related species, the existence of anatomical intermediaries in the fossil record, and biogeographical patterns of distribution on Earth.

Answers to Summing Up Question

Research Findings: Have each group present their findings as a 5-minute news report, in addition to writing up notes in this section of the lab.

What Is It—Bacterium? Protist? Fungus? [Experiment]

If you do not have access to a pond, water from any natural, unfiltered source will do.

Answers to Summing Up Questions

1. Answers will vary. (Students should include the *total* number of organism types they found.) The number and types of organisms will most likely vary between groups. This is because the distribution of organisms is not homogeneous, even when the source of water is the same!

2. Answers will vary.

3. Answers will vary.

All Plants Are Not Created Equal [Experiment]

You should provide an array of local leaves for students to look at, and make sure that the leaf identification guide you hand out has all of the appropriate leaf types included. If you do not have access to live specimens, feel free to use detailed pictures of moss, ferns, flowers, conifers, and leaves instead.

Answers to Activity 1: Procedure Questions

Step 1:

	Moss	Fern	Flowering Plant	Conifer
Leaves	Yes	Yes	Yes	Yes
Roots	No	Yes	Yes	Yes
Seeds	No	No	Yes	Yes
Spores	Yes	Yes	No	No
Stem	No	Yes	Yes	Yes

Answers to Summing Up Questions

Activity 1

1. Both mosses and ferns require water for reproduction—both have swimming sperm.

2. For flowering plants, seeds are located in the fruit; for conifers, seeds are located in the cones.

Activity 2

1. It is difficult to tell exactly what kind of tree a leaf belongs to when looking at closely related species, but for vastly different types of trees, it is relatively simple. Answers to the second part of the question will vary.

The Amazing Senses [Activity]

Safety Note: When choosing hairpins for use in the lab, make sure to select brands with round edges so that students do not accidentally scratch or poke their lab partners during Activity 5.

Answers to Summing Up Questions

Activity 1

1. Everyone has a blind spot—it's located where the optic nerve leaves the retina.

2. Answers will vary. Differences can be accounted for by the varying shapes and sizes of peoples' eyes.

Activity 2

1. Answers will vary.

2. Flexibility of the lens and strength of the eye muscles could account for the difference.

3. We need near-point accommodation to help with closeup work such as reading.

4. Decreased flexibility of the lens and weakened eye muscles account for the increase in near-point accommodation with time.

5. It enables us to read and track across a page or screen without jumping lines.

Activity 3

1. The answer should be yes, because both eyes need to be able to contract their pupils to protect their retinas.

2. If we did not have this reflex, our retinas could be damaged due to overexposure.

Activity 5

1. In the first scenario, the sound only travels through air to reach the ear, whereas in the second scenario, sound travels through bone and flesh as well.

Activity 7

1. Answers should be approximately the same for both partners.

2. The results are similar because although different people have slightly different arrangements of sensory receptors, the overall pattern is the same.

3. Different parts of the body have different distributions of touch receptors because they need different amounts of sensitivity and of protection. For example, the fact that our fingertips are very sensitive allows us to perform fine manual tasks. In terms of pain reception, a body part such as the elbow is leaned upon all the time—so, there are fewer pain receptors there than on the forearm.

Muscles and Bones [Activity]

Detailed pictures of a skeleton can be used if a model skeleton is not available for Activity 1. Any sort of bodybuilding or athletic magazines would have appropriate pictures to use for Activity 2.

Answers to Summing Up Questions

1. Deltoid, pectoralis major, latissimus dorsi (those muscles move forearm).

2. Bones: Pelvis, femur, patella, tibia, tarsals, metatarsals, phalanges.
   Muscles: Quadriceps, hamstring gastrocnemius, gluteus maximus, soleus, Achilles' tendon.

3. Wrinkling your forehead: Frontalis.
   Winking your eye: Obicularis oculi.
   Puckering your lips: Obicularis oris.

Keep Pumping [Activity]

Again, if you do not have access to stopwatches for the activity, ordinary clocks or watches with second hands should work fine. If you have students with health problems who will not be able to participate in the activities, assign them to a group with two other students who can perform the activities so that they can still complete the lab.

Answers to Activity 4: Procedure Questions

Step 1: Answers will vary, but possible responses include the following:
Raising heart rate: experiencing fear, excitement, anxiety, anger, or nervousness; ingesting stimulants such as caffeine or nicotine; eating a large meal.
Lowering heart rate: meditating; sleeping; thinking of a calm place; experiencing shock; ingesting depressants such as alcohol or tranquilizers; holding one's breath.

Answers to Summing Up Questions

Activity 1

1. Answers will vary but could include factors such as fitness, age, gender, and health.

2. Answers will vary but could include factors such as changed needs, nerves, and error.

3. Generally, students should answer that their pulse rate was faster when taken by their lab partner. This could be due to nerves, lack of concentration, and so forth.

Activity 2

1. Answers will vary. Most people find the carotid easier because it is a stronger pulse, but this is not always the case.

Activity 3

1. Pulse rate changed because the body needed more oxygen to keep the muscles moving.

2. Answers will vary but should be consistent with the data recorded in the "Procedure" portion of the lab. Reasons for varying changes in heart rate could be fitness level, effort, and so forth.

3. The answer should reflect data in Step 6 of the "Procedure" section.

4. Answers will vary. Again, factors that might explain differences in heart rate levels could include overall fitness, initial change in heart rate, and so forth.

Activity 4

1. Answers will vary but possible responses include being able to reduce anxiety, increase focus and concentration, and avoid overexertion.

Breathe In, Breathe Out [Activity]

Safety Note: In Activity 1, make sure your students only suck a little bit of water into their straws—otherwise, they could accidentally inhale water.

Answers to Summing Up Questions

Activity 1

1. Oxygen is inhaled, and carbon dioxide is exhaled.

2. Answers will vary but should have something to do with the amount of oxygen and carbon dioxide present before breath-holding.

3. The length of time after hyperventilating into the bag should be much shorter because of the quick buildup of carbon dioxide in the bag.

Activity 2

1. When you are in a sit-up position, there is less space to expand your lungs because your muscles aren't able to fully contract—this reduces your lung capacity.

2. Differences in data can be accounted for by various factors such as fitness, health, size, and gender.

Activity 3

1. Breathing rate increased.

2. Breathing rate increased because the body needed more oxygen to provide more energy to muscles.

3. Jumping while holding your breath is more difficult because the body does not have enough oxygen to supply your cells with ATP.

4. Answers will vary.

Prey vs. Predators [Activity]

Answers to Activity 2: Procedure Questions

Step 3:

Original group	Generation 1	Generation 2	Generation 3	Generation 4	Generation 5	Generation 6
6	18	54	162	486	1458	4374

Answers to Summing Up Questions

Activity 1

1. The population increased and decreased as resource availability increased and decreased over time.

2. The population and resource curves vary inversely—when the deer population increases, the amount of available resources decreases, and vice versa.

3. Answers will vary, but an example would be interactions between lynxes and hares.

Activity 2

1. The population size increased dramatically (to 4374 rabbits!).

2. The rabbit population destroyed natural habitats by eating all the plants.

3. Answers will vary, but an example would be bacteria on food left out at a buffet. Over time, exponentially growing populations use up available resources and eventually the population crashes.

Activity 3

1. At first, some balance may remain, but eventually the entire web is affected, and the number of species at every level decreases.

2. Answers will vary depending on which animal was removed from the web.

3. Answers will vary, but an example could be that over-fishing by humans is causing a decrease in the overall fish population, and other animal populations such as seals are also decreasing because of this lack of food.

4. Answers will vary but should mention something about the interconnectedness of life at all levels of an ecosystem.

Ecological Footprints [Activity]

If you do not have access to printers/word-processing programs, have students create their bumper stickers out of poster board with markers, construction paper, and other craft supplies.

Answers to Activity 2: Procedure Questions

Step 4: Answers will vary, but the list should include such factors as pollution, greenhouse gas emission, melting ice caps, climate change, resource scarcity, and so forth.

Answers to Summing Up Questions

Activity 1

1. Answers will vary, but most students should be surprised at the amount of resources it takes to provide for what they consider to be their "basic" needs.

2. Answers will vary.

3. Answers will vary, but students should come up with some creative answers; for example, collecting all the trash their family produces in a day and putting it in a pile in the living room.

Crystal Growth [Experiment]

This lab uses thymol, which may irritate the skin. Use caution. The seed crystals speed up the process of crystallization, and longer cooling promotes larger crystal size.

Answers to the Questions

1. Crystallization from a solution depends on the concentration of the solution and the rate of evaporation. Crystallization from a melt depends on temperature and the rate of cooling.

2. Yes.

3. Under ideal conditions (time, space allotment, temperature, concentration), crystal form provides a useful means for identifying minerals. Unfortunately, ideal conditions are not always possible.

4. Minerals that cool slowly develop larger crystals than minerals that cool quickly. So if you want large, well-formed minerals, take your time.

What's That Mineral? [Experiment]

For the lab on mineral identification, use your own collection of minerals (collections from Ward's Scientific or Miners Catalog). The number of minerals you require your students to identify depends on your time schedule and your particular collection of minerals. Please note!! Not all the minerals from the mineral identification tables are necessary for this lab. For example, in a mineral collection composed of quartz, calcite, magnetite, muscovite, and pyrite, your students would use hardness to identify quartz, reaction to HCl to identify calcite, a magnet or compass to identify magnetite, cleavage and color to identify muscovite, and streak and probably color and crystal form to identify pyrite.

Answers to the Questions

1. The distinguishing characteristic for the following minerals:
   a. halite   chemical—taste
   b. pyrite   cubic form with striations, streak
   c. quartz   hexagonal form, hardness
   d. biotite   cleavage, brown color, soft
   e. fluorite   isometric form, hardness
   f. garnet   isometric form, dark color, density

2. Physical properties: a mineral's crystalline structure or chemical composition:
   a. crystal form   crystalline structure
   b. color   chemical composition
   c. cleavage   crystalline structure
   d. specific gravity chemical composition

3. Metallic minerals exhibit streak. If there is no streak, the mineral is nonmetallic.

4. Streak is the more reliable method for mineral identification. Some minerals come in a variety of different colors (e.g., quartz, fluorite, and corundum) and, hence, cannot be identified by a characteristic color. Weathering may also affect a mineral's color. Because streak does not change, it is more useful for mineral identification.

5. Color.

6. The physical properties that distinguish plagioclase feldspars from orthoclase feldspars are color and striations. Plagioclase is darker than orthoclase, and plagioclase exhibits striations.

Rock Hunt [Activity]

This is simply an activity to encourage rock consciousness in the students' everyday environment.

What's That Rock? [Experiment]

This is a lab on rock identification where you use your own rocks or those students have collected. Rock collections can also be obtained from Ward's Scientific or Miners Catalog. Once again, the number of rocks you use depends on your collection. If you are using rocks collected by your students, you may find the rocks are all of one type—igneous, metamorphic, or sedimentary—depending on your area. If this is the case, you may want the students to not only identify the rock and rock type but also discuss the environment where the rock was found.

On this note, here's an interesting true story: Students in New York City find that most of the old brownstone buildings are made of Triassic sandstone quarried in Connecticut. Some, however, are built of Scottish sandstones brought across the Atlantic in the 19th century. It's hard to tell which is which. Why? Interestingly enough, both sandstones were formed at the same period under the same circumstances in the same general area. They formed during Triassic times in a northern supercontinent, before the split of the Atlantic Ocean. In the 200 million years since formation, plate tectonics has split this region onto opposite shores of the North Atlantic Ocean—part in Connecticut and part in Scotland. And now, civilization has brought them together in one city. (This tidbit from *The Practical Geologist*, by Douglas Dixon and Raymond L. Bernor, Editor.)

Answers to the Questions

1. Igneous rocks exhibit both fine- and coarse-grained textures. Fine-grained textures occur when the rock has cooled very quickly. The texture can be so fine that individual crystals are too difficult to identify with an unaided eye. Some fine-grained textures are glassy. Coarse-grained textures occur when the rock is allowed to cool slowly. Depending on the rate of cooling, most crystal grains can be easily identified.

2. Slow cooling, recrystallization, and open space. Igneous rocks that have undergone slow cooling exhibit large crystals. Metamorphic rocks subjected to increased pressures and temperatures exhibit large crystals. Sedimentary rocks precipitated from mineral-rich water or sedimentary rocks formed from the evaporation of mineral-rich water may exhibit large crystals.

3. Bedding planes, fossils, ripple marks, and cross-bedding.

4. By texture and mineral composition. Metamorphic rocks generally exhibit foliation—the realignment of crystals. The process of metamorphism also forms new minerals out of old minerals.

Top This [Activity]

This is an activity in learning about topographic maps. Students draw contour lines and construct a topographical profile. Supplement this activity by giving your students topographical maps. Ask them to determine the scale of the map and the contour interval. Have them construct a topographic profile in the area that best depicts the overall landscape, and to calculate the vertical exaggeration.

Answers to the Exercises

1. Contour lines should look something like this:

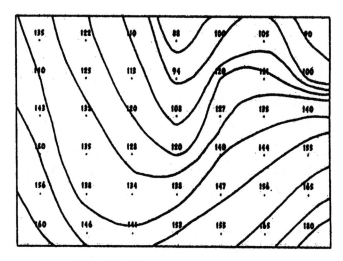

2. Contour lines should look something like this:

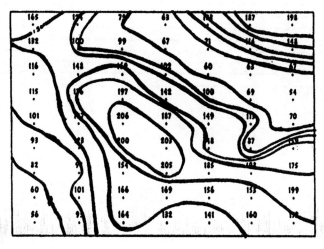

3. Elevations are as shown:

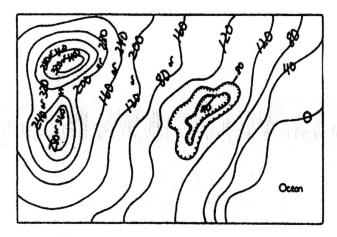

4. Topographical profile:

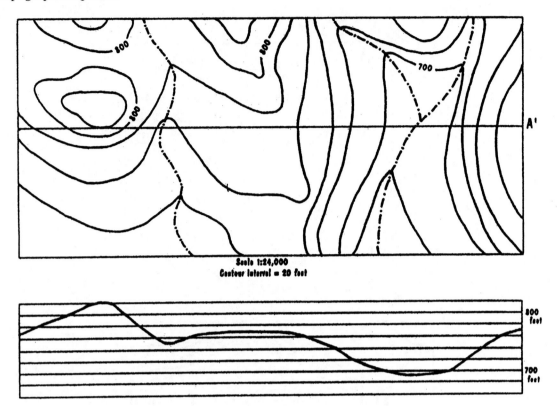

Scale 1:24,000
Contour Interval = 20 feet

800 feet

700 feet

Vertical scale is 1 inch = 100 feet = 1200 inches (1:1200)

$$\frac{1/1200}{1/24000} = \frac{24000}{1200} = 20$$

Therefore, the vertical exaggeration is 20 times greater than the true relief.

Over and Under [Activity]

This lab is supplemental rather than essential, so use if time permits. The lab is challenging and heightens student awareness of what lies beneath the Earth's surface. Measurement of dip angles can be estimated. Students should be able to tell that a 90° reading is vertical and a 45° is between vertical and horizontal. Dip direction is more important than angle. Students may enjoy coloring in the bed layers with colored pencils.

Answers to the Exercises

1. Structure is an anticline.

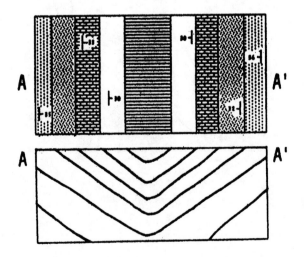

332

2. Structure is a syncline.

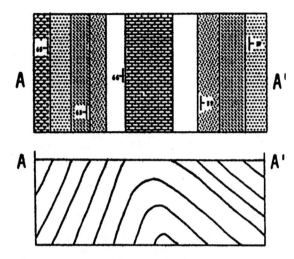

3. Structure is a plunging syncline.

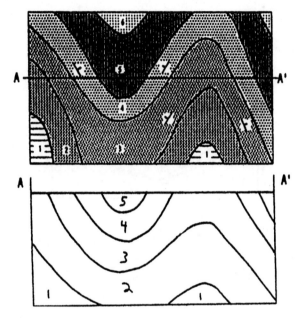

4–7. A syncline fold is displayed; strike slip fault; oldest structure is fold; youngest is intrusion.

Answers to the Questions

1. A symmetrical syncline is shown in Exercise 1. The symmetry can be determined on the map view by the dip angles and by the apparent thickness of the beds.

2. An asymmetrical anticline is shown in Exercise 2. The lack of symmetry can be determined by the dip angles, which tell us that the beds are dipping in toward the fold axis.

3. A plunging incline is shown in Exercise 3. The dip direction tells us that the beds are dipping in toward the fold axis.

4. A strike fault is shown in Exercise 4. Evidence for the fault structure is the horizontal displacement of beds. The fold structure is a syncline. The fold is the oldest structure, and the intrusion is the youngest structure.

Walking On Water [Experiment]

This is meant to follow the activity on topographical maps, *Top This*.

Students will then already know how to draw contour lines. Important here is that the groundwater flow is perpendicular to lines of equal hydraulic head. The lines of equal hydraulic head are *equipotential lines*, completely analogous to the lines of equal potential in an electric field. Electric field lines are perpendicular to equipotential lines, and groundwater flow is perpendicular to the equipotential lines of hydraulic head. Further study of these would lead to *diffusion equations*.

Answers to the Problems

1. (shown below)

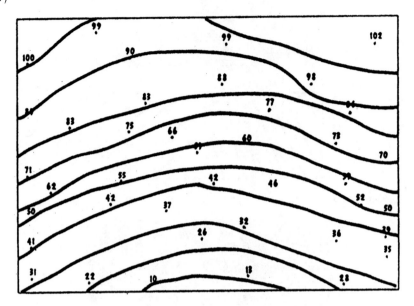

2. (shown below)

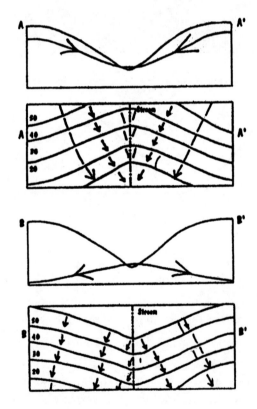

3. (shown below) Well C might be affected, but Well E will definitely be affected.

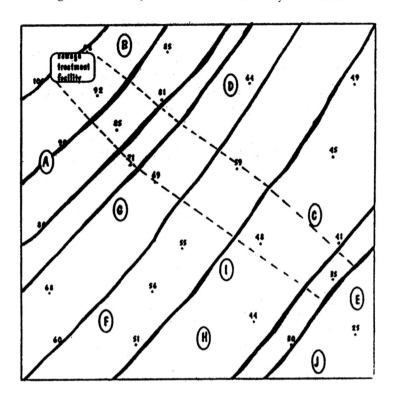

Answers to the Questions

1. The difference between Stream A and Stream B is the direction of the flow lines. In stream A, water flows from the ground into the stream. In Stream B, water flows away from the stream into the ground. Stream A represents a humid area where water is available to recharge the aquifer. In a humid area, the water table slopes toward the stream, and water flows into the stream. Stream B represents a dry area where water is scarce. In dry areas, precipitation is at a minimum, causing no direct recharge of the aquifer. The water table slopes away from the stream bed. When water fills the stream, it flows to the aquifer.

2. Yes, excessive pumping at Well H would cause a change in the flow of contamination. Well I would definitely be contaminated. Well G would most likely be affected. Well J may possibly be affected.

3. No. At point 35, however, the contamination would hit an impermeable lens, and its flow path would change to go around the lens.

Solar Power I [Experiment]

Both Solar Power I and Solar Power II complement meteorology, but they could as well be in Part 1, Heat, or in the astronomy material. Use either or both wherever they suit your course.

This is an exercise in the inverse-square law, which needs to be done during bright sunlight during the heat of the day. Amazingly, with some care, you can get results reasonably close to the "ideal" data given below. Having the foil in a jar helps to keep foil temperature closer to the inside ambient temperature. If the foil weren't enclosed, cooling by air currents would counteract its temperature rise when illuminated by the lamp or the sun.

Sample Calculations

Distance from the bulb filament to foil strip = 9.5 cm = 0.095 m, and the sun's distance in meters is 1.5×10^{11} m.

So from $\dfrac{\text{sun's wattage}}{\text{bulb's wattage}}$

We find: Sun's wattage

$$= \frac{[100][1.5 \times 10^{11}\,\text{m}]^2}{[0.095\,\text{m}]^2} = 2.5 \times 10^{26}\,\text{W}$$

335

Therefore, the number of 100-W lightbulbs is

$$\# \text{bulbs} = \frac{2.5 \times 10^{26} \text{ W}}{100 \text{ W/bulb}}$$

Not surprisingly, even if all the electric generators in the world were diverted toward just lighting the calculated number of bulbs, this would constitute only a tiny fraction of the energy radiated by the sun.

Possible sources of discrepancies include inaccurate rating of bulb's wattage; inaccurate measurement of distance; atmospheric absorption; nonperpendicular alignment of black vanes to solar rays; absorption is only by black paint, that misses energy in other wavelengths.

Solar Power II [Experiment]

The amount of solar energy flux just above the atmosphere is 2 cal/cm^2 min—the solar constant. But only three quarters of this reaches the Earth's surface after passing through the atmosphere—1.5 cal/cm^2 min. Because there are 10^4 cm^2 in 1 m^2, the solar energy flux obtained in Step 7 should be multiplied by $(10^4$ cm^2/m$^2)$ for Step 8. Following the sample calculation, the energy reaching each square meter of ground per minute would be 10,000 cal.

Sample Data and Calculations

- Volume of water: 140 mL
- Mass of water: 140 g
- Initial water temperature: 23°C
- Final water temperature: 26°C
- Temperature difference: 3°C
- Typical top diameter of Styrofoam cup: 6.9 cm

Surface area of the top of a typical Styrofoam cup is

$$\text{Area} = \pi \, (\text{diameter}/2)^2 = 3.14 \, (3.5 \text{ cm})^2 = 38 \text{ cm}^2$$

The energy collected by the cup is, therefore,

$$\text{Energy} = cm\triangle T = (1.0 \text{ cal/g °C}) \, (140 \text{ g}) \, (3°C) = 400 \text{ cal}$$

The solar flux is, therefore,

$$\text{Solar energy flux} = [\text{energy}/(\text{area} \times \text{time})] = 400 \text{ cal}/(38 \text{ cm}^2) \, (10 \text{ min}) = 1 \text{ cal/cm}^2 \text{ min}$$

Factors that might affect the amount of solar energy reaching a location on the Earth's surface include time of day, season of the year, latitude, cloud cover, humidity, air pollution, and nearby obstructions.

Indoor Clouds [Activity]

This activity is pretty lightweight and is probably the least exciting activity in the manual. But it does prompt attention to cloud formation. Consider assigning it as an out-of-class activity.

Answers to the Questions

1. Much the same in that air that is chilled undergoes condensation.

2. In the atmosphere, there isn't the confinement that restricts air currents. Relatively little circulation occurs in the capped jar, whereas air more readily rises in the atmosphere. Then expansion rather than ice promotes cooling.

3. Warmer water undergoes more evaporation, which is why warm water was used in this activity.

4. We believe warm air rises from our observation of smoke, the warmer temperature of air near the ceiling in a room, the currents over hot roads in summer betrayed by refraction in the air, and other common occurrences.

5. Air currents are swept upward when heading toward mountains. As a result, the expanding air cools, clouds form, and precipitation follows. Further along, on the other side of the mountains, dry air remains that contributes to a desert area.

Geologic Time and Relative Dating [Activity]

This lab is similar to the Practice Book activity on Relative Time, but is a bit more challenging. Have the students use their textbook to answer questions on the Geologic Time Scale. Depending on your class's ability, this lab will probably not take too much time. It can be coupled with the Practice Book activities on Relative Time or with the lab on Reading the Rock Record.

Answers to the Questions

1. Folding of layers "A" through "F", and the igneous intrusion "K" occurred before layer "L" was deposited.

2. Event "Q" is an intrusion. The principles of cross-cutting relationships and inclusions can be used to approximate the age of "Q". In the diagram, "Q" cuts into layers "B" and "C" but does not cut into "D". This tells us "Q" is younger than "D". Also, there are inclusions of "B" and "C" in intrusion "Q" (we see no other inclusions).

3. Fault "R" extends from event "A" to "J". It is a recent event that occurred after event "J" but before event "S". The fault was created by tensional forces that pull the crust apart. Tensional force causes the hanging wall (the top of the fault) to move down relative to the footwall (the bottom of the fault). "R" is classified as a normal fault.

Answer to Problem 2: Life and the Geologic Time Scale

Geologic Time Period		Life Form
Quaternary	**C**	A) Trilobite
Tertiary	**F**	B) Flowering plants
Cretaceous	**B**	C) Age of humans
Jurassic	**G**	D) Swampy environments
Triassic	**E**	E) Emergence of dinosaurs
Permian	**H**	F) Age of mammals
Carboniferous	**D**	G) True pines and redwoods
Devonian	**I**	H) First reptiles
Silurian	**J**	I) Age of fishes
Ordovician	**K**	J) Emergence of land plants
Cambrian	**A**	K) First fish

Reading the Rock Record [Activity]

This lab contains a great deal of information, but it is a great exercise to show how geologists use superposition and faunal succession to unravel the puzzle of "what came first." Demonstrate the use of Figure 1 before moving on to having the students do their own work. Show how to correlate the different rock layers by drawing parallel lines between the outcrops for the layers that share the same relative vertical position. Label the lines for clarity. Explain how the "pinched" lines indicate missing rock and, therefore, a gap in time. For example, in outcrop B, the shale layer is capped first by dolomite and then bedded sandstone. In outcrop A, the shale is capped by bedded sandstone — the dolomite is missing. The lower pinched line in outcrop A also shows missing rock (time), but more information is needed to determine the actual sequence of the lower layers.

Answers to the Questions

1. Region 1: P and S are missing below M, C is missing between L and D, B is missing between Z and X. Region 2: P is missing below S, L is missing between M and C, D Z is missing between C and B. Region 3: P is missing below S, C D is missing between L and Z, X is missing above B. Region 4: M is missing between S and L, Z is missing between D and B, X is missing above B.

2. Either the unit was not deposited in that area, or it was deposited and then eroded away before deposition of the succeeding layers—an unconformity.

3. The law of superposition! The evidence is in the stratigraphic columns. In Region 2, fish are above reptiles, and reptiles are found in the Permian. Because we are working in the Paleozoic, the fossil fish in X must be from the Permian.

4. Layer S extends from Cambrian to Ordovician, Layer L extends from Ordovician to Silurian, and Layer D extends from Silurian to Devonian. Deposition of these particular rock units must have occurred for over more than one time period. Significant, widespread fossil changes do occur at the boundaries between geological time periods, but deposition didn't stop at all locations, and not all organisms became extinct at the close of each period.

5. Most are marine-type fossils. During the Paleozoic, sea levels rose and fell several times. Shallow seas covered the continents, and marine life flourished. When sea level dropped, life moved to land, and we see reptiles. The types of fossils tell us a great deal about our planet's changing environment.

Part 5: Astronomy
Chapter 27: The Solar System
Sunballs
Ellipses
Reckoning Latitude
Tracking Mars

Sunballs [Experiment]
Beauty is not only seeing the world with wide open eyes but also knowing what to look for. Your students have all seen splotches of light beneath the trees. But now you can point out what nearly all haven't seen, and that is that the splotches are circular—or if the sun is low in the sky, elliptical. For they are images of the sun. They occur because the holes between the leaves above are small compared to the distance to the ground, and they act as pinholes (recall the activity, "Pinhole Camera"). It's nice to point out the really intriguing things around us!

Answers to the Questions

1. The shape of the hole has no bearing as long as its size is small compared to the distance to the image.

2. Measure the short diameter, for this is the undistorted diameter needed for the calculation. The long diameter is this same diameter stretched out because of the angle of sunbeams with the ground. Or position the viewing screen perpendicular to the sunbeams and get a circle.

3. The sunball will be the same shape as the eclipsed sun. And in line with pinhole images, it will be reversed. So if the bottom half of the sun is eclipsed, the image will show the top half eclipsed.

Ellipses [Activity]
Students will enjoy this light activity. It will also very likely be one of the things they'll be sure to remember from your course.

Answers to the Questions

1. The elliptical path of the Earth about the sun is nearly circular; so the ellipse drawn with pins closest together most likely is the best representation of the Earth's orbit.

2. With pins far apart, a more eccentric ellipse results—one like the path of Halley's comet. The eccentricity of Halley's comet is 0.97, compared to Earth's eccentricity of 0.0167.

3. Evidence that the sum of the distances to the foci is constant is the constant length of string made to construct the ellipses!

Reckoning Latitude [Experiment]
This experiment has two parts: building apparatus, and viewing. The viewing segment must be carried out at nighttime. Polaris turns out to be only the 53rd brightest star in the night sky. You'll find students who will expect that it should be brighter, given its importance!

You might point out that Polaris is not only not exactly over the North Pole—it's almost a degree away from the north celestial pole. For your friends in the Southern Hemisphere, sorry, there is no conveniently placed star above the south celestial pole. Polaris serves navigators well now and has been in a position to do so for the last several hundred years. But because the Earth precesses about its polar axis, like the wobble of a

spinning top, it will remain nearly over the pole only for a few more hundred years. But that should n~~
greatly worry us for the present.

The location of Polaris is easiest to find via the Big Dipper, as described in the text. It can also be located b~
using the Little Dipper. Polaris is the first star of the Little Dipper's handle. This is seen in Figure 4 of the lab
write-up. Another easily located constellation is Cassiopeia's Chair, the five-star big W in the sky (Figure 5).

Answers to the Questions

1. Answers vary according to latitude.

2. Same as the altitude in Question 1.

3. Answers will vary.

4. Answers depend on latitude.

5. If the theolite shows Polaris to be lower in the sky as one moves south, and higher in the sky as one
   moves north, then this is evidence for a round Earth.

Tracking Mars [Activity]

This is a dandy! Students plot the orbit of Mars from measurements of the sky in Tycho Brahe's time. Data
are neatly rounded off to the nearest half degree to make plotting straightforward. Corrections have been
made to avoid the gap left during the transition from the Julian calendar to the Gregorian calendar now in
current use. If you get into this, begin by asking your students what happened between October 5 and October 14 in 1582; the answer is *nothing*! These dates simply didn't exist when the changeover in calendars was
made.

The plot of this data runs nicely, and the elliptical shape of Mars's orbit is clearly evident. Once your students get the hang of it, they'll find it a pleasant and interesting experience.